W9-CTD-838

NOBEL PRIZE LIBRARY

HAUPTMANN

HEIDENSTAM

JENSEN

Nobel Prize Library

PUBLISHED UNDER THE SPONSORSHIP OF THE

NOBEL FOUNDATION & THE SWEDISH ACADEMY

Gerhart Hauptmann

Verner von Heidenstam

Johannes V. Jensen

ALEXIS GREGORY, *New York*, AND

CRM PUBLISHING, *Del Mar, California*

CONTENTS

Gerhart Hauptmann

1912

"Primarily in recognition of his fruitful, varied, and outstanding production in the realm of dramatic art"

Illustrated by R. SAVARY

PRESENTATION ADDRESS

By HANS HILDEBRAND

ACTING SECRETARY
OF THE SWEDISH ACADEMY

THERE IS AN OLD SAYING that times change and men change with them. If we look back on past ages we discover its truth. We, who are no longer young, have had the opportunity in our bustling lives to experience the truth of the saying, and every day confirms it anew. As far back as history extends we find that new things emerged, but were not at first recognized although they were to be important in the future. A seed came alive and grew to magnificent size. Certain names in contemporary science illustrate the discrepancy between modest beginnings and later developments.

The same is true of dramatic poetry. This is not the place to trace its development through twenty-five centuries. There is a tremendous difference, however, between the satyr choruses of the Dionysiac festivals, called tragedies because of the goat skins worn by the chorus, and the demands the modern age makes on dramatic poetry, and this difference indicates considerable progress.

In our time Gerhart Hauptmann has been a great name in the field of drama. He turned fifty recently; he is thus in his prime of life and can look back on an exceptionally rich career as an artist. He submitted his first work to the stage at the age of twenty-seven. At the age of thirty he proved himself a mature artist with his play *Die Weber* (*The Weavers,* 1892). This work was followed by others which confirmed his reputation. In most of his plays he deals with conditions of the low-class life which he had numerous occasions to study, especially in his native Silesia. His descriptions are based on keen observations of man and his milieu. Each of his characters is a fully developed personality—there is not a trace of types or clichés. Nobody even for a moment could doubt the truthfulness of his observations; they have established Hauptmann as a great realist. But he nowhere praises the life of these so-called low characters. On the contrary, when one has seen or read these plays and identified himself deeply with the conditions they represent, he feels the need for fresh air and asks how such misery can be abolished in the future. The realism in Hauptmann's plays leads necessarily to brighter dreams of new and better conditions and to the wish for their fulfilment.

Hauptmann has also written dramas of a totally different nature: he calls them "Märchendramen." Among them is the delightful *Hanneles Himmelfahrt* (*The Assumption of Hannele,* 1893), in which the misery of life and the bliss of heaven emerge with such striking contrast. Among these plays is also *Die versunkene Glocke* (*The Sunken Bell,* 1897), the most popular of his plays in his own country. The copy used by the Nobel Committee of the Swedish Academy bore the stamp of the sixtieth impression.

Hauptmann has also distinguished himself in the genres of historical drama and comedy. He has not published a collection of his lyrical poems, but incidental poems in his plays bear witness to his talent in this field.

In his early years he had published a few short stories, but in 1910 he brought out his novel *Der Narr in Christo Emanuel Quint* (*The Fool in Christ: Emanuel Quint*), the result of many years of work. The story "Der Apostel" ("The Apostle") of 1892 is a sketch of the final work in which we learn about the inner life of a poor man who, without any education other than that acquired from the Bible and without any critical judgment of what he has read, finally reaches the conclusion that he is the reincarnation of Christ. It is not easy to give a correct account of the development of a human soul that can be considered normal, in view of all the forces and circumstances that affect its development. But it is even more difficult to attain the truth if one describes the inner development of a soul that is in certain respects abnormal. The attempt is bold; its execution took decades of creative work. Judgment of the work has differed widely. I am happy to join the many who consider *Emanuel Quint* a masterly solution of a difficult problem.

Hauptmann's particular virtue is his penetrating and critical insight into the human soul. It is this gift that enabled him in his plays and in his novels to create truly living individuals rather than types representing some particular outlook or opinion. All the characters we meet, even the minor ones, have a full life. In his novels one admires the descriptions of the setting, as well as the sketches of the people that come in more or less close contact wth the protagonist of the story. The plays reveal his great art by their powerful concentration which holds the reader or spectator from beginning to end. Whatever subject he treats, even when he deals with life's seamy side, his is always a noble personality. That nobility and his refined art give his works their wonderful power.

The preceding remarks were intended to sketch the reasons why the Swedish Academy has awarded this year's Nobel Prize to Gerhart Hauptmann.

Dr. Hauptmann—In your significant and controversial book *Der Narr in Christo Emanuel Quint* you say: "It is impossible to uncover the necessary course of a human life in all its stages, if only because every human being is something unique from beginning to end and because the observer can comprehend his object only within the limits of his own nature."

That is indeed true. But there are many kinds of observers. The everyday man in the midst of his bustling life has neither the opportunity nor the will to study his fellow men in greater depth. We see the outside but do not care to see beneath it unless we happen to have a special interest in learning another's motives. Even those who are not drawn into the turmoil of present life, who limit their intercourse with the outside world and are on intimate terms with their immediate surroundings, do not generally go very far in their study of the human soul. We are attracted or repelled; we love or hate, if we are not indifferent. We praise or blame.

The poet, however, is not an everyday man. He is able to extend the scope of his imagination much further. For he has the divine gift of intuition. And you, Dr. Hauptmann, possess this wonderful gift to the highest degree. In your many works you have created innumerable characters. But they do not exist merely as so many types of such and such a nature. To the reader and spectator of your plays, each of your characters is a fully developed individual, living and acting together with others, but different from all of them. That is the reason for much of the magic of your work.

It has been said that at least in some of your works you have been a marked realist. You have had rich opportunities to use your gift of observation and become acquainted with the memory of whole classes of people, and you have described it faithfully. If after seeing or reading such a play one is deeply moved by it, he cannot help thinking, "These conditions must be improved." One cannot deny the existence of the seamy side of life, and it must have its place in literature in order to teach wisdom to the living.

Your manifold activities as a writer have given us other marvelous works. I shall mention only two here, *Hanneles Himmelfahrt* and *Die versunkene Glocke*. The latter seems to enjoy great popularity in your country.

Through the mouth of the ambitious and unfortunate Michael Kramer you say:

> *If someone has the effrontery to paint the man with the crown of thorns—it will take him a lifetime to do it. No pleasures for him: lonely hours, lonely days, lonely years. He must be alone with himself and with his God. He must consecrate himself daily. Nothing common must be about him or in him. And then when he struggles and toils in his solitude the Holy Ghost comes. Then he can sometimes catch a glimpse. It swells, he can feel it. Then he rests in the eternal and he has it before him in quiet and beauty. He has it without wanting it. He sees the Savior. He feels Him.*

Although in your work you have not represented the Savior with the crown of thorns, you have represented a poor man ultimately driven to the delusion that he is the second Christ. But Kramer's words reflect your own attitude. Your novel *Der Narr in Christo Emanuel Quint* appeared in 1910, but the story "Der Apostel" of 1892 shows that the plan for writing the novel had occurred to you twenty years earlier.

True art does not consist in writing down and handing to the public the thoughts of the moment, but rather in subjecting potentially useful ideas to close scrutiny, to the conflict of different opinions and the apprehensive consideration of their eventual effect. This process will gradually lead the true artist to the precious conviction, "I have finally reached the truth." You have attained the highest rank of art by painstaking but never pedantic preparatory research, by the consistency of your feelings, thoughts, and actions, and by the strict form of your plays.

The Swedish Academy has found the great artist Gerhart Hauptmann worthy of receiving this year's Nobel Prize, which his Majesty the King will now present to him.

ACCEPTANCE SPEECH

By GERHART HAUPTMANN

As the recipient of this year's Nobel Prize for Literature, I thank you for the kind and cordial words which have been addressed to me. You may rest assured that I and my nation understand and deeply appreciate the honor conferred upon me. The Nobel Prize has become a cultural concern of the entire globe, and its magnificent donor has for all times given his name a place in the cultural life of nations. Distinguished people the world over will utter the name of Nobel with the same emotions as people of former ages uttered that of a patron saint whose power of protection is beyond doubt, and the medal will be passed on from generation to generation and honored by families of all peoples.

Today I cannot but pay my share of the ever-renewed tribute of respect to this great donor, and after him to the Swedish nation that has brought him forth and is so faithfully administering the heritage of his humanitarianism. Let me also recall the memory of those men whose self-denying and lynx-like task on this earth consists in attending to the cultivation of the mind's soil, so that the weeds may be rooted out and the good shoots be nurtured. Let me thank you and express the wish that you may never tire in the most blessed of all activities and that you may never lack truly rich harvests.

And now let me drink to the eventual realization of the ideal that underlies this foundation, I mean the ideal of world peace, which comprehends the final ideals of art and science. For art and science that serve war are neither pure nor ultimate; they are so only when created by, and in turn creating, peace. And let me drink to that great, ultimate, and purely ideal Nobel Prize which humanity will bestow upon itself when brute violence is banished from the intercourse of nations, as it has been banished from that of individuals in civilized societies.

THE WEAVERS

A PLAY OF THE EIGHTEEN-FORTIES

By GERHART HAUPTMANN

Translated by Horst Frenz *and* Miles Waggoner

DRAMATIS PERSONAE

DREISSIGER, *a cotton manufacturer*
MRS. DREISSIGER, *his wife*

at Dreissiger's
PFEIFER, *a manager*
NEUMANN, *a cashier*
AN APPRENTICE
JOHANN, *a coachman*
A YOUNG GIRL

WEINHOLD, *a tutor for Dreissiger's sons*
PASTOR KITTELHAUS
MRS. KITTELHAUS, *his wife*

HEIDE, *the Chief of Police*
KUTSCHE, *a policeman*
WELZEL, *an innkeeper*
MRS. WELZEL, *his wife*
ANNA WELZEL
WIEGAND, *a carpenter*
A TRAVELING SALESMAN
A FARMER
A FORESTER
SCHMIDT, *a physician*
HORNIG, *a rag picker*
OLD WITTIG, *a smith*

WEAVERS: *Baecker—Moritz Jaeger—Old Baumert—Mother Baumert—Bertha Baumert—Emma Baumert—Fritz, Emma's son, four years old—August Baumert—Ansorge—Mrs. Heinrich—Old Hilse—Gottlieb Hilse—Luise, Gottlieb's wife—Mielchen, his daughter, six years old—Reinmann—Heiber—A weaver woman—A boy, eight years old—A large crowd of young and old weavers and weaver women.*

The action of the play takes place in the 1840's in Kaschbach, Peterswaldau, and Langenbielau, cities at the foot of the mountains known as the Eulengebirge.

ACT ONE

SCENE—*A spacious whitewashed room in Dreissiger's house at Peterswaldau, where the weavers must deliver their finished webs. At the left are uncurtained windows; in the back wall, a glass door. At the right is a similar door through which weavers, men, women, and children, continuously come and go. Along the right wall, which, like the others, is almost entirely hidden by wooden stands for cotton, there is a bench on which the weavers, as they come in, spread out their finished webs to be examined. They step forward in the order of their arrival and offer their finished products.* PFEIFER, *the manager, stands behind a large table on which the weavers lay their webs for inspection. He makes the inspection with the use of dividers and a magnifying glass. When he is finished, he lays the cotton on the scales, where an apprentice tests its weight. The same apprentice shoves the goods taken from the scales onto the stock shelves.* PFEIFER *calls out the amount to be paid to each weaver to* NEUMANN, *the cashier, who sits at a small table.*

It is a sultry day toward the end of May. The clock points to twelve. Most of the waiting weavers stand like men before the bar of justice where, tortured and anxious, they must await a life-and-death decision. They all give the impression of being crushed, like beggars. Passing from humiliation to humiliation and convinced that they are only tolerated, they are used to making themselves as inconspicuous as possible. Also, they have a stark, irresolute look—gnawing, brooding faces. Most of the men resemble each other, half-dwarf, half-schoolmaster. They are flat-chested, coughing creatures with ashen gray faces: creatures of the looms, whose knees are bent with much sitting. At first glance, their women folk are less typical. They are broken, harried, worn out, while the men still have a certain look of pathetic gravity. The women's clothes are ragged, while those of the men are patched. Some of the young girls are not without charm—they have pale waxen complexions, delicate figures, large protruding melancholy eyes.

CASHIER NEUMANN. (*Counting out money.*) That leaves 16 silver groschen and 2 pfennigs.

FIRST WEAVER WOMAN. (*In her thirties, very emaciated, puts the money away with trembling fingers.*) Thank ya, kindly, sir.

NEUMANN. (*As the woman does not move on.*) Well, is something wrong again?

FIRST WEAVER WOMAN. (*Excitedly, in begging tone.*) I'd like a few pfennigs in advance. I need it awful bad.

NEUMANN. And I need a few hundred thalers. If it was just a matter of needing—! (*Already busy counting out money to another weaver, curtly.*) Mr. Dreissiger himself has to decide about advances.

FIRST WEAVER WOMAN. Then, maybe I could talk to Mr. Dreissiger hisself?

PFEIFER. (*He was formerly a weaver. The type is unmistakable; only he is well-groomed, well-fed, well-clothed, clean-shaven; also, a heavy user of snuff. He calls across brusquely.*) Mr. Dreissiger would have plenty to do, God knows, if he had to bother himself with every trifle. That's what we're here for. (*He measures and inspects a web with the magnifying glass.*) Damn it all! There's a draft! (*He wraps a heavy scarf around his neck.*) Shut the door when ya come in.

THE APPRENTICE. (*In a loud voice to* PFEIFER.) It's just like talkin' to a block of wood.

PFEIFER. That's settled then! Weigh it! (*The weaver lays his web on the scales.*)

If ya only understood your work better. It's got lumps in it again—I can tell without looking. A good weaver doesn't put off the winding who knows how long.

BAECKER. (*Enters. A young, exceptionally strong weaver whose behavior is free and easy, almost impertinent.* PFEIFER, NEUMANN, *and* THE APPRENTICE *glance at each other understandingly when he enters.*) Damn it, I'm sweatin' like a dog again.

FIRST WEAVER. (*Softly.*) Feels like rain.

OLD BAUMERT. (*Pushes through the glass door at the right. Behind the door, waiting weavers are seen jammed together, shoulder to shoulder.* OLD BAUMERT *has hobbled forward and has laid his bundle on a bench near* BAECKER'S. *He sits down next to it and wipes the sweat from his face.*) Ya sure earn a rest here.

BAECKER. Rest is better than money.

OLD BAUMERT. Ya need money too. Good day to ya, Baecker!

BAECKER. And good day to you, Father Baumert! Who knows how long we'll have to be waitin' around here again.

FIRST WEAVER. It don't matter whether a weaver has to wait an hour or a day. He just don't count.

PFEIFER. Be quiet, back there. I can't hear myself think.

BAECKER. (*Softly.*) Today's one of his bad days again.

PFEIFER. (*To the weavers standing in front of him.*) How many times have I told you already. Ya ought to clean up the webs better. What sort of a mess is this? There are chunks of dirt in it, as long as my finger—and straw, and all kinds of rubbish.

WEAVER REIMANN. I guess I need a new pair of pincers.

THE APPRENTICE. (*Has weighed the web.*) And it's short weight, too.

PFEIFER. The kind of weavers ya have nowadays! You hate to hand out the yarn. Oh, Lord, in my time! My master would've made me pay for it. I tell you, weaving was a different thing in those days. Then, a man had to understand his business. Today it's not necessary anymore. Reimann, 10 groschen.

WEAVER REIMANN. Yes, but one pound is allowed for waste.

PFEIFER. I haven't time. That's settled. (*To the next weaver.*) What have you got?

WEAVER HEIBER. (*Puts his web up on the counter. While* PFEIFER *is inspecting it,* HEIBER *steps up to him and speaks softly and eagerly.*) Please, forgive me, Mr. Pfeifer, I would like to ask ya, sir, if perhaps ya would be so kind as to do me a favor and not deduct my advance this time.

PFEIFER. (*Measuring with the dividers and inspecting, jeers.*) Well, now! That's just fine. It looks as if about half the woof has been left on the spool again.

HEIBER. (*Continuing, as before.*) I'd be glad to make it up next week for sure. Last week I had to put in two days' work on the estate. And my wife's home, sick in bed. . . .

PFEIFER. (*Putting the web on the scales.*) Here's another piece of real sloppy work. (*Already taking a new web for inspection.*) What a selvage—now it's broad, then it's narrow. In one place the woof's all gathered together, who knows how much, then the reed has been pulled apart. And scarcely seventy threads to the inch. Whatever happened to the rest? Is that honest work? I never saw such a thing!

HEIBER, *suppressing tears, stands humiliated and helpless.*

BAECKER. (*Low, to* BAUMERT.) I guess this riffraff would like us to pay for the yarn, too.

FIRST WEAVER WOMAN. (*Who has withdrawn only a few steps from the cashier's table, stares about from time to time, seeking help, without moving from the spot. Then she takes heart and once more turns imploringly to the cashier.*) I can hardly . . . I don't know . . . if ya don't give me an advance this time . . . O, Lord, Lord. . . .

PFEIFER. (*Calls across.*) All this calling on the Lord! Just leave the Lord in peace. You haven't been bothering much about the Lord up to now. It'd be better if you'd look after your husband instead, so he isn't seen sitting in the tavern window all day long. We can't give advances. We have to account for every cent. It's not our own money. Later they'd be asking us for it. People who are industrious and understand their business and do their work in fear of God don't ever need advances. So, that's settled.

NEUMANN. And if a Bielau weaver got four times as much pay, he'd squander four times as much and be in debt in the bargain.

FIRST WEAVER WOMAN. (*In a loud voice, as if appealing to everyone's sense of justice.*) I'm certainly not lazy, but I just can't go on this way much longer. I've had two miscarriages, and my husband, he can't do no more than half the work neither; he went up to the shepherd at Zerlau, but he couldn't do nothin' for his trouble either . . . there's just so much a body can do. . . . We sure do work as much as we can. I ain't had much sleep for weeks, and everything'll be all right again if I can only get a bit of this weakness out of my bones. But ya got to have a little consideration. (*Beseeching him and fawning.*) Ya'll have to be good enough to let me have a few groschen, this time.

PFEIFER. (*Unperturbed.*) Fiedler, 11 groschen.

FIRST WEAVER WOMAN. Just a few groschen, so we can get some bread. The farmer won't give us no more credit. We got a house full of children. . . .

NEUMANN. (*Softly and with mock seriousness to* THE APPRENTICE.) Once a year the linen weaver has a brat, fa, la, la, la, la.

THE APPRENTICE. (*Chiming in.*) The first six weeks it's blind as a bat, fa, la, la, la, la.

REIMANN. (*Not touching the money that the cashier has counted out for him.*) We've always been gettin' 13½ groschen for a web.

PFEIFER. (*Calls across.*) If it doesn't suit you, Reimann, all you have to do is say the word. There are plenty of weavers. Especially weavers like you. For full weight, you'll get full pay.

REIMANN. That something should be wrong with the weight. . . .

PFEIFER. If there's nothing wrong with the cotton you bring, there'll be nothing wrong with your pay.

REIMANN. It really can't be that this web, here, should have too many flaws in it.

PFEIFER. (*Inspecting.*) He who weaves well, lives well.

HEIBER. (*He has stayed close to* PFEIFER *waiting for a favorable opportunity. He smiled with the others at* PFEIFER'S *remark; now he steps forward and speaks to him as he did before.*) I would like to ask ya, sir, if perhaps ya would be so kind and not deduct the 5 groschen advance this time. My wife's been sick in bed since before Ash Wednesday. She can't do a lick of work. And I have to pay a girl to tend the bobbin. And so—

PFEIFER. (*Takes a pinch of snuff.*) Heiber, you're not the only one I have to attend to. The others want their turn, too.

REIMANN. The way the warp was given to me—that's the way I wound it and that's the way I took it off again. I can't bring back better yarn than I take home.

PFEIFER. If ya don't like it, ya simply don't need to get any more warp here. There are plenty who'd run their feet off for it.

NEUMANN. (*To* REIMANN.) Aren't you going to take the money?

REIMANN. I just can't take such pay.

NEUMANN. (*Without troubling himself*

further about REIMANN.) Heiber, 10 groschen—take off the 5 groschen advance—leaves 5 groschen.

HEIBER. (*Steps up, looks at the money, stands there, shakes his head as if there were something he could not believe, and then quietly and carefully pockets the money.*) O my God—! (*Sighing.*) Ah, well!

OLD BAUMERT. (*Looking straight at* HEIBER.) Yes, yes, Franz! You've got cause for sighing there.

HEIBER. (*Speaking wearily.*) Ya see, I've got a sick girl layin' home. She needs a bottle of medicine.

OLD BAUMERT. What's wrong with her?

HEIBER. Ya see, she's been a sickly little thing from the time she was born. I really don't know . . . well, I can tell you: she brought it into the world with her. Such trouble's in the blood, and it keeps breakin' out over and over again.

OLD BAUMERT. There's something the matter everywhere. When you're poor, there's nothing but bad luck. There's no end to it and no salvation.

HEIBER. What have ya got in that bundle?

OLD BAUMERT. We haven't got a thing in the house. So I had our little dog killed. There ain't much to him, he was half-starved. He was a nice little dog. I couldn't kill him myself. I didn't have the heart.

PFEIFER. (*Has inspected* BAECKER'S *web, calls out.*) Baecker, 13½ groschen.

BAECKER. That's a measly hand-out for a beggar, not pay.

PFEIFER. Those who are done, have to get out. It's so crowded, we can't move around in here.

BAECKER. (*To those standing about, without lowering his voice.*) That's a measly hand-out, that's all it is. And for that a man's to work the treadle from early morning till late at night. And after a man's been workin' behind a loom for eighteen days, evenin' after evenin'—worn out, dizzy with the dust and terrible heat, then he's lucky if he gets 13½ groschen for his drudgery.

PFEIFER. We'll have no back-talk here.

BAECKER. You can't make me hold my tongue.

PFEIFER. (*Jumps up, shouting.*) We'll see about that. (*Walks toward the glass door and calls into the office.*) Mr. Dreissiger! Mr. Dreissiger, if you'll be so kind!

DREISSIGER. (*Enters. He is about forty, fat, asthmatic. With a severe look.*) What's—the matter, Pfeifer?

PFEIFER. (*Angrily.*) Baecker won't hold his tongue.

DREISSIGER. (*Draws himself up, throws his head back, and stares at* BAECKER *with quivering nostrils.*) Oh, yes—Baecker—(*to* PFEIFER.) Is that him—? (*The clerk nods.*)

BAECKER. (*Impudently.*) Yes, indeed, Mr. Dreissiger! (*Pointing to himself.*) That's him. (*Pointing to* DREISSIGER.) And that's him.

DREISSIGER. (*Indignantly.*) How can he dare?

PFEIFER. He's too well off, that's what he is. He'll skate on thin ice once too often.

BAECKER. (*Roughly.*) You shut up, you fool! Once, in the new moon, your mother must have been ridin' a broomstick with Satan to beget such a devil as you for a son.

DREISSIGER. (*In sudden anger, bellows.*) Shut up! Shut up this minute, or else—(*He trembles, takes a few steps forward.*)

BAECKER. (*With determination, standing up to him.*) I'm not deaf. I still hear good.

DREISSIGER. (*Controls himself, asks with apparent businesslike calm.*) Isn't he one of those—?

PFEIFER. He's a Bielau weaver. They can always be found where trouble is brewing.

DREISSIGER. (*Trembling.*) Then I'm warning you: if it happens once more, and if such a gang of half-drunken young louts passes my house once again, as they did last night, singing that vile song. . . .

BAECKER. I guess you mean "Bloody Justice"?

DREISSIGER. You know exactly what I mean. Let me tell you, if I hear that song once more, I'll get hold of one of you, and—on my honor, joking aside, I promise you I'll turn him over to the state's attorney. And if I find out who wrote this wretched song. . . .

BAECKER. That's a beautiful song—it is!

DREISSIGER. Another word and I'll send for the police—immediately. I won't lose any time! We know how to deal with young fellows like you. I've taken care of your kind before.

BAECKER. Well, now, that I can believe. A real manufacturer like you can gobble up two or three hundred weavers before a person has time to turn around . . . and not so much as a bone left over. Such a man's got four stomachs like a cow and teeth like a wolf. No, indeed—that's nothing at all to him!

DREISSIGER. (*To the clerks.*) See to it that that fellow doesn't get another stick of work from us.

BAECKER. Oh, it's all the same to me whether I starve behind the loom or in a ditch by the side of the road.

DREISSIGER. Get out, this minute! Get out of here!

BAECKER. (*Firmly.*) I'll take my pay first.

DREISSIGER. How much has the man got coming, Neumann?

NEUMANN. Twelve groschen and five pfennigs.

DREISSIGER. (*Takes the money from the cashier in great haste and throws it down on the counter so that a few coins roll onto the floor.*) There you are—and now hurry—get out of my sight!

BAECKER. I'll take my pay first.

DREISSIGER. There's your pay; and if you don't hurry and get out. . . . It's exactly twelve . . . my dyers are taking off for lunch. . . .

BAECKER. My pay belong in my hand. My pay belongs here. (*He points to the palm of his left hand.*)

DREISSIGER. (*To* THE APPRENTICE.) Pick it up, Tilgner.

THE APPRENTICE *picks up the money and lays it in* BAECKER'S *hand.*

BAECKER. Everything's got to be done right. (*He puts the money slowly in an old purse.*)

DREISSIGER. Well? (*As* BAECKER *still does not leave, impatiently.*) Shall I help you?

There is excited movement among the crowd of weavers. A long, deep sigh is heard, then a fall. Everyone's attention is turned to this new event.

DREISSIGER. What's happened there?

VARIOUS WEAVERS *and* WEAVER WOMEN. Someone's fainted. It's a sickly little boy. What's wrong? Is it consumption, maybe?

DREISSIGER. Why . . . what's that? Fainted? (*He goes up closer.*)

AN OLD WEAVER. He's layin' there. (*They make room. A little boy, about eight years old, is seen lying on the floor as if dead.*)

DREISSIGER. Does somebody know this boy?

OLD WEAVER. He's not from our village.

OLD BAUMERT. He looks like one of Heinrich's boys. (*He looks at him more closely.*) Yes, indeed! That is Heinrich's little Gustav.

DREISSIGER. Where do they live, these people?

OLD BAUMERT. Why, near us in Kaschbach, Mr. Dreissiger. He goes around playin' music, and in the daytime, he works at the loom. They have nine children and the tenth's on the way.

VARIOUS WEAVERS *and* WEAVER WOMEN. They sure got a lot of trouble. Their roof leaks. The woman ain't got two shirts for the nine children.

OLD BAUMERT. (*Taking hold of the*

boy.) Why, my child, what's wrong with ya? Wake up, there now!

DREISSIGER. Take hold of him—here, help me—we'll pick him up. It's incomprehensible that anybody should let a weak child like that come such a long way. Bring some water, Pfeifer!

WEAVER WOMAN. (*Helps him sit up.*) Don't ya up and die on us, boy!

DREISSIGER. Or brandy, Pfeifer, brandy is better.

BAECKER. (*Forgotten by everybody, has been watching. Now, with one hand on the doorknob, he calls across in a loud voice, mockingly.*) Give him something to eat, too, and he'll come to all right.

Exit.

DREISSIGER. That fellow will come to no good. Take him under the arm, Neumann. Slowly—slowly . . . that's it . . . there, now . . . we'll take him into my room. Why, what is it?

NEUMANN. He's said something, Mr. Dreissiger! He's moving his lips.

DREISSIGER. What is it, little boy?

THE BOY. (*Whispers.*) I'm—hungry!

DREISSIGER. (*Turns pale.*) I can't understand him.

WEAVER WOMAN. I think he said. . . .

DREISSIGER. Well, we'll see. Let's not lose any time—he can lie on my sofa. We'll hear, then, what the doctor says.

DREISSIGER, NEUMANN, *and the* WEAVER WOMAN *carry the boy into the office. There is a commotion among the weavers, as among school children when the teacher leaves the classroom. They stretch, they whisper, they shift from one foot to the other. Soon there is loud and general conversation among them.*

OLD BAUMERT. I really do believe Baecker is right.

SEVERAL WEAVERS *and* WEAVER WOMEN. He said something like that, too. That's nothing new around here—people faintin' from hunger. Yes, and who knows what'll happen this winter if this cuttin' of wages keeps on—. And the potatoes bein' so bad this year—. It won't be no different here till we're all of us flat on our backs.

OLD BAUMERT. Ya might just as well put a rope 'round your neck and hang yourself on your loom like the Nentwich weaver did. Here, take a pinch of snuff—I was in Neurode, where my brother-in-law works in the snuff factory. He gave me a few grains. You carryin' anything nice in your kerchief?

AN OLD WEAVER. It's only a little bit of barley. The wagon from the Ullbrich miller was drivin' ahead of me, and there was a little slit in one of the sacks. That comes in handy, believe me.

OLD BAUMERT. There are twenty-two mills in Peterswaldau, and still there's nothin' left over for the likes of us.

AN OLD WEAVER. Ah, we mustn't get discouraged. Something always turns up and helps a little bit.

HEIBER. When we're hungry, we have to pray to the fourteen guardian angels, and if that don't fill ya up, then ya have to put a pebble in your mouth and suck on it. Right, Baumert?

DREISSIGER *and* PFEIFER, *as well as the cashier, return.*

DREISSIGER. It was nothing of any importance. The boy's quite all right again. (*Goes around excited and puffing.*) And yet it is a disgrace. A bit of wind would blow that wisp of a child away. It's really unbelievable how people—how parents can be so irresponsible. To load him down with two bundles of cotton and send him a good seven and a half miles on the road. It's really unbelievable. I will simply have to take steps to see to it that goods brought by children will not be accepted. (*He walks silently back and forth.*) In any case, I certainly hope that nothing of this sort happens again. On whose shoulders does the blame finally rest? The manufacturers, of course. We're blamed for everything. When a poor little fellow falls asleep in the snow in the wintertime, one of these reporter chaps comes running up, and in two days the gruesome story is in all the papers. The father, the parents, the ones who send the child out . . . oh, no . . . they aren't guilty, certainly not! It must be the manufacturer; the manufacturer is the goat. The weaver is always let off easy, the manufacturer is the one who catches it; he's a man without a heart, dangerous fellow who can be bitten in the leg by every mad dog of a reporter. He lives in splendor and in comfort and pays the poor weavers starvation wages. These scribblers are absolutely silent about the fact that such a man has troubles too, and sleepless nights; that he runs great risks such as the weaver never dreams of; that often he does nothing but calculate—dividing, adding, and multiplying, calculating and recalculating until he's nearly out of his mind; that he has to consider and weigh a hundred different kinds of things, and always has to fight and compete, you might say, as a matter of life and death; that not a single day goes by without annoyances and losses. All the people who're dependent on the manufacturer, who suck him dry and want to live off of him—think of that! No, no! You ought to be in my shoes for a while, then you'd get fed up with it soon enough, I tell you. (*After a little reflection.*) How that fellow, that scoundrel there, that Baecker, behaved! Now he'll go around and tell everybody how hard-hearted I am. That at the slightest opportunity I throw the weavers out. Is that true? Am I so hard-hearted?

MANY VOICES. No, Mr. Dreissiger!

DREISSIGER. Well, it doesn't look like that to me, either. And yet these rascals go around here and sing nasty songs about us manufacturers. They talk of hunger and yet they have so much money to spend that they can consume their liquor by the quart. They ought to look around in other places, and see how things are among the linen weavers. They can really talk of hard times. But you here, you cotton weavers, you can quietly thank God that things are as they are. And I ask the old, industrious, skilled weavers who are here: Tell me, can a worker, who does a good job, earn his living, working for me or can't he?

VERY MANY VOICES. Yes, Mr. Dreissinger!

DREISSIGER. There, you see! A fellow like Baecker can't, of course. But I advise you, keep those fellows in check; if this goes too far, I'll just quit. Then I'll give up the whole business, and you'll see where you are. You'll see who'll give you work. Certainly not your fine Mr. Baecker.

FIRST WEAVER WOMAN. (*Has come up close to* DREISSIGER *and with fawning humility brushes some dust from his coat.*) You've gone and rubbed against something, Mr. Dreissiger, sir, you have.

DREISSIGER. Business is terrible, you know that yourselves. Instead of earning money, I'm actually losing it. If, in spite of this, I see to it that my weavers always have work, I expect them to appreciate it. The goods lie stocked up here in thousands of yards, and I don't know today if I'll ever sell them. Well, I've heard that a great number of weavers around here have have no work at all, and so . . . well, Pfeifer can give you the details. The fact of the matter is this: so you'll see my good intentions—naturally, I can't just hand out charity. I'm not rich enough for that. But I can, up to a certain point, give the unemployed a chance to earn at least a little something. That I'm running a tremendous risk in doing that, well, that's my own affair. I think it's always better if a man can earn a piece of bread and cheese for himself every day rather than starve. Don't you think I'm right?

MANY VOICES. Yes, yes, Mr. Dreissiger.

DREISSIGER. I am therefore willing to put an additional two hundred weavers to work. Pfeifer will explain to you, under what conditions. (*He is about to leave.*)

FIRST WEAVER WOMAN. (*Steps in his path, speaks quickly, imploringly, urgently.*) Mr. Dreissinger, sir, I wanted to ask ya real kindly, if perhaps you . . . I've been laid up twice. . . .

DREISSIGER. (*In haste.*) Speak to Pfeifer, my good woman, I'm late as it is. (*He turns away from her.*)

REIMANN. (*Stops him. In the tone of an injured and accusing man.*) Mr. Dreissiger, I really have a complaint to make. Mr. Pfeifer has . . . I always get 12½ groschen for a web, and. . . .

DREISSIGER. (*Interrupts him.*) There's the manager. Talk to him: he's the person to see.

HEIBER. (*Stops* DREISSIGER.) Mr. Dreissiger, sir, (*Stuttering, in confusion and haste.*) I wanted to ask ya if perhaps ya could . . . if maybe Mr. Pfeifer could . . . if he could. . . .

DREISSIGER. What is it you want?

HEIBER. The advance pay that I got last time. I mean that I. . . .

DREISSIGER. I really do not understand you.

HEIBER. I was pretty hard up, because. . . .

DREISSIGER. Pfeifer's business, that's Pfeifer's business. I really can't . . . take it up with Pfeifer. (*He escapes into the office.*)

The supplicants look helplessly at one another. One after the other, they step back, sighing.

PFEIFER. (*Starts the inspection again.*) Well, Annie, and what are you bringing us?

OLD BAUMERT. How much for a web, then, Mr. Pfeifer?

PFEIFER. Ten groschen for each web.

OLD BAUMERT. Ain't that something!

Excitement among the weavers, whispers and grumblings.

CURTAIN

ACT TWO

SCENE—*A small room in the cottage of* WILHELM ANSORGE *in Kaschbach in the mountains called Eulengebirge.*

The narrow room measures less than six feet from the dilapidated floor to the smoke-blackened rafters. Two young girls, EMMA *and* BERTHA BAUMERT, *sit at looms.* MOTHER BAUMERT, *a crippled old woman, sits on a stool by the bed, at her spooling wheel. Her son,* AUGUST, *twenty years old, an idiot with small body and head and long spiderlike limbs, sits on a footstool, also reeling yarn.*

The weak, rosy light of the setting sun shines through two small window openings in the left wall. These are partly pasted over with paper and partly filled with up with straw. The light falls on the pale, blond, loose hair of the girls, on their bare, bony shoulders and thin waxen necks, on the folds of their coarse chemises, which, with a short skirt of the roughest linen, constitute their entire clothing. The warm glow lights up the entire face, neck, and chest of the old woman. Her face is emaciated to a skeleton, with folds and wrinkles in the anemic skin. The sunken eyes are reddened and watery from the lint and smoke and from working by lamplight. She has a long goiter neck with sinews standing out. Her narrow chest is covered with faded shawls and rags. Part of the right wall, with the stove, stove bench, bedstead, and several gaudily tinted pictures of saints, is also lighted up. There are rags hanging on the bar of the stove to dry, and behind the stove, old worthless rubbish is piled up. On the bench are a few old pots and kitchen utensils; a heap of potato peelings is laid out to dry on a piece of paper. Skeins of yarn and reels hang from the rafters. Small baskets with bobbins stand beside the looms. In the back there is a low door without a lock; next to it, a bundle of willow switches leans against the wall. Several broken peck baskets lie about. The room is filled with the noise of the looms: the rhythmic movement of the lathe which shakes the walls and the floor, the shuffle and clicking of the shuttle moving rapidly back and forth. This blends with the low constant humming of the spooling wheels that sounds like the buzzing of bumble bees.

MOTHER BAUMERT. (*In a pitiful exhausted voice, as the girls stop their weaving and bend over their webs.*) Do ya have to make knots again?

EMMA. (*The elder of the girls, twenty-two years old, is tying up the torn threads.*) This is the worst yarn!

BERTHA. (*Fifteen years old.*) The warp sure causes a lot of trouble.

EMMA. Where's he been so long? He's been gone since nine o'clock.

MOTHER BAUMERT. I should say so! Where can he be, girls?

BERTHA. Don't ya worry, mother!

MOTHER BAUMERT. I can't help it!

EMMA *continues weaving.*

BERTHA. Wait a minute, Emma!

EMMA. What is it?

BERTHA. I thought I heard somebody comin'.

EMMA. That'll be Ansorge comin' home.

FRITZ. (*A small four-year-old boy, barefoot and dressed in rags, comes in crying.*) Mother, I'm hungry.

EMMA. Wait, Fritzi, just you wait a bit. Grandfather's comin' soon. He's bringing bread and grain.

FRITZ. But I'm so hungry, Mama.

EMMA. I just told ya. Don't be so silly. He's comin' right away. He'll bring some nice bread and some coffee grain. When we stop workin', Mama'll take the potato peelin's to the farmer, and he'll give her a bit of buttermilk for her boy.

FRITZ. But where's grandfather gone?

EMMA. He's at the manufacturer's, deliverin' a web.

FRITZ. At the manufacturer's?

EMMA. Yes, Fritzi! Down at Dreissiger's, in Peterswaldau.

FRITZ. Will he get some bread there?

EMMA. Yes, yes, they'll give him some money, and then he can buy some bread.

FRITZ. Will they give grandfather lots a money?

EMMA. Oh, stop talkin', boy. (*She continues weaving, as does* BERTHA. *Then both stop again.*)

BERTHA. August, go and ask Ansorge if he won't give us a light.

AUGUST *leaves together with* FRITZ.

MOTHER BAUMERT. (*With ever-increasing childlike fear, almost whining.*) Children, children! Where can the man be?

BERTHA. Maybe he dropped in to see Hauffen.

MOTHER BAUMERT. (*Crying.*) If he just ain't gone to the tavern.

EMMA. I hope not, Mother! But our father ain't that kind.

MOTHER BAUMERT. (*Quite beside herself with a host of fears.*) Well . . . well . . . well, tell me what'll happen if he . . . if he comes home . . . if he drinks it all up and don't bring nothin' home? There ain't a handful of salt in the house, not a piece of bread . . . we need a shovelful of fuel. . . .

BERTHA. Don't ya worry, Mother! The moon's shining. We'll go to the woods. We'll take August along and bring back some firewood.

MOTHER BAUMERT. Sure, so the forester can catch ya?

ANSORGE. (*An old weaver, with a gigantic frame, who has to bend low in order to enter the room, sticks his head and the upper part of his body through the door. His hair and beard are unkempt.*) Well, what do ya want?

BERTHA. Ya could give us a light!

ANSORGE. (*Muffled, as if speaking in the presence of a sick person.*) It's still light enough.

MOTHER BAUMERT. Now ya'll even make us sit in the dark.

ANSORGE. I've got to do the best I can. (*He goes out.*)

BERTHA. Now ya see how stingy he is.

EMMA. Yeah, we got to sit here till he gets good and ready.

MRS. HEINRICH. (*Enters. She is thirty years old, pregnant. Her face is worn from sorrow and anxious waiting.*) Good evenin' to ya all.

MOTHER BAUMERT. Well, Mother Heinrich, what's the news?

MRS. HEINRICH. (*Limping.*) I've stepped on a piece of glass.

BERTHA. Come over here and set down. I'll see if I can't get it out.

MRS. HEINRICH. (*Sits down;* BERTHA *kneels in front of her and busies herself with* MRS. HEINRICH'S *foot.*)

MOTHER BAUMERT. How's things at home, Mother Heinrich?

MRS. HEINRICH. (*Breaks out in despair.*) Soon I won't be able to stand it no more. (*She fights in vain against a flood of tears. Then she weeps silently.*)

MOTHER BAUMERT. It'd be the best for the likes of us, Mother Heinrich, if the dear Lord would have pity on us and take us out of this world.

MRS. HEINRICH. (*Losing her self-control, weeps and cries out.*) My poor children are starvin'! (*She sobs and moans.*) I just don't know what to do. Ya try as hard as ya can, ya wear yourself out till ya drop. I'm more dead than alive, and still it ain't no different. Nine hungry mouths to feed and not enough to feed them. Where am I to get the food, huh? Last night I had a little bit of bread—it wasn't enough for the two littlest ones. Who was I supposed to give it to, huh? They all cried: Mama, me, Mama, me. . . . No, no! And all this while I'm still up and about. What'll it be when I have to take to my bed? The few potatoes we had was washed away. We ain't got a bite to eat.

BERTHA. (*Has removed the splinter and washed out the wound.*) We'll put a piece of cloth around it. (*To* EMMA.) Look and see if ya can find one.

MOTHER BAUMERT. We ain't no better off, Mother Heinrich.

MRS. HEINRICH. At least ya've still got your girls. Ya've got a husband who can work for ya, but mine—he fell down again this past week. He's had another spell, and I was that scared to death—I didn't know what to do. And after he's had one of them fits, he's laid up for at least a week.

MOTHER BAUMERT. Mine ain't no better. He's ready to collapse, too. He's got trouble with his chest and his back. And there ain't a single pfennig in the house either. If he don't bring some money home today, I don't know what we're goin' to do either.

EMMA. That's so, Mother Heinrich. We're so bad off, Father had to take little Ami with him . . . we had to have him butchered so we can get something real in our stomachs again.

MRS. HEINRICH. Ain't ya even got a handful of flour left over?

MOTHER BAUMERT. Not even that much, Mother Heinrich; there ain't a pinch of salt left in the house.

MRS. HEINRICH. Well, then I don't know what to do! (*Gets up, standing brooding.*) I really don't know what to do! (*Crying out in anger and panic.*) I'd be satisfied if it was nothin' but pig swill!—but I just can't go home empty-handed again. That just won't do. God forgive me. I don't know nothin' else to do. (*She limps out quickly, stepping only on the heel of her left foot.*)

MOTHER BAUMERT. (*Calls after her, warning.*) Mother Heinrich, don't ya go an' do nothin' foolish.

BERTHA. She won't do no harm to herself. Don't ya worry.

EMMA. She always acts like that. (*She sits at the loom again and weaves for a few seconds.*)

AUGUST *enters with a candle, lighting the way for his father,* OLD BAUMERT, *who drags in a bundle of yarn.*

MOTHER BAUMERT. My God, man, where in the world have ya been so long?

OLD BAUMERT. Ya don't have to snap at me like that, right away. Just let me catch my breath first. Better look an' see who's come in with me.

MORITZ JAEGER. (*Enters, stooping, through the door. He is a well-built, average-sized, red-cheeked soldier. His Hussar's cap sits jauntily on the side of his head; he wears good clothes and shoes and a clean shirt without a collar. He stands erect and gives a military salute. In a hearty voice.*) Good evening, Auntie Baumert.

MOTHER BAUMERT. Well, well, now! So you've come home again? And ya didn't forget us? Why, set down. Come here, set down.

EMMA. (*With her skirt cleans off a wooden stool and shoves it toward* JAEGER.) Good evenin', Moritz! Did ya come back to have another look at how poor folks is living?

JAEGER. Well, now, say, Emma! I never really could believe it! Why, you've got a boy who'll soon be big enough to be a soldier. Where did ya get him?

BERTHA. (*Takes the small amount of food that her father brought in, puts the meat in a pan, and shoves it in the oven while* AUGUST *builds a fire.*) Ya know the Weaver Finger, don't ya?

MOTHER BAUMERT. He used to live here in the cottage with us. He would have married her, but his lungs was almost completely gone then. I warned the girl often enough. But would she listen to me? Now, he's dead and gone and forgotten a long time and she'll have to see how she can support the boy. But now, you tell me, Moritz, how's things been goin' with you?

OLD BAUMERT. You be quiet, Mother, can't ya see he's had plenty to eat; he's laughin' at all of us; he's got clothes like a prince and a silver pocket watch, and on top of all that, ten silver thalers in cash.

JAEGER. (*Stands with his legs apart, showing off, a boastful smile on his face.*) I can't complain. I didn't have a bad time in the army.

OLD BAUMERT. He was an orderly to a captain. Just listen to him—he talks like elegant folks.

JAEGER. I've got so used to fine talk that I can't help it.

MOTHER BAUMERT. No, no, well, I never! Such a good-for-nothin' as you was, and comin' into such money. You never was good for nothin' much; ya couldn't unwind two spools in a row. But you was always off and away, settin' wren-boxes and robin snares. You'd rather do that. Well, ain't that the truth?

JAEGER. It's true, Auntie Baumert. And I didn't catch just robins, I caught swallows, too.

EMMA. No matter how often we used to say swallows was poison.

JAEGER. It was all the same to me. But how have all of you been getting along, Auntie Baumert?

MOTHER BAUMERT. O dear Lord Jesus, it's been awful hard these last four years. I've been havin' bad pains. Just look at my fingers. I really don't know if it's the rheumatiz or what. I'm in such misery! I can hardly move a muscle. Nobody knows the kind of pain I have to put up with.

OLD BAUMERT. She really has it bad now. She won't be with us long.

BERTHA. In the mornin' we got to dress her, in the evenin' we got to undress her. We got to feed her like a little baby.

MOTHER BAUMERT. (*Continuing in a complaining, tearful voice.*) I got to be waited on, hand and foot. I ain't just sick. I'm also a burden. How often I've prayed to the good Lord if he'd only call me away. O Lord, O Lord, my life's too hard, it really is. I don't know . . . people might think . . . but I've been used to working hard from the time I was a child. I've always been able to do my share and now, all at once—(*She tries, in vain, to get up.*)—I just can't do nothin', no more! I've got a good husband and good children, but if I've got to sit by and see. . . . See how those girls look! They ain't got hardly no blood in 'em. They got as much color as a sheet. They keep workin' away at the treadle if they get anything for it or not. What kind of life is that? They ain't been away from the treadle all year long. They ain't even earned enough so they could buy just a few clothes so they could be seen in public, or could step into church and get some comfort. They look like skeletons, they do, young girls of fifteen and twenty.

BERTHA. (*At the stove.*) It's smokin' again.

OLD BAUMERT. Yeah, just look at that smoke. Do ya think something can be done about it? It'll damn soon collapse, that stove. We'll have to let it collapse, and we'll just have to swallow the soot. All of us cough, one worse than the other. Anyone as coughs, coughs, and if it chokes us, and if our lungs are coughed up with it, nobody cares a bit.

JAEGER. Why, that's Ansorge's business, he has to fix it, doesn't he?

BERTHA. A lot he cares. He does enough complainin'.

MOTHER BAUMERT. He thinks we're takin' up too much room, as it is.

OLD BAUMERT. And if we make a fuss, out we go. He ain't seen a bit of rent from us for almost half a year.

MOTHER BAUMERT. A man like that livin' alone could at least be civil.

OLD BAUMERT. He ain't got nothin' neither, Mother. Things is hard enough with him, too, even if he don't make a fuss about his troubles.

MOTHER BAUMERT. He's still got his house.

OLD BAUMERT. Oh, no, Mother, what are ya talkin' about? There ain't hardly a stick of wood in this house he can call his own.

JAEGER. (*Has sat down. He takes a short pipe with a decorative tassel out of one coat pocket and a flask of whiskey out of the other.*) This can't go on much longer. I'm amazed at how things are with you people around here. Why, dogs in the city live better than you live.

OLD BAUMERT. (*Eagerly.*) That's the truth, ain't it? You know it, too? And if ya complain, they tell ya it's just hard times.

ANSORGE. (*Enters with an earthen bowl full of soup in one hand, a half-finished basket in the other.*) Welcome home, Moritz! So you're here again?

JAEGER. Thank you, Father Ansorge.

ANSORGE. (*Shoving his bowl into the oven.*) Say, if you don't look like a count!

OLD BAUMERT. Show him your fine watch. He's brought back a new suit, too, and ten silver thalers in cash.

ANSORGE. (*Shaking his head.*) Well, well! Well, well!

EMMA. (*Putting the potato peelings into a little sack.*) I'll take the peelin's over now. Maybe it'll be enough for a little skimmed milk. (*She goes out.*)

JAEGER. (*While all pay close and eager attention to him.*) Well, now, just think how often you've made it hot as hell for me. They'll teach you manners, Moritz, you always said, just you wait, when they take you into the army. Well, now you see, it's gone pretty well with me. In half a year, I had my stripes. You have to be willing, that's the main thing. I polished the sergeant's boots; I curried his horse, I brought him his beer. I was as quick as a weasel. And I was always on my toes; damn it, my gear was always clean and sparkling. I was the first one in the stable, the first one at roll call, the first one in the saddle; and when it came to the attack—forward! Hell and damnation! I was as keen as a hunting dog. I always said to myself, nobody'll help you here, you can't get out of this job; and I'd pull myself together and do it; and then, finally, the captain said about me, in front of the whole squadron: That's the way a Hussar ought to be. (*Silence. He lights his pipe.*)

ANSORGE. (*Shaking his head.*) My, and such luck you had! Well, well! Well, well! (*He sits down on the floor, with the willow switches beside him. Holding the basket between his legs, he continues mending it.*)

OLD BAUMERT. Let's just hope that ya brought us some of your good luck along with ya. Now maybe we could have a drink with ya, huh?

JAEGER. Why, sure, Father Baumert, and when this is gone, there'll be more. (*He throws a coin down on the table.*)

ANSORGE. (*With foolish, grinning amazement.*) O Lord, such goin's on . . . over there, there's a roast sizzlin' and here's a quart of whiskey—(*He drinks from the bottle.*)—to your health, Moritz. Well, well! Well, well! (*From now on, the whiskey bottle is passed around.*)

OLD BAUMERT. If we could only have a little roast on holidays, instead of not seein' no meat at all, year in and year out. This way, ya've got to wait till a little dog crosses your path like this one did four weeks ago. And that don't happen often these days.

ANSORGE. Did ya have Ami killed?

OLD BAUMERT. He would've starved to death. . . .

ANSORGE. Well, well! Well, well!

MOTHER BAUMERT. And he was such a nice, friendly little dog.

JAEGER. Are you still so eager 'round here for roast dog?

OLD BAUMERT. O Lord, Lord, if we could only get our fill of it.

MOTHER BAUMERT. Yes, a piece of meat like that is sure rare around here.

OLD BAUMERT. Ain't ya got no appetite for such things no more? Well, just stay here with us, Moritz, and ya'll soon get it back.

ANSORGE. (*Sniffing.*) Well, well! Well, well! That's something that tastes good, and it sure gives off a nice smell.

OLD BAUMERT. (*Sniffing.*) The real thing, ya might say.

ANSORGE. Now tell us what you think, Moritz. You know how things go, out there in the world. Will things ever be different here with us weavers, or what?

JAEGER. I should hope so.

ANSORGE. We can't live and we can't die up here. Things is really bad with us, believe me. We fight to the last, but in the end we have to give in. The wolf is always at the door. In the old days, when I could still work at the looms, I could half-way get along, in spite of hunger and hardship. It's been a long time since I've been able to get some real work. I can hardly make a livin' weavin' baskets. I work till late into the night and when I fall worn out into bed, I've slaved for just a few pfennigs. You got a' education, now you tell me—can anyone really make out in such hard times? I got to lay out three thalers for taxes on the house, one thaler for land taxes, three thalers for interest. I can figure on makin' fourteen thalers. That leaves me seven thalers to live on all year. Out of that, I have to buy food, firewood, clothes, shoes, and patches and thread for mendin', and ya have to have a place to live, and goodness knows what else. Is it any wonder a man can't pay the interest?

OLD BAUMERT. Somebody sure ought to go to Berlin and explain to the King how things is with us.

JAEGER. That won't do much good, either, Father Baumert. There's already been plenty said about it in the newspapers. But the rich, they turn and twist the whole thing so . . . they out-devil the very best Christians.

OLD BAUMERT. (*Shaking his head.*) To think that in Berlin they ain't got no more sense than that.

ANSORGE. Tell me, Moritz, do you think that can really be? Ain't there a law against it? When I go and pinch and scrape and work my fingers to the bone weaving baskets and still can't pay the interest, can the farmer take my cottage away from me? There ain't a farmer who don't want his money. I just don't know what's to become of me if I've got to get out of my cottage. . . . (*Speaking with a choked voice, through tears.*) Here I was born, here my father sat at his loom, for more than forty years. How often he said to Mother: Mother, he said, when my time comes, you hold on to the cottage. This cottage I've worked for, he told her. Here, every single nail stands for a night's work, every board, a year's dry bread. Ya'd really think. . . .

JAEGER. They'll take your last pfennig, they're capable of it.

ANSORGE. Well, well! Well, well! But if it comes to that, I'd rather they carried me out than have to walk out in my old age. Dyin' ain't nothin'! My father was glad enough to die—only at the end, the very end, he was a bit scared. But when I crawled into the bed with him, he quieted down again. When ya think about it, at the time I was a boy of thirteen. I was tired, and I fell asleep by the sick man. I didn't know no better—and when I woke up, he was stone cold.

MOTHER BAUMERT. (*After a pause.*) Reach into the stove, Bertha, and hand Ansorge his soup.

BERTHA. Here it is, Father Ansorge.

ANSORGE. (*Weeping, while he eats.*) Well, well! Well, well!

OLD BAUMERT *has begun to eat meat out of the pan.*

MOTHER BAUMERT. Why, Father—Father, you wait. Let Bertha set it out on the table, proper.

OLD BAUMERT. (*Chewing.*) It was two years ago that I took the sacrament last. I sold my Sunday suit right afterward. We bought a little piece of pork with the money. I ain't had no meat since then till this very evenin'.

JAEGER. We don't need meat; the manufacturers eat it for us. They wade around in fat way up to here. If anybody doesn't believe that, he only needs to go down to Bielau or Peterswaldau. They'd be amazed —one manufacturer's mansion right after the other—one palace right after the other. With plate glass windows and little towers and fine iron fences. No, no, that doesn't look anything like hard times. There's plenty there for roasts and pastries, for carriages and coaches, for governesses, and who knows what all. They're so puffed up they don't really know what to do with all their high and mighty riches.

ANSORGE. In the old days, it was all different. In those days the manufacturers gave the weavers enough to get along on. Today, they squander it all themselves. I say that's because them people in high places don't believe in God no more, or in the devil, neither. They don't know nothin' about commandments and punishment. So they steal our last bite of bread, and weaken and undermine us wherever they can. Them people are the ones that's causin' all the trouble. If our manufacturers was good men, there wouldn't be no hard times for us.

JAEGER. You listen here, and I'll read you something nice. (*He takes a few sheets of paper from his pocket.*) Come on, August, run to the tavern and get another bottle. Why, August, you're always laughing.

MOTHER BAUMERT. I don't know what's the matter with the boy, he's always happy. No matter what happens, he laughs till his sides are ready to split. Now, quick! (AUGUST *goes out with the empty whiskey flask.*) Huh, Father, you know what tastes good, don't ya?

OLD BAUMERT. (*Chewing, his spirits rising from the food and the whiskey.*) Moritz, you're our man. You can read and write. You know how things is with the weavers. You have a heart for us poor weaver folk. You ought to take up our cause around here.

JAEGER. If that's all. That'd be fine with me. I'd be glad to give those devils of manufacturers something to think about. I wouldn't mind a bit. I'm an easy-going fellow, but when I once get my dander up and get mad, I'd take Dreissiger in one hand and Dittrich in the other and I'd knock their heads together so hard sparks would shoot out of their eyes. If we could manage to stick together, we could start such an uproar against the manufacturers. . . . We wouldn't need the King for that, or the government, either; we could simply say, we want this and that, and we do not want this or that, and they'd soon whistle a different tune. If they once see we've got spunk, they'd soon pull in their horns. I know their kind! They're cowardly bastards.

MOTHER BAUMERT. And that's really the truth. I certainly ain't bad. I was always one to say, there has to be rich people, too. But when it comes to this. . . .

JAEGER. For my part, the devil can take them all. That's what the whole bunch deserves.

BERTHA. Where's father? (OLD BAUMERT *has quietly left.*)

MOTHER BAUMERT. I don't know where he could've gone.

BERTHA. Could it be he ain't used to meat no more?

MOTHER BAUMERT. (*Beside herself, crying.*) Now, ya see, now ya see! He can't even keep it down. He's had to throw it up, all that nice little bit of good food.

OLD BAUMERT. (*Re-enters, crying with rage.*) No, no! It'll soon be all over with me. I'm too far gone. Ya finally get ahold of something good, and ya can't even keep it down. (*He sits down on the stove bench, weeping.*)

JAEGER. (*In a sudden fanatic outburst.*) And, at the same time, there are people, judges, not far from here—pot-bellies—who haven't a thing to do all year long except idle away their time. And they'll say the weavers could get along fine, if only they weren't so lazy.

ANSORGE. They ain't men, they're monsters.

JAEGER. Never mind, he's got what's coming to him. Baecker and I, we've given him a piece of our mind, and before we left, we sang "Bloody Justice."

ANSORGE. O Lord, O Lord, is that the song?

JAEGER. Yes, yes, and I have it here.

ANSORGE. I think it's called "Dreissiger's Son," ain't it?

JAEGER. I'll read it to you.

MOTHER BAUMERT. Who made up the song?

JAEGER. That, nobody knows. Now listen.

He reads, spelling it out like a schoolboy, accenting it badly, but with unmistakably strong feeling. Despair, pain, courage, hate, thirst for revenge—are all expressed.

JAEGER.

Here a bloody justice thrives
More terrible than lynching
Here sentence isn't even passed
To quickly end a poor man's life.

Men are slowly tortured here,
Here is the torture chamber,
Here every heavy sigh that's heard
Bears witness to man's misery.

OLD BAUMERT. (*Is deeply moved by the words of the song. He frequently has difficulty in resisting the temptation to interrupt* JAEGER. *Now he can no longer contain himself; stammering amid laughter and tears, to his wife.*) "Here is the torture chamber." Whoever wrote that, Mother, spoke the truth. You can bear witness to that . . . how does it go? "Here every sigh that's heard. . . ." What's the rest? . . . "bear witness . . ."

JAEGER. "Bears witness to man's misery."

OLD BAUMERT. Ya know, standin' or sittin', we sigh with misery day after day.

ANSORGE *has stopped working, his body bent over in deep emotion.* MOTHER BAUMERT *and* BERTHA *are continuously wiping their eyes.*

JAEGER. (*Continues reading.*)

The Dreissigers are hangmen all,
Their servants are the henchmen
All of them oppressing us
And never showing mercy.

You scoundrels all, you devil's brood

OLD BAUMERT. (*Trembling with rage, stamps the floor.*) Yes, devil's brood!!!

JAEGER. (*Reads.*)

You demons from the pit of hell
Who steal the poor man's house and home
A curse will be your payment.

ANSORGE. Well, well, and that deserves a curse.

OLD BAUMERT. (*Doubling his fist, threatening.*) "Who steal the poor man's house and home. . . !"

JAEGER. (*Reads.*)

Begging, pleading doesn't help,
In vain is all complaining,
"If you don't like it you can go,
And starve until you're dead."

OLD BAUMERT. What does it say? "In vain is all complaining"? Every word, every single word. . . . It's all as true as the Bible. "Begging, pleading doesn't help."

ANSORGE. Well, well! Well, well! Then nothin' will help.

JAEGER. (*Reads.*)

Now think about the misery
And pain of these poor wretches
Without a bite of bread at home
Are they not to be pitied?

Pitied! Ha! Such human feeling
Is unknown to you savages.
Your goal is known to everyone,
To bleed us poor men dry.

OLD BAUMERT. (*Springs up, in mad frenzy.*) "Bleed us poor men dry." That's right, bleed a poor man dry. Here I stand, Robert Baumert, master weaver from Kaschbach. Who can step up and say . . . I've been a good man all my life, and now look at me. What good's it done me? How do I look? What have they made of me? "Men are slowly tortured here." (*He stretches out his arms.*) Here, feel these, nothin' but skin and bones. "You scoundrels all, you devil's brood!!" (*He collapses onto a chair, weeping with anger and despair.*)

ANSORGE. (*Flings the basket into the corner, gets up, his entire body trembling with rage, stammers.*) There must be a change, I tell ya, here and now. We won't stand for it no more! We won't stand for it no more, come what may.

CURTAIN

ACT THREE

SCENE—*The tap room in the principal tavern in Peterswaldau. It is a large room, the raftered ceiling of which is supported at the center by a wooden pillar, around which there is a table. To the right of the pillar—one of its jambs hidden by the pil-*

lar—is a door in the back wall leading to another large room in which barrels and brewing utensils can be seen. In the corner to the right of the door is the bar—a high wooden counter with shelves for mugs, glasses, and the like; behind the bar is a cupboard with rows of liquor bottles; between the counter and the liquor cabinet there is a narrow space for the bartender. In front of the bar there is a table covered with a brightly colored cloth. A decorative lamp hangs above the table, around which there are a number of cane-chairs. Not far off in the right wall, a door leads to a room used for special occasions. Nearer the front, to the right, an old grandfather's clock is ticking. To the left of the entrance, against the rear wall, stands a table with bottles and glasses, and beyond it, in the corner, a large tile stove. There are three small windows in the left wall, under them a bench. In front of each window there is a large wooden table with its narrow end toward the wall. On the broad side of the tables are benches with backs and at the other narrow end, a single wooden chair. The walls are painted blue and are hung with placards, posters, and oil prints, among them the portrait of the King of Prussia, William IV.

Innkeeper WELZEL, *a good-natured giant of around fifty, is drawing beer into a glass from a barrel behind the counter.* MRS. WELZEL *is ironing at the stove. She is a dignified-looking woman, neatly dressed, not quite thirty-five years old.* ANNA WELZEL, *a well-dressed pretty girl of seventeen with magnificent reddish-blonde hair, sits behind the table, embroidering. For a moment she looks up from her work and listens to the sounds of children's voices singing a funeral hymn, off in the distance.* WIEGAND, *the carpenter, in his work clothes, sits at the same table with a glass of Bavarian beer in front of him. He gives the appearance of being the sort of man who knows what is needed to get ahead in the world: cunning, speed, and ruthless determination.* A TRAVELING SALESMAN *sits at the pillar table, busily devouring a chopped steak. He is of medium height, well-fed, rather puffy, disposed to heartiness, lively and impudent. He is dressed in the latest fashion. His baggage, consisting of traveling bag, sample case, umbrella, overcoat, and steamer rug—lie on chairs beside him.*

WELZEL. (*Carrying a glass of beer to the* SALESMAN, *aside to* WIEGAND.) The devil's loose in Peterswaldau today.

WIEGAND. (*In sharp, trumpeting voice.*) Well, of course, it's delivery day up at Dreissiger's.

MRS. WELZEL. Yes, but they weren't always so noisy.

WIEGAND. Well, it might be on account of the two hundred additional weavers that Dreissiger's gettin' ready to take on.

MRS. WELZEL. (*At her ironing.*) Yes, yes, that's it. If he wanted two hundred, probably six hundred will have showed up. We've got more'n enough of that sort.

WIEGAND. Lord, yes, there's plenty of them. And no matter how hard it goes with them, they don't die out. They bring more children into the world than we can ever use. (*For a moment, the hymn can be more clearly heard.*) And to add to it, there's a funeral today, too. Weaver Fabich died.

WELZEL. It took him long enough. He's been goin' around for years lookin' like a ghost.

WIEGAND. I tell ya, Welzel, never in all my life have I glued together such a tiny, shabby coffin. It was such a measly little corpse, it didn't even weigh ninety pounds.

SALESMAN. (*Chewing.*) I really don't understand . . . wherever you look, in all the newspapers, you read the most horrible stories about conditions among the weavers, and you get the impression that all the people here are half-starved. And then you see such a funeral! Just as I came into the village, there were brass bands, schoolteachers, children, the Pastor, and a whole string of people; my God, you'd think the Emperor of China was being buried. If these people can pay for that. . . ! (*He drinks his beer. Then he puts the glass down and suddenly speaks in a frivolous tone.*) Isn't that so, Miss? Don't you agree with me?

ANNA *smiles, embarrassed, and continues busily with her embroidery.*

SALESMAN. Those must be slippers for Papa.

WELZEL. Oh, I don't like to wear them things.

SALESMAN. Just listen to that! I'd give half my fortune if those slippers were for me.

MRS. WELZEL. He just don't appreciate such things.

WIEGAND. (*After he has coughed several times and moved his chair about, as if he wanted to speak.*) The gentleman has expressed himself mighty well about the funeral. Now tell us, young lady, isn't that just a small funeral?

SALESMAN. Yes, I must say. . . . That must cost a tremendous amount of money. Where do these people get the money for it?

WIEGAND. You'll forgive me for sayin' it, sir, there is so much folly among the poorer classes hereabouts. If you don't mind my sayin' so, they have such exaggerated ideas of the dutiful respect and the obligations that's due the deceased and the blessed dead. And when it's a matter of deceased parents, they are so superstitious that the descendants and the next of kin scrape together their last penny. And what the children can't raise, they borrow from the nearest money lender. And then they're in debts up to their necks; they'll be owing His Reverence the Pastor, the sexton, and everybody else in the neighborhood. And drinks and victuals and all the other necessary things. Oh yes, I approve of respectful duty on the part of children toward their parents, but not so that the mourners are burdened down the rest of their lives by such obligations.

SALESMAN. I beg your pardon, but I should think the Pastor would talk them out of it.

WIEGAND. Beggin' your pardon, sir, but here I would like to interpose that every little congregation has its ecclesiastical house of worship and must support its reverend pastor. The high clergy get a wonderful revenue and profit from such a big funeral. The more elaborate such a funeral can be arranged, the more profitable is the offertory that flows from it. Whoever knows the conditions of the workers hereabouts can, with unauthoritative certainty, affirm that the pastors only with reluctance tolerate small and quiet funerals.

HORNIG. (*Enters. A small, bow-legged old man with a strap over his shoulders and chest. He is a rag picker.*) Good mornin'. I'd like a drink. Well, young lady, any rags? Miss Anna, in my cart I've got beautiful hair ribbons, lingerie, ribbons, garters, pins and hairpins, hooks and eyes. I'll give them all to ya for a few rags. (*Changing his tone.*) Then, out of the rags, they'll make fine white paper, and your sweetheart'll write ya a lovely letter on it.

ANNA. Oh no, thank you, I don't want a sweetheart.

MRS. WELZEL. (*Puts a hot bolt in the iron.*) That's the way the girl is. She don't want to think of gettin' married.

SALESMAN. (*Jumps up, apparently surprised and pleased, steps up to the table, and holds out his hand to* ANNA.) That's sensible, Miss. You're just like me. O.K., let's shake on it! We'll both stay single.

ANNA. (*Blushing, gives him her hand.*) But surely you are married?

SALESMAN. God forbid, I just make believe I am. You think, perhaps, because I wear this ring? I just put it on my finger to prevent people from taking unfair advantage of my charming personality. Of you, I'm not afraid. (*He puts the ring in his pocket.*) Seriously, Miss, tell me, don't you ever want to get just the least bit married?

ANNA. (*Shaking her head.*) And why should I?

MRS. WELZEL. She'll stay single unless something very special turns up.

SALESMAN. Well, why not? One wealthy Silesian businessman married his mother's maid, and that rich manufacturer, Dreissiger, took an innkeeper's daughter, too. She isn't half as pretty as you, Miss, and now she rides in a carriage with liveried servants. Why not, indeed? (*He walks around, stretching his legs.*) I'll have a cup of coffee.

ANSORGE *and* OLD BAUMERT *enter, each with a bundle, and quietly and humbly join* HORNIG *at the front table to the left.*

WELZEL. Welcome, Father Ansorge. Is it you we're seein' again?

HORNIG. Did ya finally crawl out of your smoky nest?

ANSORGE. (*Awkwardly and visibly embarrassed.*) I went and got myself another web.

OLD BAUMERT. He's ready to work for 10 groschen.

ANSORGE. I never would've done it, but there's been an end to my basket weavin'.

WIEGAND. It's always better than nothin'. Ya know he's doin' it so ya'll have work. I'm very well acquainted with Dreissiger. A week ago I took out the storm windows for him. We were talkin' about it. He just does it out of pity.

ANSORGE. Well, well—well, well.

WELZEL. (*Setting a glass of whiskey in front of each of the weavers.*) Your health! Now tell me, Ansorge, how long has it been since ya stopped shavin'? The gentleman would like to know.

SALESMAN. (*Calls across.*) Now, Mr. Welzel, you know I didn't say that. I just noticed the master weaver because of his venerable appearance. One doesn't often run across such a powerful figure.

ANSORGE. (*Scratches his head, embarrassed.*) Well, well—well, well.

SALESMAN. Such extremely powerful, primitive men are seldom seen these days. We are so softened by civilization . . . but I find I still get pleasure out of such natural, unspoiled strength. What bushy eyebrows! Such a heavy beard. . . .

HORNIG. Well, look here, now I'll tell ya, sir—the people hereabouts are too poor to go to the barber, and they haven't been able to afford a razor in many a day. What grows, grows. They haven't anything to spend on the outer man.

SALESMAN. But I ask you, my good man, where would I. . . . (*Softly, to the tavern keeper.*) Would it be proper to offer the hairy one a glass of beer?

WELZEL. God forbid. He'll take nothin'. He's got queer notions.

SALESMAN. Well, then I won't. With your permission, Miss? (*He takes a seat at the table with her.*) I can assure you, from the time I came in, I've been so struck by your hair, such luster, such softness, such a mass of it! (*Delighted, he kisses his finger tips.*) And what color . . . like ripe wheat. What a furor you would cause if you came to Berlin with hair like that. *Parole d'honneur,* with such hair you could be presented at Court. (*Leaning back, looking at her hair.*) Exquisite, really exquisite.

WIEGAND. It's on account of her hair that she's got such a pretty nickname.

SALESMAN. What do they call her?

ANNA. (*Keeps on laughing to herself.*) Oh, don't you listen to them.

HORNIG. They call you Red Fox, don't they?

WELZEL. Now stop that! Stop turnin' the girl's head altogether. They've already put enough high and mighty ideas in her head. Today she wants a count, tomorrow it'll have to be a prince.

MRS. WELZEL. Don't ya run the girl down, man. It's no crime for a person to want to get ahead. Not everybody thinks the way you do. That wouldn't be good, either. Then nobody'd get ahead, then everybody'd always stay in the same old place. If Dreissiger's grandfather had thought the way you do, he'd still be a poor weaver. Now they're rich as can be. Old Tromtra, too, was no more than a poor weaver, now he owns twelve big estates and on top of that, he's got a title.

WIEGAND. You must admit, Welzel, on that score, your wife's right. I can vouch for that. If I'd thought like you, would I have seven journeymen today?

HORNIG. You sure know how to bide your time, we'll have to give ya credit for that. Even before the weaver's off his feet, you're already gettin' his coffin ready.

WIEGAND. You've got to tend to business if you want to get ahead.

HORNIG. Yes, you tend to yours, all right. You know better than the doctor does, when a weaver's child is goin' to die.

WIEGAND. (*No longer smiling, suddenly furious.*) And you know better than the police does where the thieves sit among the weavers, the ones who hold out a few bobbins every week. Ya come after rags and ya get a bobbin of yarn, too, if there's a chance.

HORNIG. And your livin' lays in the graveyard. The more that go to rest on your wood shavings, the better it is for you. When ya look at all the children's graves, ya pat your belly and ya say, this year's been a good one again; the little rascals dropped like June bugs from the trees. So I can afford a bottle of whiskey again this week.

WIEGAND. Anyhow, at least I don't trade in stolen goods.

HORNIG. At the most, you bill some rich cotton manufacturer twice, or you take a few extra boards from Dreissiger's barn if the moon ain't shinin'.

WIEGAND. (*Turning his back on* HORNIG.) Oh, go on talkin' to anyone you please, but leave me alone. (*Suddenly.*) Hornig, the liar!

HORNIG. Coffin-maker!

WIEGAND. (*To the others.*) He knows how to bewitch cattle.

HORNIG. Look out, let me tell ya, or I'll put the sign on you. (WIEGAND *turns pale.*)

MRS. WELZEL. (*Had gone out, and now sets a cup of coffee down in front of the* SALESMAN.) Would you perhaps rather have your coffee in the other room?

SALESMAN. Whatever put that idea in your head? (*With a longing look at* ANNA.) I'll stay here until I die.

A YOUNG FORESTER *and a* FARMER *enter, the latter carrying a whip.* (*Together.*) Good morning! (*They stop at the bar.*)

FARMER. We'll have two ginger beers.

WELZEL. Welcome to both of you! (*He pours the drinks; they both take their glasses, touch them to each other, take a sip, and place them back on the bar.*)

SALESMAN. Well, Forester, have you had a long trip?

FORESTER. Pretty far. I've come from Steinseiffersdorf.

FIRST *and* SECOND OLD WEAVERS *enter and sit down next to* ANSORGE, BAUMERT, *and* HORNIG.

SALESMAN. Pardon me, sir, are you one of Count Hochheim's foresters?

FORESTER. No, I'm one of Count Kailsch's.

SALESMAN. Oh, of course, of course—that's what I meant to say. It's most confusing here with all the counts and barons and other people of rank. You've got to have a good memory. What are you carrying the ax for?

FORESTER. I took it away from some thieves I caught stealing wood.

OLD BAUMERT. His Lordship is sure strict about a few sticks of firewood.

SALESMAN. I beg your pardon, it would

scarcely do if everybody were to take. . . .

OLD BAUMERT. Beggin' your pardon, it's the same here as everywhere else with the big and the little thieves; there are those that carry on a wholesale lumber business and get rich from stolen wood, but if a poor weaver so much as. . . .

FIRST OLD WEAVER. (*Interrupts* BAUMERT.) We don't dare pick up a single twig, but the lords, they skin us alive. There's insurance money to pay, spinnin' money, payments in kind; then we have to run errands for nothin' and work on the estate, whether we want to or not.

ANSORGE. And that's the truth: what the manufacturers leave us, the noblemen take away.

SECOND OLD WEAVER. (*Has taken a seat at the next table.*) I've said it to the gentleman hisself. Beggin' your pardon, sir, I says to him, I can't do so many days' work on the estate this year. I just can't do it! And why not? Forgive me, but the water has ruined everything. My little bit of ground's been all washed away. I've got to slave night and day if I'm to keep alive. Such a flood . . . I tell ya, I just stood there and wrung my hands. That good soil washed right down the hill and straight into my cottage; and that fine, expensive seed. . . ! Oh my Lord, I just howled into the wind. I cried for a week, till I couldn't see no more. . . . And after that I wore myself out pushin' eighty wheelbarrows of dirt up the hill.

FARMER. (*Roughly.*) You do set up an awful howl, I must say. We all have to put up with what Heaven sends us. And if it don't go good in other ways with ya, who's to blame but yourselves? When times was good, what did ya do then? Ya gambled and drank it all up, that's what ya did. If ya had put something aside at that time, ya'd have had something saved for now, and ya wouldn't have had to steal wood and yarn.

FIRST YOUNG WEAVER. (*Standing with several friends in the other room, shouts through the door.*) A farmer's always a farmer, even if he sleeps till nine every mornin'.

FIRST OLD WEAVER. That's a fact; the farmer and the nobleman, they're two of a kind. If a weaver wants a place to live, the farmer says I'll give ya a little hole to live in. You pay me a nice rent, and help me bring in my hay and my grain, and if ya don't like it, ya'll see what happens. Every one of them's just like the next one.

OLD BAUMERT. (*Fiercely.*) We're just like an old apple that everybody takes a bite out of.

FARMER. (*Irritated.*) Oh, you starved wretches, what are you good for, anyway? Can ya handle a plow? Can ya even plow a straight furrow, or pitch fifteen shocks of oats onto a wagon? You're good for nothin' but loafin', and lyin' abed with your women. You're no good at all. You're no-account bums. No use at all.

(*He pays and leaves. The* FORESTER *follows him, laughing.* WELZEL, *the* CARPENTER, *and* MRS. WELZEL *laugh out loud, the* SALESMAN *chuckles. Then the laughter quiets down, and there is silence.*)

HORNIG. A farmer like that's just like a bull. As if I didn't know how bad things was around here. All the things ya get to see up here in the villages. Four and five people layin' naked on a single straw ticking.

SALESMAN. (*In a gentle, rebuking tone.*) Permit me, my good man, to observe that there is a wide difference of opinion in regard to the distress in this region. If you can read. . . .

HORNIG. Oh, I read everything in the papers as well as you do. No, no, I know these things from goin' around and mixin' with the people. When a man's lugged a pack around for forty years, he learns a thing or two. What happened at the Fullers? The children, they scratched around in the dung heap with the neighbors' geese. Those people died there—naked—on the cold stone floor. They had to eat stinkin' weaver's glue, they was so hungry. Hunger killed them off by the hundreds.

SALESMAN. If you can read, you must be aware that the government has had a thorough investigation made and that. . . .

HORNIG. We know all that. We know all that. The government sends a gentleman who before he sets out knows everything better than if he'd seen it himself. He walks around the village a little where the brook widens and where the best houses are. He won't dirty his good, shiny shoes goin' any farther. He thinks everything is probably just as beautiful everywhere else, and climbs into his carriage, and drives home again. And then he writes to Berlin that he saw no hardships at all. If he'd had a little bit of patience, though, and had climbed around in the village up to where the brook comes in and across it or, even better, off to the side where the little shacks are scattered, the old straw huts on the hills that are sometimes so black and broken-down they wouldn't be worth the match it'd take to set 'em afire, then he'd have made an altogether different report to Berlin. Those gentlemen from the government ought to have come to me, them that didn't want to believe that there was no hardships here. I would've showed them something, I would've opened their eyes to all the hunger-holes around here.

(*The singing of the "Weavers' Song" is heard outside.*)

WELZEL. They're singin' that devil's song again.

WIEGAND. Yes, they're turnin' the whole village upside down.

MRS. WELZEL. It's like there's something in the air.

JAEGER *and* BAECKER, *arm in arm, at the head of a band of young weavers, noisily enter the other room, and then come into the bar.*

JAEGER. Squadron halt! Dismount!

The new arrivals seat themselves at the various tables at which weavers are already sitting, and start conversations with them.

HORNIG. (*Calling to* BAECKER.) Say, tell me, what's up that ya've got such a big crowd together?

BAECKER. (*Significantly.*) Maybe something's goin' to happen. Right, Moritz?

HORNIG. You don't say! Don't do nothin' foolish.

BAECKER. Blood's flowed already. Do ya want to see?

He pushes back his sleeve, stretches out his arm and shows him bleeding tattoo marks on his upper arm. Many of the young weavers at the other tables do the same.

BAECKER. We were at Barber Schmidt's havin' ourselves tattooed.

HORNIG. Well, now that's clear. No wonder there's so much noise in the streets, with such rascals tearin' around. . . !

JAEGER. (*Showing off, in a loud voice.*) Two quarts, right away, Welzel! I'll pay for it. Maybe you think I don't have the dough? Well, just you wait! If we wanted to, we could drink beer and lap up coffee till tomorrow morning as well as a traveling salesman. (*Laughter among the young weavers.*)

SALESMAN. (*With comic surprise.*) Who or whom are you talking about—me?

(*The tavern keeper, his wife, their daughter,* WIEGAND, *and the* SALESMAN, *all laugh.*)

JAEGER. Always him who asks.

SALESMAN. Allow me to say, young man, that things seem to be going right well with you.

JAEGER. I can't complain, I'm a salesman for ready-made clothing. I go fifty-fifty with the manufacturers. The hungrier the weavers grow, the fatter I get. The greater their poverty, the fuller my cupboard.

BAECKER. Well done. Your health, Moritz!

WELZEL. (*Has brought the whiskey; on the way back to the bar, he stops and, in his usual phlegmatic and even manner, turns slowly to the weavers. Quietly and emphatically.*) You let the gentleman alone. He ain't done nothin' to you.

YOUNG WEAVERS' VOICES. We ain't done nothin' to him, either.

MRS. WELZEL *has exchanged a few words with the* SALESMAN. *She takes the cup and the rest of the coffee into the next room. The* SALESMAN *follows her amidst the laughter of the weavers.*

YOUNG WEAVERS' VOICES. (*Singing.*) The Dreissigers are hangmen all, Their servants are the henchmen. . . .

WELZEL. Sh, Sh! Sing that song wherever ya want to, but I won't allow it here.

FIRST OLD WEAVER. He's quite right. Stop that singin'.

BAECKER. (*Shouts.*) But we've got to march past Dreissiger's again. He's got to hear our song once more.

WIEGAND. Don't go too far, or he might take it the wrong way.

Laughter and cries of "Ho-ho."

OLD WITTIG. (*A gray-haired blacksmith, bareheaded, wearing a leather apron and wooden shoes, and covered with soot, as if he had just come from the smithy, enters and stands at the bar, waiting for a glass of brandy.*) Let 'em make a little noise. Barkin' dogs don't bite.

OLD WEAVERS' VOICES. Wittig, Wittig!

WITTIG. Here he is. What do ya want?

OLD WEAVERS' VOICES. Wittig is here.—Wittig, Wittig!—Come here, Wittig, set with us!—Come over here, Wittig!

WITTIG. I'm awful careful about settin' with such blockheads.

JAEGER. Come on, have a drink on me.

WITTIG. Oh, you keep your liquor. When I drink, I'll pay for my own. (*He takes his glass of brandy and sits down at the table with* BAUMERT *and* ANSORGE. *He pats the latter on the belly.*) What do the weavers eat nowadays? Sauerkraut and plenty of lice.

OLD BAUMERT. (*Ecstatically.*) But what if they wasn't to put up with it no more?

WITTIG. (*With feigned surprise, staring stupidly at the weaver.*) Well, well, well, Heinerle, tell me, is that really you? (*Laughs without restraint.*) I laugh myself sick at you people. Old Baumert wants to start a rebellion. Now we're in for it: now the tailors'll start, too, then the baa-lambs'll be rising up, then the mice and the rats. Good Lord, what a time that'll be!

He holds his sides with laughter.

OLD BAUMERT. Look here, Wittig, I'm the same man I used to be. And I tell ya even now if things could be settled peaceable, it'd be better.

WITTIG. Like hell it'll be settled peaceable. Where has anything like this ever been settled peaceable? Maybe things was settled peaceable in France? Maybe Robespierre patted the hands of the rich? There it was just "allay," go ahead! Always up to the guillotine! Let's go. It had to be "along songfong." Roast geese just don't fly into your mouth.

OLD BAUMERT. If I could just halfway earn my livin'. . . .

FIRST OLD WEAVER. We're fed up, up to here, Wittig.

SECOND OLD WEAVER. We don't even want to go home, no more. . . . Whether we work or whether we lay down and sleep, we starve either way.

FIRST OLD WEAVER. At home ya go completely crazy.

ANSORGE. It's all the same to me now, no matter what happens.

OLD WEAVERS' VOICES. (*With mounting excitement.*) There's no peace left nowhere.—We ain't even got the spirit to work no more.—Up our way in Steinkunzendorf there's a man settin' by the brook all day long and washin' hisself, naked as God made him. . . . He's gone completely out of his head.

THIRD OLD WEAVER. (*Rises, moved by the spirit, and begins to "speak with tongues," raising his finger threateningly.*) Judgment Day is comin'! Don't join with the rich and the gentry. Judgment Day is comin'! Lord God of Sabaoth. . . .

Several laugh. He is pushed down into his chair.

WELZEL. All he has to do is drink just one glass of liquor and his head's in a whirl.

THIRD OLD WEAVER. (*Continues.*) Hearken, they don't believe in God nor hell nor heaven. They just mock at religion.

FIRST OLD WEAVER. That's enough, now, that's enough.

BAECKER. You let the man say his prayers. Many a man could take it to heart.

MANY VOICES. (*In a tumult.*) Let him talk—let him!

THIRD OLD WEAVER. (*Raising his voice.*) Hell has opened wide and its jaws are gaping open, wide open, crashing down all those who do harm to the poor and violence to the cause of the afflicted, saith the Lord.

Tumult. Suddenly reciting like a schoolboy.

And how strange it is.
If you will carefully observe
How they the linen weavers' work despise.

BAECKER. But we're cotton weavers. (*Laughter.*)

HORNIG. The linen weavers are even worse off. They wander like ghosts around the mountains. Here you at least have the courage to rebel.

WITTIG. Do ya think, maybe, that here the worst is over? That little bit of courage that they still have left in their bodies the manufacturers will knock right out of them.

BAECKER. Why, he said that the weavers will get so they'll work for just a slice of bread and cheese. (*Tumult.*)

VARIOUS OLD *and* YOUNG WEAVERS. Who said that?

BAECKER. That's what Dreissiger said about the weavers.

A YOUNG WEAVER. That son of a bitch ought to be strung up.

JAEGER. Listen to me, Wittig, you've always talked so much about the French Revolution. You always bragged so much. Now maybe the chance'll soon come for everybody to show how much of a man he is . . . whether he is a loud-mouth or a man of honor.

WITTIG. (*Starting up in a rage.*) Say one more word, boy! Did you ever hear the whistle of bullets? Did you ever stand at an outpost in enemy territory?

JAEGER. Now don't get mad. You know we're all comrades. I didn't mean any harm.

WITTIG. I don't give a rap for your comradeship. You puffed up fool!

POLICEMAN KUTSCHE *enters.*

SEVERAL VOICES. Sh! Sh! The Police!

There is a relatively long period of sh-*ing before complete silence reigns.*

KUTSCHE. (*Sits down by the center pillar amid the deep silence of all the others.*) I'd like a shot of whiskey, please. (*Again complete silence.*)

WITTIG. Well, Kutsche, you here to see that everything's all right with us?

KUTSCHE. (*Not listening to* WITTIG.) Good mornin', Mr. Wiegand.

WIEGAND. (*Still in the corner of the bar.*) Good mornin', Kutsche.

KUTSCHE. How's business?

WIEGAND. Fine, thanks for askin'.

BAECKER. The Chief of Police is afraid we might spoil our stomachs on all the wages we get. (*Laughter.*)

JAEGER. Isn't that so, Welzel, we've all had pork roast and gravy and dumplings and sauerkraut, and now we're getting ready to drink our champagne. (*Laughter.*)

WELZEL. Everything's the other way 'round.

KUTSCHE. And if ya did have champagne and roast, ya'd still not be satisfied. I don't have no champagne, neither, and I manage to get along.

BAECKER. (*Referring to* KUTSCHE'S *nose.*) He waters his red beet with brandy and beer. That's how it got so nice and ripe. (*Laughter.*)

WITTIG. A cop like him's got a hard life. Now, he's got to throw a starvin' little boy in jail for beggin', then he has to seduce a weaver's pretty daughter, then he has to get dead drunk and beat his wife so she goes runnin' to the neighbors for fear of her life. Ridin' about on his horse, lyin' in his featherbed . . . till nine, I tell ya, ain't that easy.

KUTSCHE. Always a'talkin'! You'll talk yourself into a big mess one of these days. It's been known for a long time what sort of a fellow you are. Even as high as the judge they've known about your rebellious tongue for a long time. I know someone who'll bring his wife and children to the poorhouse with his drinkin' and hangin' around taverns, and hisself into jail. He'll agitate and agitate until he comes to a terrible end.

WITTIG. (*Laughs bitterly.*) Who knows what's ahead? You might be right after all. (*Breaking out angrily.*) But if it comes to that, then I'll know who I can thank, who has blabbed to the manufacturers and to the nobles, and reviled and slandered me so I don't get a lick of work no more.—Who set the farmers and the millers against me so that, for a whole week, I haven't had a single horse to shoe or a wheel to put a rim on. I know who that is. I once yanked the damned scoundrel off his horse because he was thrashing a poor little nitwit boy with a horsewhip for stealin' a few green pears. I tell ya, and ya know me, put me in jail, and ya'd better be makin' out your will at the same time. If I get the slightest warnin', I'll take whatever I can get my hands on, whether it's a horseshoe or a hammer, a wagon spoke or a bucket, and I'll go lookin' for ya, and if I have to pull ya out of bed, away from your woman, I'll do it and I'll cave your skull in, as sure as my name is Wittig.

He has jumped up and is about to attack KUTSCHE.

OLD *and* YOUNG WEAVERS. (*Holding him back.*) Wittig, Wittig, don't lose your head.

KUTSCHE. (*Has stood up involuntarily; his face is pale. During what follows he keeps moving backward. The nearer he gets to the door, the braver he becomes. He speaks the last few words at the very threshold, and then immediately disappears.*) What do ya want with me? I've got nothin' to do with you. I've got to talk to one of the weavers here. I've done nothin' to you and I've got no business with you. But I'm to tell you weavers this: the Chief of Police forbids ya to sing that song—"Dreissiger's Song," or whatever it's called. And if that singin' in the streets don't stop right away, he'll see to it that you get plenty of time and rest in jail. Then ya can sing on bread and water as long as ya like.

Leaves.

WITTIG. (*Shouts after him.*) He ain't got no right to forbid us anything, and if we roar till the windows rattle and they can hear us way off in Reichenbach, and if we sing so the houses tumble down on all the manufacturers and all the policemen's helmets dance on their heads, it's nobody's business.

BAECKER. (*In the meantime has stood up, and has given the signal for the sing-*

ing to begin. He begins to sing, together with the others.)

Here a bloody justice thrives
More terrible than lynching
Here sentence isn't even passed
To quickly end a poor man's life.

WELZEL *tries to quiet them, but no one listens to him.* WIEGAND *holds his hands over his ears and runs away. The weavers get up and, singing the following verses, march after* WITTIG *and* BAECKER, *who, by nods, gestures, have signaled for everyone to leave.*

Men are slowly tortured here,
Here is the torture chamber,
Here every heavy sigh that's heard
Bears witness to the misery.

Most of the weavers sing the following verse when they are in the street; only a few young fellows are still inside the taproom, paying for their drinks. At the end of the next verse the room is empty except for WELZEL, *his wife, his daughter,* HORNIG, *and* OLD BAUMERT.

You scoundrels all, you devil's brood
You demons from the pit of hell
Who steal the poor man's house and home
A curse will be your payment.

WELZEL. (*Calmly gathers up the glasses.*) Why, they're completely out of their heads today.

OLD BAUMERT *is about to leave.*

HORNIG. Tell me, Baumert, what's afoot?

OLD BAUMERT. They'll be goin' to Dreissiger's to see if he'll add to their wages.

WELZEL. Are you goin' to join up with such madness?

OLD BAUMERT. Well, you see, Welzel, it ain't up to me. A young man sometimes may, and an old man must. (*A trifle embarrassed, leaves.*)

HORNIG. (*Rises.*) It'll sure surprise me if things don't come to a bad end here.

WELZEL. Who'd think the old fellows would completely lose their heads?

HORNIG. Well, every man has his dream.

CURTAIN

ACT FOUR

SCENE—*Peterswaldau—A living room in the house of the cotton manufacturer,* DREISSIGER. *It is luxuriously furnished in the cold style of the first half of the nineteenth century. The ceiling, stove, and doors are white; the wallpaper is a cold grayish blue, with straight lines and little flowers. The room is filled with red upholstered mahogany furniture, including chairs and cupboards, richly decorated and carved. The furniture is placed as follows: on the right, between two windows with cherry-red damask curtains, is a secretary with a drop leaf that folds down to form a desk; directly opposite it, the sofa, with an iron safe nearby; in front of the sofa a table, armchairs, and straight chairs; against the back wall, a gun case. Pictures reflecting poor taste hang in gilt frames on the walls. Above the sofa hangs a mirror with a heavily gilded rococo frame. A door on the left leads to the vestibule; an open double door in the back wall leads into the drawing room, also overloaded with uncomfortable, showy furnishings. In the drawing room,* MRS. DREISSIGER *and* MRS. KITTELHAUS, *the pastor's wife, can be seen looking at pictures while* PASTOR KITTELHAUS *converses with the tutor,* WEINHOLD, *a student of theology.*

KITTELHAUS. (*A small, friendly man, enters the front room, smoking and chatting amiably with the tutor, who is also smoking.* KITTELHAUS *looks around and, when he sees no one is in the room, shakes his head in amazement.*) Of course it is not at all surprising, Weinhold; you are young. At your age, we old fellows had—I won't say the same views—but yet, similar ones. Similar ones, at any rate. And there is, after all, something wonderful about youth—and all its beautiful ideals. Unfortunately, however, they are fleeting—fleeting as April sunshine. Just wait till you are my age. When once a man has said his say to the people from the pulpit for thirty years, fifty-two times a year, not counting holidays—then he, of necessity, becomes quieter. Think of me, Weinhold, when that time comes for you.

WEINHOLD. (*Nineteen years old, pale, emaciated, tall and thin, with long, straight, blond hair. He is very restless and nervous in his movements.*) With all respect, sir . . . I really don't know . . . there certainly is a great difference in temperaments.

KITTELHAUS. My dear Weinhold, you may be ever so restless a soul—(*In a tone of reproof.*) and that you are—you may be ever so violent—and rudely attack existing conditions, but that will subside. Yes, yes, I certainly do admit that we have colleagues who, though rather advanced in years, still play rather childish and foolish tricks. One preaches against drinking and founds temperance societies; another writes appeals which, undeniably, are most touching to read. But what does he accomplish with it? The distress among the weavers, where it exists, is not relieved thereby. And yet the peace of society is undermined by it. No, no, in such a case one might almost say, cobbler, stick to your last! A keeper of souls should not concern himself with bellies. Preach the pure word of God and, for the rest, let Him take care who provides shelter and food for the birds and sees that the lily in the field does not perish.—But now I would really like to know where our worthy host went so suddenly.

MRS. DREISSIGER. (*Comes into the front room with the Pastor's wife. She is a pretty woman, thirty years old, a robust, healthy type. A certain discrepancy is noticeable between her manner of speaking or moving and her elegant attire.*) You're quite right, Pastor. Wilhelm's always that way. When something strikes him, he runs off and leaves me alone. I've talked to him about it plenty, but you can say what you will, that's the way it is.

KITTELHAUS. That's the way with businessmen, Madam.

WEINHOLD. If I'm not mistaken, something's been happening downstairs.

DREISSIGER. (*Enters, out of breath and excited.*) Well, Rosa, has the coffee been served?

MRS. DREISSIGER. (*Pouting.*) Oh, why do you always have to run away?

DREISSIGER. (*Lightly.*) Oh, what do you know about it?

KITTELHAUS. I beg your pardon! Have you had trouble, Mr. Dreissiger?

DREISSIGER. God knows, that I have every single day, my dear Pastor. I'm used to that. Well, Rosa? I guess you're taking care of it?

MRS. DREISSIGER *in a bad temper pulls violently several times at the broad, embroidered bell pull.*

DREISSIGER. Just now—(*After walking up and down a few times.*)—Mr. Weinhold, I would have liked you to have been there. You would have had an experience. At any rate . . . come, let's have a game of whist.

KITTELHAUS. Yes, yes, by all means. Shake the dust and trouble of the day from your shoulders, and come and be one of us.

DREISSIGER. (*Has stepped to the window, pushes the drapery aside, and looks out. Involuntarily.*) Rabble!—come here, Rosa! (*She comes.*) Tell me . . . that tall, red-headed fellow there. . . .

KITTELHAUS. That is the one they call Red Baecker.

DREISSIGER. Tell me, is he by any

chance the one who insulted you, two days ago? You know, what you told me, when Johann helped you into the carriage.

MRS. DREISSIGER. (*Makes a wry face, drawls.*) I don't remember.

DREISSIGER. Now don't be that way. I've got to know. I'm fed up with this impudence. If he's the one, I'll make him answer for it. (*The "Weavers' Song" is heard.*) Just listen to it! Just listen to it!

KITTELHAUS. (*Extremely indignant.*) Won't this nonsense ever come to an end? Now, really, I too must say, it's time the police took a hand. Permit me. (*He steps to the window.*) Look at that, Weinhold! Those aren't only young people; the old, steady weavers are running with the crowd. Men whom for years I have considered to be respectable and pious are in with them. They're taking part in this unheard-of nonsense. They are trampling God's law under their feet. Perhaps you would still like to defend these people, even now?

WEINHOLD. Certainly not, sir. That is, sir, *cum grano salis.* You must realize they are just hungry, ignorant men. They are expressing their dissatisfaction in the only way they know how. I don't expect such people. . . .

MRS. KITTELHAUS. (*Small, thin, faded, more like an old maid than a married woman.*) Mr. Weinhold, Mr. Weinhold! I must beg of you!

DREISSIGER. Mr. Weinhold, I regret very much. . . . I did not take you into my house so that you should give me lectures on humanitarianism. I must request that you restrict yourself to the education of my sons, and for the rest, leave my affairs to me—completely—to me alone! Do you understand?

WEINHOLD. (*Stands a moment, motionless and deathly pale, and then bows with a strange smile, softly.*) Of course, of course, I understand. I have seen it coming: that is why I wish to leave. *Exit.*

DREISSIGER. (*Brutally.*) Then, as soon as possible. We need the room.

MRS. DREISSIGER. Please, Wilhelm, Wilhelm!

DREISSIGER. Are you out of your mind? Are you defending a man that takes sides with such vulgarity and rowdyism as this insulting song?

MRS. DREISSIGER. But hubby, hubby, he really didn't. . . .

DREISSIGER. Reverend Kittelhaus, did he or did he not defend it?

KITTELHAUS. Mr. Dreissiger, one must ascribe it to his youth.

MRS. KITTELHAUS. I don't know—the young man comes from such a good and respectable family. His father was a civil servant for forty years and never allowed the slightest reproach to fall on himself. His mother was so overjoyed that he had found such an excellent position here. And now . . . now he shows so little appreciation of it.

PFEIFER. (*Tears open the vestibule door, shouts in.*) Mr. Dreissiger, Mr. Dreissiger! They've caught him. You ought to come. They've caught one of them.

DREISSIGER. (*Hastily.*) Has someone gone for the police?

PFEIFER. The Chief of Police is comin' up the stairs right now.

DREISSIGER. (*At the door.*) Your humble servant, sir! I am very glad that you have come.

KITTELHAUS *gestures to the ladies that it would be better if they withdrew. He, his wife, and Mrs. Dreissiger disappear into the drawing room.*

DREISSIGER. (*Very excited, to the* CHIEF OF POLICE, *who has entered in the meantime.*) I have finally had my dyers catch one of the ringleaders. I couldn't put up with it any longer. This impudence simply goes beyond all bounds. It's shocking. I have guests, and these rascals dare . . . they insult my wife when she shows herself; my children aren't sure of their lives.

Chances are my guests will be beaten up. I assure you—if blameless people—such as me and my family—in a law-abiding community—can be openly and continuously insulted . . . without proper punishment, really . . . then I regret that I have different ideas of law and order.

POLICE CHIEF. (*A man of perhaps fifty, of medium height, fat, red-faced. He is wearing a cavalry uniform, saber and spurs.*) Certainly not . . . no . . . certainly not, Mr. Dreissiger!—I am at your service. Calm yourself, I am completely at your service. It is quite all right. . . . I am, in fact, very glad that you had one of the ringleaders caught. I am glad that this thing has finally come to a head. There are a few troublemakers around here that I've had it in for, for quite a long time.

DREISSIGER. You are right, a few young fellows, thoroughly shiftless rabble, lazy rascals, who lead a dissolute life, day after day, sitting around in the taverns till the last penny has trickled down their throats. But now I am determined, I will put an end to these professional slanderers, once and for all. It's in the common interest, not merely in my own.

POLICE CHIEF. By all means! Certainly —by all means, Mr. Dreissiger. Nobody could find fault with you there. And as far as it's within my power. . . .

DREISSIGER. The whip should be used on these ruffians.

POLICE CHIEF. Quite right, quite right. We must set an example.

KUTSCHE. (*Enters and salutes. As the vestibule door opens, the noise of heavy feet stumbling up the steps is heard.*) Chief, it's my duty to inform you that we have caught a man.

DREISSIGER. Would you like to see him, Chief?

POLICE CHIEF. Why, of course, of course. First of all, let's have a close look at him. Please do me the favor, Mr. Dreissiger, of not interfering. I'll see to it that you're given satisfaction, or my name isn't Heide.

DREISSIGER. I won't be satisfied—not until that man is brought before the state's attorney.

JAEGER. (*Is led in by five dyers. They have come directly from work. Their faces, hands, and clothes are stained with dye. The captured man has his cap cocked on the side of his head and displays a cheerful impudence. A few drinks of whiskey have put him in high spirits.*) You miserable wretches, you! You want to be workers, huh? You want to be comrades, huh? Why, before I'd do a thing like this—before I'd lay hands on a fellow worker of mine, I think I'd let my hand rot off first.

At a signal from the POLICE CHIEF, KUTSCHE *orders the dyers to take their hands off the victim and to guard the doors.* JAEGER, *now free, stands there impudently.*

POLICE CHIEF. (*Shouts at* JAEGER.) Take your cap off, you! (JAEGER *removes it, but very slowly. He continues to smile ironically.*) What's your name? *

JAEGER. (*Simply and quietly.*) That's none of your business!

The impact of the words creates a stir among the others.

DREISSIGER. This is too much.

POLICE CHIEF. (*Changes color, is about to burst out, but conquers his anger.*) We'll see about this later. I'm asking you what your name is! (*When there is no reply, in rage.*) Speak up, you scoundrel, or I'll have you whipped.

JAEGER. (*Perfectly cheerful and without batting an eye at the furious outburst, calls over the heads of the spectators to*

* In the original, the chief of police uses the familiar "Du," whereupon Jaeger makes the remark that the two had never gone "tending swine together," i.e., they had not been on familiar terms.

a pretty servant girl about to serve coffee. She is perplexed at the unexpected sight and stands still, open-mouthed.) Why, tell me, Emily, are you in service in high society now? Well, then, see to it that you get out of here. The wind might start blowing around here one of these days, and it'll blow everything away—overnight.

The girl stares at JAEGER. *When she realizes that the speech is meant for her, she blushes with shame, covers her eyes with her hands and runs out, leaving the dishes in confusion on the table. Again there is a commotion among the spectators.*

POLICE CHIEF. (*Almost losing control of himself, to* DREISSIGER.) As old as I am . . . I've never encountered such unheard-of impudence. . . .

JAEGER *spits on the floor.*

DREISSIGER. See here, you! You're not in a stable—understand?

POLICE CHIEF. Now, I'm at the end of my patience. For the last time—what is your name?

KITTELHAUS. (*During this past scene has been peeking out from behind the partly open door of the drawing room and listening. Now, carried away by the incident and trembling with excitement, he comes forward to intervene.*) His name's Jaeger, Chief. Moritz . . . isn't it? Moritz Jaeger. (*To* JAEGER.) Why, Jaeger, don't you remember me?

JAEGER. (*Seriously.*) You are Reverend Kittelhaus.

KITTELHAUS. Yes, your pastor, Jaeger! If I'm the one who received you as an infant into the Communion of the Saints. The one—from whose hands you first received Holy Communion. Do you remember? There—I've worked and worked and brought the Word of God to your heart. Is this the thanks I get?

JAEGER. (*Gloomily, like a schoolboy who has been scolded.*) I've paid my thaler.

KITTELHAUS. Money, money—do you really believe that that vile, miserable money will. . . . Keep your money . . . I'd much rather you did. What nonsense that is! Behave yourself—be a good Christian! Think of what you've promised. Keep God's commandments—be good and pious. Money, money. . . .

JAEGER. I'm a Quaker now, Reverend. I don't believe in anything any more.

KITTELHAUS. What? A Quaker? Don't talk that way! Try to reform and leave words that you don't understand out of this. They're pious folk, not heathens like you. Quaker! What do you mean, Quaker?

POLICE CHIEF. With your permission, Reverend. (*He steps between him and* JAEGER.) Kutsche! Tie his hands!

Wild shouting outside: "Jaeger! Let Jaeger come on out!"

DREISSIGER. (*A little bit frightened, as are the others, has stepped instinctively to the window.*) Now, what does this mean?

POLICE CHIEF. I know. It means that they want this ruffian back. But that favor we won't do them this time. Understand, Kutsche? He goes to jail.

KUTSCHE. (*The rope in his hand, hesitating.*) With all respect, I'd like to say, Chief, we'll be havin' trouble. That's a damn big crowd. A regular gang of cutthroats, Chief. Baecker is among them, and the blacksmith. . . .

KITTELHAUS. With your kind permission—in order not to create more ill-feeling, wouldn't it be more appropriate, Chief, if we tried to settle this peaceably? Perhaps Jaeger will promise that he'll go along quietly or. . . .

POLICE CHIEF. What are you thinking? This is my responsibility. I can't possibly agree to a thing like that. Come on, Kutsche! Don't lose any time!

JAEGER. (*Putting his hands together and holding them out, laughing.*) Tie them tight—as tight as you can. It won't be for long.

KUTSCHE, *with the help of the dyers, ties his hands.*

POLICE CHIEF. Now, come on, march! (*To* DREISSIGER.) If you're worried about this, have six of the dyers go along. They can put him in the middle. I'll ride ahead —Kutsche will follow. Whoever gets in our way—will be cut down.

Cries from outside: "Cock-a-doodle-doo!! Woof, woof, woof!"

POLICE CHIEF. (*Threatening, toward the window.*) Rabble! I'll cock-a-doodle-doo and woof-woof you. Get going! Forward! March!

He marches out ahead, with drawn saber; the others follow with JAEGER.

JAEGER. (*Shouts as he leaves.*) And even if Milady Dreissiger acts so proud—she's no better than the likes of us. She's served my father his bit of whiskey a hundred times. Squadron, left wheel, ma-a-arch!

Leaves, laughing.

DREISSIGER. (*After a pause, apparently composed.*) What do you think, Pastor? Shall we begin our game of whist now? I don't think anything else will interfere now. (*He lights a cigar, gives several short laughs. As soon as the cigar is lit, he laughs out loud.*) Now I'm beginning to find this business funny. That fellow! (*In a nervous burst of laughter.*) It really is indescribably funny. First the dispute at dinner with the tutor. Five minutes later, he leaves. Good riddance! Then this business. And now—let's get on with our whist.

KITTELHAUS. Yes, but. . . . (*Roars from downstairs.*) Yes, but . . . you know, those people are making a terrible row.

DREISSIGER. We'll simply retire to the other room. We'll be quite undisturbed there.

KITTELHAUS. (*Shaking his head.*) If I only knew what has happened to these people. I must admit that the tutor was right in this respect. At least—until a short time ago—I, too, was of the opinion that the weavers were humble, patient, compliant people. Don't you think so too, Mr. Dreissiger?

DREISSIGER. Certainly they used to be patient and easily managed—certainly they used to be a civilized and orderly people—as long as the so-called "humanitarians" kept their hands out of it. Then for the longest time the terrible misery of their lives was pointed out to them. Think of all the societies and committees for the relief of distress among the weavers. Finally the weaver himself believes it—and now he's all mixed up. Let some one come in and set him straight again. He won't be stopped now. Now he complains endlessly. This doesn't please him and that doesn't please him. Now, everything has to be just so.

Suddenly a swelling roar of "Hurrah!" is heard from the crowd.

KITTELHAUS. So—with all their humanitarianism, they have accomplished nothing more than literally making wolves out of lambs, overnight.

DREISSIGER. No, Reverend, by the use of cool logic we might even be able to see the good side of this affair. Perhaps such happenings won't pass unnoticed in leading circles. Possibly at last they will come to the conclusion that such things cannot go on any longer—that something must be done—if our home industries are not to collapse completely.

KITTELHAUS. Yes, but what would you say was the cause of this enormous falling off of trade?

DREISSIGER. Foreign countries have put up high tariff walls against our goods. Our best markets are thus cut off, and at home we've got to compete for our very lives. We have no protection—absolutely no protection.

PFEIFER. (*Staggers in, breathless and pale.*) Mr. Dreissiger! Oh, Mr. Dreissiger!

DREISSIGER. (*Standing in the doorway,*

about to enter the drawing room, turns, angrily.) Well, Pfeifer, what is it this time?

PFEIFER. No . . . no. . . . This is the limit.

DREISSIGER. What's wrong now?

KITTELHAUS. You're alarming us—speak up!

PFEIFER. (*Hasn't recovered himself yet.*) This is the limit! I never saw anything like it! The authorities . . . they'll make them pay for it.

DREISSIGER. What the devil's go into you? Has anyone been—killed?

PFEIFER. (*Almost weeping with fear, cries out.*) They've set Moritz Jaeger free, they've beaten up the Chief of Police, and chased him away, they've beaten up the policeman—and chased him away, too—without his helmet—his saber broken. . . . Oh, I never. . . .

DREISSIGER. Pfeifer, you've lost your mind.

KITTELHAUS. Why, that would be revolution.

PFEIFER. (*Sitting down in a chair, his whole body trembling, moaning.*) It's gettin' serious, Mr. Dreissiger! It's gettin' serious, Mr. Dreissiger.

DREISSIGER. Well, then, the entire police force isn't. . . .

PFEIFER. It's gettin' serious, Mr. Dreissiger!

DREISSIGER. Damn it all, Pfeifer, shut up!

MRS. DREISSIGER. (*Comes from the drawing room with* MRS. KITTELHAUS.) Oh, but this is really shocking, Wilhelm. Our lovely evening is being ruined. There you are, now Mrs. Kittelhaus wants to go home.

KITTELHAUS. My dear Mrs. Dreissiger, perhaps it would be best today. . . .

MRS. DREISSIGER. Wilhelm, you should put a stop to this.

DREISSIGER. You go and talk to them. You go! Go on! (*Stopping in front of the Pastor, bursts out.*) Am I really a tyrant? Am I really a slave-driver?

JOHANN, THE COACHMAN. (*Enters.*) If you please, ma'am, I've harnessed the horses. The tutor has already put Georgie and Carl in the carriage. If things get worse we'll drive off.

MRS. DREISSIGER. If what gets worse?

JOHANN. Well, I don't know, either. I'm just thinkin'—the crowds are gettin' bigger all the time. After all, they have chased off the Chief of Police along with Kutsche.

PFEIFER. I'm tellin' ya, it's gettin' serious. Mr. Dreissiger! It's gettin' serious!

MRS. DREISSIGER. (*With mounting fear.*) What's going to happen? What do these people want? They couldn't attack us, Johann, could they?

JOHANN. There are some mangey dogs among them, ma'am.

PFEIFER. It's gettin' serious—deadly serious.

DREISSIGER. Shut up, you ass! Are the doors barred?

KITTELHAUS. Do me a favor . . . do me a favor . . . I have decided to . . . please do me a favor. . . . (*To* JOHANN.) What is it that the people really want?

JOHANN. (*Embarrassed.*) The stupid good-for-nothin's, they want more pay, that's what they want.

KITTELHAUS. Good, fine! I will go out and do my duty. I will have a serious talk with them.

JOHANN. Reverend, don't do that. Words won't do no good, here.

KITTELHAUS. My dear Mr. Dreissiger, just one word more. I would like to ask you to post some men behind the door and lock it immediately after I've gone.

MRS. KITTELHAUS. Oh, Joseph, are you really going to do this?

KITTELHAUS. I'll do it, of course . . . I'll do it! I know what I'm doing. Have no fear, the Lord will protect me.

MRS. KITTELHAUS *presses his hand,*

steps back, and wipes tears from her eyes.

KITTELHAUS. (*All the time the muffled noise of a large crowd is heard from below.*) I'll act . . . I'll act as if I were just quietly going home. I want to see whether my holy office . . . whether I still command the respect of these people . . . I want to see . . . (*He takes his hat and stick.*) Forward then, in God's name. (*Leaves, accompanied by* DREISSIGER, PFEIFER, *and* JOHANN.)

MRS. KITTELHAUS. Dear Mrs. Dreissiger,—(*She bursts into tears and puts her arms around* MRS. DREISSIGER'S *neck.*) —if only nothing happens to him!

MRS. DREISSIGER. (*Absently.*) I really don't know, Mrs. Kittelhaus—I am so . . . I really don't know how I feel. Such a thing can't hardly be humanly possible. If that's how it is . . . then it's like it was a sin to be rich. You know, if somebody had told me, I don't know but what, in the long run, I would rather have stayed in—in my humble circumstances.

MRS. KITTELHAUS. Dear Mrs. Dreissiger, believe me, there are disappointments and troubles enough in all walks of life.

MRS. DREISSIGER. Yes, of course—of course. I believe that, too. And if we've got more than other people . . . Lord knows, we certainly didn't steal it. Every single pfennig's been honestly earned. Surely it can't be that the people are going to attack us. Is it my husband's fault if business is bad?

From below comes tumultuous shouting. While the two women stare at each other, pale and terrified, DREISSIGER *bursts in.*

DREISSIGER. Rosa, throw on a coat and get into the carriage. I'll follow right after you!

He hurries to the safe, opens it, and takes out various valuables.

JOHANN. (*Enters.*) Everything's ready! But hurry, before they get to the back gate!

MRS. DREISSIGER. (*Panic-stricken, throws her arms around the coachman's neck.*) Johann, dear—good Johann! Save us, dearest Johann! Save my children, oh, oh. . . .

DREISSIGER. Be reasonable! Let go of Johann!

JOHANN. Madam, madam! Aw, don't be scared. Our horses are in good shape. Nobody can catch up with them. If they don't get out of the way, they'll get run over.

Exit.

MRS. KITTELHAUS. (*In helpless anxiety.*) But my husband? What about my husband? What will become of him, Mr. Dreissiger?

DREISSIGER. He is all right, Mrs. Kittelhaus. Just calm down, he is all right.

MRS. KITTELHAUS. I know something terrible's happened to him. You just won't tell me. You just won't say.

DREISSIGER. They'll be sorry for this, you mark my words. I know exactly who is responsible for it. Such unheard of, shameless impudence will not go unpunished. A community that does harm to its pastor—it's terrible! Mad dogs, that's what they are—beasts gone mad. And they should be treated accordingly. (*To* MRS. DREISSIGER, *who stands there, as if stunned.*) Now go, and hurry up! (*Sounds of beating against the entrance door are heard.*) Don't you hear me? The mob's gone mad. (*The smashing of the downstairs windows is heard.*) They've gone absolutely insane. There's nothing left to do but to get out.

A chorus of shouts is heard, "We want Pfeifer!" "Pfeifer come out!"

MRS. DREISSIGER. Pfeifer, Pfeifer! They want Pfeifer outside.

PFEIFER. (*Rushes in.*) They're at the back gate, too. The front door won't hold out another minute. Wittig is beating it in with a stable bucket—like—like a mad man.

From downstairs, the shouts become

louder and clearer, "Pfeifer come out!" "Pfeifer come out!"

MRS. DREISSIGER *rushes off, as if pursued.* MRS. KITTELHAUS *follows.*

PFEIFER. (*Listens. His face changes color. Once he makes out the cries, he is seized with an insane fear. He speaks the following words frantically, crying, whimpering, pleading, whining all at the same time. He overwhelms* DREISSIGER *with childish caresses, strokes his cheeks and arms, kisses his hands, and, finally, like a drowning man, puts his arms around him, clutching him and not letting him go.*) Oh, good, kind, merciful Mr. Dreissiger! Don't leave me behind. I have always served you loyally—I always treated the people well. Wages were fixed—I couldn't give them more. Don't leave me in the lurch. Don't! I beg you. They'll kill me. If they find me—they'll strike me dead. O, God in heaven, God in heaven, my wife, my children. . . .

DREISSIGER. (*As he leaves, vainly trying to free himself from* PFEIFER.) Let go of me, man! We'll see, we'll see!

Leaves with PFEIFER.

The room remains empty for a few seconds. In the drawing room, window panes are being smashed. A loud crash resounds through the house, followed by a roar of "Hurray," then silence. A few seconds pass, then soft and cautious footsteps of people coming upstairs to the second floor are heard; then, timid and shy cries: "To the left!—Get upstairs!—Sh!—Slow!—Don't shove!—Help push!—Smash!—Here we are!—Move on! We're goin' to a weddin'—You go in first!—No, you go!"

Young weavers and weaver girls appear in the vestibule door. They don't dare to enter, and each one tries to push the other one in. After a few moments, they overcome their timidity, and the poor, thin figures, some of them sickly, some ragged or patched, disperse throughout DREISSIGER'S *room and the drawing room. At first they look around curiously and shyly, then they touch everything. The girls try out the sofas; they form groups that admire their reflections in the mirror. A few climb up on chairs to look at pictures and to take them down, and in the meantime a steady stream of wretched-looking figures moves in from the vestibule.*

FIRST OLD WEAVER. (*Enters.*) No, no, this is goin' too far. Downstairs they're already startin' to break things up. It's crazy. There ain't no rhyme nor reason to it. In the end, that'll be a bad thing. Nobody with a clear head . . . would go along. I'll be careful and won't take part in such goin's on!

JAEGER, BAECKER, WITTIG *with a wooden bucket,* BAUMERT *and a number of young and old weavers come storming in as if they were chasing something, yelling back and forth in hoarse voices.*

JAEGER. Where is he?

BAECKER. Where is that dirty slave-driver?

OLD BAUMERT. If we're to eat grass, let him eat sawdust.

WITTIG. When we catch him, we'll string him up.

FIRST OLD WEAVER. We'll take him by the legs and throw him out of the window so he'll never get up again.

SECOND YOUNG WEAVER. (*Enters.*) He's flown the coop.

ALL. Who?

SECOND YOUNG WEAVER. Dreissiger.

BAECKER. Pfeifer, too?

VOICES. Let's look for Pfeifer! Look for Pfeifer!

OLD BAUMERT. Look for him, Little Pfeifer—there's a weaver for ya to starve! (*Laughter.*)

JAEGER. If we can't get this beast Dreissiger—we'll make him poor.

OLD BAUMERT. He'll be as poor as a churchmouse—just as poor.

All rush to the door of the drawing room, ready to destroy everything.

BAECKER. (*Runs ahead, turns around,*

and stops the others.) Stop—listen to me! Once we're through here, we'll really get goin'. From here we'll go over to Bielau —to Dittrich's—he's the one who's got the steam power looms. . . . All the trouble comes from those factories.

ANSORGE. (*Comes in from the vestibule. After he has taken a few steps, he stands still, looks unbelievingly about, shakes his head, strikes his forehead, and says.*) Who am I? The Weaver Anton Ansorge? Has he gone crazy, Ansorge? It's true—things are buzzin' around in my head like a gadfly. What's he doin' here? He'll do whatever he wants to. Where is he, Ansorge? (*He strikes himself on the forehead.*) I ain't myself! I don't understand, I ain't quite right. Go away—you go away! Go away, you rebels! Heads off—legs off—hands off! You take my cottage, I'll take yours. Go to it!

With a yell, he goes into the drawing room. The rest follow him amid yells and laughter.

CURTAIN

ACT FIVE

SCENE—*The tiny weaver's room at* OLD HILSE'S. *To the left is a small window, in front of it a loom; to the right, a bed with a table pushed up close to it. In the corner, to the right is the stove with a bench. Around the table, on the foot bench, on the edge of the bed, and on a wooden stool, the following persons are seated:* OLD HILSE; *his old, blind, and almost deaf wife; his son,* GOTTLIEB; *and* GOTTLIEB'S *wife,* LUISE. *They are at morning prayers. A winding wheel with bobbins stands between table and loom. On top of the smoky, brown rafters, all kinds of old spinning, winding, and weaving implements are stored. Long hanks of yarn hang down; all sorts of rubbish are strewn about the room. The very low, narrow room has a door leading to the hall in the back wall. Opposite it, another door in the entrance hall stands open and affords a view into a second weaver's room similar to the first. The hall is paved with stones, the plaster is crumbling, and a dilapidated wooden stair leads to the attic. A washtub on a wooden stool is partly visible; shabby bits of laundry and household goods of the poor are scattered about. The light falls from the left into all the rooms.*

OLD HILSE. (*A bearded, heavy-boned man, now bent and worn with age, hard work, sickness, and exertion. An ex-soldier, he has lost one arm. He has a sharp nose, livid coloring. His hands tremble, and his body seems to be just skin, bones, and sinews. He has the deep-set, sore eyes characteristic of the weavers. He stands up, together with his son and daughter-in-law, and begins to pray.*) O Lord, we cannot be grateful enough that Thou this night, in Thy grace and goodness . . . hast taken pity upon us. That we have come to no harm this night. "Lord, Thy mercy reaches so far," and we are but poor, evil and sinful human beings not worthy to be trampled under Thy feet, so sinful and corrupted are we. But Thou, dear Father, willst look upon us and accept us for the sake of Thy beloved Son, our Lord and Savior, Jesus Christ. "Jesus' blood and righteousness, they are my jewels and my robe of glory. . . ." And if sometimes we despair under Thy scourge—when the fire of purification burns too raging hot, then do not count it too highly against us—forgive us our trespasses. Give us patience, O Heavenly Father, that after this suffering we may become part of Thy eternal blessedness. Amen.

MOTHER HILSE. (*Who has been bending forward in a great effort to hear, weeping.*) Father, you always say such a beautiful prayer.

LUISE *goes to the washtub,* GOTTLIEB

into the room on the other side of the hall.

OLD HILSE. Wherever is the girl?

LUISE. She went over to Peterswaldau —to Dreissiger's. She finished windin' a few hanks of yarn again last night.

OLD HILSE. (*Speaking in a very loud voice.*) Well, Mother, now I'll bring ya the wheel.

MOTHER HILSE. Yes, bring it, bring it to me, Father.

OLD HILSE. (*Placing the wheel in front of her.*) I'd be glad to do it for ya. . . .

MOTHER HILSE. No . . . no. . . . What would I be doin' then with all that time?

OLD HILSE. I'll wipe your fingers off for ya a bit, so the yarn won't get greasy— do ya hear? (*He wipes her hands with a rag.*)

LUISE. (*At the washtub.*) When did we have anything fat to eat?

OLD HILSE. If we don't have fat, we'll eat dry bread—if we don't have bread, we'll eat potatoes—and if we don't have potatoes neither, then we'll eat dry bran.

LUISE. (*Insolently.*) And if we ain't got rye flour, we'll do like the Wenglers— we'll find out where the flayer has buried an old dead horse. We'll dig it up and live off the rotten beast—for a couple of weeks—that's what we'll do, won't we?

GOTTLIEB. (*From the back room.*) What kind of damn nonsense are ya spoutin'?

OLD HILSE. Ya ought to be more careful with such godless talk! (*He goes to the loom, calls.*) Won't ya help me, Gottlieb —there's a few threads to pull through.

LUISE. (*From her work at the washtub.*) Gottlieb, you're to lend a hand to your father.

GOTTLIEB *enters. The old man and his son begin the tiresome job of reeding. They have hardly begun when* HORNIG *appears in the entrance hall.*

HORNIG. (*In the doorway.*) Good luck to your work!

OLD HILSE AND HIS SON. Thank ya, Hornig!

OLD HILSE. Tell me, when do ya sleep, anyhow? In the daytime ya go about tradin'—in the night ya stand watch.

HORNIG. Why, I don't get no sleep at all no more!

LUISE. Glad to see ya, Hornig!

OLD HILSE. Any good news?

HORNIG. A pretty piece of news. The people in Peterswaldau have risked their necks and have chased out Dreissiger and his whole family.

LUISE. (*With signs of excitement.*) Hornig's lyin' his head off again.

HORNIG. Not this time, young woman! Not this time—I have some pretty pinafores in the cart.—No, no, I'm tellin' the honest-to-God truth. They've up and chased him out. Yesterday evenin' he got to Reichenbach. By God! They didn't dare keep him there—for fear of the weavers—so he had to hurry off to Schweidnitz.

OLD HILSE. (*Picks up the thread of the warp carefully and pulls it close to the reed. His son catches the thread with a hook and pulls it through.*) Now, it's time for ya to stop, Hornig!

HORNIG. If I'm lyin', I don't want to leave this place alive, I swear. There ain't a child that don't know the story.

OLD HILSE. Now tell me, am I all mixed up, or are you?

HORNIG. Well, now. What I'm tellin' ya is as true as Amen in the church. I wouldn't of said nothin' if I hadn't been standin' right there, but that's the way I saw it. With my own eyes, just like I see you here, Gottlieb. They've smashed up the manufacturer's house, from cellar to attic. They threw the fine china from the attic window and smashed it—right down over the roof. Hundreds of pieces of cotton are layin' in the bottom of the brook! Believe me, the water can't even flow on no more; it swelled up over the banks; it turned real blue from all the indigo they poured out of the windows. The air itself was filled with all them blue clouds. No, no, they did a terrible job there. Not just in the house, mind you, . . . in the dye plant . . . in the warehouse. . . ! Banisters smashed, the floors torn up—mirrors broken—sofas, arm chairs—everything—torn and slashed—cut to pieces and smashed—trampled and hacked to pieces—damn it! believe me, it was worse than war!

OLD HILSE. And you say those were weavers from around here?

Slowly and incredulously, he shakes his head. A group of tenants of the house has gathered at the door, listening intently.

HORNIG. Well, who else? I could mention all of them by name. I led the Commissioner through the house. I talked with plenty of them. They were just as friendly as usual. They went about the whole business quietly—but they were thorough. The Commissioner talked with a lot of them. They were just as polite as usual. But they wouldn't stop. They hacked at the elegant furniture, just like they were workin' for wages.

OLD HILSE. You led the Commissioner through the house?

HORNIG. Well, I sure wasn't afraid. The people all know me, always turnin' up like a bad penny. I never had trouble with nobody. I'm in good with all of them. As sure as my name is Hornig, I went through the house. Yes—and ya can really believe it—I was sore at heart—and I can tell ya about the Commissioner—he took it to heart, too. And why? Ya couldn't hear a single word the whole time, it was that quiet. It gave ya a real solemn feelin'—the way them poor hungry devils was takin' their revenge.

LUISE. (*Bursting out with excitement, trembling and wiping her eyes with her apron.*) That's only right—that had to happen!

VOICES OF THE TENANTS. There's enough slave-drivers 'round here. There's one livin' right over there.—He's got four horses and six coaches in his stable, and he lets his weavers starve!

OLD HILSE. (*Still incredulous.*) How could that have started over there?

HORNIG. Who knows? Who knows? One says this—another that.

OLD HILSE. What do they say?

HORNIG. By God, Dreissiger is supposed to have said the weavers could eat grass if they got hungry. I don't know no more.

Commotion among the tenants, who repeat it to each other with signs of indignation.

OLD HILSE. Now just listen to me, Hornig. For all I care, ya might say to me, Father Hilse, tomorrow you've got to die. That's likely, I'd answer, why not?—You might say, Father Hilse, tomorrow the King of Prussia will come to visit ya—but that weavers, men like me and my son—should be up to such things, never in the world, never, never will I believe that.

MIELCHEN. (*A pretty girl of seven, with long, loose, flaxen hair. She runs in with a basket on her arm. She holds out a silver spoon to her mother.*) Mamma, Mamma, look what I've got! Ya can buy me a dress with it!

LUISE. Why are ya in such a hurry, child? (*With mounting excitement and curiosity.*) Tell me, what did ya come draggin' in this time? You're all out of breath. And the bobbins are still in the basket. What's the meanin' of all this, child?

OLD HILSE. Where did ya get the spoon?

LUISE. Could be she found it.

HORNIG. It's worth at least two or three thalers.

OLD HILSE. (*Beside himself.*) Get out, girl! Hurry up and get out! Will ya do what I say, or do I have to get a stick to ya! And take the spoon back where ya got it. Out with you! Do ya want to make thieves out of all of us, huh? You—I'll knock the thievin' out of ya—(*He looks for something with which to hit her.)*

MIELCHEN. (*Clinging to her mother's skirt, cries.*) Grandpapa, don't hit me—we, we—really found it. The bob-bobbin girls—they all—got—one, too.

LUISE. (*Bursts out, torn between fear and anxiety.*) There now—ya see. She found it. That's what she did. Where did ya find it?

MIELCHEN. (*Sobbing.*) In Peters—waldau—we—found 'em—in front of—Dreissiger's house.

OLD HILSE. Well, now we're in a fine mess. Hurry up, now, or I'll help ya to get goin'.

MOTHER HILSE. What's goin' on?

HORNIG. I'll tell ya what, Father Hilse. Let Gottlieb put on his coat and take the spoon to the police.

OLD HILSE. Gottlieb, put your coat on.

GOTTLIEB. (*Already doing so, eagerly.*) And then I'll go on up to the office and I'll say, they shouldn't blame us, a child like that just don't understand such things. And so I'm bringin' the spoon back. Stop that cryin', girl!

The mother takes the crying child into the back room and shuts the door on her. LUISE *returns.*

HORNIG. That might well be worth all of three thalers.

GOTTLIEB. Come, give me a piece of cloth so it don't get hurt, Luise. My, my—what an expensive thing. (*He has tears in his eyes while he wraps up the spoon.*)

LUISE. If it was ours, we could live on it for weeks.

OLD HILSE. Hurry up! Get a move on. Go as fast as ya can. That would be something! That would just about finish me. Hurry up, so we get rid of that devil's spoon. (GOTTLIEB *leaves with the spoon.*)

HORNIG. Well, I'd better be goin'. (*He talks to some of the tenants for a few seconds on his way out, then leaves.*)

PHYSICIAN SCHMIDT. (*A fidgety fat little man, with a cunning face, red from drinking, enters the house through the entrance hall.*) Good morning, people! Well, that's a fine business, that is. You can't fool me! (*Raising a warning finger.*) I know what you're up to. (*In the doorway, without coming into the room.*) Good morning, Father Hilse! (*To a woman in the hall.*) Well, Mother, how's the rheumatism? Better, eh? There you are! Now, let me see how things are with you, Father Hilse. What the devil's wrong with Mama Hilse?

LUISE. Doctor, the veins in her eyes are all dried up and she can't see at all no more.

SCHMIDT. That comes from the dust and the weaving by candlelight. Now tell me, do you know what it all means? All of Peterswaldau is on its feet, heading this way. I started out this morning in my buggy, thinking nothing was wrong, nothing at all. Then, I keep hearing the most amazing things. What in the devil's gotten into these people, Hilse? Raging like a pack of wolves. Starting a revolution, a rebellion; starting to riot; plundering and marauding. . . . Mielchen! Why, where is Mielchen? (MIELCHEN, *her eyes still red from weeping, is pushed in by her mother.*) There, Mielchen, you just reach into my coat pocket. (MIELCHEN *does so.*) Those ginger snaps are for you. Well, well, not all at once, you rascal. First, a little song! "Fox, you stole the . . ." well? "Fox, you stole . . . the goose. . . ." Just you wait, what you did—you called the sparrows on the church fence dirty names. They reported you to the teacher. Now, what do you say to that! Close to fifteen hundred people are on the march. (*Ringing of bells in the distance.*) Listen—they're ringing the alarm bells in Reichenbach. Fifteen hundred people. It's really the end of the world. Uncanny!

OLD HILSE. Are they really comin' over here to Bielau?

SCHMIDT. Yes, of course, of course.—I drove right through. Right through the whole crowd. I wanted to get out and give each one of them a pill. They trudged along, one behind the other—like misery itself—and sang a song—it really turned your stomach—you actually began to gag. My driver, Friedrich, he trembled like an old woman. We had to have some strong bitters right afterwards. I wouldn't want to be a manufacturer—not even if I could afford to have fine rubber tires on my carriage. (*Distant singing.*) Just listen! As if you beat on an old cracked boiler with your knuckles. I tell you, they'll be here on top of us in less than five minutes. Goodbye, people. Don't do anything foolish. The soldiers'll be right behind them. Don't lose your heads. The people from Peterswaldau have lost theirs. (*Bells ring close by.*) Heavens, now our bells are beginning to ring, too. It'll drive the people completely crazy. (*Goes upstairs.*)

GOTTLIEB. (*Enters again. Still in the entrance hall, panting.*) I've seen them—I've seen them. (*To a woman in the hall.*) They're here, Auntie, they're here! (*In the doorway.*) They're here, Father, they're here! They've got beanpoles and spikes and axes. They're stoppin' at Dittrich's and kickin' up a terrible row. I think he's givin' them money. Oh, my God, whatever is goin' to happen here? I won't look. So many people! So many people! If once they get goin' and make an attack—oh, damn it, damn it! Then our manufacturers'll have a bad time of it.

OLD HILSE. Why did you run so? You'll run like that till ya get your old trouble back, till you're flat on your back again, kickin' and hittin' all around ya.

GOTTLIEB. (*With increasing excitement and joy.*) I had to run, or else they would've caught me and kept me there. They were all yellin' I should hold out my hand, too. Godfather Baumert was one of them. He said to me—Come and get your two bits, you're a poor starvin' creature too. He even said—Tell your Father . . . he said I should tell ya, Father, you should come and help make the manufacturers pay back for all the terrible drudgery. (*Passionately.*) Now times've changed, he said. Now it'd be different with us weavers. We should all of us come and help bring it about. Now we'd all have our half pound of meat on Sundays and blood sausage and cabbage on Holy Days. Now everything would be changed, he said to me.

OLD HILSE. (*With repressed indignation.*) And he calls himself your godfather! And asked ya to take part in such criminal doin's? Don't ya have nothin' to do with such things, Gottlieb. The devil's got his hand in such carryin's on. That's Satan's work, what they're doin'.

LUISE. (*Overcome by passionate feeling, vehemently.*) Yes, yes, Gottlieb, just you hide behind the stove—crawl into the chimney corner—take a ladle in your hand and put a dish of buttermilk on your knee—put on a petticoat and say nice little prayers so you'll please Father! —And ya call that a man?

Laughter from the people in the entrance hall.

OLD HILSE. (*Trembling, with suppressed rage.*) And ya call that a proper wife, huh? Let me tell ya straight out—you call yourself a mother and have a vile tongue like that? Ya think ya can tell your daughter what she should do, and stir up your husband to crime and wickedness?

LUISE. (*Completely uncontrolled.*) You with your bigoted talk! It never filled one of my babies' bellies. All four of 'em laid in filth and rags on account of it. That didn't so much as dry one single diaper. I do call myself a mother, now you know it! And ya know that's why I wish all the manufacturers was in hell and damnation! It's because I am a mother—Can I keep a little worm like that alive? I've cried more than I've breathed, from the moment one of them tender, little creatures first came into the world, until death took pity on it, and took it away. You—you didn't give a damn. Ya prayed and ya sang, and I walked my feet bloody, for just a drop of skim milk. How many hundreds of nights I've racked my brains, just once to cheat the graveyard of a baby of mine. And tell me, what's the wrong that a little baby like that has done, huh? That he has to come to such a miserable end—and over there—at Dittrich's they're bathed in wine and washed in milk. No, no, I tell ya, if it starts here, ten horses won't hold me back. And this I'll say, too, if they was to attack Dittrich's, I'll be the first one—and God help them that tries to stop me. I'm fed up—and that's the truth.

OLD HILSE. You're lost—you're past helpin'.

LUISE. (*In a frenzy.*) You're the ones that's past helpin'! You're dishrags—not men! Fools to be spit at. Milksops who'd run away in fright if they so much as heard a child's rattle. Ya'd say "Thank ya kindly" three times for every thrashin' ya get. They haven't left enough blood in your veins so ya can get red in the face. Somebody ought to take a whip to ya, and beat some courage into your rotten bones! (*Leaves hurriedly.*)

A moment of embarrassment.

MOTHER HILSE. What's wrong with Luise, Father?

OLD HILSE. Nothin', Mama. What would be wrong with her?

MOTHER HILSE. Tell me, Father, am I just imaginin' it, or are the bells ringin'?

OLD HILSE. I guess they're buryin' somebody, Mother.

MOTHER HILSE. And for me the end never seems to come. Tell me, Father, why don't I ever die? (*Pause.*)

OLD HILSE. (*Leaves his work, draws himself up, solemnly.*) Gottlieb! Your wife has said such things to us. Gottlieb, look here! (*He bares his breast.*) Here laid a bullet as big as a thimble. And the King himself knows where I lost my arm. It wasn't the mice that ate it. (*He walks back and forth.*) Your wife—before she was even thought of, I shed my blood by the quart for the Fatherland. So let her rave on as much as she wants to.—That's all right with me. I don't give a damn.—Afraid? Me, afraid? What would I be afraid of, I'd like to know. Of the few soldiers who'll be rushin' after the rioters, maybe? Oh, Lord, if that was it—that wouldn't be nothin'! If I'm a bit brittle in my bones, when it comes to action, they're like iron. I wouldn't be scared to stand up against a few miserable bayonets—and, if it comes to the worst? Oh, how glad I'd be to take a rest. I certainly ain't afraid to die. Better today than tomorrow. No. No. And it'd be a good thing. For what would we be leavin'? Nobody'd weep for our poor old tortured bodies. That little heap of fear and pain and drudgery that we call life—we'd be glad enough to leave behind. But afterward, Gottlieb, afterward there's something—and if ya throw that away, too—then everything's really gone.

GOTTLIEB. Who knows what happens when you're dead? Ain't nobody seen it.

OLD HILSE. I'm tellin' ya, Gottlieb! Don't go and doubt the only thing poor folks have got. Why would I have set here—and worked the treadle like a slave for forty years and more? And watched quietly how that fellow over there lives in pride and gluttony—and makes money out of my hunger and hardship. And for what? Because I've got hope. I've got something, in all this misery. (*Pointing out the window.*) You've got your share here—me, in the world beyond. That's what I've been thinkin'. And I'd let myself be drawn and quartered—I'm that sure. It has been promised to us. Judgment Day is comin', but we are not the judges, no, on the contrary, "Vengeance is mine, saith the Lord."

A VOICE. (*Through the window.*) Weavers, come on out!

OLD HILSE. I don't care—do what ya

want. (*He sits down at the loom.*) You'll have to leave me in here.

GOTTLIEB. (*After a short struggle.*) I'll go and work, come what will.

Leaves.

Many hundreds of voices are heard near-by singing the "Weavers' Song"; it sounds like a dull, monotonous lament.

VOICES OF THE TENANTS. (*In the entrance hall.*) My God! My God! Now they're comin' like ants.—Where'd so many weavers come from?—Don't push —I want to see, too.—Look at that lanky fellow who's walkin' out front. Oh! Oh! —They're comin' in swarms!

HORNIG. (*Joins the people in the entrance hall.*) It's quite a show, ain't it? Ya don't see the likes of that every day. Ya ought to come around to Dittrich's. What they've done up there is really something. He ain't got no house, no more—no factory, no wine cellar—no nothin' at all. The wine bottles, they're drinkin' them all up . . . they don't even take the time to pull out the corks. One, two, three—the necks come off; nobody cares if they cut their mouths on the broken glass or not. Lots of 'em are runnin' around bleedin' like stuck pigs.— Now they're lookin' for the other Dittrich, the one here.

The singing of the crowd has stopped.

VOICES OF THE TENANTS. They really don't look so mad.

HORNIG. Don't ya worry. You just wait. Now they're takin' a good look at everything. See how they're lookin' over the place from all sides. Watch that little fat man—him with the stable bucket. That's the blacksmith from Peterswaldau, and a quick worker he is, too. He breaks down doors like they was pretzels—ya can believe me. If that man ever gets a manufacturer in his claws—he'll be done for!

VOICES OF THE TENANTS. Smash! Something happened! That was a stone flyin' through the window!—Now old Dittrich's gettin' scared.—He's hangin' out a sign! —What's on it?—Can't ya read? Where'd I be if I couldn't read?—Well, read it! "Your demands will be met." "Your demands will be met."

HORNIG. He could've spared hisself that. It won't help much. The weavers have their own ideas. Here it's the factory they're after. They want to put an end to the power looms. They're the things that are ruinin' the handweavers—even a blind man can see that. No, no! Those fellows won't stop now. They don't pay no attention to the judge, or to the chief of police —and certainly not to a sign. Anybody who's seen them kick up a riot, knows what it means.

VOICES OF THE TENANTS. All them people! What do they want? (*Hastily.*) They're comin' across the bridge! (*Anxiously.*) Are they comin' over on this side? (*In great surprise and fear.*) They're comin' this way, they're comin' this way. —They're pullin' the weavers out of their houses!

Everybody flees; the entrance hall is empty. A disorderly crowd of rioters, dirty, dusty, their faces red with liquor and exertion, wild-looking, exhausted, as if they had been up all night, tattered, pushes its way in, with the cry, "Come on out, weavers!" The crowd disperses through the various rooms. BAECKER *and a few* YOUNG WEAVERS, *armed with cudgels and poles, enter* OLD HILSE'S *room. When they recognize* OLD HILSE, *they are taken aback and calm down a little.*

BAECKER. Father Hilse, stop that slavin'! Let whoever wants to work the treadle. Ya don't need to work till ya've harmed yourself. We'll see to that.

FIRST YOUNG WEAVER. Ya won't have to go to bed hungry another day.

SECOND YOUNG WEAVER. Weavers'll have a roof over their heads and a shirt on their backs once more.

OLD HILSE. What's the devil makin' ya come in here for, with poles and axes?

BAECKER. These we're going to break in pieces on Dittrich's back.

SECOND YOUNG WEAVER. We'll get 'em red-hot and shove 'em down the manufacturers' throats, so they'll know how hunger burns.

THIRD YOUNG WEAVER. Come along, Father Hilse. We don't give no quarter.

SECOND YOUNG WEAVER. They took no pity on us. Neither God nor man. Now we're makin' our own justice.

OLD BAUMERT. (*Comes in, somewhat unsteady on his feet, with a newly killed chicken under his arm. He stretches out his arm.*) My dear—dear—br-brother—we are all brothers! Come to my heart, brother! (*Laughter.*)

OLD HILSE. Is that you, Willem?

OLD BAUMERT. Gustav!—Gustav, poor old wretch, come to my heart. (*Moved.*)

OLD HILSE. (*Growls.*) Let me alone.

OLD BAUMERT. Gustav, that's the way it is. A man's got to have luck! Gustav, just look at me. How do I look? A man's got to have luck. Don't I look like a count? (*Patting his belly.*) Guess what's in my belly. Food fit for a prince is in my belly. A man's got to have luck. Then he gets champagne and roast hare. I'll tell ya something—we've been makin' a mistake—we've got to help ourselves.

ALL. (*Speaking at once.*) We've got to help ourselves. Hurray!

OLD BAUMERT. And once ya've had your first good bite to eat, ya feel like a different man. Jesus! Then ya get to feelin' strong like a bull. Then the strength goes through your limbs so ya don't even see no more what ya're strikin' at. Damn it, that's fun!

JAEGER. (*In the door, armed with an old cavalry saber.*) We've made a few excellent attacks.

BAECKER. Yes, we've got the hang of it, now. One, two, three, and we're inside the house. Then it goes like wild fire—cracklin' and shiverin'—like sparks flyin' in a forge.

FIRST YOUNG WEAVER. We ought to make a little fire.

SECOND YOUNG WEAVER. We're marchin' on to Reichenbach and burnin' the houses of the rich right over their heads.

JAEGER. I bet they'd like that. Then they'd get a lot of insurance money. (*Laughter.*)

BAECKER. From here we'll march to Freiburg, to Tromtra's.

JAEGER. We ought to string up some of the officials. I've read all the trouble comes from the bureaucrats.

SECOND YOUNG WEAVER. Soon we'll be marchin' to Breslau. The crowd keeps gettin' bigger.

OLD BAUMERT. (*To* HILSE.) Have a drink, Gustav! Come on!

OLD HILSE. I never drink.

OLD BAUMERT. That was in the old times—today things is different, Gustav.

FIRST YOUNG WEAVER. Everyday ain't a holiday. (*Laughter.*)

OLD HILSE. (*Impatiently.*) You infernal firebrands, what do ya want here in my house?

OLD BAUMERT. (*Somewhat intimidated, overly friendly.*) Now look, I wanted to bring ya a little chicken—so's ya can cook some soup for Mother.

OLD HILSE. (*Perplexed, half-friendly.*) Oh, go and tell Mother.

MOTHER HILSE. (*Her hand to her ear, has been listening with difficulty. Now she wards* BAUMERT *off.*) You let me alone. I don't want no chicken soup.

OLD HILSE. You're right, Mother. Me, neither. Not that kind, anyway. And you, Baumert! I'll tell ya one thing. When old men talk like little children, then the devil claps his hands with joy. And let me tell ya this: you and me, we have nothin' in common. You're not here because I want ya here. Accordin' to law and justice and righteousness, you ain't got no business here!

A VOICE. Who ain't with us, is against us.

JAEGER. (*Threatens brutally.*) You've got the whole thing wrong. Listen here, old man, we aren't thieves.

A VOICE. We're hungry, that's all.

FIRST YOUNG WEAVER. We want to live, and that's all. And that's why we've cut the rope 'round our necks.

JAEGER. And that was right! (*Holding his fist in front of* OLD HILSE'S *face.*) Just say another word! Ya'll get a punch—right between the eyes.

BAECKER. Be quiet, be quiet! Let the old man alone.—Father Hilse, this is the way we look at it. Better dead than start the old life again.

OLD HILSE. Haven't I lived that kind of a life for sixty years or more?

BAECKER. That don't matter. There's got to be a change, anyway.

OLD HILSE. That day'll never come.

BAECKER. What they don't give us willingly, we'll take by force.

OLD HILSE. By force? (*Laughs.*) Ya might as well go and dig your own graves. They'll show you where the force is. Just wait, young man!

JAEGER. Maybe—because of the soldiers? I've been a soldier, too. We can handle a few companies of soldiers.

OLD HILSE. With your loud mouths, that I'll believe. And if ya chase a couple of them out, a dozen more'll come back.

VOICES. (*Through the window.*) The soldiers are comin'! Look out! (*Suddenly everyone is silent. For a moment, the faint sound of fifes and drums can be heard. In the stillness a short, involuntary cry.*) Damn it, I'm gettin' out! (*General laughter.*)

BAECKER. Who's talkin' of gettin' out? Who was it?

JAEGER. Who's afraid of a few lousy soldiers? I'll give the commands. I've been in the army. I know the tricks.

OLD HILSE. What'll ya shoot 'em with? With clubs, maybe, huh?

FIRST YOUNG WEAVER. Never mind that old man—he ain't quite right in the head.

SECOND YOUNG WEAVER. Yes, he is a bit crazy.

GOTTLIEB. (*Has come into the room, unnoticed, and grabs hold of the speaker.*) Ought ya to be so impudent to an old man?

FIRST YOUNG WEAVER. Let me alone. I ain't said nothin' bad.

OLD HILSE. (*Meditating.*) Oh, let him talk. Don't meddle, Gottlieb. He'll see soon enough who's crazy—me or him.

BAECKER. You goin' with us, Gottlieb?

OLD HILSE. He'll have nothin' to do with it.

LUISE. (*Comes into the entrance hall, calls in.*) Don't keep hangin' around here. Don't lose no time with such prayer-book hypocrites. Come on out to the square! Ya ought to come on to the square. Uncle Baumert is comin' as fast as he can. The Major's speakin' to the people from horseback. He's tellin' 'em to go home. If ya don't come quick, we're through.

JAEGER. (*As he leaves.*) A fine, brave man you have for a husband!

LUISE. A man for a husband? I ain't got no man for a husband.

Several in the entrance hall sing.

Once there was a man so small,
Heigh ho!
He would have a wife so tall,
Heigh diddle diddle dum, dum, dum,
hurrah!

WITTIG. (*Has entered from upstairs, a stable bucket in his hand. As he is about to go out, he stops for a minute in the entrance hall.*) Forward! Those that ain't cowards, hurray! (*He rushes out. A crowd, among them* LUISE *and* JAEGER, *follow him amid shouts of "hurray."*)

BAECKER. Good luck to ya, Father Hilse, we'll be seein' each other again. (*Is about to leave.*)

OLD HILSE. I doubt that. I won't last another five years. And you won't be out before that.

BAECKER. (*Surprised, standing still.*) Get out of where, Father Hilse?

OLD HILSE. Out of jail—where else?

BAECKER. (*Laughing wildly.*) That wouldn't be so bad. At least I'd get enough to eat there, Father Hilse.

Leaves.

OLD BAUMERT. (*Has been sitting slumped on a stool, moodily meditating; now he gets up.*) It's true, Gustav—I am sorta drunk. But even so, my head's clear enough. You've got your opinion in this matter—I've got mine. I say Baecker's right—if it ends in chains and ropes—it's better in prison than at home. There, they at least take care of ya; there, ya don't have to starve. I didn't want to join 'em. But ya see, Gustav, there comes a time when a man has to have a breath of air. (*Going slowly toward the door.*) Good luck to ya, Gustav. If something was to happen, say a prayer for me, will ya?

Leaves.

The mob of rioters has now left the stage. The entrance hall gradually fills up with curious tenants. OLD HILSE *goes about tying knots in his web.* GOTTLIEB *has taken an ax from behind the stove and instinctively is testing its edge. Both* OLD HILSE *and* GOTTLIEB *are agitated, but remain silent. From outside come the buzz and roar of a large crowd.*

MOTHER HILSE. Tell me, Father, the boards is shakin' so—what's goin' on here? What's goin' to happen? (*Pause.*)

OLD HILSE. Gottlieb!

GOTTLIEB. What do ya want?

OLD HILSE. Put down that ax.

GOTTLIEB. And who'll chop the wood? (*He leans the ax against the stove.—Pause.*)

MOTHER HILSE. Gottlieb, listen to what your father says.

A VOICE. (*Singing outside the window.*)

The little man at home will stay
Heigh-ho!
And wash the dishes all the day
Heigh diddle diddle, dum, dum, dum,
hurrah!

It fades out.

GOTTLIEB. (*Leaps up, shakes his fist at the window.*) You son of a bitch, don't make me mad!

A volley is fired.

MOTHER HILSE. (*Starts up in alarm.*) Oh, dear Lord, is it thunderin' again?

OLD HILSE. (*Instinctively folding his hands.*) Dear God in heaven, protect the poor weavers, protect my poor brothers!

There is a short silence.

OLD HILSE. (*To himself, deeply moved.*) Now the blood'll flow.

GOTTLIEB. (*When the shots were heard, jumped up and held the ax tight in his hand. He is pale and scarcely able to control his great excitement.*) Well, are we to take it layin' down, even now?

GIRL. (*Calling into the room from the entrance hall.*) Father Hilse, Father Hilse, get away from that window. A bullet came right through our window upstairs. (*Disappears.*)

MIELCHEN. (*Puts her head in through the window, laughing.*) Grandpa, Grandpa, they're shootin' with guns. A couple of 'em fell down. One of 'em turned 'round in a circle—'round and 'round like a top. One's all floppin' like a sparrow with its head tore off. Oh, and so much blood spurtin' out—! (*She disappears.*)

A WOMAN WEAVER. They've killed some of 'em.

AN OLD WEAVER. (*In the entrance hall.*) Watch out! They're goin' at the soldiers.

A SECOND WEAVER. (*Beside himself.*) Look at the women! Just look at the women! If they aren't liftin' up their skirts, and spittin' at the soldiers!

A WOMAN WEAVER. (*Calls in.*) Gottlieb, look at your wife. She's got more courage than you. She's jumpin' around in front of the bayonets like she was dancin' to music.

FOUR MEN *carry a wounded man through the entrance hall. Silence. A voice is clearly heard saying, "It's Weaver Ull-*

brich." After a few seconds, the voice says again, "He's done for, I guess—a bullet got him in the ear." The men are heard walking up the wooden stairs. Sudden shouts from outside, "Hurray, hurray!"

VOICES IN THE HOUSE. Where'd they get the stones? Ya'd better run for it! From the road construction—So long, soldiers! —Now it's rainin' pavin' stones.

Shrieks of terror and yelling are heard outside and continuing in the entrance hall. There is a cry of fear, and the entrance door is banged shut.

VOICES IN THE ENTRANCE HALL. They're loadin' again.—They're goin' to shoot again.—Father Hilse, get away from that window.

GOTTLIEB. (*Runs for the ax.*) What! Are we mad dogs? Are we to eat powder and shot instead of bread? (*Hesitating a minute with the ax in his hand. To the old man.*) Am I to stand by and let my wife get shot? No, that mustn't happen! (*As he rushes out.*) Watch out—here I come!

Leaves.

OLD HILSE. Gottlieb, Gottlieb!

MOTHER HILSE. Where's Gottlieb?

OLD HILSE. He's gone to the devil.

VOICES. (*From the entrance hall.*) Get away from the window, Father Hilse!

OLD HILSE. Not me! Not if ya all go crazy. (*To* MOTHER HILSE *with mounting excitement.*) Here my Heavenly Father put me. Right, Mother? Here we'll stay sittin' and doin' what's our duty—even if the snow was to catch fire.

He begins to weave. A volley is fired. Fatally hit, OLD HILSE *rises from his stool and then falls forward over the loom. At the same time loud cries of "Hurray" are heard. Shouting "Hurray" the people who have been standing in the entrance hall rush outside. The old woman asks several times: "Father—Father—What's wrong with ya?" The steady shouting grows more and more distant. Suddenly* MIELCHEN *comes running into the room.*

MIELCHEN. Grandpa, Grandpa, they're drivin' the soldiers out of town. They've attacked Dittrich's house. They did like at Dreissiger's, Grandpa! (*Frightened, the child sees that something is wrong—sticks her finger in her mouth and cautiously steps close to the dead man.*) Grandpa!

MOTHER HILSE. Come now, Father—say something! You're scarin' me!

CURTAIN

THE HERETIC OF SOANA

By GERHART HAUPTMANN

Translated by Harry Steinhauer

Tourists can set out for the summit of Mount Generoso in Mendrisio or take the rack railway in Capolago or start from Melida by way of Soana, which is the most difficult road of all. The whole region belongs to Ticino, a Swiss canton with an Italian population.

At a great height mountain climbers not infrequently met the figure of a bespectacled goatherd, whose appearance was striking in other ways too. His face bespoke the man of culture in spite of his tanned skin. He looked not unlike the bronze statue of John the Baptist by Donatello in the cathedral of Siena. He had dark hair which hung in curls over his brown shoulders. His dress consisted of a goatskin.

Whenever a group of strangers came near this man, the mountain guides began to laugh. When the tourists saw him, they often burst into crude roars of laughter or into loud, provocative cries. They felt justified in doing so because of the strange sight he presented. The goatherd paid no heed to them; he did not even turn his head.

All the mountain guides seemed to be on basically good terms with him. They often climbed over to him and entered into confidential conversations with him. When they returned and were asked by the strangers what sort of a weird saint this was, the guides tended to act mysterious until he was out of sight. Those tourists whose curiosity was still alive learned that this man had a dark history, was popularly called "the heretic of Soana" and enjoyed a dubious esteem mingled with superstitious fear.

When the editor of these pages was still young and fortunate enough to spend frequent glorious weeks in beautiful Soana, it was inevitable that he should now and then climb Mount Generoso and one day come face to face with the so-called "heretic of Soana." He could not forget the man's appearance. After gathering all sorts of contradictory impressions about him, he resolved to see him again, in fact simply to visit him.

The editor was strengthened in his intention by a German Swiss, the doctor of Soana, who assured him that the eccentric was not averse to receiving visits from educated people. He had visited him once himself. "I should really be angry with him," he said, "because the fellow is an unauthorized competitor of mine. But he lives very high up and far away and is, thank Heaven, only consulted in secret by those few who would not stop at being cured by the devil himself." The doctor continued, "You must know there is a belief among the people that he has sold his soul to the devil, a view that is not contested by the clergy, because it originated with them. Originally, they say, the man was under an evil spell, until he himself became a hardened villain and infernal sorcerer. As far as I am concerned, I've noticed neither claws nor horns on him."

The editor remembers his visits to the strange man very clearly. The nature of the first meeting was remarkable. A special circumstance gave it the character of an accident. At a steep spot on the road the visitor found himself face to face with a helpless mother goat which had just thrown a kid and was in the process of giving birth to a second. The distress of the lonely mother, who looked at him fearlessly as if she expected his help, and the profound mystery of birth in that vast rocky wildness, made the deepest impression on him. But he hastened his ascent, for he had concluded that this animal probably belonged to the herd of the eccentric, and wanted to summon him to help. He found him among his goats and cattle, told him what he had observed and led him to the mother in labor. Behind her the second kid was already lying in the grass, damp and bloody.

With the sure touch of a physician, with the tender love of the merciful Samaritan, the owner cared for the animal. After waiting a certain amount of time, he took each of the newborn creatures under an arm and slowly began the way back to his home, followed by the mother, whose heavy udder almost dragged on the ground. The visitor was not only rewarded with the most friendly thanks, but invited in an irresistible manner to accompany him.

The eccentric had erected several buildings on the mountain meadow that was his property. From the outside, one of these resembled a crude pile of stones. Inside it was a dry, warm stable. There the goat and her young were housed, while the visitor was led higher up to a whitewashed square building leaning against the wall of Mount Generoso and situated on a terrace overgrown with grapevine. Not far from the little gate a stream of water as thick as an arm shot out of the mountain and filled a huge stone basin which had been hewn out of the rock. Near the basin a mountain cave was locked off by an iron-bound door; this soon revealed itself to be a vaulted cellar.

This place, which, when viewed from the valley, seemed to hang at an inaccessible height, offered a splendid view; but the editor does not wish to speak about that. To be sure, when he enjoyed it for the first time, he fell from speechless astonishment into loud exclamations of rapture and back again into speechless astonishment. But his host, who at this moment emerged from the house (where he had been looking for something), suddenly seemed to be walking on softer soles. This, as well as his generally quiet, calm conduct, did not escape the visitor. It was an admonition to him to be sparing of words and chary of questions. He already liked the odd goatherd too much to run the risk of estranging him by even a hint of curiosity or importunity.

The visitor still sees the round stone table which stood on the terrace, surrounded by benches. He sees it with all the good things the "heretic of Soana" had spread on it: the most wonderful *stracchino di lecco,* delicious Italian wheat bread, salami, olives, figs and medlars, besides a jug full of red wine which he had fetched fresh from the grotto. When they sat down, the goatskin-clad, bearded host, with his long flowing locks, looked warmly into the eyes of the visitor, grasping the latter's right hand as if to indicate affection.

It is difficult to remember all that was

said at this first meeting; only some of it has remained in the memory. The goatherd wished to be called Ludovico. He related many things about the Argentine. At one point, when the ringing of the angelus bells penetrated to us from below, he remarked about this "ubiquitous irritating noise." Once the name of Seneca was mentioned. We also talked casually about Swiss politics. Finally the eccentric wanted to know some things about Germany, because it was the visitor's native land. When the time came for the visitor to depart, according to a prearranged plan, the host said, "You will always be welcome here."

Although the editor of these pages was eager for this man's story, as he frankly admits, he avoided betraying any interest in it even on subsequent visits. In chance conversations he had in Soana, he gathered some of the external reasons for Ludovico's being called the "heretic of Soana"; but the visitor was much more concerned with finding out in what sense this designation was justified, and in what peculiar inner destinies, in what special philosophy, Ludovico's way of life was rooted. But he refrained from putting questions and was richly rewarded for this.

Mostly he met Ludovico alone, either among the animals of his herd or in his cell. A few times he came upon him milking the goats with his own hands, like Robinson Crusoe, or forcing a rebellious mother to suckle her kids. At such times he seemed to merge completely with his calling of Alpine shepherd; he rejoiced in the mother goat who dragged her swollen udder on the ground, and in the ram when it was in active heat. Of one goat he said, "Doesn't he look like the Evil One himself? Just look at his eyes. What power, what flashing anger, what rage and malice! And yet what a sacred fire!" His smile took on a hard, grim character; he showed his splendid white teeth and fell into a dreamy state when he watched, with the eye of an expert, one of his demonic matadors going about his useful work.

At times the "heretic" played the pipes of Pan, and the visitor could hear their simple scale even as he approached. On such occasion the conversation naturally turned to music, about which the shepherd unfolded strange views. When he was among his herd Ludovico never spoke of anything except the animals and their habits, of the goatherd's vocation and its customs. Not infrequently he pursued the subject of animal psychology and traced the goatherd's way of life into the remotest past, betraying a scholar's knowledge of no common range. He spoke of Apollo tending the herds of Laomedon and Admetus as a servant and shepherd. "I would like to know on what instrument he made music to his flocks then." And he concluded, as if he were talking about something real, "By Heaven, I would have enjoyed listening to him." Those were the moments in which the shaggy anchorite might perhaps have created the impression that his mental powers were not quite intact. On the other hand, his thoughts received a certain justification when he demonstrated in what varied ways a herd could be influenced and guided by music. He brought them to their feet with one note and brought them to rest with another. With music he fetched them from distant places, with music he made the animals scatter or follow close on his heels.

There were also visits at which almost nothing was said. Once, when the oppressive heat of a June afternoon had penetrated to the meadows of Mount Generoso, Ludovico was lying in a blissful state of somnolence beside his cud-chewing herds. He merely gave his visitor a flashing look and motioned to him to stretch out in the grass too. When this was done and both of them had been lying there for a while in silence, he said in a drawling voice, without any introduction, something to this effect:

"You know that Eros is older than Cronus and mightier too. —Do you feel this silent fire about us? Eros! —Do you hear the cricket chirping? Eros!" —At this moment two lizards which were chasing each other shot over the prostrate shepherd with lightning speed. He repeated, "Eros! Eros!" —And, as if obeying an order he had issued, two strong bucks now got up and locked horns. He did not interfere, although the combat became more and more heated. The clang from the thrusts became louder and louder, and the number of attacks increased. And again he said, "Eros! Eros!"

And now for the first time the visitor heard words which made him listen with special attention, because they shed, or at least seemed to shed, light on the question why Ludovico was known to the people as the "heretic." "I prefer," he said, "to worship a living goat or a living bull to a man who was hanged on the gallows. I am not living in an age that does this. I hate and despise this age. Jupiter Ammon was represented with the horns of a ram. Pan has the legs of a goat; Bacchus, the horns of a bull. I mean the Bacchus Tauriformis or Tauricornis of the Romans. Mithra, the sun god, is represented as a bull. All the peoples revered the bull, the goat, the ram, and shed their sacred blood in sacrifice. To this I say: yes!—for the procreative power is the highest power, the procreative power is the creative power, procreation and creation are the same thing. Of course, the cult of this power is not the frigid bleating of monks and nuns. I once dreamed of Sita, the wife of Vishnu, who assumed human shape under the name of Rama. Priests died in her embraces. During that moment I knew something of all sorts of mysteries; of the mystery of black procreation in the green grass, of procreation in mother-of-pearl-colored lust; of raptures and stupors; of the mystery of yellow maize kernels, of all fruits, all sizes, all colors. I could have bellowed in the frenzy of pain when I caught sight of the merciless almighty Sita. I thought I would die of desire."

During this revelation the writer of these lines felt like an involuntary eavesdropper. He stood up with a few words which were designed to give the impression that he had not heard the monologue but had concentrated his thoughts on other matters. Then he tried to take his leave. But Ludovico would not permit it. And so once more, on that mountain terrace, there began a banquet, and this time its course became significant and unforgettable.

The visitor was introduced into the dwelling, the interior of the cabin described above. It was square-shaped, clean, had a fireplace and resembled the simple study of a scholar. It contained ink, pen, paper and a small library, chiefly of Greek and Latin authors. "Why should I conceal the fact from you," said the shepherd, "that I am of good family and enjoyed a misguided youth and the education of a scholar? Of course you will want to know how I changed from an unnatural to a natural man, from a prisoner into a free man, from a disturbed and morose man into a happy and contented one. Or how I excluded myself from bourgeois society and Christianity." He gave a loud laugh. "Perhaps I shall write the history of my transformation some day." The visitor, whose suspense had reached its peak, found himself once more thrown far from his goal. It did not help much when his host finally declared that the cause of his regeneration lay in the fact that he worshiped natural symbols.

In the shadow of the rock, on the terrace, at the edge of the overflowing basin

in the delicious coolness, a more sumptuous meal than the first was spread: smoked ham, cheese and wheat bread, figs, fresh medlars and wine. There had been much talk, not high-spirited but full of quiet gaiety. Finally the stone table was cleared. And now there came a moment which lives in the editor's mind as if it were yesterday.

The bronzed goatherd, as we know, created a savage impression with his long, unkept locks and beard and his goatskin. He has been compared to Donatello's Saint John the Baptist. His face did in fact have much in common with John's in fineness of line. Upon close inspection, Ludovico was really handsome, if one could forget his spectacles. To be sure, these spectacles gave his whole appearance, apart from a slightly comical expression, a strange, enigmatic and arresting quality. At the moment which I am describing, his whole person underwent a transformation. If the bronzelike quality of his body had found expression in a certain immobility, this now vanished to the extent that his features became mobile and rejuvenated. One might say that he smiled with a tinge of boyish bashfulness. "What I now ask of you," he said, "I have never proposed to anyone else. I really don't know myself where I get the courage to do it. From an old habit I still read from time to time, and even play with ink and pen. So I've written down, in the winter hours of my leisure, a simple tale which is supposed to have happened here, in and around Soana, long before my time. You will find it extremely simple, but it attracted me for all sorts of reasons, which I will not discuss now. Tell me briefly and frankly: Do you want to go back into the house with me, and do you feel inclined to forfeit some of your time to this story, which has already cost me, too, many a fruitless hour? I don't want to urge you, I would rather dissuade you. Moreover, if you say so, I will take the pages of the manuscript and throw them down into the depths right now."

Of course this did not happen. He took the wine jug, went into the house with his visitor and the two men sat facing each other. From a case made of the finest goat leather, the mountain shepherd had unfolded a manuscript, written in a monkish hand on strong paper. As though to give himself courage, he once more raised his glass to his visitor before he cast away from shore to plunge into the stream of narration. Then he began in a soft voice.

The Mountain Shepherd's Tale

On a mountain slope above Lake Lugano one may find a small hamlet among many others, which may be reached after about an hour's journey from the lake shore by way of a steep highway that winds about the mountain.

The houses of the hamlet, which, like most of the Italian places of that region, are one single gray ruin of brick and mortar, emerging like a series of boxes out of each other, front on a gorgelike valley of meadows and terraces behind the mighty slope of the towering giant Mount Generoso.

Into this valley, at the point where it really ends as a narrow gorge, a waterfall pours from the bottom of a valley situated about a hundred yards higher up. The power of the waterfall varies with the time of day and year and with the prevailing air currents; its roar constitutes perpetual music in the hamlet.

A long time ago a priest named Raffaele Francesco, who was then about twenty-five years old, was transferred to this community. He had been born in Ligornetto, which is in the canton of Ticino, and could boast that he was a member of the same family, long established there, which had produced the most significant sculptor of united Italy, who had also been born in Ligornetto and had eventually died there too.

The young priest had spent his childhood with relatives in Milan, and his student days in various theological seminaries of Switzerland and Italy. From his mother, who was descended from a noble family, he inherited the serious side of his character, which impelled him, at a very early age and without the slightest hesitation, to embrace the religious vocation.

Francesco, who wore spectacles, was distinguished from the host of his fellow pupils by exemplary industry, a strict way of life, and piety. Even his mother had to urge on him tactfully that, as a future secular priest, he might well permit himself a little joy in life, since he was not really bound to the most stringent monastic rules. However, as soon as he had received holy orders, his sole wish was to find a most remote parish, where he might dedicate himself to his heart's desire, even more than hitherto, as a sort of hermit, to the service of God, the Son and the Holy Mother.

When he came to little Soana and moved into the parsonage that adjoined the church, the mountain-dwellers soon noticed that he was an entirely different type from his predecessor. Even in appearance; for his predecessor had been a massive, bull-like peasant who used means other than ecclesiastical penances and penalties to keep the pretty women and girls of the place obedient to him. Francesco, by contrast, was pale and delicate. His eyes were deep-set. Hectic spots glowed on the impure skin that covered his cheekbones. To this were added the spectacles, which to simple folk are still a symbol of preceptorial severity and learning. After a period of from four to six weeks he had, in his own way, brought the somewhat rebellious wives and daughters under his power, and indeed to an even greater degree than the other priest.

As soon as Francesco stepped into the street through the little gate of the tiny parish yard adjoining the church, he was surrounded by children and women, who kissed his hand with genuine reverence. And the number of times in the course of the day when he was called into the confessional by the tinkling of the little church bell, mounted up, by the time evening came, to a total which elicited from his newly hired housekeeper, a woman almost seventy years old, the exclamation that she had never realized how many angels were hidden in the normally rather corrupt Soana. In short, the reputation of the young pastor Francesco Vela echoed far and wide in the region, and he soon acquired the name of saint.

Francesco did not allow any of this to affect him and was far from harboring any consciousness of doing more than discharging his duties in a tolerably competent manner. He said Masses, performed all the ecclesiastical functions of the divine Service with undiminishing zeal and in addition carried out the duties of secular instruction, for the little schoolroom was in the parsonage.

One evening at the beginning of the month of March there was a violent tug at the bell of the parish yard. When the housekeeper opened the door and shone her lantern out into the bad weather, she was confronted by a somewhat savage-looking fellow, who asked to speak to the pastor. After locking the gate the old housekeeper went in to her young master to announce the late visitor, not without visible anxiety. But Francesco, who had made it a point of duty, among others, to reject no one who needed him, whoever he might be, looked up from reading some church father and said shortly, "Go, Petronilla, bring him in."

Soon afterwards there stood before the priest's table a man of about forty, whose outward appearance was that of the people of the region, but much more neglected, indeed ragged. The man was barefoot. His threadbare, rain-soaked trousers were fastened about his hips by a belt. His shirt stood open. Above his tanned, hairy chest rose a bushy throat and a face that was overgrown with thick, black hair, out of which two dark, glowing eyes burned.

The man had hung a tattered, rain-soaked jacket over his left shoulder, as shepherds do, and he nervously twirled a small felt hat, shrunk and discolored by the wind and weather of many years, in his brown, hard fists. He had set down a long cudgel at the door.

When he was asked what he wished, the man poured out a flood of raw, unintelligible sounds and words, accompanied by wild grimaces. He spoke in the dialect of the district, to be sure, but deviated from it so much that it sounded like a foreign language even to the housekeeper, who had been born in Soana.

The young priest, who had attentively studied his visitor as he stood in the light of the small burning lamp, tried in vain to grasp the sense of his request. With much patience and by means of numerous questions, he was finally able to get this much out of him: that he was the father of seven children, some of whom he would like to send to the young priest's school. Francesco asked, "Where are you from?" And when the answer came tumbling out, "I'm from Soana," the priest was astonished and said at once, "That isn't possible! I know everyone in this place but I don't know you or your family."

The shepherd or peasant or whatever he was, now described the location of his home in excited tones, accompanying his description with many gestures; but Francesco could make no sense of it. He merely said, "If you are an inhabitant of Soana and your children have reached the legal age, they should have been in my school long ago. And I must surely have seen you or your wife or your children at a church service, at Mass or confession."

At this point the man opened his eyes wide and pressed his lips together. Instead of replying, he exhaled as though his heaving chest were congested.

"Well then, I'll write down your name. I think it's good of you to come of your own accord to take steps to prevent your children from remaining ignorant and possibly godless." At these words the ragged creature began to utter strange, croaking, animal-like sounds, so that his brown, sinewy, almost athletic body was shaken by them. "Yes," Francesco repeated in embarrassment, "I'll write down your name and look into the matter." One could see tear upon tear roll out of the stranger's reddened eyes and down his shaggy face.

"Very well, very well," said Francesco, who could not account for his visitor's excitement and was, besides, more disturbed than moved by it. "Very well, very well, your case will be investigated. Just tell me your name, my good man, and send me your children tomorrow morning." The man grew silent at this point, and looked at Francesco for a long time with a restless and tortured expression on his face. The priest asked once more, "What is your name? Tell me your name."

He had noticed, from the very beginning, a fearful, hunted quality in the movements of his guest. Now, when he was supposed to state his name and Petronilla's step became audible on the stone floor outside, he ducked down and displayed that pervasive fearsomeness that we associate mostly with the insane or the criminal. He appeared to be persecuted. He seemed to be in flight from the police.

However, he took a piece of paper and the priest's pen, walked away from the light into the darkness, toward the window sill, where the sounds of a nearby brook below and of the more distant waterfall of Soana penetrated into the room;

with some effort he managed to scrawl something legible on the paper and handed it resolutely to the priest. The latter said, "Good," and, making the sign of the Cross, added, "Go in peace." The savage went, leaving behind him a cloud of odors compounded of salami, onions, charcoal smoke, goats and cow stables. As soon as he was gone the priest threw the window wide open.

The next morning Francesco said Mass as usual, rested a while and then ate his frugal breakfast. Soon after, he was on his way to the mayor, who had to be visited early if he was to be found at home. For every day he went to Lugano, taking a train at the railway station far below on the lakeshore; he had a wholesale and retail business in Ticino cheese on one of the busiest streets of the town.

The sun shone down on the little square close to the church, which formed, so to speak, the agora of the village, surrounded by old chestnut trees, which were as yet bare of leaves. Children sat around and played on some of the stone benches, while the mothers and older daughters washed their linen at an antique marble sarcophagus overflowing with the cold mountain water which it was copiously fed, and carried the laundry away in baskets to dry. The ground was wet from rain mingled with snowflakes that had fallen the previous day; on the other side of the gorge, the mighty rocky slope of Mount Generoso, covered with newly fallen snow, towered in its own shadow, and from its inaccessible crags blew fresh mountain air toward them.

The young priest walked past the washerwomen with downcast eyes, returning their loud greetings with a nod. He briefly held out his hand to the children who pressed about him, looking at them over his spectacles like an old man; they wiped their lips on his hand with zeal and haste. The village, which began behind the square, was made accessible by a few narrow lanes. But even the main street could only be used by small vehicles, and then only at its front end. Toward the exit from the village the street became narrower and so steep that one could just about squeeze through and make one's way with a loaded mule. On this little street stood a small grocery store and a branch of the Swiss post office.

The postmaster, whose relations with Francesco's predecessor had been those of a comrade, greeted Francesco and was greeted by him in turn, but in such a way that due distance was maintained between the gravity of the consecrated priest and the casual friendliness of the layman. Not far from the post office the priest turned into a wretched little side lane which led down hazardously by means of stairways large and small, past open goat stables and all manner of dirty, windowless, cellarlike caves. Hens cackled; cats sat on rotten galleries under clusters of suspended corncobs. Here and there a goat bleated, or a cow, which for some reason had not been taken out to pasture, lowed.

It was astonishing, coming from this neighborhood, to pass through a narrow gate to the mayor's house and find oneself in a suite of small, vaulted rooms, whose ceilings craftsmen had elaborately decorated with figures in the style of Tiepolo. Tall windows and glass doors, hung with long red drapes, led from these sunny rooms to an equally sunny terrace, which was decorated with very ancient box-trees cut in conical shape and by wonderful laurel trees. Here, as everywhere, one heard the beautiful music of the waterfall and saw before one the wall of the wild mountain.

The mayor, Sor Domenico, was a well-dressed, sedate man in his middle forties, who had taken a second wife less than three months before. The beautiful, blooming woman of twenty-two, whom Francesco had found busy preparing breakfast in the gleaming kitchen, led him into the garden. When the mayor had heard the priest's story about the visit of the previous evening and had read the slip of paper which bore the name of the savage visitor in his clumsy scrawl, a smile passed over his face. After inviting the young priest to sit down, he retailed the desired information about the mysterious visitor, who was indeed a citizen of Soana, until now unknown to the priest. The mayor's narration was wholly factual and the masklike indifference of his features was never disturbed.

"Luchino Scarabota," said the mayor—it was the name which the priest's visitor had scribbled on the piece of paper—"is by no means a poor man, but for years his domestic affairs have given me and the whole community a headache, and it isn't really possible to see at this point where the whole thing is going to end. He belongs to an old family, and it is very probable that he has in his veins some of the blood of the famous Luchino Scarabota da Milano, who built the nave of the cathedral down in Como between fourteen hundred and fifteen hundred. As you know, Father, we have a number of such old, famous names in our little place."

The mayor had opened the glass door and, as he was talking, led the priest out to the terrace, where he showed him with slightly upraised hand one of the square huts in which the peasants of the region live, in the steep, funnel-shaped area which forms the source of the waterfall. But this property, hanging at a great height above all the others, differed from them not only by its isolated, seemingly inaccessible location but also by its smallness and poverty.

"Do you see, there, where I am pointing with my finger? That's where this Scarabota lives," the mayor said.

"I am surprised, Father," the speaker continued, "that you haven't heard anything about that mountain pasture and its inhabitants before this. For a decade and more these people have constituted the most disgusting nuisance in this region. Unfortunately there is no way of getting at them. The woman has been brought to court and has claimed that the seven children she has borne are not those of the man she is living with—is there anything more absurd than that?—but from Swiss summer tourists who have to pass the pasture to climb Mount Generoso. And the hag is lousy and caked with dirt and as frighteningly ugly as the night, besides.

"No, it's common knowledge that the man who called on you yesterday, and with whom she is living, is the father of her children. But this is the point: this man is also her blood brother."

The young priest turned pale.

"Of course, this incestuous couple is avoided and outlawed by everyone. In this respect the vox populi seldom errs." With this explanation the mayor continued his narrative. "Whenever one of the children has appeared here or in Arogno or in Melano, he has nearly been stoned. Where these people are known any church is regarded as desecrated if the infamous brother and sister have set foot in it, and the two outlaws, whenever they thought they might dare to make such an attempt, were made to feel this in such a terrible way that for years now they have lost all desire to attend church.

"And can we permit," the mayor continued, "such children, such cursed creatures, who are the abomination and horror of everyone, to attend our school here below, and sit on the schoolbenches among the children of good Christians? Can we be expected to allow everyone in our village, big and small, to be infected by these products of moral disgrace, these wicked, mangy beasts?"

The pale face of the priest Francesco in no way betrayed to what extent he had been moved by the narrative of Sor Domenico. He thanked him and went away with the same dignified seriousness with which he had appeared.

Soon after the conversation with the mayor, Francesco reported to his bishop concerning the case of Luchino Scarabota. A week later the bishop's answer was in his hands; it charged the young clergyman to take personal cognizance of the general situation on the so-called mountain pasture of Santa Croce. In the same letter the bishop praised the ecclesiastical zeal of the young man and confirmed that he had good cause for feeling oppressed in his conscience because of these aberrant and outlawed souls, and for being concerned about their salvation. No sinner, however far he had strayed, could be excluded from the blessings and consolation of Mother Church.

It was not until the end of the month of March that official duties and the snow conditions on Mount Generoso permitted the young clergyman of Soana to undertake the ascent to the mountain pasture of Santa Croce, with a peasant as his guide. Easter had almost come and although constant avalanches were descending the steep wall of the giant mountain and falling like muffled thunder into the gorge below the waterfall, spring had set in with full force wherever the sun was able to penetrate freely.

However little of a nature worshiper Francesco was, unlike his namesake the saint of Assisi, he could not help being affected by the tender, juicy sprouts that he saw, green and blooming about him. Though the young man did not have to become clearly aware of it, the subtle fermentation of spring was in his blood, and he was enjoying his share of that inner swelling and throbbing in all of nature which is heavenly in origin, and in all the joys that blossom from it, despite its delightful, sensuous, earthy manifestations.

The chestnut trees on the square, which the priest first had to cross with his guide, had stretched out tender, green little hands from brown, sticky buds. The children were noisy, and so were the sparrows that nested under the church roof and in countless hiding places offered by the many corners in the village. The first swallows flew in broad arcs from Soana over the abyss of the gorge, where they apparently swerved aside close to the fantastically towering, inaccessible rock massif of the mountain wall. Up there on promontories or in holes in the rock, where the foot of man had never trod, the osprey nested. These big brown couples embarked on glorious flights, and floated, for the pure fun of floating, above the mountain peaks for hours on end, circling higher and higher, as though they sought to forget themselves and move majestically into the infinite freedom of space.

Everywhere, not only in the air, not only on the brown earth, which was either plowed up or clothed in grass and narcissi, not only in everything nature permitted to rise through stalks and stems into leaves and blossoms, but in human beings also, there was a festive air, and the brown faces of the peasants who were working on the terraces between the rows of grapevine with mattock or curved knife, shone with a Sunday glow. Most of them had already slaughtered the so-called Easter lamb, a young kid, and hung it up with its hind legs tied together, on the doorpost of their home.

The women, who were assembled about the overflowing marble sarcophagus with their filled laundry baskets, were especially numerous and noisy; when the priest and his companion walked past, they interrupted their shrill merriment. At the exit from the village there were washerwomen too; here, beneath the small statue of the Madonna, a stream of water gushed out from the rock and likewise emptied into an antique marble sarcophagus. Both basins, this sarcophagus and the one that stood on the square, had been lifted quite some time ago out of an orchard full of thousand-year-old holm oaks and chestnuts, where they had stood since time immemorial, hidden under ivy and wild laurel, jutting only slightly out of the ground.

As he passed the spot, Francesco Vela crossed himself; in fact, he interrupted his walk for a moment to pay homage on bent knee to the small Madonna above the sarcophagus, who was charmingly surrounded by the gifts of wild flowers that the country folk had brought her. It was the first time he had seen this lovely little shrine, about which the bees buzzed, since he had never visited his upper part of the village before. The lower part of Soana, with its church and a few attractive middle-class homes, adorned with green shutters and placed about the chestnut square with its terrace-like pavement, gave the appearance of almost bourgeois prosperity; gardens large and small displayed blossoming almond and orange trees, tall cypresses, in short, a vegetation rather southern in character. Here, some hundred feet up, it was nothing but a poor Alpine shepherds' village, which gave out an odor of goats and cow stables. Here, too, an extremely steep mountain road began, paved with tap rock, which had been smoothed down by the large communal herd of goats going out to graze in the morning and returning at night. For this road led up and out to the communal meadow in the kettle-shaped spring region of the little Savaglia River, which forms the splendid waterfall of Soana further down and, after a brief, roaring passage through the deep gorge, disappears into Lake Lugano.

After the priest had climbed this mountain road for a short while, still guided by his companion, he stopped to catch his breath. Taking his big black plate-shaped hat from his head with his left hand, he drew a large colored handkerchief from his soutane with his right, to mop the beads of perspiration on his forehead. On the whole, an appreciation of nature, a feeling for the beauty of landscape, is not particularly well developed in an Italian priest. But the spaciousness afforded by a great height, from the so-called bird's-eye view, is after all a delight which at times affects even the naïvest person and evokes a certain degree of astonishment in him. As he looked down far below him, Francesco saw his church and the whole village that went with it as no more than a miniature picture, while round about him the mighty mountain world seemed to rise ever higher to heaven. The feeling of spring was now joined by a sense of the sublime, which may perhaps arise from a comparison of one's own smallness with the oppressively powerful works of nature and their threatening, mute proximity, and which may be tied to the partial realization that we, too, in some way share in this tremendous power. In short, Francesco felt himself sublimely great and minutely small at one and the same moment, and this caused him to make the accustomed sign of the Cross on brow and chest to protect himself against aberrations and demons.

As he climbed higher, religious questions and the practical church affairs of his diocese soon occupied the zealous young cleric's mind again. And when he stopped once more, this time at the entrance to a high rocky valley, and turned around, he caught sight of a badly neglected saint's shrine, built of stone, that had been erected here for the shepherds. This gave him the idea of seeking out all the extant shrines of his diocese, even the remotest, and restoring them to a condition that was worthy of God. He allowed his eyes to roam freely, seeking a point from which he might possibly survey all the existing shrines.

As his starting point he took his own church and the parsonage that was attached to it. It was situated, as was said, on the village square, and its outside walls merged with the steep walls of rock, past which a merry mountain brook rushed downward. This mountain brook, which crossed the square of Soana underground, emerged in a stone arch, where it watered orchards and flowering meadows, though it was badly muddied by sewage. Beyond the church, a little higher up, the oldest shrine of the region stood on a round, flat-terraced hill, although it could not be seen from this spot; it was a small chapel dedicated to the Virgin Mary, whose dusty image on the altar was surmounted by a vaulted Byzantine mosaic in the apse. This mosaic, which was well preserved in both golden background and design, in spite of its thousand or more years, depicted Christus Pantokrator. The distance from the main church to this shrine was not more than three stone's throws. Another handsome chapel, this one dedicated to Saint Anne, was located at an equal distance from it. Above Soana and behind it rose a sharply pointed mountain cone, which was of course surrounded by broad valleys and by the flanks of the Generoso chain towering above it. This mountain, shaped almost like a cone of sugar, covered with growth to its very summit and seemingly inaccessible, was called Sant' Agata, because at its peak it harbored a little chapel for this saint for use in cases of emergency. Thus there was a church and three chapels within the very narrowest circumference of the village, to which were added three or four more chapels within the larger radius of the diocese. On every hill, at every pretty turn in the road, on every peak that looked out into the distance, here and there on picturesque, rocky precipices, near and far, over gorge and lake, the pious centuries had established houses of God, so that in this respect one could still feel the profound and general piety of paganism, which, in the course of millennia, had originally consecrated all these points and had thus procured for itself divine allies against the threatening, fearful powers of this wild nature.

The young zealot contemplated with satisfaction all these institutions of Roman Catholic Christianity, which distinguish the whole canton of Ticino. At the same time, he had to admit to himself, with the pain felt by the true champion of God that an active and pure faith was not everywhere alive in them, nor even an adequately loving concern on the part of his ecclesiastical associates to safeguard all these scattered heavenly dwelling places against neglect and oblivion.

After some time they turned into the narrow footpath that leads to the summit of Generoso after a difficult ascent that took them three hours. Moreover, the bed of the Savaglia had to be crossed very soon over a dilapidated bridge; and very close by was the reservoir of the little river, which plunged down from it to a depth of a hundred yards or more in a fissure formed by its own erosion. Here Francesco heard, from various heights, depths and directions, the roaring of the wild water rushing to the reservoir and the tinkling of herd bells, and saw a man of rude exterior—it was the communal shepherd of Soana—stretched out full length on the ground, supporting himself with his hands on the bank, his head bent down to the surface of the water, slaking his thirst quite like an animal. Behind him several mother goats were grazing with their kids, while an Alsatian dog was waiting with pointed ears for orders and for the moment when his master would be finished with his drinking. "I am a shepherd too," Francesco thought, and when the other man got up from the ground and produced a piercing whistle through his fingers—a whistle that echoed from the cliffs—and threw stones a great distance at his widely scattered flocks to frighten them, to drive them on, to call them back and in general to save them from the danger of falling into the depths, Francesco thought how difficult and heavy with responsibility this task was, even with animals, to say nothing of human beings, who are always a prey to the temptations of Satan.

With redoubled zeal the priest now began to climb higher, as if there were cause to fear that the devil might possibly get to the stray sheep first. Still accompanied by his guide, whom Francesco did not consider worth conversing with, he climbed the steep and difficult ascent for an hour and more, higher and higher into the rocky wilderness of Generoso, when suddenly he saw the mountain pasture of Santa Croce lying fifty feet before him.

He refused to believe that this heap of stones and the wall in the midst of it, made of flat stones piled on each other without mortar, was the place he was looking for, as the guide assured him it was. What he had expected from the words of the mayor was a certain prosperity, whereas this dwelling could at best be regarded as a sort of refuge for sheep and goats during a sudden squall. Since it was situated on a steep slope of stone rubble and jagged blocks of rock, and as the path to it was concealed in its zigzag course, the cursed place seemed to be inaccessible. Only after the young priest had overcome his astonishment and a certain horror that took possession of him and had moved closer, did the picture of the infamous and shunned homestead take on a somewhat friendlier aspect.

Indeed, the ruin actually became transformed before the eyes of the approaching priest into sheer loveliness; for it seemed as if an avalanche of blocks and rubble which had been released from a great height had been piled up and held fast by the rudely constructed square of the homestead, so that beneath it there remained a slope of lush green free of stones, from which charming yellow marigolds climbed in delightful abundance to the ramp in front of the house door and, as though they were curious, up over the ramp and literally through the front door into the disgraceful cavehouse.

At this spectacle Francesco was taken aback. This assault of yellow field flowers against the degraded threshold, and luxuriant trains of long-stemmed blooming forget-me-nots, which likewise sought to overrun the door with their blue reflection of the sky, and under which veins of mountain water trickled away, seemed to him to be almost an open protest against human outlawry, bans and popular courts. In his astonishment, which was followed by a certain confusion, Francesco had to sit down in his black soutane on a granite boulder that was warmed by the sun. He had spent his youth in the valley, and besides, mostly indoors, in churches, lecture halls or study rooms. His feeling for nature had not been awakened. He had never before carried out an enterprise like this, into the sublime, severe loveliness of the high mountains, and he would perhaps never have undertaken it if chance, combined with duty, had not forced the ascent of the mountain upon him. Now he was overwhelmed by the novelty and grandeur of his impressions.

For the first time the young priest Francesco Vela felt the clear and truly grand sensation of existence course through him, making him forget for moments that he was a priest and why he had come here. All his notions of piety, which were intertwined with a host of ecclesiastical rules and dogmas, had not only been displaced by this sensation, but extinguished by it. Now he even forgot to cross himself. Below him lay the beautiful Lugano region of the Upper Italian Alpine world; Sant' Agata with the little pilgrims' chapel, over which the brown ospreys were still circling; the mountain of San Giorgio; the emerging peak of Mount San Salvatore; and finally, below him, at a depth that made one dizzy, lay the arm of Lake Lugano that was known as Capolago, carefully set in the valleys of the mountain relief like a longish glass plate, with a fisherman's sailboat on it, looking like a tiny moth on a hand mirror. Behind all this, in the distance, were the white peaks of the lofty Alps, which seemed to have climbed up and up with Francesco. From among them rose Mount Rosa with its seven white points, gleaming out of the silken blue sky like a diadem and a phantom.

If one is justified in speaking of mountain sickness, then one is equally entitled to speak of a state that overcomes people on mountain heights and which may best be designated as incomparable health. This health the young priest now felt in his blood like a rejuvenation. Near him, among stones in the still withered heather, was a little flower, the like of which Francesco had never seen before. It was a wonderfully lovely species of blue gentian, whose petals were an astonishingly exquisite flaming blue. The young man in the black soutane, who had wanted to pluck the little flower in his first joy of discovery, left it unmolested in its modest spot, and merely bent the heather aside to look in extended rapture at the miracle. Everywhere young bright-green leaves of dwarf beech looked out from among the stones, and from a certain distance, across the slopes of hard, gray rubble and delicate green, the flock of poor Luchino Scarabota announced itself by the tinkling of bells. This entire mountain world possessed pristine individuality, the youthful charm of extinct ages of mankind, of which there was no trace left in the valleys below.

Francesco had sent his guide home, since he wanted to make his way back undisturbed by the presence of another person and did not wish to have a witness for what he planned at Luchino's hearth. Meanwhile he had already been noticed, and a number of dirty and greasy children's heads kept looking out curiously from the smoky black door-hole of the Scarabota stone castle.

Slowly the priest began to approach it and moved into the area of the property, which revealed its owner's large stock of cattle and was dirtied by the droppings of a big herd of cows and goats. Into Francesco's nose the odor of cattle and goats rose more and more acridly, mingled with the rare, invigorating mountain air; its increasing pungency at the entrance of the dwelling was only made bearable by the charcoal smoke that issued from the interior. When Francesco appeared in the frame of the door and blocked the light with his black soutane, the children retreated into the darkness, where the priest could not see them, and they met his greeting and all that he said to them with silence. Only an old mother goat came up to him, bleated gently and sniffed at him.

Gradually the interior of the room had become brighter to the eyes of the messenger of God. He saw a stable filled with a high pile of manure, deepening towards the back into a natural cave, which had been there originally in the nagelfluh, or whatever type of rock it was. In a thick stone wall at the right, a passage had been opened up, through which the priest caught sight of the family hearth, which was now abandoned; a mountain of ashes, still burning at the center, was piled up on the floor of exposed natural rock. From a chain with a thick covering of soot on it hung a battered copper pot, which was also sooty. At this fireplace of paleolithic man stood a bench without a back, whose fist-thick, broad seat rested on two posts, of the same breadth, anchored in the rock. This seat had been worn down and polished by a century and more of tired shepherds, their wives and their children. The wood no longer seemed to be wood but a yellow, polished marble or soapstone with countless scars and cuts in it. The square room really looked more like cave, its naturally undecorated walls consisting of strata of rude blocks and slate, from which the smoke passed through the door into the stable and from there again through the door into the open air outside, having no other way of escape, except perhaps through cracks in the walls. The room was blackened by the smoke and soot of decades, so that one might almost gain the impression of being in the interior of a chimney coated with thick soot.

Francesco had just noticed the peculiar glow emanating from a pair of eyes in a corner of the hut, when the rolling and sliding of stone rubble became audible outside, and immediately afterwards the figure of Luchino Scarabota stepped into the doorway and, like a noiseless shadow, shut out the sun, causing the room to become even darker. The savage mountain shepherd was breathing heavily, not only because he had hurried down the long distance from a higher pasture soon after he had seen the priest approach, but also because this visit was an event for the outlawed fellow.

The greeting was brief. After he had cleared the soapstone bench with his coarse hands, removing the stones and plucked marsh marigolds which his cursed brood of children had used as toys, Francesco's host urged him to sit down.

The mountain shepherd blew up the fire with puffed cheeks, and this made his feverish eyes shine even more wildly in the reflected light. He nourished the flame with logs and dry twigs, so that the pungent smoke almost drove the priest out. The shepherd's behavior was of a cringing submissiveness characterized by an anxious zeal, as if everything now depended on his not losing the grace of the Higher Being who had entered his wretched dwelling. He brought over a large dirty bucket full of milk, with a layer of thick cream at its top; unfortunately it was unbelievably foul, for which reason alone Francesco would not touch it. But he also declined to eat the fresh cheese and bread, in spite of the fact that he had become hungry, because, in his superstitious fear, he was afraid of committing a sin by doing so. Finally, when the mountain shepherd had calmed down somewhat and stood facing him with a timid, expectant look, his arms hanging from his sides, the priest began to talk as follows:

"Luchino Scarabota, you shall not lose the consolation of our Holy Church, and your children shall no longer be cast out from the community of Catholic Christians if it is proved that the evil rumors about you are untrue, or if you will confess sincerely, show remorse and contrition and be prepared, with God's help, to remove the obstacle from your path. So open your heart to me, Scarabota, let me know frankly in what respect you are being maligned, and confess with complete honesty the sinful guilt which may be weighing on you."

After this speech the shepherd was silent. But suddenly a brief, wild note struggled out of his throat, a sound betraying no emotion whatever but having something gurgling and birdlike about it. Francesco proceeded in his customary way to represent to the sinner the frightful consequences of his stubbornness, and the conciliatory kindness and love of God the Father, who had shown it through the sacrifice of His only Son, the sacrifice of the Lamb that took the sins of the world upon itself. Through Jesus Christ, he concluded, every sin can be forgiven, provided that a complete confession, combined with repentance and prayer, proves to the Heavenly Father the contrition of the poor sinner.

Only after Francesco had waited a long time and had stood up, shrugging as though to go away, did the shepherd begin to choke out an unintelligible confusion of words: a sort of clucking, such as one hears from a bird of prey. With strained attention the priest sought to grasp what was comprehensible in this confusion. But this intelligible material seemed to him just as strange and wonderful as the obscure part. Only this much became clear from the frightening and oppressive host of imaginary things: that Luchino Scarabota wanted to secure his aid against all sorts of devils that lived in the mountains and were persecuting him.

It would have been unsuitable for the believing young priest to doubt the existence and activity of evil spirits. Was not Creation filled with all sorts and degrees of fallen angels from the company of Lucifer, the rebellious one, whom God had cast out? But here he felt a horror; he did not know whether it was in the face of the darkness arising from the incredible superstition he met here, or before the hopeless blindness resulting from ignorance. He decided to form, by means of specific questions, a judgment on the mental state and intellectual powers of his parishioner.

It soon became evident that this wild, demoralized creature knew nothing of God, even less about Jesus Christ the Savior, and least of all about the existence of a Holy Ghost. On the other hand, it appeared that he felt himself surrounded by demons and was possessed by a sinister persecution mania. And to him the priest was not the authorized servant of God, but rather a mighty magician, or God himself. What could Francesco do except cross himself, while the shepherd threw himself humbly on the ground and idolatrously licked his shoes and showered them with kisses from his moist, thick lips?

The young priest had never been in a situation like this. The rare mountain air, the spring, his separation from the stratum of civilization proper, caused his mind to become slightly clouded. He fell into a dreamlike trance, in which reality dissolved into floating, airy forms. This change was combined with a slight fearfulness, which counseled him several times to flee hastily down into the sphere of consecrated churches and church bells. The devil was powerful; who could know how many means and ways he had for seducing the unsuspecting, most faithful Christian and hurling him from the edge of a giddy precipice?

Francesco had not been taught that the idols of the heathen were mere empty creatures of the imagination and nothing more. The Church recognized their power explicitly, except that it represented this power as hostile to God. They were still contending with almighty God for the world, though the struggle was hopeless. For this reason the pale young priest was not a little frightened when his host fetched a wooden object from a corner of his dwelling, a horrible piece of carving which, beyond a doubt, represented a fetish. In spite of his priestly horror at the obscene object, Francesco could not help looking at the thing intently. With abhorrence and astonishment he had to admit to himself that in this place the most abominable pagan horror, namely that of a rural cult of Priapus, was still alive. It was evident that this primitive icon could represent none other than Priapus.

Francesco had scarcely taken the little innocent god of procreation in his hand, the god of agricultural fertility, who stood in such frankly high esteem among the ancients, when his strange feeling of oppressiveness was transformed into holy wrath. Instinctively he threw the shameless little mandrake into the fire, from which, however, the shepherd retrieved it immediately with the swift movement of a dog. It glowed in one spot, burned in another, but was promptly restored to its former condition of safety by the rude hands of the heathen creature. But now the object and its rescuer had to suffer a flood of reproachful words.

Luchino Scarabota did not seem to

know which of the two gods he should regard as the stronger; the one made of wood or the god of flesh and blood. However, he kept his eyes, in which terror and horror mingled with malicious rage, fixed on the new deity, whose impious daring at any rate did not indicate a state of weakness. Once he was in full swing, the emissary of the One and Only God refused to be intimidated in his sacred zeal by the dangerous glances which the benighted idolator cast in his direction. And now, without beating about the bush, he began to talk about the vile sin to which, as was generally asserted, the mountain shepherd owed his crop of children. Into these loud words of the young priest Scarabota's sister erupted, so to speak, but without uttering a word; she merely cast stealthy glances at the zealot and busied herself here and there in the cave. She was a pallid, repulsive woman, to whom water seemed to be an unknown commodity. One could catch unpleasant glimpses of her naked body through the tears in her tattered clothing.

When the priest had finished and had, for the moment, exhausted his stock of reproachful accusations, the woman sent her brother outside with a brief, barely audible word. The savage creature disappeared at once without contradiction, like the most obedient dog. Then the sinful woman, who was encrusted with dirt, and whose greasy black hair hung down over her broad hips, kissed the priest's hand with the words "Praised be Jesus Christ."

The next moment she burst into tears.

She said the priest was perfectly right in condemning her in harsh words. She had indeed sinned against God's commandment, though not at all in the manner which slander attributed to her. She alone was the sinner; her brother was completely innocent. She swore, and indeed by all the saints, that she had never committed that fearful sin of which she was accused, namely incest. True, she had lived unchastely, and since she was now confessing, she was prepared to describe the fathers of her children, though not to name them all. For she knew very few names, since, as she said, she had often sold her favors to passing strangers out of necessity.

For the rest, she had brought her children into the world in pain without help, and some of them she had had to bury here and there in the debris of Mount Generoso soon after their birth. Whether or not he could now give her absolution, she knew that God had forgiven her, for she had atoned enough through privation, suffering and anxiety.

Francesco could not but regard the tearful confession of the woman as a tissue of lies, at least as far as the crime was concerned. He felt, to be sure, that there were acts which absolutely defied confession before a human being, and which God alone learns of in the lonely silence of prayer. He respected this bashfulness in the degenerate woman, and in general could not conceal from himself the fact that in many respects she was a higher type than her brother. In the manner of her justification there lay a clear resoluteness. Her eye confessed, but neither kind persuasion nor the hangman's fiery tongs would have torn from her a confession in words. It turned out that it was she who had sent the man to Francesco. She had seen the pale young priest one day when she went to market in Lugano, where she sold the products of her pasture, and at the sight of him she had gained confidence and had hit upon the idea of commending her outlawed children to him. She alone was the head of the family and cared for her brother and children.

"I will not discuss the question," Francesco said, "whether you are guilty or not. One thing is clear: if you don't want your children to grow up like animals, you must separate from your brother. As long as you live with him, it will never be possible for you to live down the fearful reputation you have acquired. People will always assume that you are guilty of this terrible sin."

After these words obduracy and defiance seemed to gain control of the woman's mind; at any rate she made no answer, but devoted herself for some time to domestic activity, as if there were no stranger present. During this time a girl of about fifteen came in, driving some goats through the opening of the stable and then helping the woman in her work, again as if Francesco were not there. The young priest realized at once, when he merely saw the girl's shadow glide through the depth of the cave, that she must be of extraordinary beauty. He crossed himself, for a slight feeling of inexplicable terror passed through him. He did not know whether he should resume his exhortations in the presence of the youthful shepherdess. She was beyond doubt thoroughly depraved, since Satan had awakened her to life by way of the vilest sins; but there might still be a remnant of purity in her, and who could tell whether she had any inkling of her dark origin.

Her movements, at any rate, showed a great serenity, which certainly did not permit one to draw any conclusions about emotional disturbance or a burdened conscience. On the contrary, everything about her bespoke a modest self-confidence, which was not affected by the presence of the pastor. So far, she had not as much as cast a glance at Francesco, at least not in such a way as to meet his eye or in any other discernible fashion. In fact, while he himself was looking at her stealthily through his glasses, he was compelled to doubt more and more whether a child of sin, a child of such parents, could look like this. She finally vanished by way of a ladder into a sort of attic, so that Francesco was able to continue his difficult work of spiritual ministration.

"I can't leave my brother," the woman said, "for the very simple reason that he is helpless without me. He can, when necessary, write his name, and I've taught him to do so with the greatest difficulty. He can't distinguish coins and is afraid of trains, cities and people. If I leave him, he will pursue me as a poor dog pursues his lost master. He will either find me or perish miserably; and what will then happen to the children and our property? If I stay here with the children, I'd like to see the man who could get my brother away from here; they'd have to put him in chains and lock him behind iron bars in Milan."

The priest said, "This may yet happen, if you do not follow my good advice."

At that the woman's anxiety turned to rage. She had sent her brother to Francesco that he might take pity on them, not make them miserable. She preferred in that case to continue living as she had till now, hated and rejected by the people below. She was a good Catholic, but when the Church rejected someone, he had a right to give himself to the devil. And she might then perhaps really commit that great sin she was accused of but of which she was as yet innocent.

Mingled with these strained words and lone shrieks that came from the woman, Francesco heard, from above, where the girl had vanished, a sweet singing, first like the most gentle breathing, then swelling with power, and his mind was influenced more by this melodious spell than by the furious outbursts of the degenerate woman. A hot wave rose within him, mingled with an anxiety he had never felt before. The smoke-filled hole of this animal-human dwelling stable seemed to be transformed, as if by magic, into the loveliest of all crystalline grottoes of Dante's Paradise, full of angelic voices and the sounding pinions of laughing doves.

He went. It was impossible for him to

ndure such confusing influences any onger without trembling visibly. When he eached the hollowed-out pile of stones outside, he inhaled the freshness of the mountain air and was at once filled like an empty vessel with the immense impression of the mountain world. His spirit passed, as it were, into the farthest range of his eyes and consisted of the colossal masses of the earth's crust, from distant, snowy peaks to adjacent fearful abysses, under the royal brightness of the spring day. He still saw brown ospreys drawing their unselfconscious circles over the cone-shaped Sant' Agata. The idea came to him to hold a private service there for the outlawed family, and he revealed this thought to the woman, who had stepped dejectedly across the threshold of the cave, luxuriant in the yellow marigolds. "You dare not come to Soana, as you yourself know," he said. "If I invited you to do so, we would all be equally ill advised."

The woman was again moved to the point of tears, and promised to appear on a certain day before the chapel of Sant' Agata with her brother and the older children.

When the young priest had gotten far enough away from Luchino Scarabota's home and his curse-laden family so that he could no longer be seen from there, he chose a stone block that had been warmed through by the sun as a resting place in which to reflect on what he had just experienced. He told himself that while it was true he had climbed the mountain with a morbid interest, he had still done so in a sober frame of mind and with a sense of duty, and without any foretaste of what was disturbing him now with such foreboding. And what was this disturbance? He tugged, stroked and brushed his soutane for a long time, as if in that way he could rid himself of it.

When, after some time, he still did not feel the desired clarity, he took his breviary out of his pocket with an habitual movement; but even though he immediately began reading aloud, he was not freed from a certain strange indecision. He felt as if he had forgotten to attend to something, some important aspect of his mission. For this reason he kept looking back at the road from under his spectacles with a certain expectancy, and lacked the strength to continue the descent which he had begun.

So he fell into a strange reverie, out of which he was awakened by two slight incidents which his imagination, wrenched out of its accustomed groove, saw with considerable exaggeration: first of all, the right lens of his spectacles cracked with a bang under the impact of the cold mountain air, and almost immediately after that he heard a fearful panting above his head and felt a strong pressure on his shoulders.

The young priest leaped up. He laughed aloud when he recognized the cause of his panic in a spotted he-goat, which had given him proof of his unbounded confidence by planting his forehooves on his shoulders without any regard for his clerical garb.

But this was only the beginning of the animal's most intimate importunity. The shaggy goat with the strong, beautifully curved horns and flashing eyes had, it seemed, the habit of begging from passing mountain-climbers and did so in such a droll, firm and irresistible manner that one could ward him off only by taking flight. Standing above Francesco, he kept putting his hooves on the priest's chest and seemed determined to nibble at his hair, nose and fingers, after forcing the harassed victim to submit to having his pockets sniffed at and devouring a few bits of bread with incredible greed.

An old, bearded she-goat, whose bell and udder dragged on the ground, had followed the highwayman and, encouraged by him, began to harass the priest too. She was especially impressed by the breviary with its cross and gilt edges and, when Francesco was busy defending himself against a curved goat horn, she succeeded in getting possession of the little book. Taking its black-printed leaves for green ones, she began eating the sacred truths literally and greedily, according to the prescription of the prophet.

On this scene of distress, aggravated by the gathering of other animals that had been grazing by themselves, the shepherdess suddenly appeared as a rescuer. It was the very same girl of whom Francesco had first caught a fleeting glimpse in Luchino's hut. When the slim, strong girl, after driving the goats away, stood before him with her fresh cheeks flushed and her laughing eyes, he said, "You have saved me, my good girl." And, taking his breviary from the hands of the young Eve, he added, laughing too, "It is really strange that, in spite of my shepherd's office, I am so helpless against your flock."

A priest may not converse with a young girl or woman any longer than his ecclesiastical duty demands, and the congregation notices it at once if he is seen holding such a conversation outside the church. And so Francesco, mindful of his stern calling, continued his way back without delay; and yet he felt as if he had detected himself in a sinful act and had to purify himself through a remorseful confession at the earliest opportunity. He had not yet got beyond the range of the herd bells when the sound of a woman's voice penetrated to him, suddenly making him forget all his meditations again. The voice was of such quality that it did not occur to him that it could belong to the shepherdess he had just left. Francesco had not only heard the church singers of the Vatican in Rome but had formerly listened to secular singers in Milan with his mother, so the coloratura and bel canto of the prima donnas were not unknown to him. He stopped involuntarily and waited. No doubt they are tourists from Milan, he thought, and hoped that he might, if possible, catch a passing glimpse of the owner of this glorious voice. But since she did not seem willing to appear, he continued to set foot before foot, cautiously descending into the giddy depths.

What Francesco had experienced on this professional visit, as a whole and in detail, was superficially not worth mentioning, if one excludes the abominations that had as their breeding ground the hut of the poor Scarabotas, brother and sister. But the young priest felt at once that this mountain trip had become for him an event of great importance, though for the present he had not even a remote idea of the entire scope of its significance. He felt that a transformation had taken place in him, working from the inside out. He found himself in a new state, which became minute by minute more strange to him, and he grew suspicious, but by no means so suspicious as to scent the presence of Satan or to wish perhaps to throw an inkwell at him, even if he had had one in his pocket. The mountain world lay below him like a paradise. For the very first time, folding his hands involuntarily, he congratulated himself on having been entrusted by his superior with the care of this very parish. Compared with this precious valley, what was the cloth of St. Peter, which came from heaven, held by angels at its three corners? Where could the human mind find a greater majesty than in these inaccessible crags of Mount Generoso, from which one could hear continuously the muffled spring thunder of melting snow descending in avalanches?

From the day of his visit to the depraved family, Francesco, to his astonishment, could no longer find his way back into the unthinking peace of his former existence. The new countenance which Nature had assumed for him refused to fade, and she would not permit herself to be forced back in any way into her former lifeless state. The character of her influence, which plagued him not only in the daytime but in his dreams too, he recognized at once and named it temptation. And since the faith of the Church is fused with pagan superstition through the mere fact of combating it, Francesco in all seriousness traced his transformation back to the touching of that wooden object, that little mandrake which the ragged shepherd had rescued from the fire. Beyond doubt a relic still remained alive, a fragment of those abominations to which the ancients paid homage under the name of phallic worship, that shameful cult which had been suppressed in the world by the holy war of the Cross of Jesus. —Up to the moment when he had caught sight of the loathsome object, the Cross alone had been burned into Francesco's soul. He had been branded with the brand of the Cross, precisely as the sheep of a herd are marked with a white-hot stamp, and his stigma had become the essential symbol of his self, present in him in both his waking and dreaming life. Now the accursed Satan incarnate looked down at him from the crosspiece of the crucifix; this most unclean, dreadful satyr symbol was gradually usurping the place of the Cross and was in constant rivalry with it.

Francesco had reported the success of his pastoral mission to the mayor and especially to the bishop. The answer he received from the bishop was approval of his procedure. "Above all," the bishop wrote, "we must avoid any flagrant scandal." He thought it was exceedingly shrewd that Francesco had instituted a special secret service for the poor sinners on Sant' Agata, in the chapel of the Holy Mother of Mary. But the endorsement of his action by his superior could not restore Francesco's peace of mind; he could not get rid of the idea that he had come down from up there with a sort of enchantment clinging to him.

In Ligornetto, where Francesco was born and where his uncle, the famous sculptor, had spent the last ten years of his life, there still lived the same old priest who had introduced him as a boy to the saving truths of the Catholic faith and shown him the way of grace. One day, walking from Soana to Ligornetto in about three hours, he called on this old priest, who welcomed him and was visibly touched at being asked to hear the young man's confession. Of course he granted him absolution.

Francesco's scruples of conscience are expressed approximately in the following revelation which he made to the old man. He said: "Since I visited the poor sinners on the mountain pasture of Soana, I have been in a sort of possessed state. I shudder! I feel as if I had put on, not merely another coat, but actually another skin. When I hear the waterfall of Soana roar, I want most of all to climb down into the deep gorge and stand for hours under the falling masses of water, as if to purify myself both outside and in and to regain my health. When I see the crucifix in the church or the crucifix over my bed, I laugh. I can no longer weep and sigh as I used to do, or imagine the sufferings of our Savior. On the other hand, my eyes are attracted by all sorts of objects which resemble the little mandrake belonging to Luchino Scarabota. Sometimes they are quite unlike it, but I see a resemblance nevertheless. I had made curtains for the windows of my little room, so that I might work, steep myself in the study of the Church Fathers. Now I have removed these curtains. The singing of the birds, the murmur of the many brooks that run through the meadow past my house after the snow has melted, yes, even the fragrance of the narcissi used to disturb me. Now I open my windows wide, so that I may drink it all in greedily.

"All this alarms me," Francesco continued, "but this is perhaps not the worst. Still worse, perhaps, is the fact that I have fallen into the orbit of unclean devils, as though under the spell of black magic. Their pinching and clawing, their impudent tickling and provocation to sin, at every hour of the day and night, is terrible. I open my window and their magic power makes it seem as if the song of the birds in the blossoming cherry tree under my window were charged with unchastity. I am challenged by certain shapes in the bark of trees and they, yes, even certain lines of the mountains, remind me of parts of the *corporis femini.* It is a terrifying assault of crafty, malicious, ugly demons to which I am being delivered up in spite of all my prayers and chastisements. All nature, I say it to you with a shudder, sometimes murmurs, roars and thunders a tremendous phallic song into my terrified ears, thus—as I am compelled to believe against my better judgment—paying homage to the shepherd's wretched little wooden idol.

"All this," Francesco continued, "naturally increases my alarm and mental anguish, the more so because I recognize it as my duty to enter the field as a champion against the focus of infection up there on the mountain pasture. But even this is not the worst part of my confession. What is worse: something like an ineradicable poison, mingled with a sort of devilish sweetness, has penetrated the very basic duties of my calling, spreading confusion everywhere. I was at first moved with a pure and holy power by the words of Jesus about the lost sheep and the shepherd who leaves his flock to bring it back from the inaccessible rocks. But now I doubt whether this purpose still exists in its pristine purity. It has increased in passionate zeal. I awaken at night, my face bathed in tears, and I dissolve into a sobering compassion for the fate of the lost souls up there. But when I say 'lost souls,' this is perhaps the point at which a sharp line must be drawn between truth and falsehood. For the fact is that the sinful souls of Scarabota and his sister appear before my mind's eye solely and uniquely as the image of the fruit of their sin, that is, their daughter.

"Now, I ask myself whether the cause of my seemingly worthy zeal may not be a forbidden desire for her and whether I am doing right and not running the risk of eternal death by continuing my seemingly meritorious labors."

The old, experienced priest had listened to most of the youth's pedantic confession with a serious look on his face, but he smiled at several points. This was Francesco as he knew him, with his conscientious sense of outer and inner order and his need of clear accuracy and cleanliness. He said: "Francesco, do not be afraid. Just keep on the road you have always walked. You must not be surprised that the machinations of the evil enemy reveal themselves most powerfully and most dangerously when you proceed to snatch victims from him which he felt to be securely his, so to speak."

His mind set at ease, Francesco stepped out of the priest's house into the street of the little village of Ligornetto, in which he had spent his earliest youth. It is a small village, lying fairly flat on a broad valley floor surrounded by fertile fields; the vineyards wind in and out from mulberry tree to mulberry tree like solidly twisted ropes, between vegetable and grain plots. This place, too, is dominated by the mighty jagged crags of Mount Generoso, whose majesty is visible here from the west side of its broad base.

It was around midday and Ligornetto appeared to be in a state of somnolence. Francesco was barely greeted on his walk by a few cackling hens, some children at play and at the end of the village by a barking little dog. Here, at the end of the village, his uncle's home, built with the resources of a wealthy man, was thrust forward like a bolt on a door, the *buen retiro* of that Vincenzo, the sculptor. It was now uninhabited and had gone over into the possession of the canton of Ticino as a kind of memorial foundation. Francesco walked up the steps leading to the abandoned and neglected garden and then yielded to a sudden desire to see the interior of the house. Peasants who lived nearby, old acquaintances of his, gave him the key to the house.

The relation of the young priests to the arts was one which is common to his class. His famous uncle had been dead about ten years, and Francesco had not seen the rooms of the celebrated artist's home since the day of the funeral. He could not have said what suddenly moved him to visit the empty house, in which he had until now for the most part shown only a passing interest. The uncle had never been more than a celebrity to him, and his sphere of activity was alien and meaningless.

As Francesco turned the key in the lock and entered the hall through the door, which creaked on its rusty hinges, he shuddered slightly at the dusty stillness that was wafted toward him from the staircase and from all the open rooms. To the right of the entrance hall was the deceased artist's library, which revealed at once that a culturally active man had lived here. The low bookcases contained, apart from Vasari, the complete works of Winckelmann, while the Italian Parnassus was represented by the sonnets of Michelangelo, the works of Dante, Petrarch, Tasso, Ariosto and others. A collection of drawings and etchings was stored in cabinets which had been especially built for the purpose; medals of the Renaissance and all sorts of valuable rarities, among them painted Etruscan clay vases and some other antiquities of bronze and marble, were set up in the room. Here and there a particularly beautiful print of Leonardo or Michelangelo hung framed on the wall, depicting a male or female nude. The small adjoining room was practically filled from top to bottom with such objects on three of its walls.

From there you entered a room with a cupola, which was several stories high and lighted from above. Here Vincenzo had worked with modeling wood and chisel, and the plaster casts of his best works filled this almost churchlike room, forming a crowded and silent collection.

Constrained, indeed alarmed, and frightened by the echo of his own footsteps, Francesco had come this far almost with a bad conscience, and now proceeded to subject this and that work of his uncle's to a first real inspection. Beside a statue of Michelangelo a Ghiberti could be seen. There was a Dante there and works covered with stippling dots, as the models had been executed in marble in enlarged form. But these world-famous figures could not long hold the attention of the young priest. Beside them stood the statues of three young girls, the daughters of a marchese who had been broadminded enough to allow the master to portray them completely unclothed. To judge from the statues the youngest of the three ladies was not more than twelve, the second not more than fifteen and the third not over seventeen years old. Francesco came to himself only after he had contemplated the slender bodies for a long time in complete absorption. Unlike the works of the Greeks, these figures did not display their nudity as a natural nobility and image of divinity, but one experienced it as an indiscretion of the boudoir. In the first place, the copies had not been dissociated from the originals but were distinctly recognizable as copies; and these originals seemed to say: we have been indecently exposed and undressed by a brutal order against our will and our sense of modesty. When Francesco awoke from his revery, his heart was pounding and he looked fearfully in every direction. He was doing nothing that was evil but he felt it was a sin just to be alone with such figures.

He resolved to go away as quickly as possible, so that he might not actually be caught there. But when he reached the front door, instead of going out, he put the door latch into the lock from the inside and turned the key, so that he was now locked in the spectral house of the deceased and could not be surprised. After this he returned to the plaster scandal of the three graces.

His heart beating more violently, he was overcome by a wan and fearful madness. He felt a compulsion to stroke the hair of the oldest of the marchionesses as if she were alive. Although this act obviously bordered on insanity, as he himself realized, it was still in a sense commensurate with his priestly calling. But the second marchioness had to suffer being stroked on the shoulder and arm: an opulent shoulder and arm, which led to a soft, delicate hand. Soon Francesco had become a hopelessly confused and contrite sinner, through further acts of tenderness toward the third, the youngest, marchioness, finally planting a shy, criminal kiss under her left breast. He felt no better than Adam when he heard the voice of the Lord after he had eaten of the apple from the tree of knowledge. He fled. He ran as if pursued.

The following days Francesco spent partly in church in prayer, partly in his parsonage chastising himself. His contrition and remorse were great. In a fervor of devotion such as he had not known hitherto, he dared hope in the long run to triumph over the temptations of the flesh. At any rate the conflict between the principles of good and evil had broken out in him with undreamed-of frightfulness, so that it seemed that God and the devil had for the first time transplanted their theater of war into his breast. Even sleep, that part of his activity for which he was not responsible, no longer offered the young cleric any peace; for this unguarded period at night seemed especially welcome to Satan for inducing seductive and destructive delusions into the young man's normally innocent soul. One night, towards morning—he did not know whether it had happened while he was asleep or awake—in the white light of the moon, he saw the three white figures of the marchese's beautiful daughters come into his room and up to his bed. When he looked more closely, he recognized that each figure had become magically fused with the image of the young shepherdess on the pasture of Santa Croce.

Beyond a doubt a thread led from the small, toylike homestead of Scarabota to the priest's room, whose window permitted the pasture to look into it; and this thread had not been spun by angels. Francesco knew enough about the celestial hierarchy, and the infernal one too, to recognize at once whose brainchild this work was. Francesco believed in sorcery. Learned in many branches of scholastic science, he assumed that evil demons made use of the influence of the stars to accomplish certain destructive ends. He had learned that, as regards the body, man belongs to the celestial spheres; his intelligence has placed him on a level with the angels, and his will is subordinate to God; but God has permitted fallen angels to turn his will away from Him, and the realm of the demons is increased by their bond with such perverted humans. Besides, a temporal, physical emotion, exploited by the spirits of hell, can often be the cause of a man's eternal destruction. In short, the young priest trembled to the very marrow of his bones and feared the poisonous bite of the *diaboli*, the demons that smell of blood, the beast Behemoth and especially Asmodeus, the specific demon of whoring.

At first he could not bring himself to

believe that the cursed brother and sister were guilty of the sin of witchcraft and sorcery. True, he had one experience that threw him into a state of deep suspicion. Every day he undertook a spiritual purification with holy zeal and all the resources of religion, in order to purify himself of the image of the shepherd girl, but every time he did so it stood more clearly, more firmly and more plainly before him. What sort of painting was this, what sort of indestructible wooden tablet stood under it, or what sort of canvas was it that water or fire did not affect it at all?

The way this picture thrust itself forward everywhere became at times the subject of his silent and astonished observation. He would read a book; when he saw the soft face, framed by the strangely reddish, earth-brown hair, looking at him with big, dark eyes from a page, he inserted a blank leaf, which was intended to cover and conceal it. But when he turned the leaf he found that the picture penetrated every page as if there were no leaf, as indeed it penetrated drapes, doors and walls in the house and church.

Amid such anxieties and inner dissensions, the young priest was perishing with impatience because the time set for the special service on the peak of Sant' Agata would not come fast enough. He wished to perform the duty he had undertaken as quickly as possible, because he might perhaps in that way snatch the girl from the claws of the prince of hell. He wished even more to see the girl again; but what he longed for most of all was liberation from his tormented enchantment, a liberation he definitely hoped to achieve. Francesco ate little, spent the greater part of his nights awake and, growing paler and more haggard daily, acquired in the eyes of his parishioners an even greater reputation for exemplary piety.

The morning had finally come on which the priest had arranged with the poor sinners to meet in the chapel that was situated high on the cone of Sant' Agata. The extremely difficult ascent to it could not be made in less than two hours. At nine o'clock Francesco appeared on the village square, ready for the walk, serene and refreshed in his heart and viewing the world with newborn eyes. May was approaching, and a day had dawned, more exquisite than could be imagined; but the young man had already often experienced days equally beautiful, without, however, finding in nature a Garden of Eden as he did today. Today he was surrounded by paradise.

As at most other times, women and girls were standing about the sarcophagus, which was overflowing with mountain rain water; they greeted the priest with loud cries. Something in his manner and face, and the festive freshness of the young day, had given the laundresses spirit. Their skirts wedged in between their legs, so that some of them revealed their brown calves and knees, they stood bent over, working vigorously with powerful, naked arms that were tanned too. Francesco went up to the group. He found himself moved to say all sorts of friendly words that had nothing to do with his spiritual office, but concerned the good weather, good spirits and hopes for a good vintage. For the first time, probably stimulated by his visit to the house of his uncle the sculptor, the young priest condescended to study the ornamental frieze on the sarcophagus, which depicted a procession of bacchantes and prancing satyrs, dancing girls playing the flute, and Dionysos, the god of wine, wreathed in grapes, in his panther-drawn chariot. At this moment it did not seem strange to him that the ancients had covered the stone receptacle of death with figures that represented exuberant life. The women and girls, some of whom were of uncommon beauty, chattered and laughed away with him during this inspection, and at times it seemed to him that he himself was surrounded by joyful, shouting, intoxicated maenads.

This second ascent into the mountain world was like that of a man who walks with open eyes in contrast to one who is blind from birth. Francesco felt with a compelling clarity that he had suddenly regained his sight. Accordingly, the contemplation of the sarcophagus seemed to him no accident but of deep significance. Where was its dead occupant? The living water of life filled the open stone and coffin, and eternal resurrection was proclaimed on the surface of the marble in the language of the ancients. This is how the gospel had to be interpreted.

To be sure, this was a gospel that had little in common with the one he had once studied and taught. It had no relation to the leaves or letters of a book, but rather, it came welling out of the earth through the grass, plants and flowers or flowing down with the light from the center of the sun. All nature took on, as it were, a speaking life. She who had been dead and mute became alive, intimate, direct and communicative. Suddenly she seemed to tell the young priest everything she had been silent about till now. He seemed to be her favorite, her chosen son, whom she was initiating, like a mother, into the sacred mystery of her love and motherhood. All the abysses of terror, all the anxieties of his disturbed soul were no more. There was nothing left of all the darkness and fear of a supposed stormy course to hell. The whole of Nature radiated kindness and love and Francesco, rich in kindness and love, could return kindness and love to her.

Strange: as he laboriously climbed upwards through broom, beech and thickets of bramble, often sliding down from jagged stones, the spring morning enveloped him like a joyful and tremendous symphony of nature, which spoke more about the process of creating than about the created world. The mystery of a creative activity that was forever exempt from death was openly revealed. Anyone who did not hear this symphony, so it seemed to the priest, was deceiving himself when he ventured to sing with the psalmist the hymns *"Jubilate Deo omnia terra"* or *"Benedicte coeli domino."*

The waterfall of Soana rushed down in satiate abundance into its narrow gorge. Its roar sounded full and luxurious. Its speech could never fail to be heard. Muffled at one moment, becoming clear the next, the voice of satiety sounded in perpetual variation. A thundering avalanche broke loose from the gigantic shadow-wall of Mount Generoso, and when it became audible to Francesco, the avalanche itself had already poured down in noiseless streams of rolling snow into the bed of the Savaglia. Where was there anything in nature that was not in the grip of the metamorphosis of life and that was without soul? anything in which a driving will was not active? Word, writing, song and coursing heart's blood were everywhere. Did not the sun place a warm, pleasant hand on his back between his shoulders? Did the leaves of the laurel and beech thickets not whisper and sway when he touched them in passing? Did the water not flow everywhere and, softly babbling, sketch everywhere the meandering and tangled script of its channel?

Didn't he, Francesco Vela, and didn't the fiber roots of myriads of growing things, small and large, read it, and was it not its mystery that was depicted in myriads of flowers and calyxes? The priest picked up a tiny stone and found a reddish net of lines running through it; here, too, a miraculous world—spoken, painted, written—a forming form that bore testimony everywhere to the creative power of life in pictures.

And didn't the voices of the birds bear the same testimony as they united in a network of infinitely delicate, invisible threads above the eaves of the mighty valley of rock? This audible network seemed to Francesco at times to be transformed into visible threads of a silver splendor, which an inner and speaking fire caused to glitter. Was it not love made audible and visible in forms and a revelation of nature's bliss? And was it not delightful, the way this web, as often as it was dissolved or torn, was tied together again, as though by tiny weavers' shuttles, swiftly, tirelessly flying back and forth? Where were the small feathered weavers? One did not see them, except possibly when a little bird swiftly and silently changed its place; the tiniest throats poured out this speech that carried into space, drowning everything in its jubilation.

With everything welling forth, everything throbbing both within him and around him, Francesco did not know how to determine the place of death in the scheme of things. He touched the trunk of a chestnut tree and felt that he was pressing the nourishing juices upward within it. He drank in the air like a living soul and knew at once that it was this air to which he owed the breathing and hymning of his own soul. And was it not this air alone that made a speaking instrument of revelation out of his throat and tongue? Francesco stopped for a moment before a teeming, zealously active swarm of ants. A tiny dormouse had been almost wholly stripped down to its graceful skeleton by the mysterious little creatures. Did not the precious little skeleton and the dormouse that had perished and vanished in the warmth of the ant state testify to the indestructibility of life, and had not Nature, in her urge or compulsion to create, merely sought a new form? The priest saw the brown ospreys of Sant' Agata again, this time not below but high above him. Their winged and plumed bodies bore the miracle of the blood, the miracle of the pulsating heart, in majestic bliss through space. But who could fail to recognize that the changing curves of their flight delineated, on the blue silk of the sky, a clear, unmistakable writing, whose meaning and beauty were most intimately bound up with life and love? Francesco was convinced that the birds were inviting him to read it. And though they wrote by means of the path of their flight, the power of reading was not denied them. Francesco thought of the keen vision that was vouchsafed these winged fishermen. And he thought of the countless eyes of humans, birds, mammals, insects and fish, by means of which Nature views herself. With an astonishment that grew deeper and deeper, he recognized her in her infinite maternity. She saw to it that nothing in her whole maternal realm should remain hidden from her children's enjoyment; not only had she endowed them with the senses of sight, hearing, smell, taste and touch, but, Francesco felt, she was still other, countless new senses in readiness for the transformation of the aeons. What a vastness of seeing, hearing, smelling, tasting and touching there was in the world! And over the ospreys hung a white cloud. It resembled a radiant pleasure-tent. But it, too, went away and was visibly transformed.

They were profound and mystical powers that had opened the eyes of the priest Francesco. But, though he would not admit this to himself, the background for this experience was the happy circumstance that he saw four delightful hours ahead of him, including another meeting with the poor, outlawed shepherd girl. This awareness made him secure and rich, as if the time that was filled with such precious content could not come to an end. Up there, yes, up there where the little chapel stood, above which the ospreys were circling—up there, there awaited him a happiness which, so he thought, the angels must envy him. He climbed and climbed, and the most blissful zeal gave him wings. What he planned up there in unmoored proximity to heaven must surely transfigure him and put him almost on a plane with the good Eternal Shepherd Himself. *"Sursum corda! Sursum corda!"* He kept repeating to himself the greeting of St. Francis, while alongside him walked Sant' Agata, the martyr to whom the little chapel above had been dedicated and who had walked to her death at the hands of the hangman as if to a gay dance. And behind her and him, so it seemed to Francesco in his zealous ascent, there followed a procession of holy women, all of whom wanted to be present at the miracle of love on the festive summit. Mary herself, with her exquisite ambrosial flowing hair and her graceful feet, strode far ahead of the priest and his procession of sainted women, so that the earth might be covered with flowers for all those under her eye, her breath, her feet. *"Invoco te! Invoco te!"* Francesco whispered in rapture under his breath. *"Invoco te nostra benigna stella."*

Without feeling tired, the priest had reached the peak of the mountain cone, which was scarcely wider than the little church that stood on it. There was just room left for a narrow ledge and a tight little square in front of the church; in the middle of this square stood a young chestnut tree that was still without leaves. The blue gentian had spread so thickly about the sanctuary that a piece of the sky or of Mary's blue gown seemed to be strewn around the little church in the wilderness. Or one could also imagine that the mountain had simply dipped its peak in the azure of the sky.

The choirboy and the Scarabotas, brother and sister, were already there and had made themselves comfortable under the chestnut tree. Francesco turned pale, for his eyes had looked fleetingly but in vain for the young shepherdess. But he put on a stern look and opened the chapel door with a big rusty key, without showing his disappointment and the turbulent struggle that was going on in his heart. He entered the small church, in which the choirboy at once began to make some preparations behind the altar for celebrating the Mass. A little holy water was poured into the dry fountain from a bottle that had been brought up, so that the Scarabotas could dip their hard and sinful fingers in it. They sprinkled and crossed themselves and fell to their knees just inside the threshold of the door in timid reverence.

Meanwhile Francesco, driven by uneasiness, went out once more into the open, where, after walking about a little, with a sudden mute but deep emotion, he came upon the girl he was seeking; she was resting a little below the platform formed by the mountain peak, on a starry sky of gleaming blue gentian. "Come in, I'm waiting for you," the priest said. She got up with apparent indolence and looked at him calmly from under lowered lashes. At the same time she seemed to be smiling gently with a soft charm but this was merely an illusion produced by the natural shape of her sweet mouth, the lovely light in her blue eyes and the delicate dimples in her full cheeks.

At this moment the picture Francesco had cherished in his heart was fatefully renewed and enhanced. He saw a childlike, innocent Madonna face, whose maddening charm was combined with a very gentle, painful severity. The rather pronounced red of her cheeks lay on a white, not brown, skin, from which the moist red of the lips shone with the glow of the pomegranate. Every strain in the music of this childlike head was at once sweetness and bitterness, melancholy and serenity. In her eyes one could read shy retirement and at the same time a delicate challenge: both without the violence of animal impulse but artless and flowerlike. If her eyes seemed to bear in them the riddle and the fairy tale of the flower, the girl's whole appearance resembled rather a beautiful and ripe fruit. This head, as Francesco realized with astonishment, was still altogether that of a child, insofar as it expressed her soul; only a certain grapelike, swelling opulence indicated that she had crossed the boundary of childhood and had attained the state of womanhood. Her hair, which was partly earth brown in color, with lighter strands running through it, was tied around her forehead and temples to form a heavy crown. A heavy, inwardly fermenting, nobly ripe sleepiness seemed to draw the girl's eyelashes downward and gave her eyes a certain moist, overpowering tenderness. But the music of the head modulated below the ivory neck into another, whose eternal notes expressed another meaning. With her shoulders the woman began. She was a woman of youthful and yet mature fullness, almost tending toward an opulence that did not seem to belong to the childlike head. The bare feet and strongly tanned calves wore a fruitlike fullness which, it seemed to the priest, was almost too heavy for them. This head possessed the hot, sensuous mystery of its Isis-like body unconsciously, or at most with a gentle awareness. But for this very reason Francesco realized that he had fallen a hopeless victim, for life and death, to this head and to this omnipotent body.

But whatever the young priest saw, realized and felt at this moment of reunion with this creature of God, who was so heavily burdened by her heritage of sin, he did not reveal except by a slight trembling of his lips. "What is your name?" he merely asked the innocent sinner. The shepherdess gave her name as Agata and did this in a voice that seemed to Francesco like the cooing of a paradisial ring dove. "Can you read and write?" he asked. She replied, "No." "Do you know anything about the meaning of the Holy Mass?" She looked at him but did not reply. He then told her to go into the little church and went in ahead of her. Behind the altar the choirboy helped him into his vestments. Francesco put the biretta on his head and the sacred service began; never before had the young man been moved to such a solemn fervor.

He felt as if all-bountiful God had only now called him to His service. The road to priestly consecration which he had traveled now seemed to him to be nothing more than a dry, empty, deceptive precipitancy that had nothing in common with the truly divine. But now the divine hour, the sacred season, had been born within him. The Savior's love was like a heavenly rain of fire in which he stood and through which all the love in him was suddenly liberated and kindled. His heart expanded with infinite love into the whole of creation and was united with all creatures in a harmonious, rapturous pulsebeat. Out of this intoxication, which almost stupefied him, compassion for every creature, zeal for the divinely good, broke out with redoubled strength, and he believed that only now did he fully understand Holy Mother Church and her service. He now wanted to become her servant with a renewed but very different zeal.

How the journey, the ascent to this mountain peak, had unlocked to him the mystery whose meaning he had inquired from Agata! Her silence, which had made him mute too, signified for him, though he did not show it, a common knowledge through the revelation that had come to them both. Was not the Eternal Mother the essence of all transformations, and had he not lured the forsaken, lost children of God, groping about in the dark, to this peak, raised high above the ground, to reveal to them the miracle of the transubstantiation of the Son, the eternal flesh and blood of the Godhead? Thus the youth stood and raised the cup, his eyes overflowing with joy. It seemed to him as if he himself were becoming God. In this state, in which he felt himself to be one of the elect, a sacred instrument, he seemed to expand with invisible organs into all the heavens with a joy and omnipotence that lifted him, he believed, infinitely above the whole teeming spawn of the churches and their clerics. They should see him, should lift their eyes to him with astonished reverence, on the dizzy heights of the altar at which he stood. For he was standing at the altar in a very different and higher sense than the Pope, the holder of Peter's keys, does after his election. With a convulsive ecstasy he held the cup of the Eucharist and the transubstantiation, as a symbol of God's body renewing itself perpetually in the whole of creation into the infinity of space, where it shone like a second, brighter sun. And while he stood there with the raised sacrament for what seemed to him an eternity but was in reality two or three seconds, it appeared to him that the cone of Sant' Agata was covered from top to bottom with listening angels, saints and apostles. But even more beautiful was a muffled drumbeat and a round dance performed by beautifully dressed women, wearing garlands of flowers and clearly visible through the walls as they moved about the chapel. Behind them whirled the maenads of the sarcophagus in ecstatic frenzy; the goat-footed satyrs danced and skipped, some of them carrying Luchino Scarabota's wooden symbol of fertility in joyful procession.

The descent to Soana brought Francesco to that brooding disenchantment felt by a person who has drunk to the last drop from the cup of intoxication. The Scarabota family had left after the Mass: the brother, sister and daughter had kissed the young priest's hand in gratitude when they departed. As he now descended deeper and deeper, the state of mind in which he had read the Mass up above became more and more an object of suspicion to him. The peak of Sant' Agata had surely, in former times, been the seat of a pagan cult, consecrated to some idol; what had possessed him up there, apparently with the murmuring sound of the Holy Ghost, was perhaps the demonic work of that dethroned theocracy which Jesus Christ had overthrown, but whose destructive power was still tolerated by the Creator and Director of the world. Upon arriving at his vicarage in Soana, the priest was overwhelmed by the consciousness that he had been guilty of a grievous sin, and his anxiety on this account became so heavy that he entered the church, which stood wall to wall with his residence, even before taking his midday meal, to entrust himself in passionate prayer to the Highest Mediator and, if possible, to purify himself in His grace.

Feeling his own helplessness, he begged God not to deliver him up to the assaults of demons. He was aware, he confessed, that they were attacking his soul in all sorts of ways, either constricting it or extending it beyond its accustomed salutary boundaries and transforming it in a terrible way. "I was a small garden, carefully cultivated in Your honor," Francesco said to God. "Now it has been destroyed by a flood, which will perhaps rise and rise under the influence of the planets and on whose boundless waters I am drifting about in a tiny bark. Formerly I knew my way precisely. It was the same way which Your Holy Church prescribes for her servants. Now I am drifting, no longer certain of the goal and the way.

"Grant me," Francesco implored, "my former narrowness and my certainty, and command the evil angels to desist from their dangerous assaults on Your helpless servant. Lead, oh, lead us not into temptation. I went up to the poor sinners in Your service; grant that I may find my way back into the firm, restricted sphere of my sacred duties."

Francesco's prayers no longer possessed their former clarity and sharpness of contour. He asked for things that were mutually incompatible. At times he was unsure himself whether the stream of passion that bore his requests came from Heaven or from another source. That is, he did not really know whether he was not fundamentally imploring Heaven to grant him a hellish prize. His inclusion of the Scarabotas, brother and sister, in his prayers might indeed have had its origin in Christian compassion and priestly care. But was this true when he implored Heaven fervently, to the point of scalding tears, for the salvation of Agata?

For the present he could still answer this question affirmatively, for the clear stirring of the mightiest impulse, which he felt when he saw the girl again, had been transformed into a romantic feeling for something infinitely pure. This transformation prevented Francesco from noticing that the fruit of mortal sin was forcing its way into the place of Mary, the Mother of God, and was, so to speak, the incarnation of the Madonna in his prayers and thoughts. On the first of May there began in the church of Soana, as everywhere, a special service for the Virgin Mary, the observance of which lulled the young priest's alertness still more. Day after day, at about the hour of twilight, he gave a short talk, chiefly to the women and daughters of Soana, on the theme of the virtues of the Blessed Virgin. Before and after the talk the nave of the church echoed with the hymns of praise in honor of Mary; they passed through the open doors into the spring air. And the old, exquisite airs, so lovely in both words and music, mingled outside with the cheerful noise made by the sparrows and with the sweetest lament of the nightingales which came from the damp gorges nearby. At such moments Francesco, apparently absorbed in the service of Mary, was wholly given up to the service of his idol.

If the mothers and daughters of Soana had suspected that they formed for the priest a congregation which he drew into the church day after day for the glorification of this hated fruit of sin, or to have himself carried aloft, on the pious strains of the hymns to Mary, to the distant little meadow that was stuck high up on the rock, they would certainly have stoned him; but as things stood, it seemed to the astonished eyes of the whole congregation that the piety of the young cleric increased with every day. Bit by bit, young and old, rich and poor, in short, everyone from the mayor to the beggar, from the most fervent churchgoer to the most indifferent, was drawn into Francesco's sacred May-madness.

Even the long, solitary walks which he now frequently took were interpreted in the young saint's favor. And yet they were only undertaken in the hope that chance might lead Agata into his path. For in his fear that he might betray himself, he had set an interval of more than a week till the next special service for the Scarabota family; and this period of time now became unbearably long to him.

Nature still spoke to him in that open way he had first experienced on his walk to Sant' Agata, on the heights where the little sanctuary stood. Every blade of grass, every flower, every tree, every vine and ivy leaf were merely words of a language that welled up from the very base of existence, which spoke to him with a mighty roaring even in the deepest silence. Never had music penetrated his whole being like this and, as he believed, filled it with holy spirit.

Francesco had forfeited the deep, calm sleep of his nights. The mystical call which had come to him seemed, so to speak, to have slain Death and banished his brother Sleep. Each of these creative nights, pulsating with life of every sort, became a sacred period of revelation for Francesco's young body, so much so in fact that it sometimes seemed to him that the last veil was being removed from the mystery of divinity. Often, when he made the transition from the passionate dreams, which almost represented a waking state, into the waking of the senses, and outside the waterfall of Soana roared twice as loud as it did in the daytime, and the moon struggled with the darkness of the mighty abysses, and the black clouds, with a gigantic surliness, darkened the highest points of Mount Generoso, Francesco's body trembled as it never had before with fervent prayers, as a thirsty tree whose top is watered by the spring rain shudders in the wind. In this state he wrestled with God, filled with yearning to be initiated into the sacred miracle of creation as into the burning core of life, into this most holy, most inward something which permeates all Being from within. He said: "From there, O You, my almighty God, Your strongest light comes; from this core, radiating out in inexhaustible waves of fire, spreads all the bliss of existence and the mystery of the profoundest pleasure. Do not lay a finished creation into my lap, O God, but make me Your creative partner. Let me participate in Your uninterrupted work of creation; for only in this way and no other can I share in Your paradise." In order to cool the passion of his body Francesco walked back and forth in his room before open windows, so that the night air might penetrate his naked form. At the same time it seemed to him that the black storm above the gigantic rocky ridge of Mount Generoso resembled a huge bull over a heifer, snorting rain from its nostrils, grunting, shooting darting flashes out of its darkly flaming eyes and performing the generative act of fertility with its heaving haunches.

Such images were wholly pagan in nature, and the priest knew it but was no longer disturbed by it. He was already too deeply absorbed in the general numbness produced by the fermenting spring juices. The narcotic breath which filled him dissolved the limits of his narrow self and expanded him into the sphere of the general. Everywhere gods were being born in early, still lifeless nature, and the depths of Francesco's soul likewise opened and sent up images of things that lay buried in the abyss of the millions of years.

One night, in a state of half-wakefulness, he fell into a deep and, in a sense, terrible dream, which threw him into a gruesome sort of devotion. He became, as it were, the witness of a mystery from which emanated a terrible weirdness and at the same time something like the consecration of an ancient, irresistible power. Hidden somewhere in the rocks of Mount Generoso there seemed to be monasteries, from which dangerous stairways and rock steps led down into inaccessible caverns. Down these rock steps bearded men and old men in brown cowls descended in a solemn procession, one behind the other; the raptness of their movements and the withdrawn expression on their faces made him shudder; they seemed to be condemned to practice a frightful cult. These well-nigh gigantic, wild figures were venerable in an oppressive way. They descended very erectly, their hair and beards fused, mighty, shaggy, bushy. And these celebrants of a merciless and beastly worship were followed by women covered only by the opulent billows of their hair, forming heavy golden or black cloaks. While these dream monks were held rigidly and insensibly captive under the yoke of fearful instinct as they mutely descended the steps, the women displayed the humility of sacrificial animals offering themselves voluntarily to a terrible deity. In the eyes of the monks there lay a silent, senseless fury, as if the poisonous bite of a crazed animal had wounded them and infused a madness into their blood, which might be expected to erupt. On the brows of the women, on their eyelashes, which were lowered in pious devotion, there lay a sublime solemnity.

After the monks of Mount Generoso had, like living idols, finally taken their individual positions in the shallow caves formed by the wall of rock, a phallic worship began, at once ugly and sublime. Ghastly as it was—and Francesco was terrified to the depths of his soul—it was equally thrilling in its utter seriousness and fearful holiness. Near the falling water and in the magic light of the immense moon, owls circled the rocky walls with piercing shrieks, but the powerful cries of the great night birds were drowned out by the blood-congealing, anguished cries of the priestesses as they expired amid the torments of lust.

The day of the divine service for the poor outlawed Alpine shepherds had finally come again. Even the early morning, when the priest Francesco Vela awoke, was unlike any other he had ever experienced. So in the life of every superior person days break, unexpected and unbidden, like dazzling revelations. On this morning the youth did not wish to be either a saint or an archangel or even a god. Rather, he was overcome by a slight fear that saints, archangels and gods might become his enemies out of envy, for on this morning he felt himself to be exalted above saints, angels and gods. But up on Sant' Agata a disappointment was in store for him. His idol, who bore the name of the saint, had excluded herself from the church service. Questioned by the pale priest, the rude animal-like father could only produce rude, animal-like sounds, while his wife, who was at the same time his sister, excused their daughter on the score of domestic duties. Thereupon Francesco carried out his holy office with such apathy that he did not know at the end of the Mass whether he had begun it yet. Mentally, he experienced the torments of hell, and indeed entered a state of mind which could be likened to a real descent into hell and which made of him a poor damned soul.

After dismissing the ministrant as well as the Scarabotas, he descended at random one side of the steep mountain cone, still completely dazed, unaware of a goal and even less of any danger. Again he heard the nuptial cries of circling ospreys. But they sounded to him like mockery, which poured down out of a deceptively shining ether. Amidst the rubble of a dried-out rivulet he slid down, panting and running, whimpering confused prayers and curses. He felt the torments of jealousy. Although nothing had happened beyond the fact that the sinner Agata had been detained by something on the pasture of Soana, it seemed certain to the priest that she had a lover and was spending the time she had stolen from church in his villainous arms. While her absence made him suddenly aware of his great dependence on her, his feelings alternated between anxiety, dismay and rage, the urge to punish her and to beg for deliverance from his distress, that is, for the return of his love. He had by no means lost the pride of the priest yet—the wildest and most unbending pride—but had been most severely wounded. The sinner had rejected him as a man, as a servant of God and as a giver of His Sacrament. The man, the priest, the saint writhed in the convulsions of trampled vanity and foamed at the thought that she had probably preferred some beastly fellow, a shepherd or a woodcutter, to him.

His soutane torn and covered with dust, his hands bleeding and his face scratched, Francesco spent some hours climbing about wildly and blindly, up and down gorges, among broom bushes, over roaring mountain streams, and arrived at a region of Mount Generoso where the sound of shepherds' bells reached his ear. He did not for a moment doubt what place he had reached. He looked down on forsaken Soana, on his church, which could be seen clearly in the bright sun, and recognized the crowd that was now streaming in vain to the sacred place. At this very moment he ought to have been putting on his vestments in the sacristy. But he could much more easily have put a rope about the sun and pulled it down than broken the invisible bonds that drew him powerfully to the Alpine pasture.

The young priest was on the point of attaining some measure of reason when a fragrant smoke, carried by the fresh mountain air, reached his nostrils. Instinctively he looked about him searchingly and noticed, not very far away, a seated male figure; he seemed to be tending a little fire, at the edge of which a tin vessel was steaming, probably with minestrone. The seated man did not notice the priest, for he had his back turned to him. So the priest in turn could distinguish only a round head covered with blond, woolly hair, a strong, brown neck, and shoulders draped in a loose-fitting jacket which age, weather and wind had turned earth brown. The peasant, shepherd, woodcutter or whatever he was, sat bent over the little fire, whose scarcely visible flames, held down by the mountain wind, shot out horizontal tongues along the earth and flat billows of smoke into the air. He was, it soon appeared, preoccupied with some work, some carving, and was silent most of the time like someone who has forgotten God and the world in the work that engages him. When Francesco had stood there for a while, for some reason anxiously avoiding any movement, the man or boy beside the fire began to whistle softly; having swung into the rhythm of music, he suddenly sent broken fragments of some song into the air in a melodious voice.

Francesco's heart pounded wildly. It was not because he had been climbing so vigorously up and down the gorges, but for reasons which derived partly from the strangeness of his situation, partly from the peculiar impression made on him by the presence of the man beside the fire. This brown neck, this curly, yellow-white hair, the youthful physique, bursting with vigor, that could be divined behind the shabby clothes, the palpable freedom and satisfied well-being of the mountain dweller—everything together entered Francesco's mind in a flash and established a relationship in which his morbid and groundless jealousy flared up even more tormentingly.

Francesco went up to the fire. He could not have remained hidden in any case; and he was, moreover, impelled forward by irresistible forces. The mountaineer turned round, revealing a face full of youth and strength, the like of which the priest had never seen before, jumped up, and looked at the newcomer.

It was now clear to Francesco that he had a cowherd before him, since the object he was carving was a sling. He kept his eye on the brown-and-black-spotted cattle that were visible here and there, but on the whole were far away and hidden from view, climbing about among the rocks and bushes, betrayed only by the tinkling of the bells which the bull and this or that cow wore on their necks. He was a Christian; what else could he have been among all these mountain chapels and Madonna images of the region? But he also seemed to be a most devoted son of Holy Church, for, immediately recognizing the priest's gown, he kissed Francesco's hand with timid fervor and humility.

But Francesco recognized at once that the shepherd resembled the other parish children in no other respect. He was more powerfully and heavily built, his muscles were those of an athlete, his eyes seemed to have come from the blue lake down in the depths, and were equal in visual power to those of the brown ospreys who were, as always, circling about Sant' Agata. He had a low brow, his lips were thick and moist, his look and smile were of a coarse frankness. That secretive, furtive air that is common among people of the South was alien to him. All this Francesco took in as he stood eye to eye with the fair young Adam of Mount Generoso and agreed that he had never seen such a primitively beautiful peasant before.

In order to conceal the true reason for his coming and at the same time to make his presence intelligible, he told a lie: he said that he had given the sacrament to a dying man in a remote hut and had returned home with his ministrant. He had lost his way, had slid down the mountain and now wished to be shown the right way after he had taken a short rest. The shepherd believed this lie. With a coarse laugh that revealed his healthy teeth, yet with embarrassment, he followed the cleric's account and prepared a seat for him, throwing the jacket from his shoulders and spreading it out near the edge of the fire. This act bared his brown, gleaming shoulders, in fact his whole upper body down to his belt, since he wore no shirt.

To begin a conversation with this child of nature was a matter of considerable difficulty. It seemed embarrassing to him to be alone with the ecclesiastical gentleman. After he had been on his knees for a while, blowing into the fire, adding twigs, lifting the lid of the pot from time to time, uttering words in an unintelligible dialect, he suddenly gave a tremendous shout of joy which reverberated from the rocky bastions in a manifold echo.

Scarcely had this echo died away when someone could be heard approaching with loud laughter and screaming. It was a group of voices, the voices of children, from among which one could distinguish a woman's voice alternately laughing and calling for help. At the sound of this voice Francesco felt his arms and legs grow numb, and at the same time he sensed a power announcing itself which, compared with that which had produced his natural existence, contained the secret of true and real life. Francesco burned like the bush of the Lord, but outwardly he betrayed nothing of his condition. For a few seconds he lost consciousness; he felt an unfamiliar liberation, and at the same time a captivity that was as sweet as it was hopeless.

Meanwhile the feminine cries of distress, stifled by laughter, had been approaching until, at the turn of a precipitous path, a bucolic picture became visible, as innocent as it was unusual. That very spotted goat which had molested the priest on his first visit to the mountain pasture was leading a little bacchantic procession, puffing and resisting, carrying the sole bacchante of the troop astride on his back, followed by the noisy children. The beautiful girl whom, it seemed to Francesco, he was seeing for the first time, held the curving horns of the goat in a firm grip; but, however powerfully she pulled back, forcing the animal's neck toward her, she was neither able to make it stop nor to get off its back. Some prank, which she might perhaps have played for the sake of the children, had brought the girl to this helpless situation; she was not really sitting on the unsuitable mount, but touched the ground with her bare feet, so that she was not being carried but was walking, and yet could not leave the unruly, fiery billy goat without falling. Her hair had come loose, the straps of her coarse shirt had slipped from her shoulders, so that an exquisite sphere became visible, and her short skirts, which even normally scarcely reached down to her calves, were now not even adequate to cover her gorgeous knees.

It was some time before the priest realized the identity of the bacchante and that he had before him the object of his tormented yearning, whom he had been seeking so avidly. The girl's shrieks, her laughter, her involuntary wild movements, her loose, flying hair, her open mouth, her full heaving bosom, the insane character of the ride—in a sense an act of compulsion and yet deliberate—had completely altered her outward appearance. A rosy glow covered her face, where pleasure and anxiety were mingled with bashfulness, which expressed itself with droll charm, as when she lifted one of her hands from the goat's horn and directed it momentarily to the dangerously high hem of her skirt.

Francesco stood there spellbound, captivated by this picture, as if it had the power to paralyze him. Its beauty was such that the obvious similarity with a witches' ride did not even occur to him. However, it did bring back to him impressions of classical antiquity. He thought of the carvings he had recently studied on the marble sarcophagus that stood, constantly overflowing with clear mountain water, on the village square of Soana. Was it not as if this world of stone, which was nevertheless so alive, of the wreath-crowned god of wine, the dancing satyrs, the panther-drawn triumphal chariot, the girl flute players and bacchantes, was it not as if they had hidden in the stony wastes of Mount Generoso, and as if one of the divinely inspired women had suddenly torn herself away from the raging mountain cult of the maenads and amazingly stepped into the life of the present?

If Francesco had not immediately recognized Agata, the goat had indeed recognized the priest, and dragged his burden, shrieking and resisting in vain, straight towards him; by planting his two deft forehooves abruptly on the priest's lap, he enabled his rider, finally released, to glide gently from his back.

When the girl became aware of the fact that there was a stranger present, and when she recognized Francesco in this stranger, her laughter and her gaiety suddenly ended, and her face, which had just been glowing with merriment, assumed an almost defiant pallor.

"Why did you not come to church today?" Francesco asked this question, standing erect, in a tone and with an expression on his pale face that could only be interpreted as anger, although it was caused by a different emotion. Whether it was because he wanted to conceal this emotion or because he was embarrassed, indeed helpless, or whether the spiritual mentor in him had been aroused to indignation—his anger increased and came to the surface in a way that made the cowherd look up in astonishment, while the girl's face showed in turn the flush and pallor of dismay and shame.

But while Francesco was speaking and punishing with words, words that were familiar to him but did not involve his soul, his emotions were at peace, and while the veins on his alabaster brow swelled, he experienced the bliss of deliverance. The sense of utter deprivation that had assailed him only a short time before was transformed into a feeling of plenty, his tormenting hunger became satiety, and the infernal world which he had cursed but a moment earlier was now dripping with the splendor of paradise. And as his wrath flowed stronger and stronger, his bliss grew and grew. He had not forgotten the desperate state in which he had just been, but the jubilation he now felt, he had to bless, bless over and over. For this desperate state had been the bridge to happiness. Francesco had already gone so far into the magic spheres of love that the mere presence of the beloved object brought with it that enjoyment which stupefies one with happiness and does not permit one to think of deprivation, however near it may be.

With all this the young priest felt, and no longer concealed from himself, the change that had taken place within him. The true state of his being had, as it were, come to the surface naked. The mad chase he had behind him was, he well knew, not prescribed by the Church and ran outside the consecrated network of roads that clearly and strictly delineated his activity. For the first time, not only his foot but his soul, too, had left the highway, and it seemed to him that he had reached the spot on which he now stood, not so much as a human being, but rather, as a falling stone, a falling drop of water, a leaf driven by the storm.

Every one of his angry words showed Francesco that he was no longer in control of himself but was, on the contrary, compelled to seek and exercise power over Agata at any price. He took possession of her with words. The more he humiliated her, the more sonorously the harps of bliss resounded within him. Every pain he inflicted on her as a punishment awakened ecstasy within him. In fact, if the cowherd had not been there, Francesco might easily have lost his last shred of self-control in this ecstasy and, falling at the girl's feet, have betrayed the true beating of his heart.

Although she had grown up in a degenerate household, Agata had nevertheless retained to this day the innocence of a flower. Like the mountain gentian which they resembled, her blue eyes had never been seen at the lake in the valley below. She had the most limited sphere of experience. And yet, although the priest was for her not a human being at all, but rather a creature halfway between God and man, a sort of strange magician, she nevertheless suddenly divined what Francesco was trying to conceal and recorded it with a look of astonishment.

The children had led the billy goat away over the gravel and upward. The woodcutter had begun to feel uncomfortable in the presence of the priest. He took the pot from the fire and with great effort climbed up with it, probably to a comrade, who was sending bundles of brushwood down over a precipice into the depths below by means of a seemingly endless wire. From time to time one of these dark bundles traveled along the rocky bastions with a scraping sound, not unlike a brown bear or the shadow of a gigantic bird. Moreover, since the wire was invisible, the bundle seemed to fly down. When the cowherd had vanished from view after giving a powerful yodel, which echoed from the battlements and bastions of Mount Generoso, Agata kissed the hem of the priest's gown and then his hand, as though in contrition.

Francesco had mechanically made the sign of the Cross over the girl's head, and in doing so his hands had touched her hair. But now his arm trembled convulsively as if something wanted to keep another something in its power with its last ounce of strength. But the tense, resisting something could not prevent the blessing hand from extending slowly and bringing its palm closer and closer to the head of the repentant sinner, or from suddenly resting firmly and fully on it.

Francesco looked about him fearfully. He was far from fooling himself at this moment and justifying the position he was in by connecting it to the duties of his sacred office; yet all sorts of phrases came from him about confession and confirmation. And his almost unbridled passion, ready to leap, was so fearful of arousing horror and abomination when it was discovered, that it, too, sought cowardly refuge again behind the mask of the Church.

"You will come down to my school at Soana, Agata," he said. "You will learn to read and write there. I will teach you a morning and evening prayer, God's commandments too, and how you may recognize and avoid the seven cardinal sins. Then you will confess to me every week."

But Francesco, who had torn himself away after these words and descended the mountain without looking around, decided next morning, after a painful, sleepless night, to go to confession himself. When he revealed his tormented conscience, not without playing the game of hide-and-seek, to a snuff-taking archpriest in the nearby mountain town, he was most readily absolved. It was obvious that the devil was opposing the young priest's attempt to lead stray souls back into the bosom of the Church, especially since woman is always man's most direct opportunity for committing sin. After breakfasting with the archpriest in the parsonage beside an open window which admitted gentle air, sun and the song of birds, and hearing some frank words about the frequent conflict between human and ecclesiastical affairs, Francesco yielded to the delusion that he was carrying away a relieved heart.

This transformation had probably been aided in part by a few glasses of that heavy dark-violet wine which the peasants of Arogno press and of which the priest possessed a few hogsheads. At the completion of the meal the priest even led the priest and confessant to the vaulted cellar under mighty, tender-leaved chestnut trees, where this treasure was stored on beams, since he was accustomed at about this time to fill a flask, which he took with him for the further needs of the day.

But Francesco had scarcely said farewell to his confessor on the flower-studded, wind-swept meadow before the iron-bound gate of the rocky vault, and, walking briskly around a bend in the road, had hardly put enough hilly land, with trees and bushes, between them, when he began to feel an inexplicable repugnance toward his colleague's consolation and to regret all the time he had spent with him.

This grimy peasant, whose shabby soutane and sweaty underwear gave off an obnoxious odor, whose scurvy head and raw, dirt-encrusted hands demonstrated that soap was an alien commodity to him, seemed rather an animal, a block of wood, than a priest of God. Clergymen, Francesco said to himself, are, according to the Church, consecrated persons who have through their consecration received a supernatural dignity and power, so that even angels bow to them. This cleric could only be described as a travesty of this teaching. What a shame it was to see the priestly omnipotence put into such bumpkin hands, since even God was subject to such omnipotence and was compelled through the words *hoc est enim meum corpus* to descend upon the altar on which the Mass was celebrated.

Francesco hated, indeed despised, him. Then again he felt a profound regret. But finally it seemed to him that the stinking, ugly, obscene Satan had assumed his form. And he thought of those births which had taken place with the help of an incubus or succubus.

Francesco himself was astonished at such stirrings of his psyche and at the course of his thoughts. His host and confessor had hardly given him cause for them, except through his very existence; for his words at breakfast were entirely in the spirit of propriety. But Francesco was already swimming once more in such an emotion of exaltation and believed he was inhaling air of such celestial purity that, compared with this sanctified element, the everyday world seemed to him to be chained down in a state of damnation.

The day had arrived on which Francesco expected the sinful girl from the Alpine pasture in his parsonage at Soana for the first time. He had directed her to ring

the bell not far from the church door, by which he could be summoned to give confession. But midday was already approaching and the bell had not stirred and, as he instructed some half-grown girls and boys in the schoolroom, he became more and more absent-minded. Through the open window he could hear the roar of the waterfall, now swelling, then subsiding, and the priest's excitement grew whenever the sound increased. At such times he feared that he might miss the sound of the bell. The children were perplexed by his restlessness and absent-mindedness. That his mind was not on his business and not with them either, escaped the girls least of all, for they feasted on the young saint with their earthly as well as their heavenly senses. Tied to the stirrings of his youthful nature by a profound instinct, they even shared the tension that dominated him at the moment.

Shortly before the twelve o'clock bell rang, there arose a murmur of voices on the village square, which till then had lain quietly in the light of the sun, the tops of its chestnut trees covered with May blossoms. A mob of people was approaching. One could hear calmer, throaty male sounds, apparently protesting. But an irresistible stream of female words, shrieks, curses and protests suddenly drowned these out and made them inaudible. Then a fearful silence ensued. Suddenly muffled voices reached the priest's ears, but the source of these voices remained at first unintelligible to him. It was May and yet it sounded as if a chestnut tree, under the weight of a gust of wind, were suddenly shaking off its autumnal burden of fruit. The hard chestnuts were falling to the ground and bursting like drumbeats.

Francesco leaned out of the window.

With horror he saw what was going on in the square. He was so alarmed, indeed so filled with dismay, that he was brought to his senses only by the shrill, ear-piercing peal of the confession bell, which was being tugged with desperate doggedness. He hurried into the church and to the church door, and pulled the penitent—it was Agata—away from the bell into the church. Then he stepped out in front of the portal.

This much was clear: the entrance of the outlaw into the village had been noticed and the usual thing had happened. They had tried to drive her out of the abode of human beings with stones, as if she were some mangy dog or wolf. The children and mothers had soon banded together and pursued the outcast, curse-laden creature; the beauty of the girl did not in the least disturb their conviction that their stones were aimed at a dangerous animal, a monster, which spread pestilence and destruction. Meanwhile Agata, feeling certain of the priest's protection, had not allowed herself to be deflected from her goal. And so the resolute girl, persecuted and hunted, had arrived at the church door, which was still being pelted with a few stones thrown by the children.

The priest did not need to bring the agitated members of his congregation to their senses by a sermon; as soon as they saw him they scattered.

In the church Francesco had motioned to the mute, heavily breathing fugitive to follow him into the parsonage. He, too, was agitated and so they heard each other breathing fitfully. On a narrow staircase of the parsonage, between white-washed walls, stood the dismayed housekeeper, now somewhat calmer, to receive the hunted game. One could see from her face that she was prepared to help if help were needed. Only the sight of the old woman seemed to make Agata aware of the humiliating aspect of her present state. Alternating between laughter and anger, she uttered strong imprecations and so gave the priest the first opportunity to hear her voice, which, it seemed to him, sounded full, sonorous and heroic. She did not know why she was being persecuted. She regarded the town of Soana the way one would regard a nest of mud wasps or an ant heap. Furious and indignant as she was, it still did not occur to her to reflect on the cause of such dangerous malice. For she had known this condition since her childhood and assumed it to be something natural. But one fights off wasps and ants too. Even though it is animals that are attacking us, we are roused by them to hatred, to rage, to despair, according to the circumstances, and relieve our feelings by threats, tears or the stirrings of the deepest contempt. Agata did so too, while the housekeeper put the girl's ragged clothes in order and she herself pinned up the astounding mass of her hair, ranging in color from rust to ochre, which had fallen down in her hasty running.

At this moment young Francesco was suffering as never before under the compulsion of his passion. The presence of the woman who had matured in the mountain wilderness like an exquisite wild fruit, the intoxicating fire that streamed from her warm body, the fact that she, who had been distant and unattainable, was now enclosed in the narrow confines of his own dwelling—all this made Francesco clench his fists, tense his muscles and gnash his teeth, merely to keep on his feet in a situation which for some seconds threw him into total darkness. When the darkness lifted, there was an enormous commotion of images, thoughts and feelings within him: landscapes, people, the most distant memories, living moments of his domestic and professional past, fused with present ideas. As though he were fleeing from these, an inescapable future rose up before him, sweet and terrible, to which he knew he would wholly succumb. Thoughts flashed over this chaos of mental pictures, countless, restless, impotent thoughts. His conscious will, Francesco realized, had been dethroned in his mind; another will reigned, which brooked no contradiction. With horror the youth confessed to himself that he was delivered up to it for salvation or damnation. This state of mind was a sort of obsession. But if he was overcome by his fear of falling unavoidably into the crime of mortal sin, he felt at the same time like bellowing with boundless joy. His hungry eyes looked with a hitherto unknown, amazed satiety. More than that: here hunger *was* satiety and satiety, hunger. The cursed thought shot through his mind that here alone was the imperishable, divine food by which the sacrament gives heavenly nourishment to believing Christian souls. His emotions were idolatrous in nature. He condemned his uncle in Ligornetto as a bad sculptor. And why had he himself never painted? Perhaps he might still become a painter. He thought of Bernardino Luini and his great painting in the old monastery church in nearby Lugano and of the exquisite blond holy women his brush had created there. But then they were as nothing compared to this hot, most living reality.

Now Francesco did not know what to do. A warning impulse at first made him want to flee from the girl. All sorts of reasons, not all of them equally pure, moved him to seek out the mayor at once and inform him of the incident before others could do so. The mayor listened to him calmly—Francesco had fortunately found him at home—and shared the priest's view of the matter. It was but Christian and good Catholic practice not to let the bad situation on the Alpine pasture continue indefinitely, and to take an interest in the degenerate people who were enmeshed in sin and shame. As to the villagers and their conduct, he promised to take stern measures against them.

When the young priest had gone, the mayor's pretty wife, who had a quiet, aciturn way of observing people, said: "This young priest could go so far as to become a cardinal, even Pope. I believe he is consuming himself with fasting, praying and sleepless nights. But the devil pursues saints especially, with his hellish tricks and with the most secret wiles and stratagems. May the young man, with God's help, always be protected against them."

When Francesco walked back to the parsonage, as slowly as he could, he was followed by many desirous but also evil female eyes. It was known where he had been and they were resolved to submit to this pestilence of Soana only if they were compelled to do so. Girls walking upright, carrying bundles of wood on their heads, met him on the square near the marble sarcophagus; they did, it is true, greet him with submissive smiles, but afterwards they exchanged disdainful looks behind his back. Francesco strode along as though in a fever. He heard the confused song of the birds, the swelling and restrained roar of the eternal waterfall; but it was as if his feet were not on the ground, as if he were being pulled forward without a rudder, in a whirlpool of sounds and images. Suddenly he found himself in the sacristy of his church, then in the nave before the main altar, praying to the Virgin Mary on his knees for help in his emotional turmoil.

But his prayers did not express the desire that she free him from Agata. Such a desire would have found no nourishment in his heart. They were, rather, a cry for mercy. He wanted the Mother of God to understand, to forgive, if possible to approve. Francesco interrupted his prayer abruptly and broke away from the altar when the idea suddenly shot through his head that Agata might have gone away. But he found the girl still there, in the company of Petronilla.

"I have cleared everything up," Francesco said. "The way to the Church and to the priest is open to everyone. Trust me, what has happened will not recur." He was overcome by a firmness and sureness, as if he once again stood on the right path and on solid ground. Petronilla was sent to the neighboring parish with an important ecclesiastical document. The errand could unfortunately not be postponed. Moreover, the housekeeper was to report the incident to the priest there. "If you meet any people, tell them," he stated emphatically, "that Agata has come down here to the parsonage from the Alpine pasture and is receiving instruction from me in the teachings of our religion, our sacred faith. Let them come and prevent it and draw the punishment of eternal damnation down on their heads. Let them make a scene in front of the church and maltreat their fellow Christian. The stones will not strike her but me. If need be, I will personally take her back at twilight to the pasture."

When the housekeeper had gone, a lengthy silence ensued. The girl had folded her hands in her lap and still sat on the same rickety chair that Petronilla had placed near the white-washed wall for her. There were still flashes of fire in Agata's eyes, injury was mirrored in these lightning bolts of indignation and secret rage; but her full Madonna face had assumed more and more a helpless expression, until finally a silent, copious stream bathed her cheeks. Francesco had meanwhile turned his back to her and was looking out of the open window. As he let his eyes roam over the gigantic mountain wall of the Soana valley, from the fateful Alpine pasture to the lakeshore, with the everlasting murmur of the waterfall, the song of a single, sweet boy's voice penetrated to him from the luxuriant vine terraces; he was compelled to doubt that he now really held the fulfillment of his superterrestrial desires. Would Agata still be there when he turned around? And if she were there, what would happen when he turned around? Would this turning not be decisive for his whole earthly existence, even beyond that, in fact? These questions and doubts persuaded the priest to remain in his present position as long as possible, in order to pass judgment on himself, or at least take counsel with himself once more before he arrived at a decision. This was a matter of seconds, not minutes; but in these seconds, not only the entire history of his entanglement, beginning with Luchino Scarabota's first visit, but his whole conscious life became the immediate present to him. In these seconds a whole tremendous vision of the Last Judgment, with Father, Son and Holy Ghost in heaven, spread out before him over the ridge of the peak of Mount Generoso and terrified him with the blare of trumpets. One foot on Generoso, the other on a mountain peak on the other side of the lake, in his left hand the scale, in his right, his naked sword, the Archangel Michael stood like a terrible threat, while behind the Alpine pasture of Soana abominable Satan had descended with horns and claws. But almost everywhere the priest's eyes strayed there stood a woman, dressed in black and wearing a black veil, wringing her hands; she was none other than his despairing mother.

Francesco closed his eyes and then pressed both hands against his temples. When he turned around slowly, he looked for a long time with an expression of horror at the girl, who was swimming in tears, her dark, red mouth trembling painfully. Agata became frightened. Francesco's face was distorted as if it had been touched by the finger of death. Without a word he staggered over to her. And with a hoarse cry, like that of someone who has been defeated by an inexorable power, a cry that was at the same time a savage, life-hungry groan and a moan for mercy, he sank to his knees before her, a crushed man, and wrung his clasped hands.

Francesco might not perhaps have succumbed to his passion in this degree for a long time if the crime committed by the villagers against Agata had not infused a nameless, ardent element of human compassion into it. He realized what must lie in store for this creature in her future life and in a world without a protector, she who was so endowed by God with aphrodisiac beauty. Circumstances had made him her protector today; perhaps he had saved her from death by stoning. He had thereby won a personal claim on her: a thought that was not clear to him, but which nevertheless influenced his actions; working unconsciously, it swept away all sorts of inhibitions, fear and timidity. And in his mind he saw no possibility of ever again withdrawing his hand from the outcast. He would stand at her side, even if the world and God stood on the other. Such considerations, such currents, combined unexpectedly with the stream of passion, and so this stream overflowed its banks.

For the present his conduct was not yet a turning away from the right path and the consequence of a resolve to sin; it was merely a state of impotence and helplessness. He could not have said why he did what he did. In reality he did nothing. Something was happening to him. And Agata, who should now really have been terrified, was not, but seemed to have forgotten that Francesco was a stranger to her and a priest. He seemed all at once to have become her brother. And as her weeping turned into sobbing she not only permitted him, who was likewise shaken by dry sobs, to embrace her as if to comfort her, but she lowered her tear-drenched face and hid it on his breast.

Now she had become a child and he her father, insofar as he sought to calm her in her suffering. But he had never felt a woman's body so close to his and his caresses and tendernesses soon became more than paternal. To be sure, he felt clearly that the girl's sobbing pain concealed something akin to a confession. He realized that she knew to what an ugly love she owed her existence, and was submerged in the same sorrow as he was because of it. He bore her distress, her pain, with her. In this way their hearts were united. But he soon raised her sweet Madonna face to his, putting his hand to the nape of her neck and drawing her to him, bending her white brow back with his right hand; and after feasting his greedy eyes for a long time on the object he held clasped in this way, with the fire of madness in his eye, he suddenly swooped down like a hawk on her hot, tear-salted mouth and remained inseparably fused with her.

After some moments of earthly time, but eternities of numbing bliss, Francesco suddenly tore himself loose and stood firm on both feet, tasting blood on his lips. "Come," he said, "you can't go home alone without protection, so I will accompany you."

A changeable sky lay over the Alpine world when Francesco and Agata stole out of the parsonage. They turned off into a meadow path, on which they climbed down unseen from terrace to terrace between mulberry trees, through garlands of vines. Francesco knew very well what lay behind him and what boundary he had now crossed; but he could feel no remorse. He was changed, sublimated, liberated. It was a sultry night. In the plain of Lombardy, it seemed, storms were gathering, whose distant flashes of lightning spread out like a fan behind the gigantic silhouette of the mountains. The fragrance from the giant lilac tree under the windows of the parsonage floated down with the water from the network of brooks that trickled by, mingled with cool and warm currents of air. The intoxicated couple did not speak. He supported her in the dim light whenever they climbed down the wall to a lower-lying terrace, caught her in his arms too, on which occasions her breast heaved on his, his thirsty lips clung to hers. They did not really know where they wanted to go, for from the depth of the gorge of the Savaglia no road led up to the Alpine pasture. But on this point they were agreed, that they must avoid the ascent to it through the village. But their aim was not to attain some external, distant goal but to enjoy to the full what had been attained.

How full of dross, how dead and empty the world had been till now, and what a transformation it had undergone! How it had changed in the eyes of the priest and how he had changed in it! All the things that had until now meant everything to him were erased and of no worth. His father and mother, as well as his teachers, had been left behind like worms in the dust of the old, rejected world; while for him, the son of God, the new Adam, the gate of paradise had been opened again by the cherub. In this paradise, in which he now took his first enraptured steps, timelessness prevailed. He no longer felt himself to be a man of some special time or age. Equally timeless was the nocturnal world about him. And because the time of his expulsion, the world of banishment and of original sin lay behind him outside the guarded gate of paradise, he no longer felt even the slightest fear of it. No one out there could harm him in any way. It was not in the power of his superiors, nor in the power of the Pope himself, to prevent his enjoyment of even the most trivial fruit of paradise or to rob him of the smallest trifle of the highest bliss that had now become his as a gift of grace. His superiors had become inferiors. They lived forgotten in an extinct earth of wailing and gnashing of teeth. Francesco was no longer Francesco; he had just been awakened by the Divine Breath as the First Man, the only Adam, sole lord of the Garden of Eden. There lived no second man beside him in the plenitude of sinless creation. Constellations quivered with bliss, making a divine music. Clouds lowed like luxuriantly grazing cows, dark-red fruits radiated sweet rapture and delicious refreshment, tree trunks sweated fragrant resin, blossoms strewed out precious spices; but all this depended on Eve, whom God had placed among all these miracles as the fruit of fruits, the spice of spices, upon her who was herself the highest miracle. The fragrance from all the spices, their most delicate essence, the Creator had placed into the hair, skin and the fruit-flesh of her body; but her form, her substance, had no equal. Her form, her substance, was God's secret. The form moved of itself and remained exquisite alike at rest or in change. Her substance seemed to be made of the same mixture as lily and rose leaves, but it was chaster in its coolness and hotter in its fire, it was both more delicate and tougher. In this fruit there was a living, vibrant kernel; precious, trembling pulses hammered within it and, when one tasted of it, it yielded new blisses that were rarer and even more exquisite, without any loss of heavenly abundance occurring in the process.

And what was most precious in this creation, in this paradise regained, could indeed be deduced from the presence of the Creator. Here God had neither completed His work and left it alone, nor laid Himself to rest in it. On the contrary, His creative hand, His creative Spirit, His creative power were not withdrawn, they remained at the work of creating. And each of all the parts and members of paradise remained creative. Francesco-Adam, who had just emerged from the potter's workshop, felt himself a creative person within the whole sphere of his activity. With a rapture that was not of this world he felt and saw Eve, the daughter of God. The love that had formed her still clung to her, and the most precious of all the substances which the Father had employed to form her body still had an unearthly beauty that was not sullied by even a speck of earthly dust. But this creation, too, still quivered, swelled and shone from the heavenly fire of active, creative power and yearned to be fused with Adam. Adam in turn was impelled toward her, to enter with her into a new perfection.

Agata and Francesco, Francesco and Agata, the priest, the youth of good family, and the outlawed, despised child of the shepherd, were the first human pair as they climbed down into the valley hand in hand on the secret, nocturnal by-paths. They sought the deepest seclusion. Silently, their hearts filled with a nameless astonishment, with a rapture that almost caused both their hearts to burst, they descended deeper and deeper into the precious miracle of the cosmic hour.

They were moved. Because of the grace, the election they felt to be resting on them, their boundless happiness was tinged with an earnest solemnity. They had felt each other's body, had been united in a kiss, but they sensed the unfamiliar destiny to which they were moving. It was the final mystery. It was that for the sake of which God created, and for which He had put death into the world and had accepted it as part of the bargain, so to speak.

In this way the first human pair reached the narrow gorge below, sawed through by the little Savaglia River. It was very deep, and only an unfrequented footpath led upwards along the edge of the brook bed to the reservoir into which the mountain water poured from a dizzy height. At a considerable distance from it the brook was divided into two arms, which were united again by a little green island that Francesco loved and often visited because it was very lovely with its few young apple trees that had struck root there. And Adam took off his shoes and carried his Eve to it. "Come, or I shall die," he said to Agata several times. And they trampled down narcissi and Easter lilies with their heavy, almost intoxicated lovers' steps.

Even here in the gorge there was summer warmth, though the course of the brook brought coolness with it. How brief a time had passed since the turning point in the life of the pair, and how far behind them everything before the turning point lay. Since the little island was rather remote from the village, the peasant who owned it had built a hut out of stones, twigs and earth to afford some shelter against accidental storms; this provided a bed of leaves that was tolerably secure against the rain. It was this hut perhaps that had been in Adam's mind when he had headed toward the valley rather than up the mountain. The hut seemed to have been prepared to receive the lovers. Mysterious hands seemed to have been forewarned of the impending celebration of the secret creation of man; for there were clouds of light about the hut, clouds of sparks, June bugs, glowworms, worlds, Milky Ways, which sometimes rose in tremendous sheaves as if they wanted to populate empty space. They flowed and floated through the gorge at such a height that one could no longer distinguish them from the stars in the sky.

Although this spectacle was familiar to them, this silent magic nevertheless produced wonder in Francesco and Agata, and their astonishment made them hesitate a moment. Is this the place, Francesco thought, which I so often sought out and contemplated with pleasure, not dreaming what it would one day mean to me? It seemed to me a place to which I might retreat as a hermit from the misery of the world and steep myself in God's word through renunciation. But what it really was—an island on the Euphrates River or the Hiddekel, the secret, most blissful place in paradise—I would not have recognized. And the mystical, flaming spark-clouds, nuptial fires, sacrificial fires, or whatever they might be, freed him completely from the earth. When he did not forget the world altogether, he knew that it lay powerless before the gates of paradise like the seven-headed dragon, the seven-headed beast that came out of the sea. What had he in common with those who worshiped the dragon? Let him blaspheme against God's hut. His venom could not reach this spot. Never had Francesco, the priest, felt such proximity to God, such security in Him, such self-forgetfulness; and in the murmuring of the mountain brook the mountains gradually seemed to resound melodiously, the crags of rock to peal like an organ, the stars to make music with myriads of golden harps. Choirs of angels shouted in jubilation through infinity, the harmonies roared down from above like tempests, and bells, bells, ringing bells, wedding bells, small and large, deep and high, powerful and gentle, spread an oppressive, blissful solemnity through world space.—And so they sank down on the bed of leaves, entwined in each other.

There is no moment that endures, and even when one wants to cling with anxious haste to those instants that afford the highest bliss, one finds no way of holding onto them, strive as he will. His whole life, Francesco felt, consisted of steps leading to the summit of the mystery he was now experiencing. Where would one breathe in the future if one could not hold onto it? How was one to endure a damned existence if one were cast out again from the raptures of one's innermost heaven? In the midst of the superhuman intoxication of enjoyment, the youth experienced transitoriness with a stinging pain; in the enjoyment of possession he felt the torment of loss. He felt as if he must empty a cup of delicious wine and quench an equally delicious thirst; but the cup never became empty, and his thirst was never quenched. And the drinker did not want his delicious thirst to be satisfied nor the cup to be emptied; yet he sucked at it with greedy frenzy, tormented because he could never reach bottom.

Surrounded by the rushing brook, flooded by it, with glowworms dancing around them, the young couple rested in the rustling leaves, while the stars twinkled through the roof of the hut. He had taken trembling possession of all of Agata's secrets, which he had admired as unattainable treasures. He had immersed himself in her flowing hair, clung with his lips to hers. But his eye was immediately filled with envy of his mouth, which had robbed it of the sight of the sweet maiden's mouth. And bliss, more and more inconceivable, flowing, benumbing, welled up from the mysteries of her young body. What he had never hoped to possess, when it was mirrored before his eyes on hot nights, was as nothing compared to what he now had as a boundless possession.

And as he reveled, he became incredulous over and over again. The excess of his fulfillment caused him repeatedly to assure himself insatiably of his possession. For the first time his fingers, his quivering hands and palms, his arms, his chest, his hips felt woman. And she was more than woman to him. He felt as if he had regained something that he had lost, something he had wantonly thrown away, without which he had been a cripple, and with which he had now formed a bond of unity. Had he ever been separated from these lips, this hair, these breasts and arms? She was a goddess, not a woman. And she was not something that existed in itself; he burrowed his way into the core of the world, and, his ear pressed under the virginal breasts, he heard, with a shudder of bliss, the heart of the world beating away.

That numbness, that half-sleep, descended on the pair, in which the raptures of exhaustion merge with the charms of waking sensation and the charms of waking sensation merge with the raptures of the numbness produced by oblivion: in this state Francesco fell asleep in the arms of the girl, and then Agata in his. How strangely and with what confidence the shy, wild girl had yielded to the caressing compulsion of the priest, how submissively and happily she had served him. And when she fell asleep in his arms, it was with the trusting smile of the satiated infant who closes its eyes at the breast and in the arms of its mother. But Francesco contemplated the sleeping girl in amazement and loved her. Through her body passed waves of trembling, like those produced by the relaxation of life. Sometimes the girl cried out in her dream. But when she opened her languishing eyelids, she always had the same intoxicating smile, and the same dying in ultimate abandonment. Whenever the youth fell asleep it seemed to him that some power was gently, gently withdrawing from him the body he held in his embrace and which he felt with his whole body. But every time upon waking, this brief withdrawal was followed by a sensation of the highest, most gratefully experienced sweetness, an ineffable dream with a blissful, live sensation of the sweetest reality.

This was it, the fruit of paradise, from the tree that stood in the middle of the garden. He held it in the embrace of his whole body. It was the fruit from the tree of life, not from that of the knowledge of good and evil, with which the serpent had tempted Eve. It was, rather, that fruit, the enjoyment of which made one as God. In Francesco every wish for a higher, for another happiness, had died. Neither on earth nor in heaven were there raptures that could compare with his. There was no king, no god whom the youth, rioting in his extravagant excess, would not have felt to be a starving beggar. His speech had sunk to a stammer, to a convulsive breathing. He sucked in the intoxicating breath that came from between Agata's open lips. He kissed away the tears of ecstasy, hot on the girl's lashes and on her cheek. With eyes closed, looking at each other only sparingly, they both enjoyed themselves in the other, their gaze turned inward, feeling passionately and clearly. But all this was more than enjoyment—it was something that human speech cannot adequately express.

Next morning Francesco celebrated early Mass punctually. His absence had been noticed by no one, his return home, not even by Petronilla. The precipitous haste with which, after making a summary toilet, he had to rush to the sacristy to join the waiting ministrants, and to the altar before the small, waiting congregation, prevented him from coming to his senses. Reflection came when he was in the parsonage again, in his little room, where the housekeeper set the customary breakfast before him. But this reflection did not immediately yield the clarity of disenchantment. Rather, his old environment and the advancing day gave to what he had experienced the resemblance of something unreal, which faded before him like a past dream. But it was reality after all. And although it surpassed in fantastic incredibility any dream that Francesco had ever dreamed, he nevertheless could not disavow it. He had had a fearful fall, there was no quibbling about this fact; the question was whether it was at all possible to lift himself from this fall, from this fearful lapse into sin. The plunge was so deep and from such a height that the priest was compelled to despair of it. This terrible fall was without example, not only in the ecclesiastical, but also in a worldly sense. Francesco thought of the mayor and how he had talked to him about the possibility of saving the outcasts of the Alpine pasture. Only now, secretly, in his profound humiliation, did he recognize the extent of the priestly arrogance, the whole overbearing conceit with which he had been puffed up at that time. He ground his teeth in shame, he squirmed, as it were, like a vain, unmasked swindler, in his dishonor, in his naked helplessness. Had he not been a saint only a moment ago? Had not women and virgins of Soana looked up to him almost idolatrously?

And had he not succeeded in lifting the Church spirit of the place to such an extent that attending church and Masses had become popular even among the men? Now he had become a traitor to God, a deceiver and betrayer of his congregation, a traitor to the Church, a traitor to the honor of his family, a traitor to himself, yes, even a traitor to the despised, cursed, reprobate, wretched Scarabotas, whom he had really ensnared into damnation under the pretext of saving their souls.

Francesco thought of his mother. She was a proud, almost masculine woman, who had protected and guided him with a firm hand when he was a child, and whose unbending will had prescribed for him the course of his future life. He knew that her harshness towards him was nothing but ardent mother-love, that even the slightest cloud on her son's honor would wound her pride most deeply, and that a serious lapse on his part would certainly cause an incurable wound in the very seat of her life. It was strange that, in relation to her, what had really happened, what had been experienced intimately and clearly, could not even be thought about.

Francesco had sunk into the most disgusting mire, into the filth of final depravity. In it he had left behind his vows as a priest, his essence as a Christian, as his mother's son, as a human being in fact. He would have been reduced to a werewolf, that stinking, demonic beast, in the opinion of his mother and of people in general, if they had known of his crime. The youth jumped from his chair and from the breviary on the table, in which he had seemed to be absorbed. It had seemed to him as if a hail of stones had rattled against his house; not like yesterday, when they had attempted the stoning, but with a hundredfold, thousandfold power, as if the parsonage was to be destroyed or at least turned into a heap of rubble, and he buried under it like the corpse of a poisonous toad. He had heard strange sounds, fearful cries, frantic shouts, and knew that among the raging mob who tirelessly hurled stones there was not only the whole of Soana, the mayor and his wife, but also Scarabota and his family and, indeed, at the head of them all, his mother.

But after some hours had passed, such fantasies and stirrings were displaced by very different ones. Everything that had been born out of his stock-taking, out of his horror at the deed, his contrition, now seemed as if it had never existed. Francesco was dessicated by a distress he had never known, by a burning thirst. His spirit cried out as someone who is rolling about in anguish in the burning desert sand cries for water. The air seemed to be without those substances we require in order to breathe. The parsonage became a cage to the priest, and he paced restlessly between its walls like a beast of prey with aching knees, resolved, if they would not liberate him, to bang his head against the wall and smash it rather than live on like this. How is it possible to live as a dead man? he asked himself, observing the inhabitants of the village through the window. How is it that they want to breathe, how can they breathe? How can they endure their wretched existence since they do not know what I have enjoyed and now miss? And Francesco grew within himself. He looked down on popes, emperors, princes and bishops, in short, on everyone, as people commonly look down on ants. He did so even in his thirst, his misery, his deprivation. To be sure, he was no longer master of his life. An overpowering magic had made him into a completely will-less and, without Agata, completely lifeless victim of Eros, the god who is older and mightier than Zeus and the rest of the gods. He had read in the writings of the ancients about such sorcery and about this god, and had dismissed both with a superior smile. Now he felt clearly that one had to believe even in the arrow and the deep wound with which, according to the ancients, the god poisoned the blood of his victims. This wound was indeed burning, piercing, flaming, eating and gnawing within him. He felt terrible piercing pains until, when it grew dark, he set out, inwardly shouting with happiness, on the road to the same small island world that had united him yesterday with his beloved and on which he had arranged a new meeting with her.

The mountain shepherd of Ludovico, known to the inhabitants of the region as "the heretic of Soana," fell silent when he had read to the point where his manuscript broke off. The visitor would have liked to hear the end of the tale. But when he was frank enough to express this wish, his host revealed to him that his manuscript went no further. He was also of the opinion that the story could, in fact must, break off here. The visitor did not share this opinion.

What had become of Agata and Francesco, of Francesco and Agata? Did the affair remain a secret or had it been discovered? Did the lovers find a permanent or merely fleeting attraction for each other? Did Francesco's mother learn of the affair? And finally, the listener wanted to know, was the tale based on a real incident or was it a complete fiction?

"I have already told you," Ludovico replied, turning slightly pale, "that a real incident was the occasion for my scribbling." After this he was silent for a long time. "About six years ago," he continued, "a clergyman was literally driven from the altar of his church with sticks and stones. At least, when I returned to Europe from the Argentine and came to this region, this was told to me by so many people that I have no doubt of the incident itself. Moreover, the incestuous Scarabotas lived here on Mount Generoso, though not under that name. The name Agata is fictitious too; I simply took it from the chapel of Sant' Agata, above which, as you see, the brown ospreys are still circling. But the Scarabotas really did have, among other fruits of their sins, a grown daughter, and the priest was accused of having illicit relations with her. People say that he did not deny the fact nor did he ever show the slightest remorse, and the Pope, it is said, excommunicated him because of it. The Scarabotas had to leave the region. They—the parents, not the children—are supposed to have died in Rio from yellow fever."

The wine and the excitement aroused in the listener by the place, the hour, the company and especially by the work of fiction that had been read to him, combined with all sorts of mystical circumstances, made him still more importunate. He asked once more about Francesco's and Agata's fate. The shepherd could tell him nothing about this. "They are said to have been an annoyance to the region for a long time, because they desecrated and profaned the solitary shrines that are scattered about everywhere and misused them as an asylum for their wicked lust." At these words the anchorite broke into loud, unrestrained laughter that was wholly without cause and which he was unable to control for a long time.

Thoughtful and strangely moved, the reporter of this travel adventure set out on his way home. His diary contains descriptions of this descent, but he does not wish to insert them here. The so-called blue hour that appears when the sun has sunk beneath the horizon was in any case especially beautiful on that occasion. One could hear the waterfall of Soana roar. Just so, Francesco and Agata had heard it roar. Or did they really still hear its sound at that very moment? Was that spot not the location of the Scarabotas' pile of stones? Could one not hear sounds of merry children coming from there, mingled with the bleating of goats and sheep? The wanderer drew his hand across his face as if he wanted to wipe away a veil of confusion: had the little tale that he had heard really grown, like a tiny gentian flower or its like, on a meadow of this mountain world, or had this glorious, primitively powerful mountain relief, this petrified gigantomachy emerged out of the frame of this little novella? He was thinking this and similar thoughts when the sonorous sound of a woman's singing reached his ears. Was it not said that the anchorite was married? The voice carried, as in a spacious, acoustic hall, when people hold their breath to listen. Nature, too, was holding her breath. The voice seemed to be singing in the wall of rock. Sometimes, at least, it seemed to be streaming out from there, in broad waves full of the sweetest mellowness and fiery nobility. But the singer came, it turned out, from the very opposite direction, climbing up the path to Ludovico's square hut. She bore an earthenware vessel on her head, holding it lightly with her uplifted left hand, while she led her little daughter by the right hand. In this way the full and yet slender figure assumed that straight, exquisite bearing which strikes us as being so solemn, indeed sublime. At this sight a vague surmise shot through the spectator's mind like an illumination.

He had probably been discovered by this time, for the song suddenly grew silent. One could see the mounting woman come closer, completely irradiated by the splendor of the western sky. One could hear the voice of the child, and the mother replying in calm, deep tones. Then one could hear the bare soles of the woman striking the rough-hewn steps resoundingly. She had to step firmly and securely because of her burden. For the waiting wanderer these moments before meeting her possessed a tension and mystery that he had never experienced before. The woman seemed to grow. One saw her dress, tucked up high, saw a knee peeping out for a moment with every step she took, saw naked shoulders and arms emerge, saw a round, feminine face, sweet in spite of a proud self-confidence, surrounded by luxuriant hair, the color of red-brown earth, like some pristine being. Was this not the man-woman, the virago, the Syrian goddess, the sinner who fell out with God to yield herself wholly to man, her husband?

The returning wanderer had stepped aside and the resplendent canephora, returning his greeting almost imperceptibly because of her burden, strode past him. She turned both her eyes toward him while her head remained fixed ahead of her. At the same moment a proud, self-confident, knowing smile glided over her countenance. Then she lowered her eyes to the road once more, while at the same time an unearthly sparkle seemed to run through her eyelashes. The observer may have been overheated by the warmth of the day, the wine and everything else he had experienced, but this much is certain: before this woman he felt himself grow quite, quite small. These full lips, curled almost in scorn for all their enchanting sweetness, knew that there was no resisting them. There was no protection, no armor against the claims of this neck, these shoulders and this breast, which was blessed and stirred by the breath of life. She rose up out of the depth of the world and past the astonished man—and she rises and rises into eternity, as the one into whose merciless hands heaven and hell have been delivered.

THE LIFE AND WORKS OF GERHART HAUPTMANN

By FELIX A. VOIGT

Documents preserved in a number of localities on the northern slopes of the Riesengebirge, the mountain range that separates southwest Poland from Czechoslovakia, enabled Gerhart Hauptmann to trace his family lineage of four centuries, both on his father's and mother's sides. The two families—Hauptman and Straehler—must certainly have settled with the other German colonists in that part of the country, which had been depopulated in the thirteenth century by migrating Mongols. In the sixteenth century the families embraced the Protestant religion, a factor which was to be of utmost importance in the life and works of their most famous descendant. They were farmers, craftsmen, and, since the eighteenth century, frequently weavers. Memories of the latter no doubt played a part in Hauptmann's choice of the theme of *Die Weber* (*The Weavers,* 1892).

Gerhart Hauptmann's only family connection with the theater was through his maternal grandmother (born in 1801), the illegitimate daughter of a Breslau actress. Her grandson, who resembled her closely, describes her as a spirited, liberal-minded woman, very fond of the theater.

Hauptmann's mother was Maria Straehler, who in 1852 married Robert Hauptmann, proprietor of the best hotel in the spa at Salzbrunn. They had four sons, one of whom was the well known poet Carl Hauptmann (1858–1921). Gerhart, their youngest, was born on November 15, 1862.

The first twelve years of Gerhart's life were spent quietly and uneventfully at Salzbrunn, where he learned the villagers' dialect as well as German, which he spoke in his father's hotel. From 1874 to 1878 he attended high school in Breslau, the capital of the province, but apparently with no great accomplishment. Later he described his schooldays as "a time of everlasting toothache." He found it so difficult to learn his lessons that his parents thought of setting him at farming. But a short stay at an uncle's farm showed he had little interest or ability in that either.

Young Hauptmann had a vague idea he had a vocation for art and decided to study sculpture at the Breslau Art Academy, where he met little success. In 1882 he gave up the struggle and began studying history at Jena, but abandoned it after a few months when his father was forced to give up his hotel. The years that followed were a period of financial difficulties and privations for Hauptmann. However, all his hardships disappeared as if by miracle when his three brothers were married or engaged to three of the rich Thienemann sisters of Hohenhaus Castle near Dresden. With financial woes gone, Hauptmann began traveling through the whole of Europe, arriving ultimately in Italy and spending the winter of 1883 and 1884 as a sculptor in Rome. There, too, he failed to make his mark in art. Finally, a severe attack of typhus put an end to all his false starts.

In 1885, after studying in Berlin for a term, he married still another Thienemann daughter, Maria. They made their home at Erkner, then a rural suburb of the German capital. He lived in Erkner as a free-lance writer on his wife's money until pulmonary tuberculosis brought him close to the grave. At the age of twenty-three, Gerhart Hauptmann was in bad health, had little education and no profession, and appeared to be of no account whatever.

But he had devoted many years, on his own initiative, to strenuous, ceaseless reading, and had perused everything he could obtain during those first years of the naturalistic movement in literature. Also, thanks entirely to his strong determination, he had overcome his consumption. His youthful attempts at poetry—a collection of poems entitled *Das bunte Buch* (*The Motley Book,* 1888), which was never published, and an epic poem on his journey in Italy entitled *Das Promethidenlos* (1885)—had proved unsuccessful.

It was not long, however, before people began to speak about a man who lived at Erkner and apparently had the qualities of a great poet. The first writings that attracted attention to Hauptmann were two short stories entitled *"Fasching"* ("Carnival") and *"Bahnwärter Thiel"* ("Line-Keeper Thiel").

In 1888, Hauptmann spent a long time in Zurich, where his studies in the field of psychiatry under Professor August Forel added an essential ingredient to his makeup. Then came the breakthrough *Vor Sonnenaufgang* (*Before Dawn*), hi first play that was really adaptable fo the stage, was written in a few weeks Soon after its publication, in 1889, it wa discovered simultaneously by Theodo Fontane and the talented theater manage Otto Brahm. Dress rehearsal of the revo lutionary work on October 20, 1889, mad the author famous overnight. That dat marks the beginning of a new era in Ger man literature: The author becam *"Hauptmann* (captain) of the wild ban of the naturalists."

To better observe the happenings o that decadent period, Gerhart Haupt mann moved to Berlin, the young capita of the new empire. There, in a turmoi of creative fury, he wrote one play afte the other in rapid succession. The third *Einsame Menschen* (*Lonely Souls,* 1891) was translated into several languages in a very short time. His first masterwork, *Die Weber* (*The Weavers,* 1892) made him famous throughout the whole of Europe The play was translated into French by Jean Thorel and performed in the Théâ tre Libre, Paris, on May 23, 1893. Emile Zola, the naturalistic theorist and novelist, attended the rehearsals. *The Weavers* marked the first performance of a German play in Paris since 1871.

Meanwhile, the young German from Silesia found he could no longer tolerate the tense and exciting atmosphere of Berlin. Consequently, he and his brother Carl moved with their families to Schreiberhau, where they lived in a very simple house close to their native Riesengebirge.

Even this refuge failed to offer Gerhart Hauptmann the creative tranquility for which he had hoped. His marriage was an unhappy one, and it is very likely that his wife's melancholic, anxious character hampered his creative activity. It is worth noting that love pangs occupy a very small place in his first plays—even in *Lonely Souls,* which is the story of a man caught between two women. He finally found his ideal mate in a young girl named Margarete Marschalk (1875–1957), but he struggled for eleven long years before obtaining a divorce from Maria Thienemann.

Gerhart Hauptmann's fame grew from year to year. Two comedies, entitled *Kollege Crampton* (*Colleague Crampton*) and *Der Biberpelz* (*The Beaver Coat*) (1893), proved that his capacity for picturing the human condition was not confined to its seamy side. And in *Hanneles Himmelfahrt* (*Hannele,* 1892) he demonstrated he also could write verses of radiant beauty. Then, in January, 1894, he received news that his wife had taken their three sons to stay with friends in America. Maria's move was an attempt to force him to decide between her and Margarete Marschalk.

Hauptmann followed Maria without a moment's hesitation. Later he described that wild journey in his novel *Atlantis* (1912) and in *Buch der Leidenschaft* (*Book of Passion,* 1930), an autobiographical work about his marital troubles. Hauptmann spent a few months with his family in the United States and attended a performance of *Hannele* in New York before returning to Germany with his wife and family.

However, the apparent reconciliation did not last long, and the years that followed were full of stress, turmoil, and anxiety for the writer. In the autumn of 1894, Maria took the children to Dresden while Gerhart went to live alone in Berlin. There he recorded the German Peasant War of 1525 in his play *Florian Geyer* (1896), but audiences did not grasp it initially. Hauptmann sought refuge at the foot of Monte Generoso in the Swiss canton Ticino, a place to which he would return again and again. That summer, he and his young mistress journeyed to the light-flooded island of Hiddensee near Rugen on the Baltic, which became a second home for him and where, several decades later, he settled to spend the last years of his life. On Hiddensee he wrote his first play composed entirely in verse, *Die versunkene Glocke* (*The Sunken Bell,* 1896), which became a worldwide success. Unfortunately, the public, for the most part, accepted the play as a sentimental, neo-romantic poem; in reality, the author had written with his heart's blood the tragedy of his own marriage.

In 1897, Hauptmann undertook a long journey through Italy accompanied by his mistress, with whom he was to spend the rest of his life. Now he was imbued with a new spirit and Margarete Marschalk aroused the Dionysian element that slumbered within him, helping to give his work an entirely new character. Nonetheless, he never completely succeeded in recovering from the wrong he had done his first wife. It is her image, rather than Margarete's, that appears in all his works —in *Die Jungfern von Bischofsberg* (*The Maids of Bischofsberg*), in the epic *Mary,* and in the long fragments of *Der grosse Traum* (*The Great Dream*), which he began in 1914, shortly after Maria's death, but never finished. New works followed in rapid succession after 1897, poems of an entirely new type. *Fuhrmann Henschel* (*Drayman Henschel,* 1899) was a harassing tragedy worthy of Sophocles, but in naturalistic form.

In 1904 he obtained his divorce at long last and could begin a new married life with Margarete, who had borne him a son in 1900. The first part of his life was ended. *Abenteuer meiner Jugend* (*Adventure of My Youth*), as he called it in the big autobiography published in 1937, was brought to a close. Anxieties and muddled quests were finished forever.

After 1905 his life assumed a totally different aspect. Since change of scene was essential for his creative activity, he moved about at regular intervals, except during the war years. Shortly after 1900 he built a house (half-convent and half-castle) for Margarete and himself at Agnetendorf in the Riesengebirge. During this period of his life, he spent winters in Italy or the Ticino. He would then return to Agnetendorf for a few months, passing through the Black Forest on the way, to live in the mountains during spring. In summer he went to Hiddensee, where by 1930 he had established a second residence, the Haus Seedorn, which later became a place of pilgrimage for his admirers. Every autumn Hauptmann traveled to Berlin, Vienna or other cities to attend the first performances of his plays, after which he usually rested in Lugano.

Hauptmann made a trip to Greece in 1907 where he sought the gods of the earth and underworld, Demeter and Dionysus, forsaking those of Olympus. There in the theaters of Dionysus at Athens and Delphi, the essence of the "archaic" drama was revealed to him.

Hauptmann was showered with official honors, more abroad than in Germany. He received honorary degrees from Oxford University (1905), Leipzig University (1909), the German University in Prague (1921), and Columbia University in New York (1932). In 1942 Breslau granted him the title of First Honorary Citizen of its university. And in 1912, he was awarded the great honor of the Nobel Prize for Literature. The Imperial Academy of Sciences in Vienna awarded him the Grillparzer Prize three times. His fiftieth, sixtieth, and seventieth birthdays were celebrated as national holidays.

The crowning years of Gerhart Hauptmann's life were those of the Weimar Republic (1918–1933). At that time he was viewed as one of the chief representatives of German literature, and the elite of his country's intelligentsia gathered about him at Agnetendorf, on Hiddensee, at Rapallo, at Lugano, or wherever he happened to be staying.

Hauptmann, however, lacked the slightest trace of historical instinct; he was absolutely incapable not only of taking an interest in politics but even of understanding it. He once said to me, "I have always kept to the outskirts of history." He did not see the signs of the times—all he saw was people and their pains.

The barbarous advent of the Nazi regime in 1933 took him completely by surprise. He could not and would not abandon his country. His art could flourish only on his native soil and, unlike other great poets, he was not capable of writing anywhere and everywhere. He spent almost all his time at Agnetendorf. Against his wishes, his eightieth birthday was exploited by the Nazis in Vienna and in the towns of his native Silesia as an occasion for celebrations on a more than local scale. But his creative activity continued without a break.

The year 1945 saw the collapse of Germany, and at the age of eighty-three he witnessed the destruction of Dresden. Now his health broke down. Against everyone's advice he went back to Agnetendorf, which was occupied by the Russians and the Poles soon after he arrived. The Russian army of occupation showed every respect and consideration for the author of *The Weavers,* who had been a friend of Maxim Gorki's. But even they could do nothing against the Polish administration of East Germany when he was threatened with expulsion. A few days after receiving notification that he was to be expelled, he was struck down by pneumonia. On June 3, 1946, he spoke his last words: "Am I still in my house?" He was still there and remained there until his heart stopped beating three days later. At his modest funeral service eulogies were pronounced in German, Russian, and Polish.

It was not until the end of July that a special convoy could be formed to take Hauptmann's mortal remains and a large part of his personal property first to Berlin and from there to Stralsund and the island of Hiddensee he had loved so well. It was there, in the cemetery of Kloster village, that he was buried on July 28, 1946.

Margarete Hauptmann, who had been his companion for over fifty years, moved to Bavaria soon after; she settled in the vicinity of Munich where she lived until her death ten years later at eighty-two years of age.

Gerhart Hauptmann's creative activity covered a period of no less than sixty-five years. His published works include forty-seven plays, many fragments long and short, five epics in verse, and twenty-one narrative or autobiographical prose poems. In addition, there are poems, speeches, articles, and writings of all sorts, mostly unpublished. Works published after 1945 are a volume of poems, two tragedies that make up the final part of *Atridentetralogie* (Tetralogy of the Atrides): *Agamemnons Tod* (Agamemnon's Death) and *Elektra,* both 1948, the play *Herbert Engelmann,* a short story entitled "Mignon," a novel entitled *Winckelmann,* which Frank Thiess "concluded" on the basis of various variants with material of his own, and an edition of *Der grosse Traum* (*The Great Dream*) that claims to be "complete," although five cantos composed between 1938 and 1941 are not included.

There is a mass of over one hundred poetic fragments that defy proper organization, as well as first drafts of his works, diary entries, letters, and other writings, which still await publication. The mere compilation of an inventory of all the works available today would be an extremely long, tedious task. Yet there is no doubt that it is these unpublished writings that could provide the material for forming a conclusive, well-formulated judgment on the different periods of a life that was as rich as it was long.

As far as style is concerned, Gerhart Hauptmann's eludes precise classification. He has been labeled a naturalist, a realist, a romantic or neo-romantic, a symbolist, a classicist, and finally even a surrealist. None of these classifications really fits, for Hauptmann's total expression as a man and a writer is far more complex. As André Gide said, "He knew how to renovate himself continually."

Even if we overlook the youthful period, when he sought his models among the German classics, the naturalism so readily attributed to him was, in his own eyes, merely a passing phase that lasted approximately from 1887 to 1896. Plays such as *Drayman Henschel* and *Die Ratten* (*The Rats,* 1911) already left that phase behind and deserve to be called surrealist. Undoubtedly, he was a great realist all his life, one of the few writers who have succeeded in conjuring up real people before our eyes, with all their struggles, their pains, and their failures. But he combined all the essential features of every known style.

From his youth he was attracted by monasticism and mysticism; the reasons for this attraction must be sought in the history of the great Silesian mystics. At the time when he tried his hand at farming, he was strongly affected by the religious spirit of Graf von Zinzendorf, founder of a Protestant sect derived from the Moravian Brothers. The language of Martin Luther was always basic to him, and all through his life Luther's translation of the New Testament and writings were Hauptmann's daily pabulum, though he kept well away from organized religion.

Even today, few people know that in the 1890s, just when he was writing his "naturalistic" plays, he endeavored to portray Jesus Christ in essays and in poems that were rewritten again and again, and that fundamentally he was less interested in social than in religious problems. He became passionately interested in the language of the Reformation. It was that period which supplied some of his favorite themes—*Florian Geyer* in 1896; *Fragmente der Wiedertaufer* (Fragments of the Anabaptists); the terrible drama of the Inquisition, *Magnus Garbe,* written in 1914–1915 and published in 1942; the fragment *Der Dom* (The Cathedral) and *Hamlet in Wittenberg* in 1935. What he desired most was a "perpetual Reformation" in which man would really find self-determination.

Hauptmann's years of searching to define the essence of Christianity and its founder culminated in the great analytical work entitled *Der Narr in Christo Emanuel Quint* (The Fool in Christ: Emanuel Quint, 1910). In that work, Hauptmann expressed in very strong language his aversion to organized Christianity of every sort.

The author aimed his bitterest attacks at intolerance, the lack of intellectual freedom within the Church, the bloodshed of the Inquisition, the spirit of contention, a complete and frank investigation of the history of the Church, and the horror of the conquest of Mexico *Der weisse Heiland* (The White Savior, 1920). Despite a deeply felt love for Jesus Christ, which stayed with him to his death, Hautpmann turned from Christianity, seeing it as a historical phenomenon.

However, in Hauptmann's writings these themes are counterbalanced by a totally different world—the world of antiquity. As early as in *The Sunken Bell,* the crucified Savior takes the visionary form of the young god Dionysus, radiant with the ecstasy of creation.

Toward the turn of the century, Hauptmann became absorbed in the works of Plato. He had previously acquired an enormous amount of general knowledge about the ancient authors from Homer through the Greek dramatists to the late Gnostics, as well as the fathers of the church and the neoplatonic mystics. Plato's ideas come to life in what is perhaps Hauptmann's finest drama, *Und Pippa tanzt!* (And Pippa Dances!, 1906). The sparkling, fragile delicacy of glass embodies his idea of Platonic beauty: it must not be touched, only admired from a distance.

A trip to Greece in 1907, to which he had looked forward so impatiently, made a decisive impression on him. His account of the experience, *Griechischer Frühling* (Greek Spring, 1908), proves how closely he identified himself with the powers of the earth. On Corfu he started his drama *Der Bogen der Odysseus* (The Bow of Odysseus, 1914): the soil of that small island where the exhausted traveler felt at home gave him new strength, as Mother Earth had given to Antaeus.

This interest in classicism and its deities—Dionysus, Eros, the oldest of them all, and Demeter, the Great Mother—culminated in *Der Ketzer von Soana* (*The Heretic of Soana*), artistically his most mature work. It was written between 1911 and 1914 as a pendant to "The Fool in Christ: Emanuel Quint" and published in 1918. The theme is the return of a lost traveler from an unnatural world to the bosom of pure, unsullied nature. Subsequently, Hauptmann turned his attention to the Eleusinian mysteries in his *Das Demetermysterium* (The Mystery of Demeter), on which he worked steadily during the last ten years of his life but left unfinished.

Toward the end of his life, the aged writer, oppressed by the dreadful sufferings brought about the Nazi regime and the World War II, once again summoned all his dramatic power to describe the terrible fate of the Atrides from the sacrifice of Iphigenia to her return to Delphi. He did this in four tragedies, collected under the title *Atridentetralogie*. As in so many of Hauptmann's works, the idea of salvation through the voluntary sacrifice of one's life dominates the entire action.

Hauptmann once outlined his position as follows: "I am wholly a German and half a Hellene." He truly felt he had been "born as a Greek," only on northern soil. His designation, therefore, in 1932 as corresponding member of the Athens Academy, which he considered the last linear descendant of Plato's, gave him great pleasure.

Along with Christianity and the Greek classics, two poets made an impact on Hauptmann's art throughout his life—Shakespeare and Goethe. True to the old German tradition, Hauptmann struggled for no less than ten years (1924–1935) to solve the riddle of *Hamlet,* which attracted him with magic force. The play *Hamlet in Wittenberg* (1935) gave the modern playwright an opportunity to place his hero in the colorful world of the Reformation. Goethe's influence made itself felt chiefly in his language—not surprising, since Hauptmann was very familiar with the great predecessor's works.

Finally, there is the profound impact of the Indian religions. When Hauptmann was in his elderly years he kept the *Bhagavadgita* always close at hand and was constantly reading the *Upanishads*. Hauptmann considered K. E. Neumann's translation of the talks of Gautama Buddha no less important than Luther's Bible. He also made a thorough study of the Koran and still more of Lao-tzu.

Gerhart Hauptmann's bewildering profusion reaches its peak in the last of his writings, which make up an almost impenetrable maze. In this respect he resembles Goethe, whose last works were also elusive in a certain sense and demand serious study from the reader if he is to grasp their gist. For some time Hauptmann's vision of the universe had revealed a certain irrational quality or something "floating" and vague. Though he was deeply conscious of existence he refused to commit himself to a position. The truth, which he sought after but never found, was still embedded in time and not yet fully realized. For him it never achieved its marvelous, definitive crystallization. "Mebbe ay, mebbe nay!" says a simple villager in *The Weavers*. The expression in the crisp Silesian dialect interprets the quintessence of Hauptmann's thinking already at that early date. It was always difficult, not to say impossible, to get him to pronounce a clear yes or no.

All his late works, except for the fantastic short story "Das Meerwunder" ("The Sea Wonder"), were left in a fragmentary state. It is true that the monumental epic *Till Eulenspiegel* is apparently complete, but nonetheless many preliminary studies and important cantos were left unfinished.

Hauptmann's other epic poem, The Great Dream, and his novel, *Der neue Christophorus* (The New Christopher), though very long, are not complete. The author's own dream life must have been both painful and intense, and in those two works he made equal use of dreams and diary entries to discuss in his typically vague way virtually all the problems of this world and the next. Both works were begun during World War I, though there are notes which proved that the author was preoccupied with them far earlier. Both accompanied him all his life, and he was still working on them a short time before his death. Though their complex structure is often disconcerting, they are the most reliable guide to an understanding of the second half of Hauptmann's life, and the essence of his late work.

But how is it possible to discern a coherence in the life of a man whose creative activity developed in such abundance and variety through more than sixty years? Hauptmann has often been charged with not having a coherent vision of the universe. This is an extremely weighty charge, particularly in the perspective of German thinking, but it need not be taken too seriously. His life spanned the eighty-four years from 1862 to 1946. How many revolutionary upheavals Germany, Europe, the whole world experienced during that period! How could it have been possible for Hauptmann to remain unchanged, seeing that he started out from the idea that organic life is constantly transformed and renovated?

In any case, his most typical feature is the refusal to accept a system of any kind, and in particular that of pure scientific thinking, which is concerned with what is already done and is therefore dead. Heraclitus and Plato, not Aristotle and Kant, were his philosophers. We weaker vessels are awed by all grand phenomena, whether spiritual or natural (and in my opinion Hauptmann belonged to both those realms), so we attempt to "grasp" or "comprehend" them in simpler words, to get inside them and size them up. But when we do that we merely violate those phenomena and so deprive them of their unique, inimitable character. That is no way to do justice to Gerhart Hauptmann, a man who marked a new departure in the history of his nation's spiritual life. Nor is it the right way to form a valid judgment of his worth. Yet, out of respect for the unique, inimitable, undescribable nature of the individual that judgment must be pronounced.

In Hauptmann's eyes, the true essence of nature and the world consisted in the tension between opposites, in the struggle that Heraclitus extolled as the begetter of all things. How else would he have been a dramatist? So long as the world continues to evolve—until, to quote Goethe, "all that urges, all that surges . . . rests eternally in the Lord God"—man will always be caught up in the ancestral drama that shatters him. Only a great tragic poet has the strength to look this Medusa in the eye without going mad. Hauptmann observed naked existence with horror and emotion, but also with a sublime sangfroid, and expressed it anew in a work of art. It is only in this sense, and not out of any sentimental, bourgeois sympathy, that Gerhart Hauptmann became the poet of compassion, that is to say, one who shared the sufferings of all creation.

Felix A. Voigt is Professor of German Literature at the University of Würzburg.
Translated by Robert Allen.

THE 1912 PRIZE

By GUNNAR AHLSTRÖM

In 1912, when the Nobel Prize for Literature was awarded to Gerhart Hauptmann, the event marked the entry of contemporaneity into the Nobel annals. The new crop had finally been sown. Until then such worthy oldsters as Sully-Prudhomme, Björnstjerne Björnson, Frédéric Mistral, Theodor Mommsen, and Paul Heyse had been honored—together with such more-or-less venerated figures from romantic or exotic schools as Henryk Sienkiewicz, Rudyard Kipling, Selma Lagerlöf, and Maurice Maeterlinck. Sometimes the laurels had been distributed to hoary classics presented with official recommendations, sometimes they were voted to writers enshrouded in the mystery of distant lands or epochs, ranging from catacombs to medieval towers, from the Indian jungle to Swedish fairy tales.

But the new laureate was a true man of his times. For years Hauptmann had been famous chiefly for *The Weavers,* his drama about the workers of Silesia. Critics credited him all kinds of revolutionary qualities which were scarcely in accord with the official policies of Kaiser Wilhelm's Germany. In London the *Pall Mall Gazette* commented in a way that was characteristic of most thinking at the time: "The award of the Nobel Prize to Herr Hauptmann will probably not be greeted by the Kaiser with unmixed joy. It is a triumph for the Vaterland to have won the Prize four times while France has won it only twice and no other country has even won it more than once. But on the other hand, Herr Hauptmann represents a school of dramatic art with which the Kaiser can scarcely be in sympathy."

The award was accompanied by a kind of agitation. An atmosphere of instability characterized the debates and meetings of the Nobel Committee. From France came the rumble of public disapproval, and a sharper protest came from England.

A great change had taken place within the Swedish Academy itself, and on the Nobel Committee. On June 15, 1912, C. D. af Wirsén died in Stockholm. From the very beginning he had been closely involved with the awards. Although he wrote a rather seraphic kind of poetry, he was known chiefly as a militantly conservative literary critic, and his journalistic signature, C.D.W., had for years been the target of the younger generation's scorn. Since 1894, he had served as permanent secretary of the Swedish Academy, and it was in this capacity that he was particularly effective in setting up the necessary administrative apparatus for the awards.

In 1912, af Wirsén's chair was vacant, and it was filled only toward the end of the year. In the meantime, the duties were assumed by af Wirsén's old friend, Hans

Hildebrand, the former director general of historical monuments, a handsome, white-bearded old man, who, that year, was scheduled to make the traditional address to the laureates. These new circumstances gave added importance to the 1912 choice for the literature award, since it might signal some change in policy.

There were thirty-one candidates that year, and they were without exception very well qualified. France sent an official nomination for Henri Fabre and his *Souvenirs entomologiques;* but there were other, more brilliant stars in the French literary firmament. Foremost among them was Pierre Loti, whose claims were once more put forward. Another name was added to this elite group—Henri Bergson—a nomination submitted by Andrew Lang, the famed scholar of Saint Andrew's. Ernest Lavisse was also nominated by a Swedish group.

New countries entered the competition. Switzerland came out in behalf of Spitteler's *Olympian Spring* (which was to win the Prize in 1919). Of even greater importance, however, was the arrival on the scene of the New World, represented by serious challengers. Until 1912, the United States had been represented either marginally or absurdly by local figures or impossible poets. This time, however, it was a choice nomination, Henry James, strongly backed by university circles, especially those of Harvard and Columbia. The Royal Society of Great Britain had two names to recommend. A document signed by seventy colleagues was sent in support of Thomas Hardy, which was scarcely surprising. The name of James George Frazer, the Cambridge anthropologist and scholar of mythology, whose *Golden Bough* had opened a triumphal career throughout the world, appeared for the first time. It is also of interest to note that George Bernard Shaw was also nominated for the first time—by the Norwegians, however, not by the British.

There was, then, no lack of first rate candidates, and it was among such that Gerhart Hauptmann was to be distinguished. His position, for many reasons, was a special one. He had been proposed for the first time ten years before, thus meeting the unwritten seniority requirement. He had achieved, moreover, an international reputation firmly based on the success of his plays in the theaters of many nations. In the opinion of many he was a singular Teutonic genius, somewhat in the mold of Goethe, and his work summed up with great virtuosity many varied literary currents. Gerhart Hauptmann seemed to fulfill the requirements of the most widely diversified camps.

In the last analysis it was a broad sensitivity, a sort of personal universalism, and an eclecticism that brought Hauptmann the Nobel Prize. The most diverse schools of literature could find something in him to admire.

When Hauptmann was first proposed in 1902, there was no end of discussion. To begin with, Richard M. Meyer, a distinguished professor of literature at the University of Berlin, had offered his prestigious support. "In those German circles that concern themselves lovingly and seriously with literature, there is no doubt that Gerhart Hauptmann is the most gifted author of our times," he wrote. He went on to demonstrate how Hauptmann's naturalism is stamped with "a highly idealistic orientation." But in 1902, the Nobel Committee was inclined toward Theodor Mommsen.

Four years later Hauptmann's case was reconsidered. The Swedish Academy received a printed petition on the position occupied by Hauptmann in the cultural life of his country and on his mastery as a writer. It was signed by thirty-five German and Austrian personalities, professors of literature and members of the various academies. The missive made an impression, and the candidacy subsequently was strengthened by the successes achieved by Hauptmann in the following years, especially when his religious novel *The Fool in Christ: Emanuel Quint* came out in 1910. This explains why Erich Schmidt could be brief in nominating him in 1912, merely referring to the documentation already submitted in previous years. Everything leads us to believe, moreover, that he was directly in contact with the Nobel Committee. Thus it was no surprise to those in the know when the Academy met on November 14 and voted the prize to Hauptmann, "primarily in recognition of his fruitful, varied, and outstanding production in the realm of dramatic art."

Translated by Dale McAdoo.

Verner von Heidenstam

1916

"In recognition of his significance as the leading representative of a new era in our literature"

Illustrated by *GASTON BARRET*

BECAUSE OF WORLD WAR I, NO NOBEL PRIZE CEREMONIES WERE HELD IN 1916 AND CONSEQUENTLY THERE WERE NO PRESENTATION OR ACCEPTANCE SPEECHES

POEMS

By VERNER VON HEIDENSTAM

Translated by Charles Wharton Stork

THE WEDDING OF THE SISTERS OF ISIS.

I. *Prolog: Chorus of the Sisters of Isis.*

Raise the garlands, O ye virgin sisters,
From your hair unto the drowsy night!
O'er the desert now the twilight glisters.
Would the hour of evening ne'er took flight!
Would those girls of Thebes, each one so tender
Bearing to the well her polished jar,
Might be ever lovely, ever slender,
Ever youthful as to-night they are!
Would yon boys that on the mountains blue
To their flocks now call
Might stay children, and their lambkins too
Be but lambkins small!
Lift your voices, virgins pure, in weeping,
O'er each myrtle wreath let sweet tears well!
Bar the world from out the temple, keeping
But the sweet that in this eve doth dwell,
But the innocence of youthful creatures!
Let a refuge here for that be made,
Which with yonder boys and girls will fade,
Wearing only long-lost memory's features!

II.

After a listless day, when the cool of an eve in December
Came like a rapture of rest upon Thebes, the over-thronged city,

Then did the handmaids of Isis meet on the roof of the temple;
Vestured in white, they enringed a bowl of glittering copper.
Brimful of water, it shone, the mighty bowl on its tripod.
Oft was it used so, because in the stars it mirrored could women
Skilled in star-cunning divine the joys and griefs of the future.

Then did the eldest priestess, the ninety-year Bent-Amenemma,
Heavily rise. On her breast a beaten-gold image of Isis
Gleamed. From her tenderest years for that moonlight faith she had striven
Chaste and inviolate law of the pure, the gentle-eyed Isis.
Strictly she governed the rest. Through the city,—nay, throughout Egypt,—
Flew the insulting words that her savage tongue had been hurling
Long against Hator-Secket, the Goddess of Pleasure. She bowed her
Silently over the bowl and read in the fate-written water.
Anxious and hushed, the circle waited; but lo! with a sudden
Gesture she flung back her whitened hair! "Ye priestesses holy,
Never the stars have given an answer more grim than this evening.
Darkly, sepulchrally clanks a threatening doom there above us:
One of us shall to-night so deeply sin, that atonement
Greater by sevenfold than the sin shall of us be demanded."

Whispering then, the priestesses rose, but the pretty Ahanna
Twitched the old woman's robe and said: "O worthy high priestess,
Ask of the sinner's name, that she straight be exposed without mercy!"
Lifting a hand as dried as a mummy, and moved unto weeping,
Thus did the other reply, the ninety-year Bent-Amenemma:
"Spare we that question to-night; to-morrow it well may be answered.
Seems not the blow sufficient to thee? Would my zeal, then, be grateful,
If thou thyself should'st be crushed by the weight of the starry foreboding?"

So she ended. And, foll'wing the bowl which the sisters in silence
Carried, they slowly went down from the roof in mournful procession.

. . . . .

Eve became night, and around the failing fires in the market
Shivering boys attended the voice of the teller of stories.
Clad in his chequered coat with bells on sleeves and on hem, he

Sang in the waning glare of the flame, which tinted his figure
Ghastly pale as a powdered buffoon. On a height in the desert,
Far from the market-place, far from the hundred gates of the city,
Rose in stupendous bulk the dusky temple of Isis.
Open it was, as ever, but guarded by staring-eyed sphinxes
And by the faith of mankind;—superstition and faith are the same, lo!—
Through the pylon and fore-court the way was open to all men.
Farther might none proceed, for there in the innermost shrine sat,—
Hewn of gray-black granite that came from afar in the southland,
Rock-hard, mysteriously dark, and half concealed in her mantle,—
Isis, with Horus on knee, in her horns the disc of the full-moon.

Warden's place by the statue that night was assigned to Ahanna.
Stiffly erect as the goddess; her chin, her cheek, and her forehead
Vividly lighted with red, but with heavy shadows extending
Over her eyes, she stood, her bare arms crossed on her bosom,
Close to the altar-fire with its wind-blown, flickering streamers.
Roused by a squeaking bat, that flew with wings nearly singeing
Back and forth by the flame, she looked about and beheld then—
Far through the lotos-columns, which all from bottom to top were
Stained blue and red with symbolical pictures of mythic tradition—
Deep in the darkness, a man in flowing raiment of scarlet.
Pallid with consternation, she sprang back and held o'er the fire
Hands outstretched in imploring as unto a spectre. The Red One,
Carelessly humming, advanced to the light none the less, and forthwith she
Knew him to be a priest of Hator, whose robe was embroidered
Down all its trailing expanse with figures of pipes and of tambours.

Poised on a bull-like neck, his head rose straight and defiant.
Jewels a-many he bore on his youthful arms, and he chanted
Low, while his teeth shone white and the temple rang with his laughter:
"I, merry Hator's priest, who have sipped till the close of the evening
Wine sweet as ever was drunk in Thebes, the opulent city,
Now have a tickling desire to eat here my supper untroubled,
Toasting my loaf at the embers that glow on the altar of Isis.
Sit, that we may divide it like brother and sister, my darling!
Then, timid child, thou shalt give me thy lips for a kiss to repay me."

Blushing red with shame and terror, the maiden pushed from her
Sidewise the loaf that he broke so calmly over the fire.
Frantic with haste, she caught from the altar utensils a bell then,
Massive its clapper of gold, with handle carven of amber
Brought by seamen of Sidon from regions of uttermost Thule.
Hollowly now in the lonely depths of the temple resounded
Four quick metallic blows, like wing-beats close to each other.
Harshly the great doors ground and sandals hurriedly pattered,
White-robed priestesses came from stairway and passage; amazed, they
Saw there the priest of Hator. But bitterly spoke the high priestess,
Eldest among them all, the ninety-year Bent-Amenemma:
"This is the sin predestined. In Isis' presence our sister
Stood with a man. In Isis' presence now must she be offered!
Sevenfold more than the sin the offering demanded, and therefore
Six more, the youngest, I doom to fall by the knife as atonement."
Therewith she felt for and drew a knife, but a thunderous wind-gust
Blew out the altar-flame. The trembling, terrified sisters,
Huddling close together, their prayers and formulas muttered.
Bent-Amenemma, famed for supernatural wisdom,
Spoke, after blowing asunder the heap of blackening embers:
"Sisters, that was a sign to spare the young girls. Let us hasten
Even to-night unto Thebes to the priests of Hator for counsel!"

. . . . .

When with the sisters she neared the house of the famed and audacious
Brothers of Hator, she heard a clamor of drinking within it.
Stretched supine on a couch lay the jesting high priest of the order.
Boys from Goshen were swinging on handles covered with silver
Elegant peacock fans that shone with the gleam of a hundred
Sapphires and emeralds. Then in time with the tinkle of cithers
All arose for the dance. The caps and cloaks of the dancers
Glittered with cloth of silver, with opals and gay-colored tassels.
Darkly Bent-Amenemma stood forth in the midst of the banquet's
Carelessly rippling commotion, and making her way to the high priest,
Spoke with accents of sternest command: "Thou prince of vain pleasures,
Break off thy scandalous feast, let the juggling fiddles be silent!
Cast off thy panther-skin dress and put on the raiment of sorrow!

For by the stars a sin was foretold." The ninety-year woman,
Pale and bent, would but tell in a whisper that which had happened,
Writhing her hands in despair and terror, while tears without ceasing
Poured down her wrinkled cheeks. The merry high priest, as he heard her,—
He who, most like a child with friendly eyes full of wonder,
Took his days as they came and strewed on him legends and fancies;
He who, soon as a priest bore tidings of grief to the dwelling,
Drove him forth with showers of figs and bunches of wine-grapes,—
He, the lover of scoffing, was smitten with shame and, embarrassed,
Knotted his fingers so tightly around the sable and hairy
Goat-skin bottle of wine, that purple drops of the vintage
Sprinkled his hand.—"My sister, oh wisdom-renownèd, my sister"—
Shy and abashed he began, and gave her his hand, on whose fingers
Wine was glowing like blood. "But half is it proved, oh my sister.
True, by the stars was foretold a sin, but the name of the sinner
Thou did'st omit to ask. Bring thy bowl and seek in the water
Whether the stars have writ that the sinner's name is Ahanna!"

Now had the bowl been brought and set on its copper-green tripod,
High aloft was it raised in the sheltered court of the palace.
There did the southern stars through the limpid night of the desert
Brightly gaze on the bowl. At the threshold-stone in the doorway,
Diffident, stood the high priest. His brothers, who else were accustomed
Only to revel and jest, were standing like boys newly punished
Round the bowl of the sisters; the strains of music were silent,
Sweet-breathing incense was quenched in the sandy square of the courtyard.

Straight'ning her crooked back, out stepped then Bent-Amenemma,
Grim with menace, and read the far-famed oracular surface.
Upright for long she stood, but slowly sank more together,
Anxiously groping about with her fingers over her kirtle,
Staring with fixed, keen gaze at the fiery star-script. In horror
Trembling, she sank on her knees. Her chin and cheek were sunk forward
Deep in the mirroring water. In dumb desperation she clenched her
Teeth on the edge of the shimmering bowl, and fell with an outcry
Vehemently back, while she dragged the bowl along in her falling;
Drenched with the sacred water, she lay a-swoon in the courtyard.

Forward the high priest hurried, he seized the hands of his brothers
Warmly, nor did his attire, that shone with jeweled adornments,
Gleam more brilliantly now than his eyes all radiant with rapture.
Nodding, he shouted aloud, as amid the flutes thrown aside there,
Fans, too, and trampled goblets, he went his way through the courtyard:
"Thine was the sinner's name, thine own, oh Bent-Amenemma!
When thou at Isis' foot drov'st away a man from thy sister,
Thou did'st wrong even Isis. Ah, why should we ever be laying
Our false words on the lips of the gods? For these women here wot of
Only one kind of sin, the sin to which others are subject.
Wine, the kiss of a girl, and the daring jest that will startle
Senile women and men—to the gods above these are blameless.
Moon and stars and sun are gifts of the gods, but so likewise
She the beloved of my youth and my loaf of bread. As like brothers,
Sharing the loaf and the goat-skin flask, we are sitting together,
In the convivial air sprouts the seed from which may in secret
Grow the all-brothering hour.—The sacrifice of atonement
Must be sevenfold more than the sin was. Therefore, my sister,
Give to eternal Hator of Isis' handmaidens seven.
Day and night shall the seven, for thus I interpret the judgment,
Ever be fettered, each one to the priest of Hator she favors."
Ill did the priestesses, though, repress their heart-hidden gladness,
When they were dragged away mid the Hator priests' exultation.
After the smith had been brought from Thebes, afar through the desert
Rang the quick-riveting strokes of the hammer; but when these were silent,
Loud to the lonely night from the fast-barred house of the brothers
Rattling tambours proclaimed the nuptial feast of the sisters.

III.

Epilog: Hymn of the Priests of Hator to Ptah.

As bounteous love shines bright in every thread
Of the rich robe the husband's hand hath spread
As gift for the beloved one of his soul,
So bright, O God, thy love shines from the whole.
O love-abounding God! O Father good!
Say, hast thou nearer to our threshold stood
Than now, when wine from goat-skin flasks is streaming,

While gentle, string-sped music whispers low,
And we, the sons of hate, are brothers, deeming
That all the world with peace and love must glow?
If thou hast wrought whatever we perceive,
In evil also—we must then believe—
Reflected glimmers of thy glory shine.
Thus evil, too, is as a child of thine.
What God hath wrought must needs be free of blame.
What mortals "wickedness" and "sin" may name
Is wickedness and sin but in their sight.
There is a heavenly voice which earth misjudges quite.

WHAT SHALL I THINK?

When Mahmoud Khan, elated by the wine
Of conquest, entered Sumnat's plundered shrine,—
Where to the columns breaking the expanse
Of swamps, illimitable, foul and dreary,
His soldiers tied their chargers, battle-weary,
And now drew lots for captured shield and lance,—
Right against Shiva's giant image, towering
Sternly, in shining silver all arrayed,
With sixteen arms and one great eyeball glowering,
He raised his famed and dreaded blade,—
Evilest of sledges
That the evilest smith
(As the East alleges)
E'er smote anvil with.

Inside the court, where the dim sun, declining,
Shed spectral green on pool and colonnade
And fettered hounds with blood-stained whips were flayed,
'Twas black with men save for their helmets' shining.
Here cups and fans and dancers' robes were scattered;
There amid laugh and shriek were women led,

By ropes that cut their bare knees till they bled,
Past elephants and captured idols, battered,
With heads knocked off in one of the caprices
Found in all minds of true barbarian mould,
Mid drinking-vessels, too, of tarnished gold,
And skins of Kashmir goats with silken fleeces.

A Brahmin gray
Timidly stepped into the conqueror's way.
His small head stuck absurdly out
From his great cap with silver fringed about
Like a potato from a silver cup.
To Shiva's altar he advanced forthright,
And, feverishly trembling, then spoke up:
"Hurl in thy wrath, O Mahmoud Khan, to-night
My body to the temple-river eels,
But tell what thought at thy brown forehead's base is
Of man, the thought that boundlessly disgraces
All manhood as *thy* nature it reveals!"

The chieftain smiled with aspect so appalling
That his own warriors hid their eyes before
The blow. Therewith they heard his weapon falling
With hollow sound as on a dungeon door.
Now sprang, when Shiva's form in twain was crumbled,
Out of the cloven belly far and wide
A rainbow fount of gems on every side,
Where diamonds, sapphires, pearls, and mohurs tumbled.
All of the temple's spoil, a very glut
From rajah's harem and from peasant's hut,
From widows and from orphans, there was gleaming
In open day before the robber horde.
Like peas from an inverted basket streaming,
The great pearls down the polished stairway poured.

So Mahmoud Khan smiled grimly once again,
And to the gray old Brahmin answered then,
While the old man so shook to see his pelf

That the eleven bells which fringed his vest
Tinkled with ruby tongues their tiny best:
"When man's god is the priesthood's money-chest,
What shall I think, forsooth, of man himself?"

THE HAPPY ARTISTS.

Yes, human beings,—these same bulks we see
In square and street since, doubtless to oppress them,
The clothes-idea struck man's family,—
Have form and color, if they but undress them.

I stretched my canvas, took up with precision
My charcoal. Then the model in that cold
And blue-gray light let fall her garment's fold,
And a nude beauty stood before our vision.
We merry lads were seated all around,
While through the frosted windows came up-soaring
The muffled, multitudinous thunder-sound
Of smoky Paris, like Niagara's roaring.

I was the youngest student, to my woe.
How gladly I recall now the occasion
In the first week when I as "le nouveau"
Danced for my fellow-students' delectation,
Wearing a mighty Phrygian chapeau!
Each man politely bade me buy him soap;
If I forgot, though, I should get a thwacking.
With punch I sued for grace, but had to mope
In thirst while all the rest their lips were smacking.

I had to serve our Baal, the fire-place,
Which glowed like any wine-warm prelate's face.
My blue-and-yellow matchbox with a snicker
They scrutinized, and straightway bade me spell

For hours together "sä-ker-hets-tänd-stickor"
And say: "The Swedish language sounds like hell."
I soon made friends and, better yet, what ho!
One day my youthful happiness was doubled
When o'er the threshold slouched a fresh "nouveau,"
And I had rest while he in turn was troubled.

We were like mad-cap boys and acted so.
What painter lacks the impulse or the leisure
To climb forthwith the giddiest peak of pleasure,
When his tobacco and his punch-bowl glow,
Like sunny morning with new-fallen snow,
Such was the spirit of our band's employment.
What clamor at the Café Star there was
Among these men, who sent their brains to grass
And took the whole world for their eyes' enjoyment!
Across their pencil-butts benignly gazing,
They saw the gorgeous town and the attire
Of long-gloved ladies, costumes quite amazing:
Their eyes' delight was all they could desire.

And yet their handwork never wholly filled me,
Though I with charcoal sought to play my part.
I had at home a shelf of books that thrilled me.
I scanned the world through printed symbol swart,
And through the beggar's rags I strove to see
The inner man. I looked unceasingly
With my cold mind and with my burning heart.
Time's war-cry in the din I could betoken.
In wrath I gripped my charcoal with the will
To make it glow; I tried my utmost skill,
A foot I drew, a heel—with that 'twas broken.

Paris I wept not for, but jealous, lonely,
I bade farewell to that gay artist set,
Who with small genius of the soul had yet
A genius gathered in the eye-sight only.

NAMELESS AND IMMORTAL.

Finished, in Pæstum's rose-embowering garden,
Stood Neptune's temple, and the man who planned
Sat near. His young wife, on his shoulder leaning,
Spun with the yellow distaff in her hand.
She listened to the piping of the herdsmen
Who tended on the hills their droves of swine,
And with an almost childish joy she murmured,
Twisting the flax about her fingers fine:
"My cup of happiness is filled to brimming.
The man who brings me home to Naxos' strand,
Now he has built yon glorious Neptune temple,
Returns, immortal, to his native land."

Then solemnly her husband answered her:
"No, when we die, our name will pass away
A few years after, but yon temple there
Will still be standing as it stands to-day.
Think you an artist in his time of power
Sees in the background multitudes that shout?
Nay, inward, only inward, turns his eye,
And he knows nothing of the world without.
'Tis therefore that the bard would weep hot blood
If he deliver not his pregnant soul;
But he would kiss each line wherein he sees
His spirit live again, true-born and whole.
'Tis in such lines as these he lives and moves.
He strives for immortality—but mark!
'Tis for his writings, never for himself;
The man's true reputation is his work.
What's Homer? At the very best a myth!
We seek to clasp a more enduring fame.
We see the pulses leap on Homer's brow,
For 'Iliad' has become his mighty name."

He rose, as if to go, but suddenly
She caught him by the cloak and held him fast
And murmured, while a hundred smiles dissolved
In the one look that furtively she cast:
"Still on a column there your name is carved.
If this proud vaunt be earnest, as you say,
Take from among the tools there at your feet
The biggest sledge and hew the name away!"

He turned, he shot at her a keen, quick glance,
But when she sat there calmly as before,
Twisting the flax into an even thread
And gazing at the masts along the shore,
He bent him down impulsively and took
The biggest sledge; his knuckles were distended
And then grew white as wax, so hard he gripped
Upon the haft. The lifted sledge descended.
It scattered sparks from out the column's side,
And at his feet the steps were sprinkled o'er
With rain of pointed shards. From that time forth
The temple bore the artist's name no more.

Then with a cry of joy his young wife sprang
Quickly from flax and distaff to the place,
And mid the scattered fragments of his fame
She fell and clasped his knees in her embrace.
"Ah, now," she cried, "no words can tell my joy,
As we return to Naxos whence we came.
Now is my lord a thousand times more great
And 'Pæstum's Temple' is his mighty name!"

So evening fell. A single ship went out
With lowered sail, a Naxos flag had she.
Slowly she rowed far out against the sun
And vanished on the mirror of the sea.

A thousand years and more have passed away,
Leveling Pæstum with the verdant plain,

But still the temple stands, and in its shade
The fiddlers wake Arcadian joys again.
The master's name may no man surely know,
But all who see the temple's gleaming height
May see his very soul in yonder form
And share to-day the architect's delight.
He is to me an old beloved friend—
Though far away, I know him in good truth—
A schoolmate, brother, comrade of my youth.

SINGERS IN THE STEEPLE.

At the belfry window the ringer stood,
A vigorous form of giant size.
His thatch of red hair, unkempt and rude,
Was blown down over his eyes.
——Ding! Dong!——
He tramped at the treadle and sang his song:

"Thou mighty thundering church-bell, thou,
With lips and tongue of metal that ring,
Thou callest the people to worship now,
But this my own psalm I prefer to sing.
The weary week-days back to Monday
Are slaves to the rich man, the money-lord.
The only day that steals from his hoard
A paltry copper is Sunday.
His life is a heaven. Ours instead
Is a hell. We are ragged and eat hard bread.
At home our loved ones are sighing,
While starved we row for a surfeited race
Their barge of trade with sweat in our face
And weep at the oars we are plying."
——Ding! Dong!——
"May vengeance dire consume them!

When shall I ring in redress of wrong,
And God's own judgment doom them?

"From our starving flesh they cut off a pound
To make the money-lord fat and round.
But beware, money-lord, your knell will be rung!
Oppression is old but freedom is young.
She comes as a thief in the night.
She waits not to knock, but in she breaks
She tramples your carpets and hers she makes
Whatever you snatched with your might.

"There's a mine of powder by no means small
In the cellars under your castle wall.
A spark, and the mob will rally."
——Ding! Dong!——
"We bring an armful of stones along,
With torches we sally
From hovel and alley.
We shame your wife, we stick your swine,
We spill on the street your costliest wine.
Your roan must pull where we have striven.
And when to ashes your castle is burned,
Our hell will be turned
At once into your proud heaven.

"From our huts to the square we all drag out
Our straw and our tatters clout by clout.
On them shall your throne be, O money-king,
And your plundered purse for your apple we'll bring.
And drummers shall come and stand around
To thunder and pound
On your kitchen saucepans furiously,
And fifers shall toot in time with them
On crystal decanters your requiem.
Above, your house totters, while sparks begem
Your smoke-woven canopy.
Your dirge to the skies will groan now,

And beggars will bring live coals to fire
The straw-heap that is your throne now.
They dance in a ring around your pyre,
While I sing bass in the men's deep song.
And I ring in so loudly your final hour
That earth re-echoes my strokes of power."
——Ding! Dong!——

Up on the tower beams beside him sat
His wife in silence. Then she followed him
Down the steep ladder's length, she followed on
In silent thought down churchyard pathways trim.
Beside their cottage lay a narrow plot
Of garden by a hill, all baked and dry.
Thither she went alone, but in her ears
Still rang the deep bell and her husband's cry.
He, harsh and wild, slunk off as was his wont
To drink and gamble at a neighbor's house.
She sat her down among the stones beneath
The mingled maple and wild cherry boughs.
To save her Sunday shoes she loosened them
And slowly took them off. With playful air
She wove for fun a chain of maple leaves
And fastened on some cherries here and there.
Then she sprang up, hearing a man's voice nigh
And sound of more men coming, vaulted o'er
The latticed garden gate with nimble bound,
And ran until she reached the steeple door.
There she stepped in, afraid she might be caught
Running bare-footed on a Sabbath day.
In the dark steeple, under the round bell,
She, young and sunburnt, held her leaf array.

She listened long; at last, when no one came,
Quickly around her neck the wreath she threw
And climbed the steep rungs higher, higher yet,
Until the floor had vanished from her view.

Dull in the wood-work whined the eddying draught.
With bended foot and practiced hand she stood
Upon the rungs as upon tight-stretched cords
And held on steadfastly with resolute mood.
Through loop-holes she could see the market-place,
But all was dark beneath her in the tower.
At every step the bell became more large,
And men grew smaller on the street below her.
Breathless and flushed and warm she reached the bell;
Like to a loved and trusted friend she found it,
And when she smote her knuckles on its rim,
Whispered vibrations fluttered all around it.
But higher still the narrow steps led on.
Boldly at last with lifted hands she swung
Up to the narrow beam. The bell below,
Dumbly upon its bright-worn axis hung.
One arm across the beam, she twined her chain
Of maple leaves around the brazen crest,
So that the green-gray giant suddenly
Was as a maiden for her bridal dressed.

The service done, the ringer came, but paused
In dumb surprise, his arm against a beam,
To note the verdant head-dress of the bell
With reddish-purple cherries all agleam.
His wife had often rung the bell before;
She waited not his grumble or his frown
But on the well-worn treadle of the bell
She set her foot, strong-sinewed, bare and brown.
The bell swayed heavily from side to side,
Now the first deafening strokes were heard to ring.
With that the frightened jackdaws raised a cry,
And tower, roof and beams began to swing.

——Ding! Dong!——
She tramped at the treadle and sang *her* song:
"From the tower's quivering height
Ring forth over square and street!

Afar lies the plain with its waving wheat
And the woods where the sun glows bright.
Not only over the fields and bays,
Where, O bell, thy notes are hurled,
But over the weeks and years I gaze
To the brothering-time of the world.
I see not savage and weaponed men,
Not kindled cities aflame—
Such a world would be but again
The old world, the ill world, the same.

"Nay, the city is festive. Bells are clanging.
At every doorway garlands are seen.
Between the houses festoons are hanging,
The street is all like an arbor of green.
A forest of flags on the house-tops is swaying
And streamers by thousands and thousands are playing.
The mightiest pennon gleams and arches
From the golden vane of the steeple.
Like brothers below pass the people,
For rich man with poor man marches.
They meet not for strife but for shaking of hands,
As now are gathered the reaper bands
For the haying-feast at midsummer time.
Then my daughter's daughter shall climb
To the bell where the rafters sway,
And, brown of hue and young and strong
As I, shall ring in the brothering-day."
——Ding! Dong!——
"Then, drawn by white horses with plumes of white
At a walk, a carriage comes in sight,
A carriage with silvered wagon-prong."
——Ding! Dong!——
"Around it are children in white arrayed.
The rain of flowers has overlaid
So deeply the stones of the street below
That softly the wheels as on carpets go.
On the carriage, the goal of every eye

Stands a mighty cup exalted high,
A bowl whereon wreaths of corn-flowers twine,
And along the rim these letters shine:
Not joy to the rich, to the poor man care;
Our toil and our pleasure alike we share.

"The crowd makes way for the carriage to come,
The murmurs grow silent, the people stand dumb;
Only the sound of the bells is rolled,
Like a seraph-song from the blue down-sailing.
Then the heads are bared, both young and old.
Then matrons and maidens look pale and cold
As they stand by their balcony railing.
Unsparing, each tears in pieces
The necklace that brother or husband gave,
Strips off the rings that sparkle so brave,
And her arms from jewels releases.
They climb on the railings one and all
And into the mighty cup let fall
Their wealth, where the flowers blending
Hide with their petals the bad gold's gleam.
Like rain-drops in banded light descending,
From festive balconies falls the stream."
——Ding! Dong!——
"With sudden tears the most hardened of men
Swears to abide by his fellows then
In weal or woe his whole life long
As a son, a brother, one of their clay.
The tender woman in man shall bring
Redemption to all the world and ring
In the future's brothering-day."

A PEOPLE.

I.

The People.

(Cf. Nahum III, 18)

The prophet Nahum speaketh thus
To Nineveh, to Assyria's king:
"The pilots of thy people slumber,
And each one of thy chieftains, Prince,
Dwelleth apart and doeth naught;
Thy scattered people roam the mountains,
For no voice ever summoneth them."

I tremble at the word: a people!
So full of song, so full of wailing,
Of thunderbolts and trump o' doom.
I shrink together at the word
As at a heaven-towering giant,
Whose foot is crunching in my ribs
As I might crunch a mussel-shell.
A people! Toward the sky it flames.
In a dark valley waggons rattle,
And savage men in wild-beast skins,
With naked children, wasted women,
Plod ever forward, ever forward,
Forgetful of the roads they followed
And no more knowing whence they came.
The children ask, but no one answers.
There rises from the throng of elders,
With ice-gray beard and shaggy mantle,
One-eyed, a raven on his shoulder,
And sword unsheathed, a wonder-man.

He motions to the bards—and sadly
They sing of their forgotten birthplace,
When midnight stareth on the tents.
He speaks—around the altar-stone
That, blood-smeared, stands beneath the oak-tree
He sets new images of gods
And stands himself as god among them.
Then groweth leaf-o'ershadowed Birka,*
Where amid oar-song viking vessels
Cut glad the waves. On yon high prow
Stands the dread fifty-winter sea-king
With captured bride and hails his home.
Soon speech as soft as festal raiment
Is woven, timed to gentler breathing.
Then holy bells ring, centuries hurry
Like shadow of clouds across the lands.

Now all grows still, as mournful-still
As when a limpid St. John's Eve
Sets heavenly glint on sound and bay;
But in the heart's deep secrecy
Dwells dread, when anxious lips are silent.
My people, though your hand be cold,
The frost that chills is of the dawn.
Your pilots slumber, O my people,
And each one of your chieftains, too,
Dwelleth apart and doeth naught.

II.

Sweden.

Oh Sweden, Sweden, Sweden, native land,
The home and haven of our longing!
The cow-bells ring where armies used to stand,
Whose deeds are story, but with hand in hand

* Birka, or Birch Island, was a port of the vikings near to where Stockholm now stands.

To swear the ancient troth again thy sons are thronging.
Fall, winter snow! And sigh, thou wood's deep breast!
Burn, all ye stars, from summer heavens peeping!
Sweden, mother, be our strife, our rest,
Thou land wherein our sons shall build their nest,
Beneath whose church-yard stones our noble sires are sleeping.

III.

Fellow-Citizens.

As sure as we have a fatherland
We are heirs to it one with another,
By common right in an equal band,
The rich and his needy brother.
Let each have his voice as we did of old
When a shield was the freeman's measure,
And not all be reckoned like sacks of gold
By a merchant counting his treasure.

We fought for our homes together when
Our coast by the foe was blighted.
It was not alone the gentlemen
Drew sword when the beacons were lighted.
Not only the gentlemen sank to earth
But also the faithful yeomen;
'Tis a blot on our flag that we reckon worth
By wealth, and poor men are no men.

'Tis a shame to do as we oft have done,—
Give strangers the highest places,
But beat our own doors with many a stone
And publish our own disgraces.
We are weary of bleeding by our own knife,
When the heart from the head we sever;
We would be as one folk with a single life,
Which we are and would be forever.

V.

Soldier's Song.

Beat the drums there, boys! Go ahead, make way!
Hurrah for country and king!
Hurrah for the Riksdag, where old men stay,
Pound the gavel and scratch at their heads all day,
And cough and blink at the ceiling so gray
Ere they let the gold-pieces ring!

But when it's time that for people and king
Our blood on the snow shall run,
They don't tie a man with a money-bag string,
For then, young or old, the man's the thing.
All right, then, comrades. Strike up and sing!
We'll be as one people, as *one*.

We'll be as an eagle, faithful and dumb
Mid petty clamor and clangor.
When the thunder rolls at the beat of the drum,
Then between the gray crags our banner shall come.
We'll be heard when we swoop from our rocky home
And yell with the might of anger.

VI.

Invocation and Promise.

If the neighbor-lands three should cry: "Forget
Your greatness of bygone ages!"
I'd answer: "Arise, O North, who yet
May'st be what my dream presages!"
The vision of greatness may bring again
New deeds like those of our betters.
Come, open the graves—nay, give us men
For Science and Art and Letters!
Aye, close to a cliff let our people stand
Where a fool his poor neck may shatter.

There are other things, men, to hold in your hand
Than a brim-full Egyptian platter.
It were better the plate should be split in two
Than that hearts should rot when still living.
That no race may be more great than you,—
That's the goal, why count we the striving?

It were better to feel the avenger's might
Than that years unto naught should have hasted,
It were better our people should perish quite
And our fields and cities be wasted.
It is braver to take the dice's hap
Than to mope till our fire is expended;
It is finer to hear the bow-string snap
Than never the bow to have bended.

I wake in the night, but I hear no sound
Save the waters seething and churning.
Like a soldier of Judah, prone on the ground,
I could pray with passionate yearning.
I ask not years when the sun shines bright,
Nor for golden crops I importune.
Kind Fate, let the blazing thunderbolt smite
My people with years of misfortune!

Yea, smite us and lash us but into one,
And the bluest of springs will follow.
Ye smile, my folk, but with face as of stone,
Ye sing, but your joy is hollow.
Ye rather would dance in silk, forsooth,
Than solve your own riddle truly,
Ye might awake to the deeds of your youth
In the night when ye sorrow newly.

Then on, shy daughter, in hardship bred,
Look up and let sloth forsake thee!
We love thee so that, if thou wert dead,
Our love could once more awake thee.

Though the bed be hard, though the midnight lowers,
We'll be true while the tempest rages,
Thou people, thou land, thou speech that is ours,
Thou voice of our souls to the ages!

A DAY.

With twinkling stars the sky is crowned,
Although the peasant with his light
Is stumbling on his farm-yard round.
Now to the woods with deep, soft sound
Goes fluttering the Bird of Night.
The cottage clock is striking five,
The streak of morn is gleaming,
The factory wheels are all alive,
The fire and sparks are streaming.

To north, where pine- and fir-trees float,
The earliest rays have hurried
To tinge the heath. A cow-horn's note
Across the smooth lake is carried.
The beams now touch a pale white peak,
Or on some torrent settle
That frozen hangs on ledges bleak.
Above a Lapp's tent whirls the reek,
And flames leap round his kettle.
Out on the snow, with branching horns
His deer stand in a ring there.
No house, no tower yon land adorns,
Nor is there bell to sing there.
Night seethes around, an ocean vast,
For all things come to night at last.

Thou sun, whose might bestoweth
On each least plant a quickening dower,

Grant us thy bright creative power
As long as day still gloweth!
Keen is our heart, but time is short.
Oh, hark to our imploring,—
Thou whom our fathers once would court,—
On us thy radiance pouring.
Go forth, go forth, thou new-born day,
With morning-song and hammer-play,
May dusk-fear come not o'er us!
Kindle brave strife, our hearth-stone guard;
Send, lightning-like, a spirit sword
To flash the road before us!
Shine far across our folk and land,
Make rich our soul, make firm our hand,
So that with gladness we may bear
Such years as age shall bring,
And still like sowers onward fare
Into the world's new Spring!

AT THE END OF THE WAY.

Wise, O Man, thou only shalt become
When thou winn'st unto the evening coolness
Of the topmost height, the Earth o'erlooking.
Turn thee at the ending of the way,
Rest an hour, O king, and look behind thee!
All is clear there, all is reconciled,
And the realm of youth once more is gleaming,
Strewn as erst with light and morning dew.

STARTING ON THE JOURNEY.

Already I'm upon the bridge that leads
From Earth unto a land beyond my ken,
And far to me is now what once was near.
Beneath, as formerly, the race of men
Praise, blame, and forge their darts for warlike deeds;
But now I see that true and noble creeds
Even on my foemen's shields are blazoned clear.
No more does life bewilder with its riot,
I am as lonely as a man may be;
Still is the air, austere and winter-quiet;
Self is forgot, and I go forward free.
I loose my shoes and cast aside my stave.
Softly I go, for I would not defile
With dust a world so pure, all white as snow.
Beneath, men soon may carry to a grave
A wretched shape of human clay, the while
Mumbling a name—'twas mine once long ago.

WE MORTALS.

We that hardly meet before we sunder,—
Born alike of clay, alike of wonder,—
On life's headland where the tempests rave,
Shall we loveless bide till fate shall summon?
Solitude awaits us all in common,
And the same sad sigh of grass on grave.

THE DOVE OF THOUGHT.

Lone the dove of thought goes lagging
Through the storm, with pinions dragging
O'er an autumn lake the while.
Earth's aflame, the heart's a-fever.
Seek, my dove,—alas! thou never
Comest to Oblivion's isle.

Hapless dove, shall one brief minute,
Flaming, fright thee to a swoon?
Sleep thou on my hand. Full soon,
Hushed and hurt, thou'lt lie within it.

MOONLIGHT.

'Tis strange that I sit here in wakeful mood,
Though day has brought me nor joy nor gain;
But all of which ever my life was fain,
And all that was hidden in gloom and pain,
Is trembling to-night in yon silvery flood.

MY LIFE.

Glide on, my life! I love thee not so much
That I would set thine hours with busy care
In a shop-window for a common show.

I never say: "Come, press the master hand
That lures to birth such wondrous lovely flowers!"

When I have been betrayed by trusted friends
And heavy fortune follows in my path,
I do not bear with me a silver cup
Of tears and say to him who passes by:
"Oh, lay thine arm about my neck and weep,
And pity me, and let us both lament!"

O thou wide world, my greatest grief
Is but the shadow of a cloud.
I go in silence to my grave.

THE HEAVIEST ROAD.

Hard do you press on me, dark hand,
And heavily you rest upon my head.
I vowed that unlamenting I would stand;
Boldly set garlands on my hair instead.
The sorrow of the old is other
Than bird-song grief in springtime's glow.
Around me chilling shadows gather.
The heaviest road is still to go.

ALONE BY THE LAKE.

Here spread the waters dark and deep,
Where now your ashes are lying.
Oh, tell me, my father, will you keep
The promise you made when dying?
Then rise, O wraith, from your watery grave,

Speak the word that was uttered never,
Oh, give the token that none yet gave,
If the dead may live on forever!

From the dark the surf rolls in its foam,
With a curve of white it enrings me;
A storm-cloud points to the starry dome,
As though some token it flings me;
But the desolate night is hushed in gloom,
And naught in answer it brings me.

No answer for him who does not see
What you, ye stars, are outpouring.
I am one with you from eternity,
With the winds and the surf's loud roaring.
Then shine for me, stars, and guide me on,
For you are my father since *he* is gone!

PRAYER AMID FLAMES.

Holy Spirit, I worship thee.
Fire and Victor-Song is thy name.
Shine in our need, O spirit of power,
Shine o'er the gulf of our dread last hour,
Burn into ashes our mortal frame!—
Even in death mine arms shall be
Outstretched in prayer to thy deathless flame.

THE JEWEL.

Happiness is a woman's jewel.
Gods remorseless, fates unsparing,
Scanty bread—aye, that's the cruel,
    Bracing life for men!

THE SHIPWRECKED MAN.

After the storm
Smilingly he warms his outstretched hands
Over the quickly failing fire,
Lone on the cliff.
With the morn, embarked on his fragile raft,
He will be saved or die.

THE WITCH'S COUNSEL.

You ask: "Pray teach me how to set a trap
Within whose meshes Fortune may be caught."
Sit down again, my child,—'tis lightly taught—
And wait with folded hands across your lap.
Each day the butterfly of Fortune swings
Around us, seeking us on wings of gold.
But who can teach how one may safely hold
The butterfly and never break its wings?

THE CHARLES MEN

By VERNER VON HEIDENSTAM

Translated by Charles Wharton Stork

PART I

CONTENTS

The Green Corridor

In the castle attic, where the fire-chief sold brandy and ale, a tall, narrow-shouldered customer had been thrust down the stairs and his empty pewter pot thrown after him, so that it rolled between his shoes. His worsted stockings were mended and dirty. He had tied his neck-cloth over his mouth and unshaven cheeks, and he continued to stand with his hands in his coat-tail pockets.

"Show out crazy Ekerot!" said the fire-chief. "He has spit tobacco plug into the ale, stuck Peter Painter with a bodkin, and is full of mischief all through. Then shut up the folding table! There is a command to bar the castle gates, for now it will soon be over with His Royal Majesty's life."

One of the wardens was Charles XI's faithful old servant, Hakon. He had a tranquil face, but walked so bowlegged in his stiff clothes that he looked as if he had just dismounted from a horse. He picked up the pot and stuck it good-naturedly under Ekerot's arm.

"I shall follow you, constable," he said, —"or lieutenant, or whatever I should call you."

"Lars Ekerot is a captain in His Gracious Majesty's battlefleet," answered Ekerot, "and travelled and learned in tongues he is, too. Here in the castle attic one sees no distinction between folk and folk. I shall leave a report and complain of it, that I shall. Have I not told you that soon fire shall rain from heaven, and every rafter in this house break out into bright flame? Mercenary councillors, unrighteous judgments, execration, and lamentation,—that has become our daily bread, and the wrath of Heaven rests heavy on the land."

"Lieutenant—or captain—you need not spread talk of worse misfortunes than those which God has already given us to bear. Round about in the suburbs has the fire made way, and for ten years we have had failure of harvest and famine. Four bushels of rye already cost twelve rix-dollars in silver. Soon fodder will run short even in the royal stable, and the boats with imported grain lie frozen solid out by the coast."

Ekerot went down the steps beside him and looked around without fixing his small, restless eyes on any definite object. Sometimes he stood still, nodding and talking to himself in an undertone.

Through the loopholes came glimpses of the castle grounds far below and the covered terrace with obelisks and sentries who went back and forth in the trumpeters' gallery. Beyond the snow-covered towers and roofs, small groups of people moved on the frozen Mälar between King's Island and Söder. The light of the March evening shone slanting through one of the halls in the western wing of the castle, so that it appeared as if light had been kindled in the chandelier.

"Yes, yes," mumbled Ekerot, "that shall all burn, all—all that which was our shame, all that which was our greatness. I have seen shining fellows in the heavens, and when I sit with my pipe at night, I see in the tobacco smoke wonderful planets, which show me that the old order of the world is upset. In Hungary and Germany rain down swarms of Arabia's grasshoppers. The fire-spurting mountains cast up glowing stones. Two years ago we had grass finger-high in the park in February and heard the birds of spring, but in September I picked strawberries at Essing. It is in such times that the Lord God opens the eyes of his elect so that they see what is hid."

"In God's name, do not talk so!" stammered Hakon. "Do you see your visions waking or asleep?"

"Between the two."

"I promise that I shall report every word to His Royal Majesty himself, if you, lieutenant, will recount for me quite veraciously all that you have seen and known. Do you see down below there the two windows where the shutters are closed? It isn't half an hour since I was in there. There His Royal Majesty sits in a chair made into a bed with covers and pillows, and he has become so small and dried up that he is only nose and lips. And he cannot raise his head. His poor Majesty, who has to endure such agony, though he is but some forty and odd years! Formerly, when he came limping through the door, I was most glad if I could slip out, but though I am only the least among servants, he can now put his arms around my neck and press me to him with streaming tears. I do not believe that he feels much more warmly for his son than he did for his wife. When he sends for him, he is brief of speech and mostly sits and looks at him. He speaks now only of his kingdom—and again of his kingdom. Up to a week ago I saw on his knee house-inspections and tariffs and such trifles, but now he has written down his secret instructions to his son and laid the letter in a sealed iron casket. As soon as any one steps into the room, it is as if both with his feverishly gleaming eyes and his words he stammered a constant: 'Help me, help me to uphold the kingdom, to make my son worthy and prudent. The kingdom, the kingdom!' "

Hakon passed his hand across his forehead, and they went on down the steps from loophole to loophole.

"In the room below us to the left is Her Majesty, the queen dowager. She has locked herself up during these last days, and not even Tessin slips in with his portfolios. No one knows just what she is about, but I can well believe that she does her best to banish her sad thoughts with a game of cards. There's a tinkling and jingling of watch-charms on the edge of the card table, and a crunching and a rustling and a frizzling of lace and ruffs—and a cane with a gold knob slips to the floor—"

"And the pretty Lady Hedwig Stenbock, who stands behind the chair, picks it up."

"That she certainly doesn't, for she is long since married and old and ugly, and at her own home. You live only in that which was and that which is to be."

"That may be." Ekerot screwed up his eyes and pointed to the north wing of the castle, which had just been reared by Tessin, after the old one had been levelled to the earth. Some scaffolds were still standing with fir branches on the highest pinnacles.

"Well, who lives under that long box-lid? Fie! There lives no one at all—and neither will any one come to live there, that I know. Why couldn't it be left to stand as it was? Devil take the Gottorp woman that put all this building nonsense into the head of His Royal Majesty! You see, warder, just as every man has his soul, so every old house has in it all sorts of spooks and other creatures of darkness, which are disturbed and uncomfortable when people come with pick-axe and trowel. Do you remember the Green Corridor which used to run under the section of the roof above the old castle church? It was there that for the first time I got my eyes opened. Oh, I'll tell you all about it. I will tell you the whole story, warder, if you will follow me home and then keep your promise to relate every word to His Royal Majesty himself."

Having now come down to the entrance door, they went on the drawbridge across the castle moat. A courier with a leathern bag on his back was just about to dismount from his horse, and his answer to the many questions was heard through the trampling of feet and the orders.

"For six miles north of Stockholm seen only three human beings—They sat by the side of the road and fed on an animal that had died a natural death. In Norrland a pound of meal mixed with bark cost five rix-dollars in silver. Soldiers starving to death—Regiments hardly half their complement—"

Ekerot nodded assentingly, as if all this had been known to him long since, and he continued to walk beside Hakon with his pewter pot under his arm and his hands stuck in his coat tails.

When they had come up to his attic room at Trångsund he gave Hakon a mistrustful side-look, and when he stuck the key into the lock he ascertained carefully that the door had not been opened in his absence. The room was large and bare. In the window stood a cage with a squirrel, and on one wall was a medley of unlike pieces of money nailed up in rows. There were bright Elbing rix-dollars, small and large copper coins, a five-ducat piece of Reval, and even a couple of Palmstruch's old bank-notes, which had been worthless for thirty years. Ekerot advanced, inspected, and counted the money.

"A fool," he said, "sinks his possessions so deep that he cannot himself keep watch over them, but I want to have them under my eyes, so that I can easily count them into a sack, when the great fire comes."

Out of one corner, Ekerot carefully took five logs, which he put in the fireplace and lighted with a piece of tarred stick. Thereupon he and Hakon filled their pipes, and as there were no chairs, they sat on the floor in front of the blaze.

"Well, let us hear now," said Hakon.

Ekerot narrated:

Never have I seen anything so frightful as the Green Corridor. That was at the time when I was constable with the battle-fleet. Now they have given me my little pension of two hundred and fifty dollars. Oh, to be sure. I was as good as driven from the service because people were afraid lest otherwise I should end as admiral-in-chief. And *that* Hans Wachtmeister wants to be himself. "The fellow is crazy!" he screamed on the deck, when I politely asked him to raise his hat before he ordered me into the rigging. And so it was all up with me. Crazy Ekerot I was called wherever I came and went. So it keeps on. A poor journeyman carries a comrade to the grave; then he carries his master to the grave; and at last, for a groat, he carries one after another, gets himself a glazed hat and a long black coat, and when he is in a hurry rolls of braid fall out of his pocket—and children take to their heels and weep and scream: "The corpse bearer, the corpse bearer!" But though one may become such a bugbear, at the beginning we are, to be sure, all baked of the same dough. Report that now, word for word, to His Royal Majesty in person. Ah well, at that time I was quite skilful in drawing and sketching. A few days before that quarrel with Wachtmeister, I therefore received a gracious command to take with me another constable, who was called Nils, and appear in the store-room above the old papist church in the castle tower that stood by the river. There we were to draw a broken lantern of a galleon, according to which the queen dowager wished to have a new one made for her sloops on the Mälar.

When we had sat there in that manner for a day, gambling and worrying over the smashed lantern of the galleon, which the devil himself couldn't have drawn, a merry fit came upon me, and I cried: "Nils, have you ever seen a dog with five legs?"

When Nils shrugged his shoulders, I went on: "I saw one just now in Iron Square. He walked on four legs, and the fifth he had in his mouth."

Nils got angry, and to provoke him I cried still louder: "Clever you are not. Let's see if you are brave. I'll wager you this pewter pint measure filled with good Spanish wine and with a ducat at the bottom that I shall go alone at guard-bell through the Green Corridor."

Nils replied: "I know that when you set your mind on anything it's no use trying to keep you from it, and I don't want that you should think me stingy of gifts. Therefore, my dear Ekerot, I take your wager as you desire, but I will not bear the responsibility to your old mother if any ill befalls you. Therefore I prefer to go home to my place. In daytime this splendid building is fine enough to see; but at night strange things are supposed to happen here, and I'd rather sleep in the wretchedest hole in the suburb."

I called him poltroon, and let him ramble off home. As soon as I was alone, I noticed that it had already begun to grow dark, and, in order to harden myself, I went up the two or three winding stairways to the Green Corridor and looked through the keyhole.

The green paint had fallen down in many places, so that the older bright red color shone out. Along the walls stood all sorts of household furniture that had been worn out and carried up there. I saw cabinets and chairs, and representations of dogs and horses, and in the far corner a bed with drawn curtains. On the sides were hidden recesses, where there was a dropping and dripping from the leaky roofing.

It was Walpurgis Night and therefore somewhat light, and this restored me to a certain feeling of security, so that I could sit down and wait, but I knew that wondrous beings had their resort up there under the roof. The warders called them night-goblins, because only at twilight did they lift up the dark boards and stick out their heads. They were not larger than a three-years' child, were brown all over, naked, and had the bodies of women. Often they would sit mounted on a cabinet and wave their arms, and he who happened to touch a night-goblin died within the year. They were wont to spring about in the attics, and sometimes they shrieked in the privies and clattered under the seats, so that the court ladies dared not go there, but rather lay in bed with colic all night.

As soon as I heard the guard-bell, I opened the door wide.

I took a step forward, but my terror was so great that I remained standing with hands on the door-jamb and only stared. Through a bare space in one of the chalked panes I looked all the way up to the tower of Brunkeberg, and that strengthened me so that I sprang right into the Green Corridor, in order that the ringing should not be still before I had got back. As long as it sounded, the creatures of darkness would have no power.

In about the middle of the corridor I suddenly saw something dark shoot forward along the curtain-bed and slink down in one of the armchairs to hide or wait. My left knee gave way of itself, and I heard the echo of my scream through the attics. It was from that time that my eyes were opened so that men called me crazy.

Against the light of the window, I saw that a man was sitting in the chair. He remained as motionless as I. All at once he seized me by the arm and whispered through his teeth: *"Figlio di un cane!* Spy? What are you? The queen dowager's warder?"

"God bless me!" I stammered, for now I understood that it was a fellow human being, and by the trembling and fumbling hands I comprehended that he was no less frightened than I myself. I even noticed that he was in his stocking feet, and had his shoes stuck in his bosom.

I summoned my wits and described my foolish enterprise, and finally I was believed.

"Such a damned, dilapidated old nest," growled the man, to excuse his own astonishment. "There are such drippings from the roof that my feet are wet through. As sure as I live, there shall be a new house here. My good man, if you can find the way, help me through this labyrinth of attics to the ballroom. Who I am is no matter."

"Very good," I answered, though I recognized the gracious Chamberlain Tessin.

He was silent, and took me by the coat tail, and so I turned and went before him. I imagine that at bottom we were both equally pleased at having happened upon each other. When we came down to the ballroom, he ordered me to stand outside the door, but I heard the night-goblins jumping in the dark behind us, and I kept my hand on the lock, so that I was instantly able to open the door again and steal in after him unnoticed. Through the window I saw the river, and within, around the walls, stood a multitude of leaning side-scenes, painted with trimmed trees and white temples.

Tessin stood in the middle of the hall and clapped his hands thrice.

A lady rose behind the side-scenes, and opened a little dark lantern. Who should it be but Hedwig Stenbock, the queen dowager's highborn lady-in-waiting! "Look, look, look," I thought, biting my lips, "has that foreign dandy there climbed so high already?"

"Hedwig, my dearest of all in the world!" said he. "Let us go directly to your room. No arguments, *ma chère!*"

Hedwig Stenbock was then nearly thirty-five, and she went so stiffly and rigidly to meet him that I should not have believed she had either heart or soul, had she not all at once become wholly transformed and showed the blood in her cheeks, when he embraced her.

Then I forgot myself, and burst out half aloud, "Aha, yes!"

Tessin turned around, but he was so hot that he only knitted his eyebrows and spilled out all his words in explaining my presence.

"We might have needed some assistant in any case," said he, "and Ekerot may be as good as any one else. If he knows how to keep silent, he shall not be without reward."

He then ordered me to take the dark lantern and go through the empty conference chambers—thanks for the favor!—and on, by a course which he described, to the corridor where the queen dowager's ladies dwelt—sweet sleep, my pretties! As soon as I had carefully ascertained that no flies in court dress were buzzing around there, I was to return and so report.

I had, however, something else to announce, when I did come back. I had heard the night-goblins clatter inside the door of the Art Room, and had seen them running with small sparks of fire in their hands down the stairs to the Archive Hall, where the affairs of the kingdom lay in the wall cabinets. Finally, in the aforesaid corridor I had come upon one of the queen dowager's warders, who sat asleep over his dark lantern with his back against the wall.

"He has been sent there since I left," said Hedwig Stenbock, and again she stood as stiff and straight as at first. "He does not suspect that the bird is already flown. But how to get back?"

She pushed Tessin's arms from her and became thoughtful.

"Long have I feared and suspected. Tonight scandal has come upon us. Her Majesty is jealous."

Tessin clutched in the air with his hands as if toward invisible swords and daggers, and his eyes flashed and sparkled.

"Jealous! Of me? She is forty and grizzled, and she is somewhat hoarse and rough of voice like a man. Shall I never escape hearing that babble? With whom should I have laid my plans and sought gracious protection, if not with Sweden's

Hedwig Eleonora?" He bowed. "Yet fear not, my dearest one, for no shame shall attach to your days, but this very night you shall follow me hence. A sleigh can always be had—and then—*addio!* In Italy I have friends."

"God in heaven knows," she answered, "that I will always follow you wherever you desire, and for men I care not at all, but will rather be by you than forsake you, yet we must first consider with a certain friend what is wisest. I am thinking of Erik Lindskiöld, who this evening sits and drinks with His Majesty. Ekerot shall go down across the courtyard to the king's little staircase and wait there till Lindskiöld comes. Then—with many apologies—he shall entreat him to hurry up here—to me."

Tessin made a dissuasive motion with his hand, but I paid little heed to the cavalier, finding a greater pleasure in obeying such a noble lady.

It had drawn far into the night when I came back with Lindskiöld. He interrogated me fully about everything. His peruke swayed, and he swore kindly, guffawed, and was as noisy as if the whole castle were his.

When he came into the ballroom, he bent one knee, while he threw his hat into the air and cried: "Are ye altogether staggering mad, my worthy folk, who of love would partake and never forsake, though all to hinder you watch and wake? Your inclination gives more delectation than elevation. Paff, poof! A poor master builder, who thrives by adventure, though good luck bewilder, may not without censure suppose himself worth, sir, a lady of birth, sir. That day began mankind's vexation when Adam awoke at Eve's creation and said, impelled by a new proclivity: 'Congratulations on your nativity!' "

"Fiddlededilly, reeling—silly!" muttered Tessin to his lady. "That's what they call the Swedish *esprit.* Lindskiöld is drunk."

"Only a trifle. He is in the most favorable mood."

Lindskiöld did not hear them, but went on so that the wide hall rang: "I have long suspected this, and the titled class is likely to take it ill. But travel to Italy! Ah, bah! Here the chamberlain has a land that needs his genius. Let him look me in the whites of the eyes, and say whether he can travel from the designs for the royal castle that he has spread out on my table, whether anything in the world is as dear to him as his art."

Tessin became blood-red, and looked down in the light of the lantern.

"I have determined to marry Chamberlain Tessin," said Hedwig Stenbock, "and that is how this has happened."

Linkskiöld laid his hand on his heart: "Of course, of course! says the royal widow. A wreath will I twine, the best to be had, of flower and vine from my Lindevad. I was born at no manor, with chapel and banner, and my sire was a smith, but they made him forthwith—aha, burgomaster of Skenninge. Think if the chamberlain had sprung from Skenninge. How would he have built then? A new royal castle in the Skenninge style? A sight for the city, or the devil may get me! What pride would be his to be just who he is!"

Lindskiöld seized Tessin by the arm in a lofty, threatening way, with a gesture as if he suddenly threw off a spattered masquerade cloak.

"Let him calm his ardor for a moon or so. To begin with, the chamberlain now kisses the hand of his chosen one, goes three steps backwards, makes a reverence, and then follows with me. Silent, when I talk in the halls of the king! Ekerot goes back to the dowager's warder, blows out his lantern, wakes him with a sound and expressive box on the ear, and throws his shoes after him when he runs, so that he believes it is the night-goblins. Afterwards the gracious young lady returns unseen and tranquil to her room. It is fully determined that she, in due time, shall go along on a trip to Pomerania. Then the chamberlain overtakes her, and marries her in all secrecy. His Majesty I shall see to here at home. The Gottorp misfortune—I mean the royal dowager—crafty woman —her the devil himself cannot control, but the high-noble set, them I've heard assessed before the Royal Commission, and I shall know them well enough to remind them what they are worth. New times are at hand here. Ah, my children, my children, if you knew how the breast fills, when one stands at the helm of state and steers according to distant beacons, whose name one dares not once utter to His Royal Majesty himself. But for the present, rely on my word. Here where we now stand, the chamberlain shall build his immortality."

Confusedly Tessin drew his hand to his lips, and when I had performed my errand with the warder, he handed me, with a supercilious grimace, the two Palmstruch notes that hang there on the wall.

"There you have your promised reward, if you are silent," he said.

But then began my visions and misfortunes, and when I sat sick in my room at home, my ailments became a by-word in the square—gout, lung trouble, snuff disease, accidental bullets in the leg—and buzzing in the head. And when I pulled out the Palmstruch notes which the dishonorable villain stuck into my coat pocket, I found that they had lost all value many Lord's years before. Report that now to His Royal Majesty's person!

Ekerot would have related still more, but there was a violent banging on the door, and a messenger called Hakon to the king, who was worse.

Some days later, on the second day after Easter, people said that the king lay at the point of death, but Ekerot only nodded in his usual way as if it had all been known to him before. A crowd of men and maid-servants, who had been dismissed in the country because of the famine, stood homeless and despairing on the streets in the snow, and Ekerot went from group to group with his hands in his coat tails, and listened and nodded. By night he composed letters of prophecy, which he then presented to the court pastor superior, Wallin. "The unfortunate," he wrote, "are accustomed to see in the darkness, so that in the end they can discern that which is dim and hidden to those blinded by the light of prosperity."

One windy April day, when he had just stuck his last letter of prophecy under Wallin's entry door and come home to his room, he sat down at the window and prattled with the squirrel. Now and then he chewed at some dried pears, which he picked out of a drawer. Just as he was sitting so, he heard the tocsin and alarm, and when he stretched himself out through the window, he saw the castle roof enveloped in yellow smoke. Turning around to the room, he began to take down the coins from the wall, counting them accurately into his pocket. He trembled, and his teeth chattered, as, with the squirrel cage under one arm and the pewter pot under the other, he toddled down the stairs to the street.

He was jostled against the house wall, and stood staring up at the castle, where roaring streaks of fire already spurted forth under the dark rafters. Soon all three of the wings flamed like huge bonfires, and the thunderous noise of the conflagration drowned the tocsin and the trumpet flourishes.

"Look, look!" he said. "The night-goblins must out into the light of day. Look how they jump in rows along the roof-ridges with fire in their hands! Now they climb up on the tower roof and hop over the new Tessin addition, which disturbed their comfort. They want to burn themselves in it. This is only the beginning. It will all burn—all."

Soldiers and warders thronged on the castle bridge amid barrels of water and itinerant chairs, cabinets, and paintings. Under the two lions that held the coat-of-arms above the door of the gate stepped forth Hedwig Eleonora, the mother of the Charleses. Two courtiers supported and almost carried her, for she shrunk together, and constantly wanted to stand still and look back. The wind raised the mantilla over her silver-gray hair, and the next moment drew it as a veil over her eyes red with weeping, her proud aquiline nose, and thickly painted cheeks.

"The pyre is burning under your son's body," shouted Ekerot, pointing. "And the throne on which your grandson has ascended is burning, and before you close your eyes his whole realm shall be burned in ashes. Don't you remember that he was born with blood on his hands?"

He made his way anxiously along the wall and around the corner to Trångsund. Sparks rose to heaven like stars, and beyond the churchyard wall one saw the great castle tower called the Three Crowns, which rose four full stories above the highest roof. With every story that the fire conquered, the smoke burst out through the loopholes as from cannon. That's the night-goblins, thought he, who fire victory salutes, while the citadel of the Vasa kings is burning. Again and again, the smoke enveloped the ancient arms of the realm on the spire of the tower—and again, dizzyingly high, gleamed forth the golden crowns, like three storm birds resting on their wings. The ringers of St. Nicholas Church climbed up the steps to swing even the great bell and the preliminary bell, but when they heard the rumble, as the tower floors and vaulting plunged down together, pulling the spire and arms with them in the fall, they turned and fled. Smitten with terror, children and women began to sob and run, and it was told that people at the South Gate saw an insane man steal out with a squirrel cage and a pewter pot, singing in an undertone an old song of penance.

A Sermon

In Great Church the audience arose from their pews and looked toward the armory, before which Charles XII dismounted from his carriage.

He was a handsome, but slender and undeveloped boy. His hat, edged with plumes, sat comically in its smallness upon the great curly peruke, and when the king stuck it under his arm, his gestures were nervous and embarrassed. He walked trippingly, a trifle bent in the knees, as was the fashion, and his eyes were lowered. His costume of mourning was precious with ermine on the facings and blonde lace around the gloves, and on his high-heeled shoes of cordovan leather he had buckles and ribbon rosettes.

Bewildered by the inquisitive glances, he took his place in the royal pew, under the gilded crown upborne by genii. He sat stiffly, facing the altar, but was unable to collect his thoughts around the sacred ceremonies. When, at last, the minister stepped into the pulpit and with an epigram and a vigorous blow on the back of the book aroused a subdued murmur, the king reddened and felt himself caught in the very act. Directly, however, his thoughts became the same rebels as they were just before, and went their own ways. To cover his shyness, he began to pluck off the black points on the ermine.

"Look at un," said a woman in one of the bottom pews. "He still needs to wear out his father's rod. Has the devil bit un i' th' fingers?"

"That's for her to say, the dirty wench,

who has traipsed into a higher pew than belongs to her!" answered a grand lady, and pushed her headlong out into the aisle.

The old man with a cane, who stood down by the door and had the office of going around and cuffing on the neck those of the congregation who went to sleep, tapped on the floor and menaced with his hand, but the scuffle was heard as far up as the pews of the nobility, so that the fine gentlemen turned their heads, and the preacher straightway interpolated the following words:

"Concord, I said, Christian concord! Whither does she repair with her mild sweet-gruel? To the populace, perchance? Hold her fast! In God's house or around His Royal Majesty's own person, perchance? Well for him who finds her! Therefore I say unto you, ye princes of the earth, seek diligently for concord and love, and lift not into strife the sword which God has placed in your hand, but lift it only for the defence of your subjects."

At this allusion the young king again blushed red and laughed shamefacedly. Even Hedwig Eleonora, the queen dowager, in the royal pew just opposite to him, nodded simperingly, but the young princesses beside her laughed most of all. Ulrica Eleanora sat tolerably stiff, but Hedwig Sophia leaned forward with her slim long neck. In happy consciousness that she wore gloves, so that her malformed thumbs were not visible, she held the prayerbook in front of her mouth.

The king now became bolder and looked around. In what a strange temple of the Lord he found himself on this day! The whole church was overcrowded with the furniture and objects of art which had been saved from the fire at the castle. Only the middle aisle was free. In the corner up by the altar stood, rolled up, Ehrenstrahl's representations of the Crucifixion and the Last Judgment, and behind the tomb of the Skyttes he recognized the plume-tufts and the green curtains from the bed on which his father, sitting crosswise and supported on pillows, had given up the ghost. The recollection of this, however, moved him not, since he had scarcely felt for his father anything but fear. He had seen in him rather the deputy appointed by God than the dear blood-relation, and in his thoughts as in his speech he preferred to call him plainly and simply, the *old* king. Like two questing bees, his eyes wandered over the numerous familiar objects, and tarried long at last on a coat-of-arms on the nearest pillar.

There, since several years, rested beneath the floor his teacher, Nordenhjelm, the good-hearted old Norcopensis whom he had loved with childish enthusiasm. He recalled hours of study early in winter mornings, when he sat and learned the four branches of ciphering, and poked at the wick with the candle-snuffers, or when Nordenhjelm told stories of the heroes of Greece and Rome. Since the old king's death he had walked in a dream. He understood that he must not show gayety, that lamentation was the only thing he had license to claim, but at the same time he saw that there were many who were quite ready in private to court his favor by amusing him though attracting as little attention as possible, now with one prank, now with another. Even His Excellency Piper could at the same time dry his tears and beg the king not to forsake his youthful sports but play a game of shuttlecock. The gloomy, serious faces about him afflicted him sometimes, so that the tears sprang into his own eyes, but from the most secret depth of his boyish soul rose the dizzying, triumphal intoxication of victory. The morose and stiff-necked old men whom he had formerly feared and shunned, he had suddenly found humble and submissive. Sometimes at table, while they were sitting with their most anxious

expression, he had audaciously filliped fruit seeds into their faces so as to see them laugh all at once, and then go away again and range themselves in a lugubrious ring around the queen dowager. The burning of the castle, with its adventures and dangers, had been for him a day of curiosity and excitement. It had even been almost the jolliest day he had yet had in his life, though he himself did not dare to think so. The affright of the others and his grandmother's faintings had only made that wild spectacle the more strange and extraordinary. Now all the old life was done. The old king was dead, and his stronghold in ashes. All the new, all, all that Sweden longed for, should now mount on high with him like a flame of fire—and there he sat, lonesome and fourteen years old.

It seemed to him next that Nordenhjelm stood at the pulpit behind the speaker and dictated the words. Only for an instant had the minister shaken the clown's staff with bells so as to make himself intimate with his listeners. Then he addressed himself to the king in sight of all the congregation, earnestly, strictly, yes, even commandingly. He required him, in the name of God, not to let himself be led to vanity and pride by sycophants and hangers-on, but to dedicate his actions unselfishly to the unselfish people of Sweden, so that when, in the fullness of years, he closed his weary eyes, he might be followed by the blessings of thousands, and might enter into God's glory.

The voice of truth sang and thundered beneath the arches of the church, and a lump rose in the young king's throat. He tried afresh to link his thoughts to other, indifferent things, but every word struck his upright childish heart, and he sat with bowed head.

It was a relaxation for him when the carriage took him again to Karlberg. There he bolted himself into his apartments, and not even the resolute summons of the dowager could induce him to go down to table.

In the room outside his sleeping-chamber lay the books which were used in his rarer lesson-hours. Already he liked to philosophize over the riddles of creation, and he was always fascinated by the sciences, but he began to despise books like a merry troubadour intoxicated with life. The uppermost work dealt with geography, and, after turning the page back and forth, he threw it to one side. Then, vehemently and at random, he drew out instead the bottom book. With it he remained sitting.

It was broken at the corners and severely worn, and the contents was only a few manuscript pages with the evening prayers that he had learned to recite as a child. Many sentences and words had already been frozen out of his memory, but as he now saw the familiar lines before him, he needed only to read them through two or three times to know them by heart.

In the evening he ate only a cup of beer-soup, and the warders then began to undress him. He bore his violent emotions with such propriety that they only thought he was tired, and when they lifted the peruke from his short-clipped and dark-brown, somewhat wavy hair, and he climbed up in his shirt into the great bed, he looked like a little girl.

The dog Pompey crept up by his feet, and below the foot of the bed a lighted candle was set in a basin of silver filled with water. The king was afraid of the dark, and it had therefore become the custom that the door to the outer room should be left open, and that a page or playmate should spend the night there. This evening, however, the king ordered with decision that the door hereafter should be closed. Only when they heard that did the warders begin to wonder and become uneasy, noticing that he was disturbed in spirit.

"Ah bah!" grumbled old Hakon, the faithful servant from his father's days, who obstinately continued to treat the king as a child. "To what shall that serve?"

"It shall be as I have said," answered the king. "And from to-morrow on the night-light is not necessary either."

The warders bowed as they went backwards from the sleeping apartment, but when Hakon had closed the door, he sat down on the threshold outside. One of the warders, who was named Hultman, also remained there standing. They heard how the king turned and threw himself on the mattress, and when Hakon finally stretched himself up to the keyhole, he saw indistinctly in the glimmer of the night-light that his young lord was sitting upright in bed.

Gusts of the night wind roared and rattled out on the castle terrace and in the lindens of Karlberg Park, but within doors it was already hushed and still. Yet Hakon thought, to his wonderment, that he could distinguish a muffled, almost whispering human voice, and even detached words. He became attentive and listened.

He heard then that the king recited with half-raised voice the prayers he had taught himself to pray in his earliest childhood.

"Teach me to control myself and not to be misled by flattering talk to presumption and self-will, and thereby to sin against the regard which I owe to God and men."

Old Hakon brought his knees together and clasped his hands for prayer, and, through the stillness and the soft rustle of the blast, he heard continually the words of the king.

"Though the son of a king and hereditary heir to a mighty kingdom, I yet would always humbly consider that these things are a special grace and blessing of God, on which account I must strive after Christian virtues and knowledge, so that I may become skilful and worthy in so great a calling. Almighty Lord, Thou who dost raise up kings and put them down, teach me ever to obey Thy commands, so that I may never to my own ruin and the oppression of others misuse the power that Thou lendest me. For Thy holy name's sake. Amen."

The Successor to the Throne

How dull it was! How long were the days at the little court, where the black-clad councillors of state yawned in armchairs and stared in front of them, as if they pondered how it was that they were similarly shod on both feet, and had not a jack-boot on one and a silken slipper on the other. And so they yawned again—and out on the stairway the warders yawned, and down in the kitchen the cooks tasted the viands with their fingers in the grease, and said to one another: "Is that sour enough, so that the great gentlemen will at once make wry faces?"

The coachmen harnessed horses with black plumes and ribbons in front of black carriages. Black broadcloth was being cut out or sewed on all the tables. In the church on Grayfriars' Island, where the old king had been interred, the black canopies and tapestries still hung, and the king's funeral knell was heard far out into the country. When, finally, the coronation train moved forth over the snowy streets, all went in mourning, and only the young king wore his purple. The echo of the last festal salutes had hardly rolled over Tyskbagareberg, before the same intolerable dulness again settled over the throne in the dark Yuletide days.

Then, one sullen gray noon, the dowager's master cook stamped on the floor. In his hands he held a pot with boiled tomatoes.

"Ach, du Lieber! There's something to

o here to-day. His Grace, the Duke of Iolstein, who is to be expected here hortly, has sent us a costly gift. Her Ma-esty and Mistress Greta Wrangel have lready tasted the fruit, and Tessin, who a travelled man, is coming down into e kitchen himself to advise us in the reparation. Don't stand there gaping, oys. Dishcloths to the saucepans! Rub nd polish!"

The remote little court in the outermost orner of the world had that day gotten omething to think of. At table the talk 'as of nothing else than the tomatoes, nd each and all had something to say bout their smell and flavor. Meanwhile ere was drinking, and the old council-ors who had been invited, growing mel-ow, forgot their intrigues and said drolly greeable things to one another.

After the meal the king took Councillor ars Wallenstedt by the coat-button, and ed him along to the window recess, like panting grumble-bear with a ring rough its nose.

"Tell me," inquired the king earnestly, how should a prince sacrifice himself for is people? That sermon of last spring ever leaves my mind."

Wallenstedt had the habit when he alked of puffing out his lips as if he were aying "Pooh!"

Accustomed to the king's precocious nd penetrating questions, he answered: A prince should sacrifice all small mis-ivings, gather all power to himself, be-ome his people's archetype and will. 'hat was truly a pious discourse we heard at time in church, but does not the Most everend Bishop Spegel say that subjects hould be as thralls to their lord? The ouncillors and nobles now quarrel but or their share of the power since the time f Your Majesty's revered father. And)xenstjerna and Gyllenstjerna and—ah, vell—they have their ears to the ground. ut it was for that reason I always ven-ured to support Your Majesty's will that even at your youthful years you should shift the heavy weight of government from the shoulders of Her Majesty the queen dowager."

When Cronhjelm, the king's tutor, who stood in the recess, heard the words about the weight of government, he wrote with his finger on the moisture of the window-pane: "The old woman feels that burden as deliciously light as her head-dress."

"Yes, yes, my dear Wallenstedt," the king meanwhile answered. "I, too, have always felt within me that my will urged me in that direction. On Atland's throne a man must sit. It is a wondrous trouble-some thing to will. How is that? To-day I feel that I will ride to Kungsör and hunt bears. But why? I might equally well will something else. Will is to me a fetter, a chain drawn tight around my breast, from which I cannot twist myself free. It is the master, and I am the servant."

Wax candles were already lighted when he stepped into his outer apartment. On the table stood the sealed iron box in which the old king had deposited his final secret and fatherly instructions. Many days had elapsed since the retiring guar-dians of the realm had let it leave their hands, but he had not yet been able to bring himself to open the lid. One night, to be sure, he had violently torn off the seal, but he had then shrunk back. This evening he felt that the will was come.

But when he set the key in the rattling iron, his old fear of the dark fell upon him. He saw before him the old king's coffin of tin, on which had just fallen the spadefuls of earth, and it came over him that now he was to stand eye to eye with the dead. He called in Hakon, and bade him lay wood on the fire. Meanwhile he turned the key, threw back the lid, and with chilly trembling unfolded the closely written paper.

"Take the power into your own hand," stood there, "and beware of the great lords who are about you, of whom many have

French stomachs. Those who chatter most eagerly hanker only after their own interests, and the best at times keep their own counsel."

When he had read to the end the anxious and mistrustful warnings of the departed, he did not notice that Hakon had left the apartment.

Now he was lord over all the land of Sweden. The high dignitaries had thronged outside his door to declare him of age. Did they even know themselves whether their words were dictated by the hope of favor or by pure intentions? Did they not love him more than they did their own sons or brothers? But nevertheless he could not talk familiarly with these old men, who weighed and adjusted their speech. And could he talk with those of his own age, a crowd of shyly courteous playmates, who knew naught of the affairs of the day? Alone he went about as never before, and alone he had to carry the old king's sceptre. Nothing could be greater than Sweden, and of all Sweden's kings he willed to be the foremost and best. Had he not received a token of it from the hands of Almighty God, in that he was exalted to be a ruler so young, with the many years of a long life before him? The old, which had brought down the wrath of God, was now passed away. Song rose on high, there was jubilation of drums and trumpets.

He arose, and his hand fell with a light blow on the edge of the table.

Piper was right. Piper had said that Sweden was a great realm with a little court in a small town at the world's end. There was to be no more of that. He had himself set the crown upon his head, and had ridden to the church with it. Had he not already received it from God at the hour of his birth, on the June morning when the glittering star of the Lion's Heart ascended above the rim of the east? The floor-cloth on the streets, in which his horses' hoofs had beaten holes, he had given to the peasantry for clothing, b the nobles had had to go on foot, and t very councillors of state had borne h canopy and waited on him like warde Why should he dissimulate, why shou he confer honor on men whom he d not honor in his soul? Had he ever giv a royal charter? The Estates, but not h had had to take oath. His kingly vow had sworn in silence before God, as stood at the altar. Now, now was he lo over all the land of Sweden!

He went to the hanging mirror, ey complacently the small pock-marks in h girlish skin, and compressed with his fi gers the stern furrow in his brow.

Then he pointed into space, sat himse astride on a chair, and galloped arour the room.

"Forward, boys, forward for your kin Jump, Brilliant, jump, jump!"

He imagined he was riding over meadow against the enemy and that hu dreds of bullets struck him on the breas but fell flattened in the grass. Round abo on the heights stood spectators, and at distance the very king of France came c a white horse and waved his hat.

In the hall below, the old dignitari still stood in conversation. When th heard the racket, they were still a mome and listened, but Cronhjelm wrote in t moisture and grumbled half aloud: "Th is only His Majesty who is occupied wi the management of the realm. He is devi ing marks of favor for us in return f declaring him of age."

Wallenstedt blew out his lips and ga him a furious glance.

When the king had galloped all aroun his room, a sudden recollection struc him, and he went to the door.

"Klinckowström!" he cried, "Klinckov ström, can you tell me why I have ju now taken such a fancy for riding t Kungsör and hunting bears?"

Klinckowström, a merry page with re cheeks and a light tongue, answered: "B cause it's pitch dark and infernal weather, and because no bear is started, so that hunting is impossible. Shall I give orders for horses and torch-riders?"

"Have you any better suggestion?"

"All other suggestions are better, but—"

"No, you are right. We must ride to Kungsör just because it seems impossible, and because we will it."

When, a little later, the king rode down Queen Street, he passed close to a suburban place which extended below St. Clare's churchyard to a yellow-painted house. There an old widow known as Mother Malin kept an inn. The grounds were fenced in with boards, on which the builders at work on the castle, when in summer they emptied their glasses at Mother Malin's, had painted arches of triumph and obelisks and dancing Italians. In one corner lay a pleasure-house having a fireplace and chimney. One window was on Queen Street, the other faced inward on plum trees and flowerbeds, now covered with snow. For several weeks Mother Malin had daily carried food to the pleasure-house, but no one of her old customers knew anything with certainty as to the guest she lodged within. At a sale of a noble family, whom narrowed circumstances had bowed to the earth, she had purchased for her guest a piano, and in the evenings behind the closed shutters were heard strange melodies, accompanied by a weak and delicate voice.

Just as the king's torch-bearers approached, Mother Malin was standing at a crevice of the planks, looking out upon the dark street.

"It's he himself," she burst out, and thumped on the door of the pleasure-house. "It's the king that's coming. Put out the light and peep through the heart in the shutter!"

At that moment the king dashed by in wild career.

"So handsome he is o' the cheeks, the gracious young lord!" she said, and went down again to her inn. "And pure and holy is his life, too. But why should he tempt God and set the crown on his head with his own hands? That's why he slipped on the way, and the box of sacred ointment thudded on the floor of the church."

The night went by, and so did month after month. In the garden the chestnut trees became green again, as well as the plum trees behind the barberry and currant bushes. The Maypole was raised, and the court drove by to Karlberg.

Beside the king sat the Duke of Holstein, who had come to marry his sister, Princess Hedwig Sophia, and make an end of the intolerable dulness. As they drove past the pleasure-house, he happened by accident to throw a glance through the wide open window.

In the evening came a man with his cape-collar up, who knocked stealthily at the inn, but Mother Malin regarded him mistrustfully. "Be off to the devil with your cape-collar!" said she.

He laughed loudly and talked broken Swedish.

"I lie here on one of the German galleons, and would but have a mug of berry juice in your garden. *Schnell!*"

He thrust a couple of coins into her hand and pushed her aside. She was near to giving him a blow, but, as it was, she counted her money and thought things over. She put the mug of syrup on the earthen bench in the garden, but she herself sat behind the half-closed shutters to keep the new customer under her eyes.

He sipped a little at the juice, wrote with his heel on the sand, and looked about him. When he had sat awhile and thought himself unobserved, he arose and turned down his collar. He was a young, handsome gentleman, of a daring and merry appearance, and he walked slowly along the path.

"Impudent villain!" muttered Mother

Malin. "I vow he's going to knock at the door of the pleasure-house."

When the door remained shut, he shrank several paces aside to the open window, and stuck his hat under his arm in knightly fashion. Then he sat on the window-sill and spoke softly and eagerly.

With that Mother Malin's patience gave way, and she went out. She walked on the sand path, twisting a thread of yarn between her fingers and holding her head slyly bent forward. Meanwhile she meditated on the abuse which she should utter. But when she had gone a little way, the young gentleman flew from out the barberry hedge, and roared with the most disrespectful wrath, "Ha, you crone, march! I am the Duke of Holstein. But not a word of this!"

Mother Malin was so astonished that she could only turn completely around and smite herself on the knee. Again, when she went back into the house, she smote her knee, and could not comprehend that it was she, precisely, in her little abode, who had come to experience anything so great and extraordinary.

It then happened often in the bright, summer evenings, when the chestnuts stood without showing a breath of wind, that the duke came to the place. The door of the pleasure-house was never opened, no matter how insinuatingly he rapped, but he sat on the window-sill; and Mother Malin, who had meanwhile got a shining ducat in her kirtle-pocket, served there both syrup and wine, and once even a raisin-cake, on which she had written with white of egg: "No prince on earth has nobler worth."

On this particular evening the duke tarried longer than at other times, and within the pleasure-house the piano sounded.

As he finally rose to go, he said: "Power, power? Why to be sure, all cry out for it. Why should you alone be silent? Consider that your father has played away his last sovereign. Adieu, adieu! If you fail with the lion, you bid fair next to hold the door open for the wolf."

The duke stood before the window. It was hushed and still, for down at the inn all had by now gone to bed.

"You do not answer," he continued. "Is it shyness? Then answer with a sign. One stroke on the piano means Yes, but if you trill with your little finger-tips it means No, irrevocably No."

He went lingeringly down the path. The night heavens were bright, the ground without shadow, and he felt about in a gooseberry bush without being able to find any fruit. Then a chord sounded softly from the piano. He pressed his hat down on his head, and drew his cloak about him, and hastened from the garden with cheerful steps.

After that night, Mother Malin went about in vain waiting to open the gate at dusk for the great lord. In ill humor, she began at last to draw from her pocket and count over the ducats, and she cursed herself because she had not at the right time known how to entice to her yet more.

Meanwhile, one evening, a barber's widow had been buried in the churchyard of St. Clare, and after the twelve torch-bearers had gone, two journeymen remained to keep watch. They sat on planks by the grave and spoke ill of the house of mourning.

"They ought to smart for it. The old hag lay covered in a cambric bonnet with crape ribbons, like a noble, and both spice-cakes and preserves stood on the table, but here to us they haven't even sent a stoop of small beer."

"I see across the wall that light is shining through the heart in Mother Malin's shutters. Shouldn't we go there and knock?"

They went out on the street to the yellow wooden house and thumped on the tin.

Mother Malin set one of the shutters ajar.

"You come just in the nick of time, lads," said she, when she recognized them. "No one has treats to offer in these days, but you can earn a pretty penny."

She pushed open the shutter still further and lowered her voice.

"Here you have each of you a whole Charles-piece. Yes, look at it, you noisy lads; it'll stand taking hold of. Within here stands a royal page, who is soon coming down to you. At dawn, as usual, some night-cuckoos from the court are to ride by here. Pretend then to trip up and thrash the young gentleman, and afterwards take to your heels. That's all."

"That seems right enough," said the journeymen, and thumbed the coins. "The hardest thing will be not to lay on in the excitement so that it cuts."

They went back to the churchyard gate and waited, and they heard Mother Malin whispering with the page up in the room.

The time grew long. A star flamed over the dead-house in the summer heat, the fire-watch called on Brunkeberg, and the dawn drew near.

There was a creaking and squeaking on Mother Malin's steps, and the page, walking with knees somewhat turned in and arranging the buttons of his coat, came down to the journeymen.

In the alley off Queen Street was heard roistering and trampling of horses. First rode Klinckowström, who was so drunk that he had to hold himself on by his horse's mane. Behind him could be seen the king, the Duke of Holstein, and some ten other riders. All had blades in their hands, and all but the king were in only their shirts. He was mad with drink, and with his sword knocked in window-panes, lifted off signboards, and cut at wooden doors. There was no one now in the whole world whom he need obey. He could now do anything whatever that occurred to him, and no one would have a single word of reproach. Let them but dare! At supper he had struck the dishes from the pages' hands and thrown fragments of cake on his comrades' clothes, so that they had white marks as from snowballs. The intolerable old was now done with. The old men might yawn and clear their throats by their snuff-jars as they pleased. They had no longer anything to attend to but to be fools. He dedicated his old kingdom of bears to joy and the spirit of youth. The whole of Europe should be amazed. Now he was lord over all the land of Sweden!

Meanwhile the unknown page had laid himself on the ground in the churchyard gate, and the journeymen pinched and beat to their heart's content, and clutched at his throat.

"Who's there?" shouted the king, and set upon the journeymen, who straightway fled between grave-mounds and crosses. He was close at their heels, and stabbed one of them several times in the left arm, so that the blood dripped. At last, in defence, they lifted one of the planks by the half-filled grave of the barber's widow. Then the king laughed and rode back to the wicket gate.

"One of ours?" he inquired of the unknown, who had picked himself up again. "What, are you so tipsy that you don't even know our password: Snuff on all perukes? No matter. Sit up behind our friend Klinckan, and hold him fast on his Wallach. Forward!"

Singing and hallooing, the shirt-clad band dashed on along street and hillside, waving and making long noses at the sleep-dazed folk who came to the gates. When the panes tinkled about Chief Marshall Stenbock, that most worthy old man went himself to the window in his dressing-gown and, bowing, began to lament that, at last, it was necessary for him to flee the realm. But the king tore his wig from him, and cut it in two halves with his sword.

"This is life!" shouted the Duke of Holstein. "Hats in the air! If we could only take along all the royal lady wooers who sit and peep in their bed-chambers. Wigs in the air! Rise in your stirrups and piddle over your horses' heads! Soho, boys! Devil take you. *Vivat Carolus,* king of Sweden and of scandals!"

Shirts were fluttering out; hats, wigs, and gloves lay on the street; hoofs struck sparks, and the horses rushed forward as in a fire.

When the wild riders had come back to the castle, they sprang from their saddles, and let the horses run as best they could. Upon the stairs they broke the lampshades and fired pistol shots at a marble Venus.

"Vorwärts!" shouted the king, as he stormed with all his following into the chapel, and slashed amain at the pews. "They shall get splinters in their breeches here o' Sunday."

The duke pounded on the floor demanding silence, and Klinckowström, who had set to throwing dice in the circle of the altar, held his hand over his mouth so as to keep still.

"Dearly beloved listeners!" began the duke. "Nothing could make this earnest occasion more solemn than if my exalted and charming brother-in-law in this morning hour would give us, his faithful servants, a hint as to the choice of his heart. Let us speak of ladies that woo! Let us think of the baggage from Bavaria who scampered all the way hither with her sweet mother, though there was hardly any lodging for her after the castle was burned. Oohoo! says the owl. Only eight little tulip-red summers older than Your Majesty. Or of the Princess of Wurtemburg, who already showed her amorousness by paying suit to Your Majesty's father of most blessed memory, and who is sickly in the chest. Don't cough during the ceremony! Or of the Princess of Mechlenburg-Grabow, who with her mother is also supposed to be climbing into her travelling-coach. Or of the Prussian princess, who is only two never-so-little sugar-grain years older; or the Danish princess, the tooty-tooty little pink-and-gold bird, who is only five small rose-leaf years older. All of them are bent upon wooing, and sprucing themselves up and beautifying their pictures, because their love afflicts them full sore."

The king became abashed and replied: "Have I not always said that surely no man need think of being married before he is forty?"

As the duke noted his embarrassment he winked at the page from the inn and pounded anew on the floor.

"Very good. His Majesty of Sweden will not parcel out his glory and the love of his subjects in anything else than manly courage and joy. Snuff on all wigs! Were I the monarch of the Swedes, I should therefore frighten the old fellows out of their wits by summoning the prettiest ladies and minxes to my festivities. *Potztausend!* They should sit before us on the saddle and stay with us till the cock crowed the third time. But, as if I would talk any longer! Set your knees to the pew-ends! Hey! Beat and break, snap and crack! Stamp on the floor!—*Herr Gott,* bring water! The king is sick. Water or wine—just wine—wine!"

The king had grown pale, and put his hand to his forehead. It was nothing to him that the others were flaming red and reeled about. At bottom, perhaps, he loved none of them deeply. What did it matter if they called one another drunken? But never should any such thing be said of him, the chosen of God.

"That's enough now, boys!" he said, trying to thrust his sword into the scabbard, whereupon he noticed that he had lost it. Instead, therefore, he very calmly stuck the weapon through the skirt of his coat, and walked with resolute step toward the door.

The duke seized the unknown page by the arm, whispered, and made signs with his hands. The page hurried immediately fter the king, opened the door for him, nd followed him upstairs.

"Never shall I taste wine again!" hought the king. "I could not bear if eople said that I stuttered in my speech nd held pages to my breast. Why should after that be respected more than they? And wine does not taste so much better han small beer. That depends on habit. A really wise man drinks water."

They went together along the stairs and orridors, and came, at length, to his leeping apartment. Here Wallenstedt and couple of other high nobles were aleady waiting. Wallenstedt puffed up his ips.

"Six o'clock in the morning," he began, 'is the usual time for us to consider the ffairs of government."

"If it concerns a criminal matter, yes," answered the king; "otherwise I will receive no counsel, but will regulate and decide as seems to me right."

He did not pick up the poker, as did his father. He was as wakefully solicitous about his dignity as a nobly-born young ady about court propriety. Smiling and bowing, he went straight up to the gentlemen, so that they had to leave the room backwards.

"That is our return for setting a boy on the throne," they dinned maliciously into the ears of Wallenstedt.

The page, however, had already locked the door behind them with a subdued bang. That pleased the king. He stood leaning against the end of the high bed beside the casket in which his father had gathered together jewels and valuables of all sorts, and which had now been fetched up from the treasure-vault known as the Elephant.

"What is your name?" he asked the page. "Why don't you answer?"

The page breathed hard, fumbling and plucking at his clothes.

"Well, but answer me, boy! You know your own name, I suppose. You stand almost with your back to me so that I cannot see you."

The page now stepped forward into the middle of the room, lifted the peruke from his head, tossed it on the night-table, and answered: "My name is Rhoda—Rhoda d'Elleville."

The king saw that it was a very young girl with dark-pencilled eyebrows. Her yellow hair was crisply curled with a curling-iron, and a lightly shadowed line trembled around her mouth.

She sprang forward, threw her arms about his neck, and impetuously kissed him on the left cheek.

For the first time the youth of sixteen lost his self-command. Flames rose before his eyes, his cheek became grayish-white, and his hands hung impotent. He only saw that the page's coat was unbuttoned over the breast, so that lace was hanging from it. She continued to hold him fast in her arms, and pressed a long kiss upon his mouth.

He neither responded to it nor made resistance. He only raised his hands little by little and lifted her arms back over his head like a ring. Then, stammering, and bowing deeply and ceremoniously, he moved aside.

"Pardon, mademoiselle!" He scraped with his foot, clicked his heels, and, bowing again with each step, moved still further away. "Pardon, mademoiselle, pardon!"

How thoroughly had she not studied beforehand every word she meant to say! But now she remembered nothing. She spoke at random and without herself any longer knowing what she said.

"Mercy, sire! The good God may be excused if He punishes such presumption as mine."

She bent her knee to the carpet.

"I have seen you on horseback, sire; I have seen you from my window. In imagination I have seen you, before I made the long journey up here, have seen my hero, my Alexander."

At once he went forward to her, took her under the elbows, and conducted her in precocious cavalier fashion to a chair.

"Not so, not so. Sit, sit!"

She kept hold of his hand, and wrinkled her brow a little, as she looked him brightly in the eyes—and then she burst into a ringing laugh of relief.

"Ah, well, you are human after all, sire. Not a trace of the preacher. You are the first Swede I have met who understands that the eyes of virtue look inward and do not evilly squint at others. Your favorites drink and throw dice and pay attentions to women without your saying anything about it. You barely notice it. Let us speak of virtue, sire."

Perfume, the scent of her hair, of a woman, tortured him so violently that he was near to vomiting. The contact, the feel of her warm hand, nauseated him like touching a rat or a corpse. He believed himself offended and defiled both as the king, specially chosen of God, and as a man in that a stranger had touched his clothes and face and hands. Another, and that a woman, had taken hold of him as of a prey, a conquered captive. The person who had touched him straightway became an enemy, with whom he wished to fight, whom he wished to strike down in punishment of lese-majesty.

"When I was yet but a child," she continued, "my confessor fell in love with me. He wrung his hands and strove with himself and babbled prayers, and I played with the madman and made a fool of him. Sire, how different you are from him! You never strive with yourself. You are wholly and completely indifferent, sire. That is all. Virtue with you is so innate that"—she laughed playfully—"I do not know if I can even call it virtue."

He tried to twist his hand free, and exerted his strength more and more. How had not the duke, the pages, and the warders dinned in his ears about lady wooers and pretty mamselles in the last weeks! Was this, too, a game behind his back? Should he, then, have no peace?

"Pardon, mademoiselle!"

"I know, sire, that for whole hours you can sit and turn over Tessin's etchings and that you look especially at pictures with tall young ladies. That is perhaps only the esteem for art which you have inherited from your noble lady grandmother; but will it always remain so? I am no dead representation, sire."

Though bowing constantly, he now tore himself free with such vehemenec that at the same time he jerked Rhoda d'Elleville up from the chair.

"No, you are a live page, mademoiselle and the *page* I order to go down into the chapel and send the comrades to the east anteroom."

She saw at once that the game was hopelessly lost, and the shadowed expression around her mouth became deeper and more weary.

"The page must obey," answered she.

When the king was left alone, he became again tranquil as before. Only at times there passed over his thoughts a flash of indignation. The unexpected adventure had chased the wine fumes from his head, and he wished not to go to rest like a weakling after the pranks of the night, but to continue them hour after hour.

He threw off his coat. In his shirtsleeves, with sword in hand, he went out to his comrades in the east anteroom.

This room was sprinkled with dried stains of blood. The boards of the floor had been drenched and embrowned with pools of blood, and by the portraits on the wall, whose eyes were poked out, hung lumps of hair and of long-congealed blood.

In the room outside a lowing was heard. A calf was led in and brought forward to the middle of the floor.

The king bit his under lip so that it grew white, and with a single whistling blow struck off the calf's head. With blood oozing under his nails, he then threw the head through the broken window down on the passers-by.

Outside the door, meanwhile, the duke whispered hurriedly with Rhoda d'Elleville.

"So no one is likely to get my exalted brother-in-law out of his stiff-neckedness. Old Hjärne of the funny face talks of cooking a love potion, but that's likely to be of little avail. Had he not inherited his father's coldness, he would with his bravado have become a Swedish Borgia. If he can't soon get to be a demi-god, he'll become a devil. When such a bird doesn't find flapping-room for its wings, it breaks apart the walls of its own nest. Hist! Some one's coming. Don't forget! This evening at nine at Mother Malin's. Have on hand some figs and raisins!"

Behind them on the stairs came faithful old Hakon, leading two goats. He stood still, threw his hands aloft, and sighed anxiously:

"What have they made of my young lord? Never has such a thing been seen in the home of Sweden's kings. Almighty God, have pity and give us yet greater misfortune than before, because the quiet that has now come upon us can be borne neither by the Swedes nor by such a prince!"

Midsummer Sport

Two little girls stood in a pasture with a sieve, and near by, on a mossy stone, lazy and half-asleep, sat their brother, Axel Frederick, who to-day completed his twentieth year. His intended, the frightened little Ulrica, who had come to the place on a visit, bent down juniper twigs over the sieve and cut at them with her sickle. The little girls spread their hands to hold the twigs and help all they could, and melting snow dripped from the birches and alders.

"Oh, oh, even grandfather has come out in this heavenly weather," said Ulrica, pointing down at the great house.

The little girls then began to shout and hop. They took the sieve between them and went off to the great house, while they swung the sieve in time and warbled:

The birds of springtime, they sing so well.
Come little goat-girls, come!
To-night we'll have music and dance in the dell.

On the other side of the fence, where the neighbor's land began, Elias, the farm-servant, brought down the last load of wood from the forest. The water dripped from his wooden shoes, and the two red oxen, Silverhorn and Yeoman, had sprigs of rowan in their yoke as a protection against witchcraft. Elias, too, began to join in:

The birds of springtime they sing so light.
Come, my goat, oh, come!
The flowers will push through the turf to-night.

But with that he broke off and, bending over the fence, said to Axel Frederick, "Powder smells ill when people shoot, and soot falls from the chimneys, so surely the thaw will last."

The entry of the great house was covered with a snowy thatch of turf, where in summer a goat was wont to browse among the house-leeks and limewort. Below on the bench sat grandfather in his gray frock coat with pewter buttons, and Ulrica led forward the little girls so that they might greet him. They were clad in basted-up smocks, which were home-dyed with whortleberry juice, and every time the little girls curtsied, they made lilac circles on the wet steps of the stairs.

Grandfather patted Ulrica on the cheek with the back of his hand.

"You will grow up in time no doubt, little one, and become a help to Axel Frederick."

"If I were only quite certain of it, grandfather. It is so big here, and there is so much to manage that I am not accustomed to."

"Ah, yes. And pity it is for Axel Frederick that he lost both father and mother so early, and had no one but his aunts and his old grandfather. But still we have looked after him in every way, and you, little one, must of course learn to take our place. The hardest thing is his frail health, the fine boy.—Ah, dear children, God be thanked for this day of spring and for blessed years of peace!"

Grandfather felt of the cut juniper and praised it because it was moist, so that it would take up a great deal of dust.

Behind him in the kitchen window stood the two aunts, cooking a mash of castoreum and laurel berries for a sick heifer. Both of them had plain black clothes and ice-gray hair combed back.

"Why isn't Axel Frederick with you?" they asked of Ulrica. "Remember that for supper he is to have his favorite dish, honey-pudding dipped in syrup, and there is to be pork with shallot."

"Yes, yes," said grandfather; "and then let the servants have a rest for to-night."

Ulrica hastened into the maids' room, where the servants were picking tow, but she had not taken many steps before her timid and undeveloped little face again took on an anxious and listening expression.

"But, Ulrica!" called grandfather. "I don't understand this, Ulrica! Come here, Ulrica!"

She hung the bunch of keys she had just taken up behind the door-post in the entry, and went out.

"Isn't that a rider coming off there?" asked grandfather. "Three months now I've been spared from letters. I grow so full of dread when I get a letter. Look at him, look at him! He digs his paw into his bag."

The rider came to a standstill a moment by the steps, and delivered a sealed and folded paper.

The aunts elbowed their way forward on both sides of grandfather, and reached him his spectacles, but his hands trembled so that he could hardly break the seal. They all wanted to read the writing at the same time, and Ulrica forgot herself so far that she leaned over grandfather's arm, pointed along the lines, and spelled aloud before the others.

At last she struck her hands together and stared in front of her, while tears mounted to her eyes.

"Axel Frederick, Axel Frederick!" she cried, and ran over the sanded court to the pasture. "For heaven's sake!"

"What the mischief is the matter with you now?" answered Axel Frederick, throwing away the withered fern which he was chewing. He had a full, pink face and an agreeable, careless voice.

She did not come to a halt before she had taken his hand.

"Axel Frederick, you don't know. There's an order that the regiment shall hold itself in readiness to gather under the flag. It's on account of the Danes' invasion into Holstein."

He followed her back to the great house, and she squeezed and squeezed his wrist.

"Dear children," stammered grandfather, "that I must needs live to see such a visitation! We have war upon us."

Axel Frederick stood and pondered.

Finally he looked up and answered, "I won't go."

Grandfather tramped around on the

steps, and about him the aunts went back and forth.

"You are already enrolled, dear child. The only thing would be if we could perhaps hire some one else."

"One can surely do that," replied Axel Frederick indifferently.

He went into the house, and Ulrica sprang up the stairs with her apron before her eyes, and threw herself on her bed.

In the evening, when the honey-pudding was eaten, and they all sat around the table, grandfather wanted, as usual, to work on a hundred-mesh net, but he trembled too much.

"It has gone ill up there in Stockholm," said he. "Ballets, masquerades, streets covered with carpets, comedians and conjurers of all sorts—that has been the daily food with our new 'King Christina.' I've heard all about it. When the money ran out, he began to give away the crown jewels. Now our gracious lord must spell out another lesson."

Axel Frederick moved back his candlestick, and sat leaning indolently forward with his elbows on the table, while the aunts and Ulrica, her eyes red with weeping, cleared the table. Grandfather nodded and coughed and went on with his talk.

"In all these years of peace there has been nothing but greed and extortion, and the very worst fellows have pushed themselves nearest to the throne. Now these fatted oxen are behaving ill, I fancy. Ha-ha! You should but have seen the old times when grandfather was young, and was called to the nobles' banner. The king's standard that was kept in the royal wardrobe was unfurled, and the horse with the kettledrum was equipped in its long saddle-cloth with crowns in the corner, and then we assembled in our tight, braided coats, while the trumpets began to play."

Grandfather took the yarn and tried to tie it, but threw it aside again and rose.

"You should only have seen, Axel Frederick. Even in the moonlight, as we stood drawn up on the icy ground and sang psalms before the advance, I recognized the Närkingers' red uniforms with white facings, which were like striped tulips; and the yellow Kronobergers, and the gray boys from Kalmar, and the gay blue Dalecarlian regiment, and the West Gotlanders, who were yellow and black. That was a feast to behold, but quiet as in the Lord's house. Well, there have come other men and other coats. Everything now is to be severe and simple."

There was silence in the room awhile.

After that Axel Frederick said, as if to himself, "If my togs and gear were in good order, there might be merry times in a camp."

Grandfather shook his head.

"You are frail in health, Axel Frederick, and it will be hard to march down through the whole kingdom to Denmark."

"Yes, march I won't, but I might, though, have Elias with me and the brown long-wagon."

"That you may of course have any time, but you have no cloth tent with stakes and ridge-tree and pegs and whatever else there ought to be now."

"Elias could very well purchase that for me on the way. As to uniform, I'm passably well off."

"Let's see now, let's see now." Grandfather became eager and toddled off over the floor to open the wardrobe. "Ulrica, come here, Ulrica, and read how it stands there in His Royal Majesty's" (he bowed) "edict which lies on the table! Here we have the cloak with brass buttons, lined with smooth Swedish baize. That is right. And the vest is here, too. Read now about the coat!"

Ulrica trimmed the tallow candle, and sat down at the table with hands over her brow, while she read monotonously, spelling out the words, in a loud voice: "Coat of blue unstretched cloth, red collar, lined with madder-red baize, twelve brass buttons in front, four above and three below the pocket-flap, and one button on each side, three small on each sleeve."

"Eight—twelve—that's right. Now we come to the breeches."

"Breeches of good buckskin or deerskin with three buttons covered with chamois."

"They are fearfully chafed. There will soon be eyes in the seat. However, Elias could very well see to getting you a new pair on the way. But the hat and gloves. Where are the hat and gloves?"

"They're lying in the chest in the entry," said Axel Frederick.

Ulrica read: "Gloves with large gauntlets of yellow shamozed ox-leather, stiffened and reinforced, with the grip of buck- or goat-skin. Shoes of good Swedish wax-leather with straps cut in one piece. Bottom of an insole and a middlesole. Shoe-buckles of brass."

"The shoes and wax-leather boots are here, and are fairly good. You can have my spurs. You shall be a fine-looking Swedish soldier, my dear boy."

"Neckcloth: one of black Swedish wool-crepon two-and-a-half feet long and a full nine inches wide with a leather cord half a yard long at each end, and two of white."

"That Elias must get for you at Örebro."

"Pistols: two pairs. Holsters of black leather with tops of gathered broadcloth."

"You must take mine. And my broadsword is in excellent condition with calfskin sheath and sword-band of elk-leather. That's how a Swedish warrior ought to look. We must now think, too, of equipping Elias and putting in haversacks and all."

Axel Frederick stretched his arms.

"It's surely the best thing for me to go up and lie down and take a good rest beforehand."

There was now noise and commotion in the great house. There was nailing and battering every day, there was flaming and sputtering in the fireplace, and by night the candle was burning. The one room that stayed dark was Axel Frederick's.

On the last night no one but Axel Frederick went to rest, and when the dawn had come on so far that all lights could be put out, the aunts waked him and gave him something warm to drink in bed with drops of *aqua fortis,* for they had heard that he coughed in the night.

When he came down into the hall, the others were gathered there already, even the maids and the men-servants, and the table was spread for all in common. They ate without saying a single word, but when the meal was over, and they arose, the Bible was brought to grandfather, and Ulrica read with choked voice. When she had ceased, grandfather clasped his hands and spoke with eyes closed:

"Like as my forefathers have done, even so will I now in the hour of departure lay my hands upon you, my daughter's son, and bless you, for many are my years, and who knows when the hourglass has run out? God, the Most High, I invoke from my lowly dwelling, that He may lead you to honor, and that the heavy trials which await us may only exalt our little nation to be greater and more glorious."

Axel Frederick stood at the corner of the table, fingering and balancing the plate, until from outside was heard a clatter, as the brown long-wagon was driven up.

All now went out, and Axel Frederick sat up beside Elias, wrapped in grandfather's wolf-skin coat and much heated, for in the spring weather the water was dripping from roof and tree.

"Here is the butter firkin," said the aunts, "and here the bread sack. Hearken now, Elias! In the seat-box are the curdcake and the flask with the *aqua fortis.* If the strain and peril are too hard, dear Axel Frederick, never forget that the way home is short."

But grandfather pressed in among them and stuck his hands down in the back of the wagon.

"Is the chest tied on right? And let's see now! Here is the sprinkling-brush and the whisk-cloth and the scraper—and here we have the fodder-bag and the water-bottle. That's as it ought to be. The lead-mould, bullet-cutter, and casting ladle are in the chest."

Ulrica stood behind them without any one noticing her.

She said very softly, "Axel Frederick, when it is summer, I shall go out some evening and bind joy-threads and sorrow-threads on the rye, to see which has grown highest the next morning—"

"Now it's all ready," broke in grandfather, who had not heard her; "and God be with both you and Elias!"

Round about on the side of the road stood the farm-folk and the day-laborers.

But just as Elias raised his whip, Axel Frederick laid his hand over the reins.

"This journey may turn out ill," said he.

"Still it would look badly," answered Elias, "to unharness and unsaddle now."

Axel Frederick stuck his hand back into the sleeve of his coat, and between the lines of silent people the wagon rolled away.

The weeks passed, and the trees blossomed. It was a slow march with the Närke regiment through the wilds of Sweden, and Axel Frederick sat in his coat and slept beside Elias, warm on the brow and with his gloves of goat's-hair very moist. A little way from Landskrona, the brown long-wagon had fallen behind the regimental baggage, and the horse stood in the blaze of the sun, and browsed beside the ditch. Both master and man fell asleep, shoulder to shoulder.

The horse whisked at a gad-fly, the water purled in the ditch, and a couple of vagrants threw their bad language at the sleepers; but they continued to sit in the same untroubled repose.

Then there came behind them at a gallop a shabbily dressed rider with a large flaxen peruke, who pulled up his horse beside the wagon.

Elias nudged Axel Frederick, and picked up the reins, but Axel Frederick, unwilling to open his eyes, only said: "Yes, drive on, Elias! I need to get a good rest before my hardships."

Elias gave him another nudge in the side.

"Rouse yourself, rouse yourself!" he whispered.

Drowsily Axel Frederick opened one eye—but in that instant he grew blood-red over all his face, he rose, and saluted from the middle of the wagon.

He recognized at once from pictures that it was the eighteen-year-old king himself. Yet what a transformation! Was this majestic and commanding youth, who had grown up so quickly, the same that a few months before beheaded calves and broke windows? He was not above middle height, and his face was small; but the brow was high and noble, and from the large deep-blue eyes beamed an enchanting radiance.

"The gentleman should throw off his coat, so that I can inspect his uniform," he said deliberately. "The earth is green long since."

Axel Frederick panted and struggled to get off his grandfather's accursed pelisse, and the king surveyed coat and buttons, fingered them, pulled at them, and counted.

"That is fair," said he with a precociously earnest expression; "and now we shall all become entirely new men."

Axel Frederick stood dazed and erect, looking fixedly at the wagon wheel.

Then the king added slowly, "In a few days we may perhaps have the fortune to stand before the enemy. I have been told that in battle nothing is as hard as thirst. If the gentlemen should some time meet me in the tumult of the strife, let him step forward and lend me his drinking-flask."

The king once more gave his horse the spurs, and Axel Frederick sat down. He had never loved or hated, never been worried or carried away with enthusiasm, and he pondered the king's words.

The pelisse came to lie between him and Elias. When at dusk the wagon clattered into Landskrona, the regiment had already pitched their tents. Axel Frederick looked about for the covered drinking-table of which he had dreamed. Instead he found only taciturn comrades, who pressed one another's hands, and looked away in crowds across the Straits of Oresund, where the waves were rushing under the cloudy summer heavens, and where flags and pennons fluttered over the forest of masts of the Swedish fleet.

Next morning Elias put the horse and wagon into a barn, because the Crown had taken over all vessels, and only on the day after the fleet had sailed could he follow on a fishing-boat to Zeeland. He remained standing on the shore, almost out in the water, when the monstrous anchors, dripping with mud, were hoisted up by the creaking cables. On mast after mast rose the swelling sails, and the sunlight glittered on the lanterns and glass windows of the poops. The billows danced and shot by, mirroring in flaming coils the lofty, swaying forms of the galleons, which with their laurel garlands and tridents pointed out across the sea to the unexplored land of wonder, toward adventure and achievement. The masses of cloud, after resting long on the waves, had sunk into the sea, and the atmosphere was blue as in a saga.

Then the king forgot himself; the boy in his soul conquered so that he began to clap his hands. He stood in the poop just in front of the lantern, and around him the gray-haired warriors of his father's time smiled, and also began to clap. Even His Excellency Piper sprang up the ladder as nimbly as a ship's-boy. There were no longer any old and decrepit men or greedy bickerers; it was an army of youths.

As if at a mysterious sign, music and drums began to sound at the same moment, swords flew from their sheaths, and, rising above Admiral Anckarstierna's words through the speaking-trumpet, a hymn was sung from the nineteen warships and the hundred smaller vessels.

Elias recognized Axel Frederick, who sat on grandfather's pelisse, hemmed in by the cargo of gabions, sacks for earth, and trench entanglements. But when Elias saw that he, too, slowly rose and drew his blade like the others, and saw how the fleet gradually vanished on the water, he passed his hand over his eyes, shaking his head.

He returned toward the barn, muttering, "How will he look after himself with his fragile health till I can catch up?"

A few days afterward Elias came alone with his long-wagon on the Småland roads. Peasant women, who recognized him from the time he had driven past with the sleeping officer, set their entry doors ajar, and asked if it was true that the Swedes had landed at Zeeland, and that the king had thanked God on his knees for the victory, but had stammered from embarrassment.

He nodded assentingly without replying.

Day after day he drove northward, step by step, walking with the reins the whole way beside the wagon, which was covered with a piece of an old sail.

When at last, one evening, he came to the hedge in front of the great house, all immediately recognized by the noise that it was the brown long-wagon, and the horse neighed. Amazed, they went to the window, grandfather himself came out on the steps, and Ulrica stood in the middle of the courtyard.

Elias walked as slowly as ever with the reins in his hands, and at the steps the horse stood still of itself.

Then Elias carefully drew the sail from the wagon, and there stood a long, narrow, nailed-up coffin, with a yellowed wreath of beech-leaves on the lid.

"I brought him home with me," said Elias. "He received a shot in the breast as he sprang forward and handed His Royal Majesty his drinking-flask."

Gunnel the Stewardess

In a vault of the fortress at Riga, Gunnel the stewardess, an old woman of eighty, sat and spun. Her long arms were veinous and sinewy, her breast was lean and flat like an old man's. Some thin white wisps of hair hung down over her eyes, and she had a cloth knotted about her head like a round cap.

The spinning-wheel whirred, and a trumpeter lad lay on the stone floor in front of the fire.

"Grandma," said he, "can't you sing something while you are spinning? I've never heard you do otherwise than nag and scold."

For a brief moment she turned towards him her tired and wickedly chilling eyes.

"Sing? Perhaps of your mother, who was set on a wagon and carried to the Muscovites? Perhaps of your father, whom they hanged at the chimney of the house on the bridge? Curse will I the night when I was born, and myself will I curse and every human being I have met. Name me a single one who is not even worse than his repute."

"If you sing a song, you'll be cheerful, grandma, and I should be so glad to have you cheerful, this evening."

"He whom you see playing or laughing is only a master of deception. Misery and shame is all, and it is for the sake of our sins and our baseness that now the Saxons have come and besieged our city. Why don't you go in the evening and do your duty on the wall as at otherwhiles, instead of lying here in your laziness?"

"Grandma, can't you say a single pleasant word to me as I go?"

"Thrash you I should, if I were not so infirm and bent with my years that I no more can lift my countenance to heaven. Do you not want me to tell your fortune? Do they not call me the Sibyl? Shall I tell you that the crooked line over your eyebrows signifies an early death? I see years ahead into the future, but as far as I see I find only evil and low purposes. You are worse than I, and I am worse than my mother, and all that which is born is worse than that which dies."

He arose from the floor and stirred the logs.

"I will tell you, grandma, wherefore I sat myself by you this evening, and wherefore I asked of you a kindly word. The old governor-general has ordered to-day that before the following night all women, young and aged, sound and sick, shall go their way, so as not to consume the bread of the men. Those who refuse shall be punished with death. How can you, who in ten years have never gone further than across the castle courtyard to the storehouse, now be able to range about in wood and waste in the midst of the winter cold?"

She laughed and trod the spinning-wheel faster and faster.

"Haha! I have been waiting for this after I tended so faithfully the noble lord's storeroom and all that was his. And you, Jan? Aren't you worried at having no one any longer to bake for you at the oven and make your bed on the folding-bench? What other feeling is there in children? Praised be GOD, be GOD, Who at the end casts us all under the scourge of His wrath!"

Jan clasped his hands about his curly brown hair.

"Grandma, grandma!"

"Go, I tell you, and let me sit in peace and spin my tow, till I open the door myself and go out of it to be quit of this earthly life!"

He took a few steps forward toward the spinning-wheel, but thereupon turned about and went out of the vault.

The spinning-wheel whirred and whirred, until the fire burned out. Next morning, when Jan the trumpeter came back, the vault stood empty.

The siege was long and severe. After divine service had been held, all the women went out of the city in the snowy days of February, and the feeble or sick were set upon litters and wagons. All Riga became a cloister for men, who had nothing to give to the flocks of begging women that now and then stole out in front of the wall. The men had scarcely bread for their own necessities, and the starved horses tore each other to pieces in the stalls, or devoured the mangers, and gnawed great holes in the wooden walls. Smoke hung over the burned suburbs, and at night the soldiers were often wakened by warning tocsins, and took down their broadswords from the ceiling.

In the evenings, however, when Jan the trumpeter came home to the vault which he and his grandmother had had as a living-room, he almost always found the folding-bench made up as a bed, and a bowl with mouldy meat beside it on a chair. He was ashamed of saying anything about it to the others, but he was really terrified. He believed that his grandmother had perished in the snowdrifts, and that now, remorseful over her former hardness, she went about again without rest. In his fright he shook as with ague, and many a night he preferred to sleep hungry in the snow on the wall. After he had strengthened himself with prayer, however, he became easier, and finally he felt himself more surprised and anxious when he now and then found the folding-bench untouched and the chair empty. Then he would seat himself at the spinning-wheel and, treading it very softly, would listen to the familiar whirring which he had heard day after day since his birth.

Now it happened one morning that the governor-general, the celebrated Erik Dahlberg, a man of seventy-five, heard violent shooting. He rose with impatient anger from his sketches and fortification models of wax. As a reminder of his bright youthful excursions in the service of beauty, splendid etchings of Roman ruins hung on the wall, but his formerly mild countenance had become wrinkled with melancholy, and an expression of harshness stiffened around the narrow, compressed, almost white lips. He adjusted his great spliced wig, and tremblingly ran his nails over his thin moustache. When he went down the stairs, he struck heavily on the stones with his cane, and said:

"Ah, we Swedes, we blood-kindred to the Vasa kings, who in their old age could only find fault and quarrel and at the last sat in their own rooms afraid of the dark, —we have in our soul a black seed, from which with the years is raised a branching tree filled with the bitterest gall-apples."

He became bitterer and harsher in spirit the farther he went, and when he finally stood at the wall, he spoke to no one.

Several battalions had been drawn up with flags and music, but afterwards the shooting had quieted, and through the gate returned scattered bands of weary and bleeding men who had just repulsed the enemy's attack. Last of them all, came a thin and feeble old man, who had himself a red sabre wound on the breast, but who painfully carried in his arms in front of him a wounded boy.

Erik Dahlberg raised his hand over his brows to look. Was not the fallen boy Jan the trumpeter, the lad from the castle? He recognized him by his curly brown hair.

At the arch of the gate the exhausted bearer sank down against the stone pillar, and remained there sitting with his wound and with the dead boy on his knee. Some soldiers, bending down to examine the wound, slit up the bloody shirt above the breast.

"What!" they shouted, and stepped back. "It's a woman!"

Wondering, they bent down still lower to look at her face. She had sunk her head sidewise against the wall, and the fur cap slid down, so that the white locks of her hair fell forward.

"It's Gunnel the stewardess, the Sibyl!"

She breathed heavily and opened her dulling eyes.

"I didn't want to leave the boy alone in this world of evil, but after I had put on men's clothes and served night and day among the others on the wall, I thought that I was eating a man's bread without wrong."

Soldiers and officers looked dubiously at Erik Dahlberg, whose commands she had transgressed. He continued to stand there, reserved and harshly gloomy, while the stick in his hand trembled and tapped on the stone paving.

Slowly he turned to the battalion and the thin lips moved.

"Lower your colors!" he said.

French Mons

A hide-covered field wagon had stuck in one of the swamps of Poland, and the horse had already been unhitched. On the wagon stood a young man who had just come to the army to work his way up. His comrades called him French Mons, because as tutor he had followed some distinguished lords to France, and had there filled his chest with all sorts of odd things. Captain Olof Oxehufvud and several subalterns and soldiers waited alongside in the mud, and the snowstorm struck them in the face.

"The wagon and chest must be left behind," said Oxehufvud.

French Mons opened the chest, and pulled out as much as he could carry.

"What a pied dressing-gown with all that needlework and tassels!" exclaimed Oxehufvud and the subalterns. "What miserable little slippers! And false calves! And a bonnet!"

"That's a *cadeau* from ma—"

"Kick it into the slush!"

"—From mama."

"Look at the little peruke!"

"And the medium peruke!"

"And the great spliced peruke!"

Oxehufvud could now control himself no longer, but took him by the leg.

"Kick the damned stuff into the slush, I say!"

The delicate blonde countenance of French Mons flamed up, and he struck his hand on his sword.

"Master Captain, such an import—"

"Such an important person as you can freely hold up the march, you think?"

"No. Such a victorious army, I would say, surely need not go in shabby clothes, with dressing-gowns from the time of King Orre."

"Stuff and nonsense! Little schoolmaster! Consummate ass!"

"The captain treats me like a menial, yet I have had education, have travelled in France, yes, have stood eye to eye with Vauban himself."

"Well, what did Vauban say?"

"What did he say?"

"Just so."

" 'Get out!' he said, for it was at his own gate, and I was in his way."

"Lord! Lord! Get down from the wagon and be quick about it! Come here, two of you fellows, and take this beggar in lady's chair style!"

French Mons rolled up the slippers and wigs in the dotted dressing-gown and took it on his back, while he held a lorgnette before his eyes.

When he had been carried to the bank, Oxehufvud stood in front of him, tall and slim, with brilliant red cheeks and small dark moustaches.

"Hark now, monsieur, what do you want in the field? Do you want to work up?"

"Though not of noble rank, I aspire to it. Who knows if perhaps even I may not sit some time with a certificate of nobility in my pocket?"

"You may ennoble yourself in fools' hell! In this army no one says a word about nobility, but every one must work his way up the best he may."

Oxehufvud had now abused him so long as leader that his comradely heart began to thaw, and he added grumblingly in a somewhat milder tone, "Behave yourself gallantly, and you may get your officer's commission to start with! We have already broken so many Swedish dandies of your sort and made men of them. There by that little wood you see a large house with a white stairway. Since we are in all no more than five-and-twenty men, I can't afford to leave you a single soldier. Reconnoitre and spy diligently on the enemy, so that no one falls on us from the rear!"

Oxehufvud marched off with his little band, and French Mons went up to the house with his bundle on his back.

No human being was visible, and he stationed himself irresolutely in the lee of the wall. He was cold and wet through, but above all he was troubled by the dirt and mud on his boots. Would he not be able to keep equally good watch from one of the windows? A well-made bed with a silken coverlet and a foot-muff was exactly what he longed for.

Transversely under the house went a dark carriage-door, and thither with great caution he slunk along the wall. When he had dried his moist lorgnette, he leaned forward and looked in with stealthy alertness.

There was a stamping and clattering, and he distinguished two gleaming eyes. With throbbing heart he took a step back and drew his sword. A black horse rushed out and ran back and forth in the courtyard, while it threw the snow high in the air with its hind feet.

"I won't catch that black fellow," thought French Mons. "If a soldier sits on such a wild horse, the dead owner will rise from the swamp, jump up behind, and pull him from the saddle. They tell of such things in the evening by the campfire."

He threatened the horse with his sword, and went in, pushing the door open on the other side so that the light would be better. He saw now that the door to the house was walled up.

Snorting and stamping, the horse came back, but French Mons chased him out again. Then he went out and called up to the window. A gray-haired serving-woman stuck out her head.

"Does a friend of King Stanislaus or of the Saxon drunkard dwell here?" he asked.

"Here dwells an old recluse, who is no one's enemy and no one's friend."

"Good. Then he cannot deny shelter to a frozen Swedish soldier."

The serving-woman vanished and finally returned after a time with a ladder, on which he climbed in.

The room was large, and the ugly but clean wooden chairs stood in a stiff row along the bare walls. When he chanced to push back one of the chairs with his scabbard, the serving-woman hastened at once to move it back to its proper place. Two girls dressed in blue, with pale faces and curled hair, came and went without saying a word. As soon as one got a few steps behind, she ran anxiously forward to the other's side. They rubbed against each other and groped with their long fingers, and though it was still bright daylight, they carried two lighted lamps.

When the serving-woman had rubbed the mud from his boots and sufficiently dried the wet places that the soles had made on the floor, she quietly and carefully opened the door to the next room.

"Don't walk too roughly!" she whispered.

There stood a man of middle age in a dressing-gown and with the most impudent and pointed nose, but no one had ever worn a more elegantly curled peruke, and on his white fingers gleamed rings with jewels.

French Mons set down his bundle, and eyed him with his lorgnette. Much pleased with his venerable exterior, he thereupon made a wide gesture with his arms, and bowed to the floor.

"My intentions are courteous," he said, "and humbly I beg the favor of knowing with what nobleman I have the good fortune to speak."

"Sit down, my good sir. I am nothing but a forgotten old recluse, but since you are a man of quality, I shall at once explain various things that may seem remarkable."

The two gentlemen sat down stiff and straight with hands on their knees.

"Formerly I was a merry companion, and my coat of brocade was the talk of all Warsaw, but on my thirtieth birthday, when I sat drinking with my comrades, I lifted my glass and spoke somewhat in this fashion: My friends, with every year your eyes become harder and your hearts more shrunken. One believes in King Stanislaus of the white cheeks, and the other in King August with the big belly. Afterwards you forge your plots accordingly, and seek for appointments and rewards. I will not go to the grave with the horrible recollection that each of my brothers was at the last a Cain. I set friendship much higher than love, because it is a bond exclusively between souls, and therefore to-day I say unto you farewell, while we are all still young. Of me you shall never hear anything further, but such as I now see you, you shall still go about me in my room before my eyes and keep me company, when I sit alone and old. When the serving-woman outside the door hears that I prattle half aloud, she will say: 'Now the old man is talking with the friends of his youth.' "

"And after you had so bade them farewell?"

"Then I went home and had the door walled up. My servants have to get themselves out and in as best they may."

"With a host of such delicate sensibilities a guest will surely get on well."

"Get on well? What are you thinking of? My twin daughters who walk about the room here with their lamps are insane. Their mother was an abducted nun. No, a guest would not get on in the least."

"You mean, perhaps, that my coming disturbs."

"Ah well, I won't exactly say that. But there are ghosts here."

His nostrils rose at the corners, and he got up and rubbed his hands in satisfaction.

"I consider it my duty as host to tell the truth as well first as last. There is a dead lackey who goes about again, and whose name is Jonathan. He stands in window-recesses and behind doors in brown livery with black braid. His servant zeal so sticks to the poor fellow even after death that he watches over and serves guests when they least expect it. Fortunately guests are rare here. Tell me, are you a count?"

"I? No."

"Are you a baron?"

"No, I'm not a baron yet."

"Are you not at least a plain nobleman?"

"Is it my lord's intention to insult?"

French Mons flushed with embarrassment. "The certificate has been my dearest dream," he thought, "and would to God I carried it already in my coat pocket. Then no one any longer should cry, 'Little schoolmaster!' Then it should be: 'I saw the marks of nobility on that man long before he got his certificate.' "

"How can such a simple question wound you?" exclaimed the recluse, with yet more enjoyment.

"Of course I am noble. My family is extremely old."

"That would be another thing. That's very good. Though Jonathan had a Christian burial and all that, he is such an out-and-out aristocratic lackey that he starts all sorts of malicious tricks as soon as he has before him a parvenu or a plebeian."

French Mons stroked his small moustache with the nail of his little finger and swung his lorgnette uncomfortably.

"Is my lord a connoisseur of Syracusan wine?" he asked.

"No."

"I too think much more of a glass of Frontignac. My favorite dish is ragout with mushrooms, though I shall never speak ill of a *haché* of lamb with thyme. Much in this part of the world depends on the sauce. Oh, I do not long to be back home with oatmeal and pitchy darkness."

"Pitch darkness? Are you thinking of the summer nights?"

"They are bright."

"And winter evenings are bright, too, for then you have snow. If you are afraid of pitch darkness, never travel southward again! Have you in your land any great artists and scholars?"

"We have not and never shall have."

"You do not over-value your countrymen."

"I have seen a little of the great world, my lord. I have travelled in France a good two months, my lord. I have even been a whole evening with *roi Soleil.*"

"You? Have you been with Louis XIV?"

"That I have—at the theatre—though I only got a wretched standing-place in the parterre. Since Augustus there has not lived so majestic a sovereign. Only look at his style of bowing!"

"The king of Sweden is a man, too."

"That he is, for he makes us noticed in foreign countries, but how poor for all that!"

"Mightily poor in Warsaw lately. When Stanislaus stepped into the church for coronation with his spouse, who is always frightened and tremulous, he not only got as a present from the Swedes the newly wrought crown, sceptre, apple, sword, ermine, belt, and shoes, but also a banner, tapestries on the church walls, the plates on the table, coronation money to be scattered about, and soldiers who kept guard and fired the jubilation salute—and at the last he thanked His Excellency Piper and kissed his hand.—Are you poor yourself?"

"Poor? I?"

French Mons thought of the two wretched Charles-pieces that were sewed under the lining of his coat, and were all he possessed, but he rapped his lorgnette on the table and hastened to say: "My expenses are enormous—and play amuses me—I never go without ten louis d'or in my purse."

"Will you lend me five louis d'or?"

French Mons looked up at the ceiling.

"Just to-day, unluckily, I forgot my purse in a coat on my tent-post. But I shall deem myself happy to have the trifle sent you at the first opportunity. My lord, do not regard us awkward Swedes as any *grands seigneurs*. However high I mount, still Mons always peeps out between the seams."

"You were mightily awkward lately at our Polish election, when Arvid Horn sat with his note-book and registered all who voted against the Swedish orders, and when our land-marshal broke his staff in despair.—But now consider my house as your own. The tobacco pipe lies by the flask of scented water, the scented water on the powder-box, the powder-box on the tobacco keg, the tobacco keg on the commode. That you must hunt out as time goes on."

With these words he took up a leather-bound book and sat down to read.

"I beg you to trouble yourself no further," answered French Mons, looking at him sidelong through his lorgnette with wakening mistrust. Within his soul he thought: "Just wait till I'm sitting with my certificate in my big state carriage! Then it will be: 'That gentleman is our newly made knight, Magnus Gabriel.' "

The two girls every now and then pattered past through the room, and threw the light of their lamps upon him, and every time he rose and bowed. As the recluse meanwhile continued to read and gradually appeared to forget his presence entirely, he finally took his bundle and went back into the outer room.

"It's getting dark," he said to the serving-woman, "and I am too tired to keep company longer."

"We have arranged the gentleman's bed here to the left in the great hall. That is the only room that has a fire."

The hall was whitewashed and long, with inhospitable rows of chairs and a couple of rough folding-tables. Just by the door stood a bed with curtains of Holland linen. The old woman lighted the four candles in the sconces and left him alone.

Chilled, he looked about him and laid his sword on the table. Then he unpacked his bundle. Three of the candles he blew out, and on them hung the little peruke and the medium peruke and the spliced peruke, but with the fourth he threw the light under the bed and in the window recesses and then set it back in the socket.

"Impudent pack!" he muttered. "I'd rather have stood outside in the snow, but since I'm now inside here, it's a matter of keeping awake, peeping about, and going often to the window to listen and spy."

He tried to lock the door from inside, but it was without both bolt and key. After he had worked in vain for a long time to get off his wet boots, whose musty smell annoyed him, he put on his dressing-gown and lay down in his boots on the bed.

At times he heard a muffled stamping and snorting from the wild horses in the carriage entrance under the floor of the hall, but after a while it grew more quiet, and he began to think that the candle did not light sufficiently, because all the corners and recesses were dark. He raised his lorgnette, sharpened his gaze, and turned his eyes on all sides, but otherwise lay quite motionless.

Then he saw by the door-jamb close behind the curtain at the head of his bed a tall, thin lackey in a brown coat with black braid.

A cramp-like dread caught him by the throat, he grew dizzy, but he thought: "It is only the good God who wishes to try me because I am dreaming of distinctions and certificates."

Softly and almost imperceptibly he caught hold of both sides of the bed so as to control his shuddering body, and then he stuck his right leg out between the curtains.

"Jonathan," said he, "pull off my boot!"

The lackey grinned so that his dark mouth twisted itself up to his ears, but he did not move from his place.

French Mons chattered his teeth, but he did not draw back his leg.

"Jonathan, is this the way you serve folk of the nobility?"

The lackey grinned still worse, and made a disdainful gesture of refusal with his hand.

French Mons now understood that the lackey had seen through his deception and treated him as a parvenu and a plebeian, and his terror grew so great that he panted and moaned softly, but his leg he held continually outstretched.

"Pull off my boot, Jonathan!"

His voice was now barely a whisper.

The lackey rubbed his hands on his hips and grinned, but remained standing by the door-jamb.

At that moment the horse down below in the carriage entrance neighed long and piercingly, and far off in the snowstorm many horses answered.

French Mons threw himself from the bed.

"I'm neglecting my duty," he cried. "That's the enemy!"

He sprang forward to the table to grasp his sword, but the lackey walked beside him with long steps and stared him in the eyes.

Then he again grew paralyzed and stood still. Meanwhile the lackey took the sword with one hand, stretched out the other over the candlestick, and with two fingers lifted the great spliced wig on high and then drew it as an extinguisher over the burning candle.

"Good God in heaven!" stammered French Mons. "I have seldom gone into Thy house and have rather pampered myself and played with all sorts of vanity, but help me for this one time so that I do not neglect my duty and become a disgrace! Then Thou may'st punish me eternally."

Neighings were heard ever nearer and nearer, and the wild horse rushed stamping and snorting from its retreat.

Then French Mons bent down with his clenched hands over his head, and threw himself in the dark upon the lackey.

"You spook of Beelzebub!" he shouted.

He pulled the sword to him and struck on all sides in the dark, and chairs fell to the floor. He could nowhere lay hold on Jonathan, but at last he struck his hand against the wall, and the door opened. The two sisters with their lamps and their pale, wide-eyed countenances entered in only their chemises, without the wit to feel any embarrassment about it. They only rubbed against each other and stared at the stranger who had waked them with his racket. On this occasion he did not give himself time to bow, but shoved up the window and hopped to the ground. In his dressing-gown, with sword in hand he ran along the house and heard behind him a harsh voice from the window, but he did not know whether it was that of the recluse or of Jonathan, or whether they were both one and the same.

"I said that you were a fool," cried the voice, "a great fool, a fool without peer, and I wanted to be even with you. But if the horsemen get to see you, and there is a hand-to-hand fight, my house, my home, my nook will be an ash-heap before the cock crows."

Without looking back, French Mons sprang in among the trees, thinking all the while: "Now's the chance for an officer's commission! And then the certificate, the certificate!"

The moonlight shone through the snowstorm, and he saw Polacks with waving plumes flit by like shadows. When they came too near, he threw himself down beside a heap of twigs or set himself behind a tree trunk.

At last he discovered an old snow-covered barricade. Behind the logs a soldier rose and asked in a whisper: "Who goes there?"

"God with us! Good comrade!" answered French Mons, and climbed into the triangle. "The enemy is upon us!"

"I have long thought I heard hoofs,"

said Oxehufvud softly. "Perhaps it would be wisest to run down and occupy the house."

"Captain, do not command me to show the way! I was received there as a guest; I am a chevalier and would rather be shot."

"And how were you treated there?"

"Like an excellency."

"We shall see. It seems to be too late now. Take aim! Fire!"

A swarm of Polacks galloped forward and struck with their spears across the logs, but the first volley threw them from the saddle.

"Oohaho! oohaho!" rang through the wood. Riding shadows and long lines of men on foot gathered as far as the eye could see. In the half light they resembled the dark bushes that swayed in the wind.

"I fancy we're going to have a pretty party with the enemy," said Oxehufvud. "We are five-and-twenty men, and around us stand fully three battalions."

"Now we are only twenty-four," answered French Mons as he took the musket from a fallen soldier.

"Now we are only nineteen," said Oxehufvud after a time.

Shot rained over the triangle and killed man after man. As soon as the riders shrank back, the Swedes stopped shooting, but when the silence once more enticed the Polacks and inspired them with the belief that there was no longer any man living behind the barricade, they were met at once by shot and swords and stones and boughs of trees. So the raging strife continued hour after hour.

Oxehufvud stole along the stockade and counted half aloud: "Eight, ten, thirteen—we're not many now. A sorry number."

He, too, had taken a musket, and on his knees was picking up the ammunition from the cartridge-box of one of the fallen.

"Comrade," said he, and without rising he drew French Mons to him in his dressing-gown. "I gave it to you rough, comrade, at noon on the swamp."

"Now we are only seven," answered French Mons, loading and firing. "But soon we shall have held out three hours."

"Comrade, you are not the first who has shown me that the Swedes should not always laugh at their dandies. You see, comrade, it happens sometimes in this world that he who begins with a great peruke may end with a great deed."

"Now we are only two."

"Hardly two, for I have got mine already," answered Oxehufvud, and sank back against the logs. "Hardly two."

French Mons now stood alone among the dead. He tore up his dressing-gown and twisted some rags about his left arm, which was bleeding violently. His waistcoat, too, he cast away, and the lorgnette he stuffed into the leg of his boot. Then he lay down among the others as far in among the branches and twigs as he could creep.

The next time the Polacks galloped forward, all was still.

They vaulted over the logs with a wild cry and began to plunder, but when they saw him, bloody and half undressed, they let him lie, and at daybreak they went away.

"Now," thought French Mons, "now I have my officer's commission. The certificate comes later."

He crept out between the logs, and up by the house in the snow he happened upon the peruke, which had been thrown after him from the window.

"The wretch!" he whispered. "That's my thanks for saving his nest."

All day he went through the woods with his peruke under his arm, and only late in the evening was he challenged by the outposts of the Swedish camp.

Tents and cabins of brush were set up in the woods without any sheltering entrenchments. On wagons or before their huts the women sat on a separate lane and cradled their children on their knees or whispered gently and quietly with their soldiers. Round the fires the clay pipes puffed in scarred hands. There Cornet Brokenhjelm and the dauntless Lieutenant Pistol related their adventures. Lieutenant Orbom let his neighbor feel with his fingers the shot from Klissov which still remained behind his right ear after having gone in under his left eye and through his head. Per Adlerfelt, the dancing-master, lamented that the enemy always, as at Duna, shot so low that at last they would mar his handsome legs. There the lively Dumky jested, still wearing on his arm the garter which as a page he had got from a Silesian duchess. Svante Horn, who was being bandaged by his faithful servant, Lidbom, muttered that he could never charge without immediately getting a Cossack spear or sword in his body. Before him stood the genial gray-haired surgeon, Teuffenweisser, who continually put on and took off his spectacles, and always required a dram before he attended rich patients. All conversed of the fortune of war, which allowed one man to grow gray under hardships and honors, but let another fall by the first shot in the spring of his days. No drinking-songs rang out, but the king had kettledrums and oboes play merrily all night. It was a camp where that soft noise was like the murmur of a clear forest brook under leafage dewy with June.

Against the wish of the king, his bodyguards had wound his tent with hay and on that had laid sod, so that it was like a charcoal-kiln. It stood, not in the middle of the camp, but on the outermost edge and almost in darkness. Within, by the tent-pole, they had built a fireplace of stones and had brought there time and again a red-hot cannon-ball. There was a wash-basin of pure silver, and on the table, beside the Life of Alexander the Great and the gold-bound Bible, stood a little silver-plated image of the dog Pompey, which had died. But the light blue silken brocade on the chair and field-bed was already worn and spotted. In the middle of the tent crouched the dogs, Turk and Snuffler, but the king lay among the fir-twigs on the ground. The small beer was done, and the lackey Hultman had had nothing but a glass of melted snow and two slack-baked biscuits to offer him for supper. After that he had spread his cape over him and put on his embroidered nightcap. There now, at the midday height of his victories, slept the king of the Swedes, and his narrow head was turned toward the languishing gleam of the last glowing cannon-ball. It was long now since he had read the evening prayer which he had formerly stammered out in his room while the wind raged in the lindens of Karlberg Park. His god had gradually darkened into the thunderous god of the Old Testament, to the avenging Lord of Sabaoth, whose commands he heard in his soul without needing to pray for them; and it was Thor and the Asar who drove around this camp in the rumbling of the nocturnal storm, and who with their trumpets hailed their youngest-born on earth.

Then the dogs began to whimper and growl, and the half-grown Max of Wurtemberg, the Little Prince, came, overjoyed and beaming, to the opening of the tent.

"Your Majesty," he cried, with his ringing boyish voice, "awake, awake! Five-and-twenty Smålanders have been out and played with the enemy."

Behind him stood French Mons, propped against the gallant Captain Schmiedeberg, who himself still went on a crutch after an engagement over the baggage, where he with twelve men had fought against three hundred Polacks.

French Mons had never carried his head more proudly and contentedly, though he reeled with weariness; but when he heard that he was standing before the king's tent, he stopped short in anxiety. He stooped and tremblingly wiped the bloodstains from his hands. His hat, the medium peruke, and the little peruke he threw upon the ground, and without considering the regulations, put on the great spliced peruke. When he got himself in order, he extended his arms along his sides and told his story stammeringly with chattering teeth.

The king, who continued to sit on the fir-twigs, then slowly repeated it, investigating every word so as not to miss a single detail of the adventure. He rejoiced as a child would at a wonderful saga. Finally he gave him his hand.

"Oxehufvud spoke rightly," he said. "The gentlemen have had a pretty party with the enemy. It has been quiet enough here in camp, and I should myself have gladly been along. Since the Polish recluse begged in jest the loan of five louis d'or, I will leave him ten, and the gentleman shall go back and throw them in to him through the window."

French Mons went backward through the tent door, and Schmiedeberg caught him around the waist and conducted him into a ring of inquisitive, expectant comrades. There were ensigns and lieutenants and captains, who were his equals in age, but who had already risen higher in rank than he.

"French Mons," they murmured, "now no one any longer dares laugh at your lorgnettes and your wigs. But how did it go with your commission and certificate? The certificate!"

"Quiet, quiet!" said Schmiedeberg. "There are other rewards for the poor fellow. If His Royal Majesty might prevail, he would give no rewards, but would wish that each and all should fight and fall for honor alone."

No one dared contradict Schmiedeberg, and dropping the arm of his new-found charge, he limped on his crutch a few steps nearer the fire.

"Didn't you see?" he whispered—"didn't you see that His Royal Majesty took him by the hand almost as an equal?"

"There I got my certificate for time and eternity," said French Mons.

In his dripping spliced wig and ragged shirt he stood all the while upright with arms at his sides, and he still stammered in his speech and chattered his teeth.

"And your charter as baron," answered Schmiedeberg softly, "you get when you fall."

The Queen of the Marauders

The tocsin in the church tower at Narva had ceased. In a breach of the battered rampart lay the fallen Swedish heroes, over whose despoiled and naked bodies the Russians stormed into the city with wild cries. Some Cossacks, who had sewed a live cat into the belly of an innkeeper, were still laughing in a circle around their victim, but the gigantic Peter Alexievitch, the czar, soon burst his way through the midst of the throng on street and courtyard and cut down his own men to check their misdeeds. His right arm up to the shoulder was drenched with the blood of his own subjects. Weary of murder, troop after troop finally assembled in the square and the churchyard. Under the pretext that the churches had been desecrated by the misbelievers who lay buried there, bands of soldiers began to violate and plunder the graves. Stones were pried up from the floor of the church with crowbars, and outside the graves were opened with shovels. Pillagers broke the copper and tin caskets into pieces, and threw dice for the silver handles and plates. The streets, where at the first mêlée the inhabitants had thrown down firebrands and tiles, and where the blood of the slain was still running in the gutters, were for many days piled up with rusty or half-blackened coffins. The hair on some of the bodies had grown so that it hung out between the boards. Some of the dead lay embalmed and well preserved, though brown and withered, but from most of the coffins yellow skeletons grinned forth from collapsed and mouldered shrouds. People who stole anxiously among them read the coffin-plates in the twilight, and now and then recognized the name of a near relative, a mother or a sister. Sometimes they saw the ravagers pull out the decayed remains and throw them into the river. Sometimes, again, protected by night, they themselves succeeded in carrying them off and burying them outside the city. So in the dusk one might encounter an old man or woman who came stealing along toilsomely with children or serving-maids, carrying a coffin.

One night a swarm of pillagers bivouacked in a corner of the churchyard. Hi! what fun it was to pile up a bonfire of bed-slats and bolsters and chairs and coffin-ends and what the devil else could be dragged forth! Flames and sparks blazed up as high as the attic window of the parsonage. Round about stood coffins propped one against another. The bottom of one of the uppermost had been broken, so that the treasurer, of blessed memory, who was inside it, stood there upright with his spliced wig on his head and looked as if he thought: "I pray you, into what company have I been conducted?"

"Haha! little father," the robbers called to him, as they roasted August apples and onions at the flames; "you surely want something to wet your whistle, you there!"

The glow of the fire lighted up the living-room of the parsonage, and the sparks flew in through the broken panes. In the rooms stood only a broken table and a chair, upon which sat the parson with his head propped on his hands.

"Who knows? Perhaps it might succeed," he mumbled, and raised himself as if he had found the key to a long-considered problem.

His silver-white beard spread itself all over his breast, and his hair hung down to his shoulders. In his youth, as chaplain, he had gone in for a little of everything, and he had never pushed back a cup that was offered him. Afterwards, as a widower in the parsonage, he had worshipped God with joy and mirth and a brimming bowl, and it was bruited about that he did not reach first for his Bible if a well-formed wench happened to be in his company. He therefore even now took misfortune more bravely and resignedly than others, and his heart was as undaunted as his soldierly body was unbowed by years.

He went out into the entry and cautiously pulled out the five or six rusty nails that held down a couple of boards above a little narrow recess under the stairs. Then he lifted the boards aside.

"Come out, my child!" he said.

When no one obeyed him, his voice grew somewhat more severe, and he repeated his words: "Come out, Lina! Both the other maids have been bound and carried away. It was verily at the last minute that I got you in here. But it is almost a day since then, and you cannot live without meat and drink. Eh?"

When he was not obeyed, he threw back his head in annoyance, and he now spoke in accents of harsh command: "Why don't you obey? Do you think there is food here? There's not so much as a pinch of salt left in the house. You must be got away, you understand. If it goes ill with you, if a plunderer gets you on the way, I can only say this: clasp your arms about his neck and follow with him on his horse's back wherever it carries you. Many a time in the rough-and-tumble of war have I seen such a love, and then I have slung the soldier's cloak over my priest's frock and waved my hat for a lucky end to the song. Don't you hear, lass? When your late father, who was a tippler—if I must tell the truth—was my stable-boy and pulled me out of a hole in the ice once, I promised for the future to provide for him and his child. Besides, he was Swedish born, as I was. Well, haven't I always been a fatherly master to you, or what has Her Grace to object? Have her wits deserted her, eh?"

Something now began to move in the pitch-black recess. An elbow struck against the wall, there was a rustling and scraping, and with that Lina Andersdaughter stepped out, barefooted, in nothing but her chemise and a torn red jacket without sleeves but with a whole back to it, over which hung the braid of her brown hair.

The light of the fire fell in through the window. Squatted together, she held her chemise between her knees, but her fresh, downward-bent face with broad, open features was as merry as if she had just stepped out of her settle-bed on a bright winter morning in the light of the dawn.

The blood ran impetuously enough through the veins of the white-haired chaplain, but in that moment he was but master and father.

"I did not know that in my simple house folk had learned such a ceremonious feeling of delicacy," said he, and gave her a friendly pat on the bare shoulders.

She looked up.

"No," she said, "it's only because I'm so wretchedly cold."

"Ah, well, that's natural. That's the way I like people to talk in my house. But I have no garments to give you. My own hang on me in tatters. The house may burn at any time. I myself can maybe sneak out on my way unaccosted, and I have a Riga rix-dollar in my pocket. Who asks about a ragged old man? It's another affair with you, Lina. I know these wild fellows. I know but one way to get you off, but I myself shrink from telling it. Naturally, you are afraid."

"Afraid I'm not. It will go with me as it may. To be sure, I am no better than the others. Only I'm perishing of cold."

"Come here to the door, then, but don't be frightened. Do you see out there in the doorway the rascals have set a little wooden casket. It cannot be very heavy, but I think you will have room in it. If you dare lay yourself in the casket, perhaps I can smuggle you out of the town."

"That I surely dare."

Her teeth chattered, and she trembled, but she straightened herself up a little, let the chemise hang free, and went out on the stones in the doorway.

The pastor lifted off the moist lid, which was loose, and found nothing in the plundered casket but shavings and a brown blanket.

"That was just what I needed," she shivered. She pulled up the blanket, wrapped it over her, stepped up, and laid herself on her back in the shavings.

The pastor bent over her, laid both his hands on her shoulders, and looked into her fearless eyes. She might be eighteen or nineteen years old. Her hair was stroked smoothly back to the braid.

As he stood so, it came over him that he had not always looked on her in the past with as pure and fatherly feelings as he himself had wished and as he had pretended to do. But now he did so. His long white hair fell down as far as her cheeks.

"May it go well with you, child! I am old. It matters little whether my life goes on for a while still or is destroyed in the day that now is. I have been in many a piece of mischief and many an ill deed in my time, and for the forgiveness of my sins I will also for once have part in something good."

He nodded and nodded toward her and raised himself.

There outside the clamor sounded louder than ever. He laid on the lid and fastened in as well as he could the long screws that had been left in their places. Then he knelt, knotted a rope crosswise around the casket, and with strong arms lifted the heavy burden on his back. Bending forward and staggering, he strode out into the open air.

"Look there!" shouted one of the pillagers at the fire, but his nearest comrade silenced him with the word: "Let the poor old man alone! That's only a miserable beggar's casket."

Sweat trickled out over the old man's face, and his back and arms ached and smarted under the heavy weight. Step by step he moved forward through the dark streets. Every now and then he had to set the casket down on the ground to take breath, but then he stood with his hand on the lid in constant fear of being challenged and hustled away or of being stabbed by some roving band of soldier revellers. Several times he had to step to one side because of the heavy wagons, loaded with men and women, who were to be taken hundreds of miles into Russia to people the waste regions. The great conquering czar was a sower who did not count the seeds he strewed.

When finally the old war-pastor reached the town gate, and the watch came to meet him, he roused his strength to the utmost with all the collected will-power of his anxiety. With a single arm he held the casket in place on his back, while with his free hand he drew the Riga rixdollar from his pocket and handed it to the sentry as a bribe.

The soldier motioned to him to go on.

He wanted again to move his foot forward, but now he was unable. Through the town gate he saw the river glimmer on the open plain, but then it grew dark before his eyes. Still afraid for his burden in his helplessness, he softly and cautiously lowered the casket beside him on the stone flagging. Thereupon he fell forward and died.

The other men of the watch sprang forward and began to curse and complain. No casket could remain standing there in the door of the gateway.

The officers, who were sitting and gambling in a room of the casemate, now came likewise to the spot. One of them, a little dry, weather-beaten figure with rectangular spectacles, who was more like a clerk than a soldier, took a lantern, came forward, and held the lid slightly ajar with his scabbard.

First he drew back his head precipitately, nearly dropping the lantern. The next time he bent down and looked in, he dwelt on the action longer and more searchingly, and afterwards passed his hands over his whole face to hide his thoughts. Then he unhooked his spectacles and stood pondering. When he bent the third time, he sent the light back and forward through the crevice,—and there inside lay Lina Andersdaughter quite calmly, screwing up her eyes at him in the lantern's light without herself knowing what was going on.

"I'm hungry," she said.

He laid aside the lantern and went a couple of paces up and down through the door with hands crossed behind his back. There came then into his frigid expression a sly and merrily vibrating life, and unnoticed he took some August apples and thrust them into the casket. Thereupon he began to give commands.

"Come here, boys! Let eight men take the casket to General Ogilvy, salute him and say that this is a small gift from his humble servant, Ivan Alexievitch. Eight of you others who have just come from working on the walls go after it, and roll up your leather aprons like trumpets in which you are to blow the regimental march. But in front of all, two men are to go with rushlights. Forward, march!"

The savage soldiers looked openıouthed at one another and obeyed. aughing, they lifted the casket on their ıuskets. Two long stalks, tarred and visted about with straw, were brought ırward from a corner of the gateway and ghted at the lantern; and as the proces-on set itself in motion into the field to-ard the camp, the musicians tooted the ıarch in their aprons:

O you, who have chosen a gun to bear,
You care not for lodging or bed, lad,
You feed like a prince on the finest fare,
Of girls and of lice you've enough and to spare,
But when will you ever be paid, lad?

Vhen they came to the camp, the soldiers ıshed together around them in the torch-ght. General Ogilvy, who was sitting at ıble, came out of his tent.

"Beloved little father," said one of the earers, "Lieutenant Ivan Alexievitch umbly sends you this gift."

Ogilvy grew pale and bit his lips under is bushy gray moustache. His face, wrin-led and strained to harshness, was at bot-ım good-natured and friendly.

"Is he out of his right mind?" he thun-ered with pretended wrath, though in eality he was as frightened as a boy. Put down the casket and break off the d!"

The soldiers pried it open with their lades, and the dark lid rattled to one de.

Ogilvy stared. With that he burst out ıughing. He guffawed so that he had to t down on an earthen bench. And the ıldiers laughed, too. They laughed down ırough the whole lane of tents, so that ıey reeled and tottered and had to sup-ort themselves one against another like runkards. Lina Andersdaughter lay there ı the casket with a half-eaten apple in er hand and made great eyes. She had ow become warm again, and was as looming of cheek as a doll.

"By all the saints," Ogilvy burst out. "Not even in the catacombs of St. Anthony has man seen such a miracle. This is a corpse that ought to be sent to the czar himself."

"By no means," answered one of his officers. "I sent him two little fair-haired baggages day before yesterday, but he cares only for thin brunettes."

"So it is," answered Ogilvy, and turned himself, bending, toward Narva. "Salute Ivan Alexievitch and say that, when the casket is returned, there shall lie in the bottom of it a captain's commission.—Hey, sweetheart!"

He went forward and stroked Lina Andersdaughter under the chin.

But at that she sat up, took hold of his hair, and gave him a resounding box on the ear, and after that another.

He did not let it affect him in the least, but continued to laugh.

"That's the way I like them," he said; "that's the way I like them. I will make you Queen of the Marauders, my chick, and as token thereof I give you here a bracelet with a turquoise in the clasp. A band of our worst rabble stole it just now from the casket of Countess Horn in Narva."

He shook the chain from his wrist, and she caught it eagerly to her.

When, later in the evening, the cloth was laid in the tent, Lina Andersdaughter sat at the table beside Ogilvy. She had now got French clothes of flowered brocade, and wore a headdress with blonde lace. But what hands! She managed to eat with gloves, but under them swelled the big, broad fingers, and the red shone between the buttons.

"Hoho! hoho!" shouted the generals. "Those hands make a man merrier than he would get with a whole flask of Hungary. Help! Tighten our belts! Hold us under the arms! It will be the death of us!"

Meanwhile she filled her plate, munched sweetmeats, and sat with her spoon in the air. If anything tasted bad, she made a face. Eat she could. Drink, on the contrary, she would not, but only took a swallow in her mouth, and then spurted the wine over the generals. But all their curses and worst expressions she picked up, while she sat ever alike blooming and gay.

"Help! help!" shrieked the generals, choked with laughter. "Blow out the light so we can't see her! Hold our foreheads! Help! Will you have a little puff of a tobacco pipe, mademoiselle?"

"Go to the deuce! Can't I sit in peace?" answered Lina Andersdaughter.

There was one thing, though, that Ogilvy skilfully concealed, so that the laughers should not turn to him and nudge him in the ribs and pull his coat tails and say: "Oho, little father, you've got into water too deep for your bald head. Bless you, little father, bless you and your little mishap!"

He pretended always to treat her with slightly indifferent familiarity, but he never sat so near her that his dog could not jump up between them. He never took hold of her so that any one saw it, and never when no one saw it either, for then he knew that her hand would catch him on the face, so that the glove would split, and the red shine out in all its strength. It was a fact that, notwithstanding, she now and then gave him a slap in the middle of the face, and no one did she snub worse than him. But at all this he only laughed with the others, so that never before had there been in the camp such a clamor and bedlam.

Sometimes he thought of knouting her, but he was ashamed before the others, because everything could be heard through the tent, and he feared that they then would the more easily guess how things stood, and how little he got along with the girl. "Wait," he thought, "we shall be sitting alone sometimes behind locked doors. Just wait! Till then thin may go on as they do."

"Help, help!" shouted the genera "That's how she carries her train. V must take hold of it. Lord, Lord, no; b just look!"

"Take it up, you," said she. "Take up, you. That's what you are for."

And so the generals were cuffed a bore her train, both when she came to t table and when she went.

Then it happened one evening, wh she sat among the drinking old men, th an adjutant stepped in, hesitating and e barrassed. He turned to Ogilvy.

"Dare I be frank?"

"Naturally, my lad."

"And whatever I say will be forgiven

"By my honor. Only speak out!"

"The czar is on his way out to t camp."

"Very good, he is my gracious lord."

The adjutant pointed at Lina Ande daughter.

"The czar has a fancy for tall br nettes," said Ogilvy.

"Your Excellency, in these last days has changed his taste."

"God! Call the troops to arms—a forward with the three-horse wagon!"

Now the alarm was struck. Dru rolled, trumpets blared, weapons cl tered, and shouts and trampling filled t night. The drinking party was broken u and Lina Andersdaughter was set in baggage wagon.

Beside the peasant who was driving soldier sprang up with a lighted lante and she heard the peasant softly inqu of him the purpose of the flight.

"The czar," answered the soldier in monotone, and pointed with his thu over his shoulder at the girl.

At that the peasant shrunk together at a frost-cold breeze, and whipped t small, shaggy horses more and mo wildly. He hallooed and beat and urg them into a thundering gallop. The lantern light fell caressingly on the fir bushes and the burnt homesteads; the wagon banged and tottered among the stones, and creaked in its joints.

Lina Andersdaughter lay on her back in the hay, and looked at the stars. Whither was she carried? What fate awaited her? She wondered and wondered. On her wrist hung the bracelet as a talisman, a pledge for the accomplishing of Ogilvy's wonderful prediction. Queen of the Marauders! It sounded so grand, though at first she had but gradually discovered what the word really betokened. She stroked and plucked at the small silver rings. Then she sat up and scanned the stony road in the lantern's light. Cautiously she moved further and further out. Unnoticed, she climbed slowly over the wagon-sill and lowered her feet to the ground. Would she be crushed and left lying? For a few steps she dragged along. Then she lost her hold, stumbled, and fell lacerated among the bushes.

On thundered the baggage wagon with its three galloping horses, and the lantern light vanished. Then she got up and wiped off the blood from her cheeks, while she wandered forth into the trackless woods.

When she met barbarous-looking fugitives, and they saw her pretty face, they at once picked berries and mushrooms for her and followed along. She got a whole court of ragamuffins, and she treated them so ill that they scarcely dared to touch her dress, but sometimes they stabbed one another. Finally she took service with a skipper's wife, who was to sail with her husband to Danzig. Scarcely had it begun to grow dark when the ragamuffins came out one after another and took service for nothing. The skipper sat on his cabin in the moonlight, blew his shepherd's pipe, and congratulated himself on having got such a willing crew. And never had the old woman seen a stronger serving-maid. But hardly had they put to sea when Lina Andersdaughter sat herself beside the skipper with her arms crossed, and all the ragamuffins lay on their backs and sang in tune with the pipe.

"Do you think I'll scour your bunks?" said she.

"Beat her, beat her," cried the old woman, but the skipper only moved nearer, and blew and blew on his pipe. Night and day the vessel rocked on the bright waves with slack sail, and the skipper played for Lina Andersdaughter, who danced with her ragamuffins; but down in the cabin sat the old woman, crying and lamenting.

When they came to Danzig, the skipper stuck the pipe under his arm and slunk off the vessel at night with Lina Andersdaughter and her ragamuffins. They guessed now that she thought of going to the Swedish troops in Poland and compelling the king himself to give her his hand.

When she with her followers stepped, humming, in among the Swedish women of the camp, there was uproar and alarm, because for two days they had sat by their wagons without food. The last provisions had been delivered to the sutlers and divided among the soldiers. Then she stepped forward to the first corporal she happened on and set her hands on her hips.

"Aren't you ashamed," said she, "to let my women starve, when in spite of all you can't get along without them?"

"*Your* women? Who are you?"

She pointed to her bracelet. "I am Lina Andersdaughter, the Queen of the Marauders, and now take five men and follow us!"

He looked toward his captain, the reckless Jacob Elfsberg; he looked at her pretty face and at his men. How the line surrounded her with their muskets, and the women armed themselves with whip-handles and pokers! At night, when the light of the camp-fire tinged the heavens, the king, inquisitive, got into his saddle. As the wild throng came back with well-laden wagons and oxen and sheep, the troops cheered louder than ever: "Hurrah for King Charles! Hurrah for Queen Caroline!"

The women thronged about the king's horse, so that the lackeys had to hold them back, and Lina Andersdaughter went to him to shake hands with him. But he thereupon rose in his stirrups, and shouted over the women's heads to the corporal and the five soldiers: "That's well maraudered, boys!"

From that moment she would never hear the king named, and whenever she met a man, she flung her sharpest abuse right in his face, whether he was plain private or general. When Malcomb Björkman, the young guardsman—who, however, was already famous for his exploits and wounds—held out his hand to her, she scornfully laid in it her ragged, empty purse; and she was never angrier than when she heard General Meyerfelt whistling as he rode before his dragoons, or recognized Colonel Grothusen's yellow-brown cheeks and raven-black wig. But if a wounded wretch lay beside the road, she offered him the last drop from her tin flask and lifted him into her wagon. Frost and scratches soon calloused her cheeks. High on the baggage wagon she sat with the butt of a whip and commanded all the wild camp-followers, loose women, lawful wives, and thievish fellows that streamed to them from east and west. When at night the flare of a fire arose toward heaven, the soldiers knew that Queen Caroline was out on a plundering raid.

Days and years went by. Then, after the jolly winter quarters in Saxony, when the troops were marching toward the Ukraine, the king commanded that all women should leave the army.

"Teach him to mind his own affairs!" muttered Lina Andersdaughter, and she very tranquilly drove on.

But when the army came to the Beresina, there was murmuring and lamenting among the women. They gathered around Lina Andersdaughter's cart and wrung their hands and lifted their babies on high.

"See what you have to answer for! The troops have already crossed the river and broken all the bridges behind them. They have left us as prey to the Cossacks."

She sat with her whip on her knee and with high boots, but on her wrist still gleamed the silver chain with its turquoise. All the more violently did the terrified women sob and moan around her, and from the closed baggage wagons, which were like boxes, crept out painted and powdered Saxon hussies. Some of them, none the less, had satin gowns and gold necklaces. From all sides came women she had never seen before.

"Dirty wenches!" muttered she. "Now at last I have a chance to see the smuggled goods that the captains and lieutenants brought along in their wagons. What have you to do among my poor baggage crones? But now we all come to know what a man amounts to when his haversack is getting light."

Then they caught hold of her clothes, and called upon her as if she alone could seal their fate.

"Is there no one," she asked, "who knows the psalm, 'When I am borne through the Vale of Death'? Sing it, sing it!"

Some of the women struck up the psalm with choked and nearly whispering voices, but the others rushed down to the river, hunted out boats and wreckage from the bridges, and rowed themselves across. Each and every one who had a husband or a beloved in the army had hoped that even at the last she would be taken along and hidden; but all the worst women of the rabble, who belonged nei-

ther to this man nor to that, stood with their rags or their tasteless, ridiculous gowns in a ring around Lina Andersdaughter. Meanwhile swarms of Cossacks, who had crossed the river to snap up any straggling marauders, were sneaking up through the bushes on their hands and knees.

Then her heart failed her, and she stepped down from the wagon.

"Poor children!" she said, and patted the hussies on the cheek. "Poor children, I will not desert you. But now—devil take me!—do you pray to God that He will make your blood-red sins white, for I have nothing else to offer you than to shame the men and die a hero's death."

She opened the wagon chest and hunted out from among her plunder some pikes and Polish sabres, which she put into the hands of the softly singing women. Thereupon she herself grasped a musket without powder or shot, and set herself among the others around the cart to wait. So they stood in the sunset light on the highest part of the shore.

Then the women on the river saw the Cossacks rush forward to the cart and cut down one after another of them with the idea that they were men in disguise. They wanted to turn their boats, and soldiers sprang down from their ranks to the water and opened fire.

"Hurrah for King Charles," they cried with a thousand intermingled voices; "and hurrah—No, it's too late. Look, look! There is Queen Caroline dying a virgin in the midst of the harlots with a musket in her hand!"

Mazeppa and His Ambassador

In a splendidly decorated sleeping apartment stood a high bed with plumes at the corners. Behind the half-drawn bed-curtain lay an old man of sixty-three with the coverlet pulled up under his beard, his long white hair spread over the pillow. His whole forehead was hidden under a plaster. It was Mazeppa.

Beside the bed, among cups of medicine on the carpet, lay several books of Latin and French poetry, and at the door a little wizened priest carried on a whispered conversation with two green-clad messengers from Czar Peter.

"He scarcely comprehends your words," whispered the priest, giving a painfully searching look toward the sick man. "He even lies speechless for long periods. Who could have imagined that the old man with his joy of life would suddenly lie on his death-bed?"

"Ivan Stefanovitch," one of the strangers said with raised voice, approaching the bed, "our magnanimous czar, your lord, sends you greeting. Do you remember? Those three Cossacks of yours who stole off to him and related that you secretly planned a rebellion against his overlordship, he has had them fettered and returned to you as gifts of friendship. Ivan Stefanovitch, he relies on your loyalty."

Mazeppa's eyes opened feebly and his lips moved, but he was only able to utter an unintelligible whisper.

"We understand you," cried the messengers, speaking all at once. "We understand you. You greet him and thank him for his favor, and we are to say to him that you are bowed under your years and that you have already turned all your thoughts to that which is not of this world."

"I fear," murmured the priest to them aside, "that here it will soon be over."

The messengers nodded sadly, and backed out of the sleeping apartment.

As soon as they were out, the priest bolted the door.

"They have gone," he said.

Mazeppa sat up and tore the plaster from his brow, throwing it far across the carpet. His dark wide-open eyes gleamed and twinkled. A flush rose and paled on his cheeks, and under the handsomely curving nose shone teeth as white and fresh as a youth's. He tossed away the coverlet and, fully clad from tip to toe in long-coat and boots with spurs, he sprang from the bed, and jestingly pinched the priest in the ribs.

"You little rascal priest, you! You vagabond! This time we didn't manage badly. In Moscow they will believe that old Mazeppa is lying helpless and harmless. God be gracious to his pious soul! Hahahey! You little rascal priest, you! You arch-hypocrite!"

The priest laughed dryly. He was a deposed bishop from Bulgaria, and his round head with its short nose and deep-sunken eyes was like a skull.

Mazzepa grew still livelier.

"Mazeppa dying! Ay, ask his mistresses! Only ask them! No, my great Muscovite czar, you, now I am going to live and be quits with you."

"The czar suspects you, my lord, but he wishes to disarm you with magnanimity. He can be like that."

"And I should have been conquered by it, if one night at table, when we were drunk, he had not struck me on the ear. I value my ear as he does his, and an insult I can never forgive. It sticks in the soul and frets and gnaws. If I am not a king by birth, I am one in soul. And what does he want with his German coats on my splendid Cossacks? Now to business! Relate your adventures, you liar!"

"My lord, dressed as a mendicant monk, I went forth on my way to the Swedish headquarters. Sometimes I set a tavern lass on my knee and a can on the table corner, but when I peeped down and saw the toes sticking out of my ragged shoes, I thought to myself: This is Mazeppa's ambassador!"

"Very good, but how did you find the dandy?"

"The dandy?"

"To be sure. His Swedish Majesty, King Carolus. Don't you believe he dandifies as much with his grimy rags as any French prince of scented water with his silk stockings? And he possesses that wonderful Northern recklessness which continually snaps a riding-whip and cries: 'Rubbish! that's nothing! It's no matter!'—He has never been able to grieve for a misfortune longer than overnight. That has been the secret of his power. Woe to him and his fate when he sits up night after night without sleep! I am curious to see him. I long for it. But tell on!"

"First I found him in wig and armor on the tavern lass's neckcloth or pinafore, and on the glass from which I drank, and on the icing I ate, and on table-cloths and chest-lids and tobacco-boxes and market-booths. No one spoke of anything else than of him, and the children arranged themselves and played at Swedish divine service. The old peasants called him the sword-pope of the Protestants chosen by God Himself, and took off their hats in speaking of him."

"Ah yes, but how did you find him himself, when you came to headquarters?"

"I warn you. I predict misfortunes. I saw an omen. I found him puffed up and haughty of spirit."

"As a great personality of whom the world begins to disapprove."

"Marlborough, after an audience in Saxony, left his camp with a shrug of the shoulders, and sovereigns begin to laugh at him behind his back. His own generals have grown weary."

"He has become a hero of the rabble, you think. Well, even then, that's the sort of man I need to gather the wild hordes. If you do not assure me that you have seen him eat and drink, I cannot believe that he is a living human being. Then I should have to say: The young prince of the Swedes fell in the tumult of victory at Narva, but his shade rides ever on before s troops. Snow falls and falls, and drums ttle and rumble, and the thinning bat-lions do not know and do not under-and whither he leads them. When the emy recognize him in the powder-noke, they lower their muskets in super-itious awe and dare not shoot, and he oes not notice that sometimes he cuts own men who are making ready to fall n their knees. Hired assassins throw own their weapons at sight of him and ve themselves up—and he lets them go npunished. Don't talk to him about states nd treaties! He does not fight for posses-ons as men do; he wields the sword of od to revenge and reward. What did he quire just now as the reward of victory the conclusion of peace? Money? and? Of Austria he required a councillor ho had slandered him at table and a varm of Russian soldiers who had fled over the border—and freedom of con-ience for the Protestants. Of Prussia he emanded the imprisonment of a colonel ho had given counsel to the czar, and anishment for a writer who had cavilled his stipulations against the Pietists. Of axony he demanded Patkull and all Swe-ish renegades, but freedom for the rinces Sobieski and all Saxons who had one over to the Swedes. King August imself he compelled to pack up the old olish regalia in a velvet trunk and send em to King Stanislaus. And now, since e has deposed King August in Poland, e wants to depose the czar or challenge im to a duel, but their crowns and gov-rnments he would not even take as a gift. ince antiquity no stranger man has held e sword or a sceptre."

Mazeppa, while he was speaking, rasped one of the bedposts so hard that e plumes of the silken canopy shook.

But the other lifted three fingers and plied: "I have warned you. Everything at he touches he dedicates to misery nd death. Yet he is the patron saint of adventurers. He has raised adventure to stability and greatness. You too, my lord, are an adventurer, and I myself am the worst adventurer of you all. Therefore I will be compliant."

He lowered his hand and drew near with disrespectful familiarity. "You, Ivan Stefanovitch! Have you never wondered that I directed my steps to your particular door?"

"You were driven from your episcopal see because of your unfaith and your pranks."

"It really amounted to a little pilfering of small import. There were on the ikon-stand a couple of emeralds—"

"Which you replaced with bits of glass and in all secrecy sold, so that you might live more bountifully and in a manner more worthy a servant of the church."

"Let us say no more about it!—So I heard of Mazeppa, the former page at Johann Casimir's court, who in his pow-dered wig was attentive to the wayward sex so long that a jealous husband at last bound him naked on a horse's back and drove him forth into the wilderness. And there he built up a kingdom of adventur-ers. Saint Andrew guarded you, Mazeppa. I needed a little master who would be ashamed to strike off a good head, who would let me read my Greek and my Machiavelli in peace, and to whom I might say: 'Agreed, old fellow! It's all a shadow play, even this that you are lord and I servant.' Therefore I came to you. My adventurer's blood cannot bear to sit still, and I weary of your wine mixed with water, for you are a great miser, Ma-zeppa; but as you are now pondering a financial transaction in musket-balls, I follow you. And as the Swedish king no longer listens to his generals or to the beseeching letters from his grandmother and his people, and comes hither by the most perilous and impossible roads, he wishes to accept your offer of an alliance.

With you and your Cossacks he will march against your lord. Here are the papers."

The priest shook off his cope and stood in Cossack dress with pistols in his girdle, and from his bosom he drew forth some folded papers.

Mazeppa grew pale, seized them, and held them pressed long to his mouth, while he sank his forehead and bowed as before the invisible image of a saint.

"Drums, drums!" he stammered in agitation.

But when the priest had got to the door, he checked him.

"No, don't let the drums strike up before to-morrow."

Thereupon he went to a plain wooden table in a little side-room, and sat down over his account books. He had his bailiffs summoned, and calculated and calculated, and prescribed greater economy in the milk department. Half a merry knight of the roads and half a learned but thrifty proprietor of lands, he finally superintended the packing of his many trunks and boxes. Sometimes he bent down and helped. Last of all, next morning he put on an old-fashioned and much-adorned Cossack costume. Impetuous and active, he sprang up from his chair as soon as he had sat down, but he remained standing before the mirror for some little time, now and then running his delicate, small white hand through his beard.

As soon as the music was heard, he mounted to the saddle and kept his charger constantly at a gallop.

When, after a time, he had come to the Swedes and was riding one morning through a flurry of snow in the king's retinue, the priest, as if by accident, pulled up his horse alongside him. Round about the troops marched past, sprinkled with grime, their weapons and cannon covered to prevent rusting. Baggage wagons clattered along with their weight of provision sacks and sick men, and sometimes wit a covered coffin. Last were driven masse herds of cattle. Drunken Zaporogean prancing Cossacks, and eagerly drum ming Polish Wallachians rode in gree and red cloaks and with high brass he mets on which bells were tinkling. Som were brandishing tufted spears and bow or long flint-locks inlaid with silver an ivory. Others played on a sort of wailin wooden pipe. It was a colorful, legendar sort of march, that went over untrodde and unknown forest paths, over froze marshes, and under snowy fir trees to ward the mysterious East.

"Mazeppa," the priest began in a lo voice, "you promised to come to th Swedes with thirty thousand Cossacks, bu hardly four thousand followed you."

Mazeppa kept his roan at a gallop, an nodded in silence, and the priest neve wearied of his gibes.

"Day before yesterday half of thes went off. Yesterday more still. Soon yo will have barely a couple of hundred fel lows, barely the servants who watch ove your trunks and the two barrels wit your money. Your uprising was betraye your cities are burned, your few faithfu men nailed on boards and thrown int rivers. Soon you will be nothing but gorgeous knight in the train of the Swed ish king."

As Mazeppa was still, the priest con tinued: "To-day I too will abandon you because the small beer of the Swede tastes sour to me, and my toes stick ou too far from my shoes. Your ambassado needs a richer lord. Farewell, Ivan Stefan ovitch!"

Mazeppa replied, "As long as I hav still my head and my philosophy, I re main Mazeppa. While my Cossack turned and broke away, I had the het-ma staff and mace carried before me, and rode on to the king as if I had come i front of Xerxes' millions. And he, wit his impoverished realm, his discontente generals, and his sinking sun, came toward me like the most fortunate among princes. What does it trouble him and me how many ride behind us? He has had enough of kingly honor, and wishes also to be a chosen man of God. He thinks of history as a man in love does of his sweetheart: he would not win her favor by his birth but by his person. If we two, he and I, should one day be the last survivors and sit in an earthen hut on the steppe, we should still continue to talk philosophy and treat each other as at a coronation dinner."

"You speak of his sinking sun. You have seen the omen, even you! He can no longer talk without boasting like a baggage driver."

"It is easy to be modest as long as everybody praises."

Mazeppa threw back his white-haired head with lofty contempt, and galloped forward to the king, who raised his hat and bowed and bowed again in his saddle.

Round about several of the generals joked as loudly as possible so that the king might hear them.

"When I come to Moscow," said Anders Lagerkrona, "I shall mend the seat of my trousers with the czar's night-cap."

"Pshaw!" answered Axel Sparre. "There is an old prophecy that a Sparre will some day be governor at the Kremlin."

"This way!" cried the ensigns. "Shoot down any one who dares to hinder such a great and exalted prince from marching forward wherever he chooses."

The king smiled and hummed: "Russia must run, Russia must run." But when the speakers were no longer within his hearing, they were transformed and became absent and melancholy.

"Your Majesty!" cried Mazeppa in crisp Latin and with kindling eyes, "Your Majesty's conquering arms go on so far that one fine morning we shall have hardly eight miles more to Asia."

"As to that the authorities used to disagree," answered the king, moved, but hunting for the Latin words, his gaze fettered by Mazeppa's white and pleasingly mobile hands. "If the border is not far off, we must go there, so that we can say we were also in Asia."

The voices died away, and the priest reined in his horse.

"Asia!" he muttered, "Asia doesn't lie in the middle of Europe. But ride on, ride on with you, my adventurous lords! I have changed my name and dress so many times that none of you Swedes will ever notice what I was. But do not forget that it was the ragged monk, the vagabond, Mazeppa's ambassador, who by his cunning negotiations laid his blue-frozen finger on your and your demi-god's fate and directed you into the wildernesses. You are right, King Carolus, and you, Mazeppa. Everything depends at the last on individual men."

It snowed and snowed, and he sat motionless on his lean horse, while the battalions marched by, silent and impatient. When the last soldiers turned and looked back at the solitary, unknown rider, and saw his little compressed death-skull head, they were seized with fear and hastened their steps.

Fifty Years Later

When the porridge had been eaten and the branch candles of tallow which shone on both sides of the pewter dish stood more than half burnt out, the chairs were drawn close to the fire. The manor-house was one of the smallest and poorest in the district, but in the evening no poverty was visible there. The straw lay soft as a carpet over the floor planks, fresh juniper had been set beside the dark and streaming windows, the gleam from the open fireplace tinted with yellow the whitewashed wooden walls. Recently, too, a goblet of sherry had been offered about. All knew, furthermore, that the most festive time of the evening was now come. Even the two servant-girls, who wore today their best holiday jackets, cleared the table as slowly as possible and hid themselves, waiting, by the door, for now old Captain Höök, a Charles man, brought out his tobacco-box and drew in the chair of honor to the middle place before the fire. It was, however, only after he had unlaced his brogans and laid his crossed feet with their thick white stockings on the fender to warm them thoroughly that he seemed to feel himself fully at ease. To be sure, he alone had carried on the conversation almost all the evening, and now at last spoke of Ehrencrona, who had received the Order of the Sword from King Frederick and never could wear it otherwise than in a snuff-box. But in the same moment he became stern and reflective, and slipped into a new history. It was, indeed, alleged that he generally lied roundly, but nobody cared about that, for the principal thing was that he should keep on with his tales.

He was already an elderly man with a frost-bitten lump of a nose. Both his hair, which was brushed forward, and his moustaches, which were twisted youthfully, had always been so light that nobody noticed whether the years had made one or another strand still whiter. And he sat on the chair in his scanty, buttoned-up coat as upright as formerly. Without any transition he began in his usual way.

Yes, the autumn when I went astray in the woods I was certainly badly off. I mean the autumn down in Severia. Lewenhaupt had just made us destroy our last wagons, and was leading us along the Soza River to find a ford, so that when on the other side we might be able to grope our way forward to the king's army; but many foot-soldiers had stopped to plunder the wagons. I was an ensign at that time. Together with several others, I was sent back by Major-General Stackelberg to master the fellows, but the Russians were already among them, and I scarcely knew in the darkness how I could manage to save myself across the river. When, dripping with water and mud, I stood in the heather on the farther bank, I stumbled on a dragoon private. He was from my own regiment, and we called him Long Jan, because he was one of the tallest and slimmest lads that ever lifted a Swedish blade. His chest was narrow, but his hands were large. His arms and legs seemed to have hardly a single muscle, and there was not a particle of down on his lean and simple face—a face any one would know again by the slanting eyes and the thick under lip.—God knows why he had ever been taken along.—But in that moment I was as glad to get sight of that lanky spectre as if I had met a sweetheart, and at random, but still as fast as we were able, we turned our steps into the forest.

At the start we leaped along so as to get warm and dry our clothes, and not until dawn did we lie down to sleep.

For many days after, we struggled on through the woods and swamps, and our clothes were still as wet as before. Once we took them off and hung them on a branch, but in the misty autumn air this helped but little, and we were only so much the colder when we succeeded, with great difficulty, in pulling them on again. As to our boots, there was no talk of getting them off. They dried temporarily during our progress, but soon became as completely soaked in a marsh, and one shower of rain followed another.

I had with me a bit of meat and a piece of black bread, which I divided with my silent and, as it seemed, submissive brother in misfortune, and after that we chewed leaves and twigs and anything we could find. Hunger, though, was not nearly such a gnawing plague as the continual chilly dampness, which made our teeth chatter even in our sleep. As our strength failed, our joints stiffened, so that we could not move them without pain.

One evening we heard an unexpected barking, and for a moment I realized that I flushed with joy, but immediately after came hesitation, with thoughts of danger. I turned to the opposite direction, and Long Jan followed me, silently as always, but when we had walked awhile, I noticed that we only came much nearer to the barking. Then I took the soldier by the arm and turned again toward the other side, but, similarly drawn by an irresistible inner attraction, we kept walking so that we came nearer and nearer to the dog. When I finally let go of Long Jan's arm, he still went on.

"Halt!" I called after him, excruciated with the damp and yet little minded to go straight into a hostile place where most likely axes would be the first things to greet us.

"Halt, halt!" repeated Long Jan obediently, but in spite of that continued to go on.

Then I raced up to him and caught him by the belt. As long as I held him, he stood quite straight and motionless, but as soon as I let go my hold, he went on.

"Halt! Stand!" I thundered, raging as if I had found myself under fire, and dumbfounded at such an abrupt and insubordinate obstinacy in a soldier who had learned our iron-hard discipline. "Will you not obey your own ensign, fellow?"

"Halt! Stand!" he repeated, but continued on as before, as though no longer master of his own feet.

"Come on, then, in Jesus' name!" I burst out; "we can't get it worse than it has been already. But now you have made yourself an ensign, though you are barely one of the rank and file, and me a common soldier. Be so good as to lay that up in your memory!"

Long Jan answered nothing, neither perhaps did he hear me. I resigned myself to following him, and after a few minutes we came out on a level clearing with many barns and houses. Right beside us stood a great wooden building with many stories. The sunset glittered on the raindrops which hung on the cementing moss between the rough logs of the wall, and the window-panes glimmered as if lighted by countless chandeliers; but the door was locked, and no smoke came from the chimneys. The house was as a corpse with closed mouth and without breath, but with eyes hideously lighted by a cold gleam from without. Tied to a stake behind a straw-stack that had crookedly collapsed, a lean dog crept back and forth along the ground and wagged his tail when he saw us.

Long Jan went straight forward to the door and banged on it, but no one opened. Then he drew his blade and smashed in the nearest window with the hilt. At that moment we heard from within a frightened woman's voice shouting again and again to some one who was called Varvara. The broken glass fell tinkling, the leaden frame was bent on all sides into long hanging strips. Then running steps were heard in the house. The next moment the door was opened by a well-grown and stately serving-maid with a broad, light braid of hair down her back and a multitude of jingling silver pieces on her black hood and red and green bodice. In her hand she held an unlighted lantern, which in her terror she had presumably seized from habit.

"We'll do no harm," I said, trying as well as I could to explain myself in the bothersome speech. "Heaven forbid such a horror, most gracious young lady! But we are nearly starved and above all we require—"

"Dry clothes," broke in Long Jan, shivering.

That was the first time in the long wandering that I had heard this peculiar chap utter anything of his own accord, and then he had had the impudence into the bargain to take the word out of my mouth. When the girl turned around and left the door half open, he did indeed stand aside to give me place, but I remarked irritably: "The Herr Ensign will surely go first."

"God deliver me from any such thing," he answered, and smacked his boot-heels together. But, partly cheered by the peaceful reception, partly still angry, I added in such a sharp tone of voice that he could not doubt my seriousness: "Or else devil take the ensign!"

Then he dragged his long legs in through the door ahead of me and, as the house had no entry, we found ourselves at once in a large hall, where a heating-stove of variegated porcelain rose like a tower to the middle of the ceiling. Along the walls, which consisted entirely of rough-hewn logs caulked with moss, stood several black-varnished chairs, and on a shelf gleamed pots of pewter.

The serving-maid ran away and called Varvara, who finally appeared, dazed and frightened, in the farthest corner of the darkened hall. There the two girls tarried, whispering anxiously.

After a while, however, they grew easier; and they could not keep from giving each other a look and feeling more accommodating when I unexpectedly called them "gracious young ladies," and accordingly feigned not to understand that they were poor serfs. That was a drop of warm oil on the hard wax, and they now told us that the noble masters had gone away two weeks ago at the report of the Swedes' approach. They separately assured us that in the whole house, yes, in the whole place, there was nothing left of any value whatever, but that they would gladly do their best to serve the strangers.

Varvara had pretty teeth, but she was too small and fat and black-fleeced, and after a while she let out such a piercin laugh that I was annoyed. The yellow haired girl, who was called Katarina, o the other hand, I could not keep fron pinching on the ear in fun, when sh brought in wood to the stove. Meanwhil Long Jan had, without further ceremony pulled off his tattered blue coat, and as h had neither shirt nor vest, he soon stoo naked to the waist in all his miserabl leanness, so that no one could keep seri ous any longer—no one but himself Never had I seen a cheerful twitch pas over that stolid face. After we had each o us got a sheepskin coat and stilled th worst hunger with a little mashed turni and kvass, we laid us down by the stov with broadswords between our knees, an I ventured to order the Herr Ensign t watch with me alternately, in case an one could possibly have any evil in mind I also forbade the two serving-maids t leave the hall, and reading my prayer aloud in Swedish, entrusted us to th Almighty.

But!—The Almighty lets us human be ings now and then give each other sur prises. When no one addressed me, went on sleeping for hours, till I wa waked by a piercing warmth, which a other times I should have called a pain but which now at least reminded me tha I was no longer a wandering skeleton, bu a living man again. And still, who will no understand my terror when I saw th heated hall dark and empty, and hear shrieks and clamor from the room ad joining.

I at once took my broadsword an sprang to the door. There I saw a blazin cook-stove, and before it stood Long Ja in a checkered dressing-gown of brigh silk and high-heeled shoes. Obviously th rascal had also skill in foraging, for a fowl sat already on the spit, and in a bubbling pot he threw, higgledy-piggledy everything he could gather from the half sobbing girls. In the midst of this he took out of a broken cupboard one splendid glass after another, smashed it to pieces on the edge of the fireplace, and threw the fragments on the floor. I went forward and took the lanky loon around the body, but was not in a condition to remove him from the spot. His incredible obstinacy gave a giant's strength to his slim body, and I was still exhausted by all the sufferings we had gone through. When he turned his face toward me, his eyes were glassily fixed, but I noticed a whiff of wine. Quite taken aback, I now let him go. He was drunk.

The yellow-haired Katarina, who really seemed much more amused than frightened, meanwhile came up to me and told me in her soft voice—ho! old Captain Höök was young in those days and a pretty fellow— . . . Where were we now? Oh, yes, she said that he had gone from room to room, hunted through everything, and broken the vases and clocks. Finally, in the cellar he had searched through all the vaults except one—except one—one —one, to which the key was lost, she added hurriedly.

"But you, poor fellow, may also need something," she said to me, and pushed me into another room, which might have been called palatial. Around the walls hung woven greenish tapestries, on which Diana hunted a deer. The most splendid garments lay spread out over the slippery and shining floor; the armchairs were gilded, and beside a dish in the middle of the table stood mugs which were not filled with sickening kvass, not even with ale, but with a clear, yellow wine.

I, too, now lost my reason at the vision of all this magnificence, and my mistrust was somewhat eased because the two girls themselves seemed heartily delighted at having the chance to waste and destroy. They, too, felt themselves on hostile ground in the house where they had formerly had to go about as obedient and humble thralls. It was for them a moment of victory to be able to destroy the delicacies which they had never tasted, to throw themselves into proud reclining-chairs before which they had been forced to bow to the floor, and to trample on the costly garments which they had been scarcely deemed worthy to touch. They selected for me a coat of stiff cloth-of-silver, which had tails spread out with whalebone so that they were like a swelling skirt; and I got stockings and red shoes on the feet from which that evening I had ripped the boots with difficulty. Just the same, I did not dare to throw off the broadsword from my body, because I could not altogether put aside all doubts as to an ambush.

With the wholly childlike frankness of a little heart-subduer Katarina clapped her hands, which in fact were neither white nor soft, and confessed that she felt really jolly, since with me, who was of the same class, they could be as they chose; whereas before the ensign, who was a fine gentleman, they always had to be careful.

I sat down to the table in one of the armchairs, which was nearly buried under my glittering coat tails, and on either side I invited one of the girls, and clinked glasses with them and drank.

"The Herr Ensign is of very high extraction," said I. "He will end as, it may be—yes, a councillor of state."—That was up to then my most unseasonable remark, because people who wield the pen—"But the gracious young ladies know that the highborn sometimes, by an unlucky hap, may be born both foolish and simple-witted, and it is therefore that I regard myself obliged sometimes to screw up his wits a little into the right groove, so to speak."

I have always had a fault as a soldier. I have been able both to hack and to hew at the right time, but in the very act I have been too good-natured and accommodating. Therefore, too, I let Long Jan rummage in the kitchen however he chose, while I myself ate and drank to my heart's content. But with every gulp I felt how the wine kept on taking away my wits. That I did not become more forward than I was toward my merry hostesses depended less on the virtue with which the Almighty has sometimes wisely endowed beauty than on the hardships I had gone through, which quickly enough changed the wine into a sleeping potion. Reflection told me that I should push the mug aside, but, in addition to the distress of the last days, the wine was irresistible. I fell asleep sitting with hands crossed over the pommel of my sword.

"Now I hear tiptoeing steps," said I to myself in my dreams. "They are coming yet nearer behind my chair. Now I must draw steel. But what's that! I can move neither hand nor foot, though I am so much awake that I can see Diana and her greyhounds on the tapestry. All the air is dancing vapor, which rustles around the faces of the prattling girls and the flames of the waxlights. I am helplessly drunk. Of that there is no doubt, but now I am asleep again, and there's a tiptoeing behind my chair. A hidden serf stands there with his axe. Even now he's lifting it. The next instant I shall feel it as a lightning-flash through my head—and then all's over. Why won't the chair stand still? I can't hold myself on, if you jump. Whoa, there, Whiteface! I'd have you know there's nothing in the world that can scare me. But to hold myself on, sitting backward on the loins of one of the king's galloping chargers—that I can't. . . . Bang! Look there! Now I'm lying there in the middle of the stone pavement. . . . Fie! What are you laughing for? And then the vault in the cellar. . . . Why did you say just now that there was one . . . one . . . one two, one two, one two, lads in blue, two three, in grief and glee, three four, their land adore, four five, and boldly strive, five six, for Carolus Rex."

Finally I raised myself on my aching elbow and sang the whole of Psalm Number Six from the first to the last verse, and that with such a powerful voice that it seemed to me as if everything evil must have shrunk away in terror.

Many times have I treated myself to a booze, but never one that gave me worse agony. When I awoke in the morning, I sprang at once from the floor, where I was lying at full length on my back by the chair. I was still so sure of an ambush that I was wholly surprised when I found both the girls sleeping on a sheepskin under the table, on which a light was burning in the socket. Out in the kitchen I heard strange voices and came there upon an old one-eyed witch who was called Natalia, and a shaggy serf who was called Makar, and who to the smallest detail resembled the man of whom I had dreamed. They confessed that they had kept themselves hidden in the attic, but had now crept out when they noted that we intended no harm. They related that in the neighboring village there had also been several families during the night, but that at the report of our coming these had straightway loaded their belongings on a wagon and driven off at a gallop.

For the first time now I could honestly feel myself free from all apprehension, and with joy I went back to the hall, bent over the girls, and kissed Katarina both vigorously and long.

She woke up and laughed and turned over on her side to sleep further, but I kissed her yet again, and then she defended herself and jumped up, brisk and cheerful.

"You are a fine girl, Katarina, and I don't need to mistrust you any longer," said I. "Fetch me a little fresh water now and some salt."

While she came and went to set out my breakfast I often took her about her none too slender waist, and kissed her. At last she kissed me back, too, and leaned against the cloth-of-silver on my breast, and cried and laughed alternately. We went back and forth through the many rooms, but at a certain door she always checked herself, because back of it the ensign had been pleased to go to rest in one of the noble master's own down beds. Finally we sat down in a yellow reclining-chair, and I took her on my knee and wound her thick plait about my wrist. It was no falsehood either when I whispered into her ear that my hardened soldier's heart had seldom beaten more warmly.

I think with regret of the happy days that followed, and rather than recall them hour by hour, I leave it to you, especially to the young ones, to make use of your imaginations. Still, I always set Makar every evening as a guard before the house and never left off my broadsword. Sometimes Katarina in play would pull it from me, hold it out with both hands on the hilt, and go tramping through the rooms, while the autumn rain beat on the window-panes. The loosely suspended tapestries were set in motion by the draught she made, so that the pictures seemed to breathe and bow. There was an echo every time when, with her black hat pulled down like an old-fashioned morion, she shouted her "Forward!" Then I built barricades of tables and gilded leather chairs, until in the midst of the assault I leaped forth and overpowered both the amazon and her weapon. I had no longer any thought of my comrades, who meanwhile were perhaps hungering and bleeding, and my only wish was always to stay where I now found myself.

Katarina always smelt of lavender. We had barred off a corner room for our share of the house, and thither she carried her big chest, which was entirely plastered over with blue-checkered paper. This contained her clothes and other belongings, and it never was opened without filling the room with lavender scent. It was her favorite diversion to lie on her knees in front of the chest, pull out all her garments with a multitude of small boxes and receptacles, and then pack them in again with the greatest care. When I found that too tedious, or the room sometimes grew too cold, I persuaded her to go out with me to the great hall, where we sat down by the stove. Then I tried to fasten her attention by telling the life history of my long broadsword, which I did not shorten by a word. I knew for sure that it had the death of eleven men on its conscience, and on my arm I could show scars both of bullet-grazes and cuts. But she did not ask much about them. If I told the saga of Prince Gideon of Maxibrander, she grew impatient. "That is something that never happened," she said, and began eagerly to sew together green and red scallops of cloth on two fur boots, which were clearly intended to become a masterpiece of their kind.

The Herr Ensign lived in a continual booze and showed for the women the most open disdain. Katarina found this, too, very fortunate, she confessed, because it was so hard for a person in her class to reprove so high a gentleman, if he became attentive. One morning, in the midst of this, Herr Ensign called to mind the locked vault down in the cellar, which we had both forgotten. He went straightway there, and Katarina grew so beside herself with alarm that she could not conceal it. Pressing both my hands, she begged and prayed me to hold him back, and so completely was I then the prisoner of my heart that, although all my previous doubts awoke to life again, I let myself be forced to seek help for her.

We went down after Herr Ensign into the lighted cellar, where he was already absorbed in breaking open a locked wooden door.

"Let that alone!" I commanded him,

and he assented, but kept on, nevertheless, with his immovable stubbornness, breaking and prying.

Then I excused myself before my wailing followers with the plea that a common soldier such as I could not command an officer—and at that moment the door gave way.

Within the vault a lamp burned under a gilded Russian Madonna, and beside a table with various sorts of food stood a made-up bed. Between the bed and the wall moved something round and dark, which, when we went nearer, showed itself to be the bent back of an old man. When the old man saw himself unearthed, he crept forward, embraced Herr Ensign's knees, and begged and conjured him to give pardon. He admitted that he was the master of the house and that he had concealed himself after he had sent away his family, but promised to be our most humble servant if we had pity on his life.

"Be easy!" answered I, and helped the tottering old fellow up from the ground. "But then you shall be our drummer when we go to table."

When we ate that evening in the great hall, Herr Ensign as usual had the splendid chair, and beside him sat I and Katarina. At a table a little to the left stood the white-bearded and trembling master of the house with a brass mortar, and Makar with two pot-lids. They made their cooking utensils thunder in time to the melancholy folk-songs which ugly old Natalia sang, as she sat between the two on the edge of the table.

I don't know why, but her wailing voice gradually robbed me of all my brisk gayety, and I began to think of my thousands upon thousands of absent comrades. I had between my vest and shirt a whole packet of letters which anxious relatives had written to their dear ones in the field, and which they had begged me to deliver to them, if I ever should get on to the king's camp. I drew the letters from my bosom. They were not secret, for I had received many of them unsealed on my last evening at Riga. I pushed the candlestick nearer, eyed by chance a letter written in uncertain style, and read:

Give this into the hands of John.

My dere son:—

Receive thy father's blessing, though separated from him by both land and watter and right nere the heathenish parts of the urth, where crocodiles, scorpions and other harmful crawling things strike fere. . . .

I drew a wry face, mayhap, but I felt my sacred responsibility, and my mind grew all the heavier. I noticed that Katarina pressed my foot more energetically than usual, but I pressed back and thought that it was only a love token. When at last I had laid the letters together, I discovered that she sat quite pale, and could not take any wine or food. I bent a little to one side, so that she might be able to whisper but the old gentleman at the table stared at her unexpectedly, while he the more eagerly let his blows ring on the brass mortar, which he held out like a bell.

I remained in doubt and did not know rightly what trick I should invent. Then I trumped up the excuse that I was freezing. I went into the sleeping-room and after pretending to search in the dark awhile, called, "Katarina, my girl, where have you put the sheepskin coat?"

When she came in, she rushed straight up to me and threw herself on my neck with stifled sobbing.

"You didn't hear," she whispered, "that Makar just now in the midst of the noise told the master that he had got together more than sixty of the serfs, and that, as soon as he gives them a signal by breaking the window in the great hall, they are coming in to cut down both of you."

I remained fairly cool and sought to console her, but, choked with weeping, she told how she herself at the beginning was with the rest in wanting to entice us into a trap, but that she now no longer believed she could live on a day without me.

I pressed her to me hard and kissed her burning mouth and throbbing temples, and yet in that moment a strange repose fell upon my soul. My acquaintance with her became all at once nearly as something in the past. I have since, in my gray years, regretted this bitterly and wondered at myself, who at that especial moment had so little to give her. Reading the letter, the sudden danger . . . I don't know fully which was most to blame. To be sure, it depended on both.

"If I could take you along," I stammered.

She shook her head, as I could very clearly perceive in the half-light from the open door, and drew me instead to the window, where she begged me to steal off. Then I lashed myself into a sort of pretended anger, threw her from me over the polished floor, and cried with raised voice, "For whom do you take me, lass?"

With that I drew my broadsword and went out into the great hall, and when Herr Ensign got sight of me so, he rose from the table directly and also drew.

Then the master raised the mortar to throw it at the misty window-pane, but we stood right in front of him with our weapons, and his shaking knees became all the more bowed. He grew shorter and shorter, and the pestle rang between his fingers. Natalia crossed herself in silence, and Makar, who saw his master ready to sink, supported him from behind under the elbows and let the pot-lids fall clattering to the floor. Every now and then he tried to snatch the pestle to throw it at the window-pane, but then the old man shut his hand around the shaft without daring to let it go.

So we stood a long while facing one another, and we heard the kettle purr in the kitchen.

But soon we heard also the tap of steps, for the serfs had spied through the window from without and seen all. The kitchen door was filled with dirt-gray sheepskin coats, on which a bright button glinted here and there. Then a shot rang out and blew the smoke over the shaggy hides.

Now I wholly forgot our ensign game and shoved Long Jan aside so as to go at them for life and death, but just at this moment, even better than at any other time, was I to learn whom I had for a comrade. He stood still, obstinate as ever, seized me around both arms and swung me aside with the irresistible strength which his thin limbs gathered, I don't know from where.

"Ensign," said he, "if you have made yourself a private and me the ensign, then you ought also to know our custom in war that an officer goes first into the firing."

Like a thunderbolt he burst in among the sheep-skin coats, and with his great flat hands held the blade that with one blow cut the lintel over his neck and with another peeled off the poor wretches' hides and clothes. I heard yet another shot, and saw axes and hay-forks. His right arm twitched and grew bloody, and he could now only wield his weapon with the other, but I was at his side, hewing and thrusting.

We were forced into one corner of the kitchen, and my inflated fool's mantle of cloth-of-silver was cut to pieces so that the black stubs of whale-bone stuck out through the holes. Blackened with smoke so that he was unrecognizable, Long Jan tottered against my shoulder, and I took him by his uninjured hand and squeezed it in brotherly fashion with the words, "Now I've learned what you amount to, Jan, and if we get out of this, we shall nevermore leave each other."

He answered nothing. One eye was shut, the other was staring wide, and he fell heavily in front of me to the floor.

That was the last time I saw Long Jan, at whom I had so often laughed, and who had so often vexed me, but to whom I was now glad to offer the respectful grasp of a friend and an equal.

For a moment I sought involuntarily to defend his body, but gradually I perceived it would be useless in that last forlorn hope. A moment later I was groping around once more amid underbrush and mud, wet through with rain, and with a wound over one dexter finger.

I had, however, the luck to stumble upon a detail of twenty other wandering Swedes, and climbed up in a fir-tree to get my eye to the kernel of the far-stretching glow that tinted the lowering sky above the wood.

"What do you see?" asked my comrades.

"I see pitch-black darkness. But if I shut my eyes, I see still more. Then I see before me a hostile camp. Below me I see the soggy turf, which sucks hard about our feet, greedy for the honor of being the death-bed of a few poor wretches. Behind me I see the miles on miles of wilderness, where our brothers' corpses grow yellow beneath the fallen October leaves, where no hens cluck before the burnt homesteads, and no horse can find any food except the bark of twigs. But still farther away lies the sea, and beyond that I see a long road with tumble-down fences that climbs up to an old red-painted homestead. Within there, the turnips have just been taken from the table, and while the venerable old man opens his leather Bible, where a black cock's feather lies as marker to the first chapter of the Book of Revelation, he falls into musing and wonders if we perchance have by now got ahead with reinforcements to the king's camp, and if his dear boy may now be reading by the fire his half illegible letter."

Certainly I didn't say all this at that time, but I know that I thought it. Katarina was already an almost silenced memory.

"What do you see now?" asked my comrades. "You have climbed higher up."

Across the trees I saw beacons or campfires hanging within the yellow mist like lumps of melted iron, and as I strained my eyes, the row of gray tent-roofs in the light of the pitch beacons reminded me of a misty coast-line.

"That glow," I whispered to my comrades, "is a great apple with many kernels, and we need to have our swords ready. But wait! that was not Russian. Didn't you hear the two outposts who called to each other? As sure as I live was not that our own beloved mother-speech? If I didn't seven times hear 'devil,' may the devil take me!"

How did I come down from the fir? That I hardly remember. On all sides I shook outstretched hands and moved between blue and yellow coats from embrace to embrace. How many longed-for embraces did I not have to give, how many adventures to describe! I went about ever further into the camp, sometimes carried, sometimes dragged, sometimes met with ringing laughter, as they got sight of my ragged fool's-mantle, round which the projecting whalebones shook with every motion. Within me was a roar of joy.

"I have a letter to Captain Bagge," I shouted.

"Shot long ago."

"I have also a letter to Cederstjerne, Lieutenant."

"Shot."

I stumbled over a dead horse, which with its stiffened grin was almost scorched by a smouldering fire of logs. The rain had quenched the flames, and in the illuminated smoke behind the embers I saw a seated circle of grim-looking officers. Among them lay on the ground at full length a man with a fur hood drawn down and a cape collar over his face. I wanted to step over him and waved my packet of letters, but a hand seized me by the shoulder and I was harshly stopped short by the words, "Are you out of your wits? Don't you see it is His Majesty?"

Then I struck my heels together as I raised the hand with the packet to my head, and the tears that burst forth ran down my cheeks.

Captain Höök arose and finished his story as he bade good-night, but when he went out into the entry, the others heard that he remained standing on the winding stair.

Then one of the servant-girls drew her holiday jacket about her and loosened the last stump of one branch candle from the round table. As she carried it, she held one hand underneath, so that no grease should fall on the straw. Thereupon she went out carefully to light the captain, for they all knew that he, a Charles man, was so afraid of the dark that he never dared go alone across the attic.

The Fortified House

Surprised by the winter cold, the Swedes in crowded confusion had taken up their quarters behind the walls of Hadjash. Soon there was not a house to be found that was not filled with the frost-bitten and the dying. Cries of distress were heard out in the street, and here and there beside the steps lay amputated fingers, feet, and legs. Vehicles stood fastened to each other, so tightly packed from the city gate to the market-place that the chilly-pale soldiers, who streamed in from all sides, had to crawl between the wheels and runners. Buckled in their harness and turned away from the wind, the horses, their loins white with frost, had already stood many days without food. No one took care of them, and several of the drivers sat frozen to death with hands stuck into their sleeves. Some wagons were like oblong boxes or coffins, where from the chink of the flat lid stared out mournful faces, which read in a prayer-book or gazed longingly with feverish delirium at the sheltering houses. A thousand unfortunates, in muffled tones or silently, cried to God for mercy. Under the sheltered side of the city wall dead soldiers stood in lines, many with red Cossack coats buttoned over their ragged Swedish uniforms and with sheepskins around their naked feet. Wood-doves and sparrows, which were so stiff with frost that they could be caught with the hand, had fallen on the hats and shoulders of the standing corpses, and fluttered their wings when the chaplains went by to give a Last Communion in brandy.

Up at the market-place among burnt areas stood an unusually large house, from which could be heard loud voices. A soldier delivered a fagot to an ensign who stood in the doorway, and when the soldier went back into the street, he shrugged his shoulders and said to whomsoever cared to hear him: "It's only the gentlemen quarreling in the chancellery."

The ensign at the door had lately arrived with Lewenhaupt's forces. He carried the fagot into the room, and threw it down by the fireplace. The voices within ceased immediately, but as soon as he had closed the door, they began with renewed heat.

It was His Excellency Piper who stood in the middle of the floor, his countenance wrinkled and furrowed, with glowing cheeks and trembling nostrils.

"I say that the whole affair is madness," he burst out, "madness, madness!"

Hermelin, with his pointed nose, was

constantly twitching his eyes and his hands, while he sprang back and forth in the room like a tame rat; but Field Marshal Rehnskiöld, who, with his handsome, stately figure, was standing by the fireplace, only whistled and hummed. If he had not whistled and hummed, the quarrel would have been finished by this time, because for once they were all fully agreed; but the fact that he whistled and hummed instead of being silent or at least speaking, that could be endured no longer. Lewenhaupt at the window took snuff and snapped shut his snuff-box. His pepper-brown eyes protruded from his head, and it looked as if his comical peruke became ever bigger and bigger. If Rehnskiöld had not continued to whistle and hum, he would have controlled himself to-day as yesterday and on all other occasions, but now wrath rose to his brow.

He shut his snuff-box for the last time, and mumbled between his teeth, "I do not ask that His Majesty should understand statesmanship. But can he lead troops? Does he show real insight at a single encounter or attack? Trained and proved old warriors, who never can be replaced, he offers daily for an empty bravado. If our men are to storm a wall, it is considered superfluous that they bind themselves protecting fagots or shields, and therefore they are wretchedly massacred. To speak freely, my worthy sirs, I can forgive an Uppsala student many a boyish freak, but I demand otherwise of a general in the field. Truly it avails not to carry on a campaign under the command of such a master."

"Furthermore," continued Piper, "His Majesty does not at present incommode you, general, with any particularly hard command. At the beginning, before one man had succeeded in distinguishing himself more than another, it went better; but now His Majesty goes around mediating and reconciling with a foolish smile so that one could go crazy."

He raised his arms in the air with a wrath which had lost all sense and bounds, notwithstanding he was altogether at one with Lewenhaupt. While he was still speaking, he turned about and betook himself impetuously to the inner apartments. The door slammed with such a clatter that Rehnskiöld found himself yet more called upon to whistle and hum. If he only had chosen to say something! But no, he did not. Gyllenkrook, who sat at the table and examined departure-checks, was blazing in the face, and a little withered-looking officer at his side whispered venomously into his ear: "A pair of diamond earrings given to Piper's countess might perhaps even yet help Lewenhaupt to new appointments."

If Rehnskiöld had now ceased to whistle and hum, Lewenhaupt would still have been able to control himself, to take up the roll of papers he carried under his coat and sit down at a corner of the table; but instead, the venerable and at other times taciturn man grew worse and worse. He turned about undecidedly and went toward the entrance door, but there he suddenly stood still, drew himself up, and smacked his heels together as if he had been a mere private. Now Rehnskiöld became quiet. The door opened. An icy gust of wind rushed into the room, and the ensign announced with as loud and long-drawn a voice as a sentry who calls his comrades to arms: "Hi–s Majesty!"

The king was no longer the dazzled and wondering half-grown youth of aforetime. Only the boyish figure with the narrow shoulders was the same. His coat was sooty and dirty. The wrinkle around the short, protruding upper lip had become deeper and rather morose. On the nose and one cheek he had frost-bite, and his eyelids were red-edged and swollen with protracted cold, but around the formerly bald vertex of his head the combed-back hair stood up like a pointed crown.

He held a fur cap in both hands, and tried to conceal his embarrassment and diffidence behind a stiff and cold ceremoniousness, while bowing and smiling to each and all of those present.

They bowed again and again still more deeply, and when he had advanced to the middle of the floor, he stood still and bowed awkwardly toward the sides, though with somewhat more haste, being apparently wholly occupied with what he was about to say. Thereupon he remained a long while standing quite silent.

Then he went forward to Rehnskiöld and, with a brief inclination, took him by one of his coat buttons.

"I would beg," he said, "that Your Excellency provide me with two or three men of the common soldiers as escort for a little excursion. I have already two dragoons with me."

"But, Your Majesty! the country is overrun with Cossacks. To ride in here to the city from Your Majesty's quarters with so small an escort was already a feat of daring."

"Oh, nonsense, nonsense! Your Excellency will do as I have said. Some one of the generals present, who is at leisure, may also mount and take one of his men."

Lewenhaupt bowed.

The king regarded him a trifle irresolutely without answering, and remained standing after Rehnskiöld hastened out. None of the others in the circle considered it necessary to break the silence or to move.

Only after a very long pause did the king bow again to every one separately, and go out into the open air.

"Well?" inquired Lewenhaupt and clapped the ensign on the shoulder with a return of his natural kindliness. "The ensign shall go along! This is the first time the ensign has stood eye to eye with His Majesty."

"I had never expected he would be like that."

"He is always like that. He is too kingly to command."

They followed after the king, who clambered over wagons and fallen animals. His motions were agile, never abrupt, but measured and quite slow, so that he never for a moment lost his dignity. When he had finally made his way forward through the throng to the city gate, he mounted to the saddle with his attendants, who were now seven men.

The horses stumbled on the icy street, and some fell, but Lewenhaupt's remonstrances only induced the king to use his spurs yet more heartlessly. The lackey Hultman had read aloud to him all night or had related sagas, and had at length coaxed him into laughing at the prophecy that, had he not been exalted by God to be a king, he would for his whole life have become an unsociable floor-pacer, who devised much more wonderful verses than those of the late Messenius of Disa on Bollhus, but especially the mightiest battle stories. He tried to think of Rolf Gotriksson, who ever rode foremost of all his men, but to-day it did not please him to bound his thoughts within the playroom of a saga. The restlessness, which during the last few days had struck its claws into his mind, would not let go of its royal prey. At the chancellery he had just seen the heated faces. Ever since the pranks of his boyhood he had been wrapt in his own imaginary world of the past. He had sat deaf to the piercing cries of distress along the way, while he became distrustful of each and all who exhibited a more sensitive hearing. To-day, as at other times, he hardly noted that they offered him the best-rested horse and the freshest cake of bread, that in the morning they laid a purse with five hundred ducats in his pocket, that the horsemen at the first *mêlée* would form a ring about him and offer themselves to that death which he had challenged. On the other hand, he noticed that the soldiers saluted him with gloomy silence, and misfortunes had made him suspicious even of those nearest to him. The most cautious opposition, the most concealed disapproval, he made a note of without betraying himself, and every word remained and gnawed at his soul. Every hour it seemed to him that he lost an officer on whom he had formerly relied, and his heart became all the colder. His thwarted ambition chafed and bled under the weight of failure, and he breathed more lightly the farther behind him he left his headquarters.

Suddenly Lewenhaupt came to a stand, debating within himself how to exercise an influence upon the king.

"My heroic Ajax!" said he, and patted his steaming horse, "you are indeed an old manger-biter, but I have no right to founder you for no good cause, and I myself am beginning to get on in years as you are. But in Jesus' name, lads, let him who can follow the king!"

When he saw the ensign's anxious sidelong look toward the king, he spoke with lowered voice: "Be faithful, boy! His Majesty does not roar out as we others do. He is too kingly to chide or bicker."

The king feigned to notice nothing. More and more wildly over ice and snow he kept up the silent horse-race without goal or purpose. He had now only four attendants. After another hour one of the remaining horses fell with a broken foreleg, and the rider out of pity shot a bullet through its ear, after which he himself, alone and on foot, went to meet an uncertain fate in the cold.

At last the ensign was the only man who was able to follow the king, and they had now come among bushes and saplings, where they could proceed but at a foot-pace. On the hill above them rose a gray and sooty house with narrow grated windows, the courtyard being surrounded by a wall.

At this moment there was a shot.

"How was that?" inquired the king, and looked around.

"The pellet piped nastily when it went by my ear, but it only bit the corner of my hat," answered the ensign, without the least experience of how he ought to conduct himself before the king. He had a slight Småland accent, and laughed contentedly with his whole blond countenance.

Enchanted by the good fortune of being man by man with him whom he regarded as above all other living human beings, he continued: "Shall we then go up there and take them by the beard?"

The answer pleased the king in the highest degree, and with a leap he stood on the ground.

"We'll tie our steeds here in the bushes," he said, exhilarated and with bright color on his cheek. "Afterwards let us go up and run them all through as easily as whistling."

They left the panting horses and, bending forward, climbed up the hill among the bushes. Over the wall looked down several Cossack heads with hanging hair, yellow and grinning as those of beheaded criminals.

"Look!" whispered the king, and smote his hands together. "They're trying to pull shut the rotten gate, the fox-tails!"

His glance, but recently so expressionless, became now flickering and anon open and shining. He drew his broadsword and raised it with both hands above his head. Like a young man's god he stormed in through the half-open door. The ensign, who cut and thrust by his side, was often close to being struck from behind by his weapon. A musket-shot blackened the king's right temple. Four men were cut down in the gateway, and the fifth of the band fled with a fire-shovel into the courtyard, pursued by the king.

Then the king wiped off the blood from his sword on the snow, while he laid two ducats in the Cossack's shovel and burst out with rising spirits, "It is no pleasure to fight with these wretches who never strike back and only run. Come back when you have bought yourself a decent sword."

The Cossack, who understood nothing, stared at the gold-pieces, sneaked along the wall to the gate, and fled. Ever farther and farther away on the plain he called his roving comrades with a dismal and lamenting "Oohaho! Oohaho!"

The king hummed to himself as if chaffing with an unseen enemy: "Little Cossack man, little Cossack man, go gather up your rascals!"

The walls around the courtyard were mouldering and black. From the wilderness sounded an endlessly prolonged minor tone as from an aeolian harp, and the king inquisitively shouldered in the door of the dwelling-house. This consisted of a single large and half-dark room, and before the fireplace lay a heap of blood-stained clothing, which plunderers of corpses had taken from fallen Swedes. The door was thrown shut again by the cross-draught, and the king went to the stable-buildings at the side. There was no door there, and a sound was now heard the more plainly. Within in the darkness lay a starved white horse bound to an iron ring in the wall.

A lifted broadsword would not have checked the king, but the uncertain dusk caused the man of imagination to stand on the threshold, fearful of the dark. Yet he gave no sign of this, but beckoned the ensign. They stepped in down a steep stairway to a cellar. Here there was a well, and at the arm of the creaking windlass that brought up the water, a deaf Cossack, wholly unaware of danger, was driving around with whip and reins a human figure in the uniform of a Swedish officer.

When they had loosed the rope and had bound the Cossack in the place of the prisoner, they recognized the Holsteiner, Feuerhausen, who had served as major in a regiment of dragoon recruits, but had been cut off by the Cossacks and harnessed as a draught animal for hoisting water.

He fell on his knees, and stammered in broken Swedish: "Your Majesty! I gan't pelief my eyes . . . My gratitude—" . . .

The king cheerily interrupted his talk, and turned to the ensign: "Bring up the two horses to the stable! Three men cannot ride comfortably on two horses, and therefore we shall stay here till a few Cossacks come by, from whom we can take a new horse. Do you, sir, stand guard at the gate."

After that the king went back to the dwelling-house, and shut the door after him. The horses which, desperate with hunger, had been greedily gnawing the bark from the bushes, were meanwhile led up to the stable, and the ensign mounted guard.

Slowly the hours went by. When it began to draw towards dusk, the storm increased in bitterness, and in the light of sunset the snow whirled over the desolate snow-plain. Deathly yellow Cossack faces raised themselves spying above the bushes, and borne in the wind sounded the roving plunderers' "Oohaho! Oohaho! Oohaho!"

Then Feuerhausen stepped out of the stable, where he had sat between the horses so as not to get frost in his wounds from the ropes with which he had been bound. He went forward to the barred doors of the dwelling-house.

"Your Majesty!" he stammered, "the Cossacks are gathering more and more, and darkness is coming soon. I and the ensign can both sit on one horse. If we delay here, this night will be Your Mightiest Majesty's last, which Gott in His secret dispensation forbit!"

The king answered from within, "It must be as we said. Three men do not ride comfortably on two horses."

The Holsteiner shook his head and went down to the ensign.

"Such is His Majesty, you damt Swedes. From the stable I heard him walk and walk back and forvart. Sickness and conscience-torture will come. Like a *pater familiae* the Muscovite czar stands among his subjects. A confectioner he sets up as his friend, and a simple servant-girl he raises to his glorious imperial throne. Detestable are his gestures when he gets drunk, and he treats women *à la françois;* but his first and last wort always runs, 'For Russia's goot!' King Carolus leafs his lants as smoking ash-heaps, and does not possess a single frient, not efen among his nearest. King Carolus is more lonely than the meanest wagon-drifer. He has not once a comrade's knee to weep on. Among nobles and fine ladies and perukes he comes like a spectre out of a thousant-year mausoleum—and spectres mostly go about witout company. Is he a man of state? Oh, haf mercy! No sense for the public. Is he a general? Good-by! No sense for the big masses. Only to make bridges and set up gabions, clap his hants at captured flags and a couple of kettledrums. No sense for state and army, only for men."

"That may be also a sense," replied the ensign.

He walked vigorously back and forward, for his fingers were already so stiff with cold that he scarcely could hold his drawn blade.

The Holsteiner shifted the ragged coat-collar around his cheeks and went on with muffled voice and eager gestures: "King Carolus laughs with delight when the bridge breaks, and men and beasts are miserably drownt. No heart in his breast. To the deuce wit him! King Carolus is such a little Swedish half-genius as wanders out in the worlt and beats the drum and parades and makes a fiasco, and the parterre whistles, Whee!"

"And that is why the Swedes go to death for him," answered the ensign; "that is just why."

"Not angry, my dearest fellow! Your teeth shone so in a laugh when we first met."

"I like to hear the Herr Major talk, but I'm freezing. Will not the major go up and listen at the king's door?"

The Holsteiner went up to the door and listened. When he came back, he said, "He only walks and walks, and sighs heavily like a man in anguish of soul. So it always is now, they say. His Majesty nefer sleeps any more at night. The comedy-actor knows he is not up to his part, and of all life's torments wounded ambition becomes the bitterest."

"Then it should also be the last for us to jest at. Dare I beg the major to rub my right hand with snow; it is getting numb."

The Holsteiner did as he desired, and turned back to the king's door. He struck his forehead with both hands. His gray-sprinkled, bushy moustaches stood straight out, and he mumbled, "Gott, Gott! Soon it will be too dark to retreat."

The ensign called, "Good sir, I should like to ask if you would rub my face with snow. My cheeks are freezing stiff. Of the pain in my foot I will not speak. Ah, I can't bear it."

The Holsteiner filled his hands with snow. "Let me stand guard," he said, "only for an hour."

"No, no. The king has commanded that I stay here at the entrance."

"Och, the king! I know him. I will make him cheerful, talk philosophy, tell of gallant exploits. He is always amused to hear of a lover who climbs adventurously through a window. He often looks at the beautiful side of womankint. That appeals to his imagination, but not to his flesh, for he is witout feeling. Ant he is bashful. If the fair one ever wishes to tread him under her silken shoe, she must herself attack, but pretent to flee, and all the others must strive against the *liaison*. The most mighty lady, his grandmother, spoiled everything with her shriek of 'Marriage, marriage!' King Carolus is from top to toe like the Swedish queen Christina, though he is genuinely masculine. The two should have married each other on the same throne. That would haf been a fine little pair. Oh, pfui, pfui! you Swedes. If a man gallops his horses and lets people and kingdom be massacred, he is still pure-hearted and supreme among all, if only his bloot is too slow for amours. Oh, excuse me! I know pure-hearted heroes who were faithfully in love with two, three different maidens or wives in one and the same week."

"Yes, we are so, we are so. But for Christ's pity you must rub my hand again. And excuse my moaning and groaning!"

Just inside the gate, which could not be shut, lay the fallen Cossacks, white as marble with the hoar frost. The yellow sky became gray, and ever nearer and more manifold in the twilight sounded the wailing cries, "Oohaho! Oohaho! Oohaho!"

Now the king opened his door and came down across the court.

The pains in his head, from which he had begun to suffer, had been increased by his ride in the wind and made his glance heavy. His countenance bore traces of lonely soul-strife, but as he drew near, his mouth resumed its usual embarrassed smile. His temple was still blackened after the musket-shot.

"It's freshening up," he said, and producing from his coat a loaf of bread, he broke it in three, so that every one had as large a piece as he did. After that, he lifted off his riding-cape, and fastened it himself about the shoulders of the sentinel ensign.

Abashed over his own conduct, he then took the Holsteiner forcibly by the arm and led him up through the courtyard, while they chewed at their hard bread.

Now, if ever, thought the Holsteiner, is the time to win the king's attention with a clever turn of speech, and afterwards talk sense with him.

"The accommodation might be worse," he began, at the same time biting and chewing. "Ah, good old days! That reminds me of a gallant adventure outside of Dresden."

The king kept on holding him by the arm, and the Holsteiner lowered his voice. The story was lively and salacious, and the king grew inquisitive. The coarsest allusions always lured out his set smile. He listened with a despairing and half-absent man's need of momentary diversion.

Only when the Holsteiner with cunning deftness began to shift the conversation over to some words about their immediate danger did the king again become serious.

"Bagatelle, bagatelle!" he replied. "It is nothing at all worth mentioning, except that we must behave ourselves well and sustain our reputation to the last man. If the rascals come on, we will all three place ourselves at the gate and pink them with our swords."

The Holsteiner stroked his forehead and felt around. He began to talk about the stars that were just shining out. He set forth a theory for measuring their distance from the earth. The king now listened to him with a quite different sort of attention. He broke into the question keenly, resourcefully, and with an unwearied desire to think out new, surprising methods in his own way. One assertion gave a hand to another, and soon the conversation dwelt on the universe and the immortality of the soul, to return afresh to the stars. More and more of them flickered in the heavens, and the king described what he knew about the sun-dial. He stood up his broadsword with its scabbard in the snow and directed the point toward the Polestar, so that next morning they might be able to tell the time.

"The heart of the universe," he said, "must be either the earth or the star that stands over the land of the Swedes. No land must be of more account than the Swedish land."

Outside the wall the Cossacks were calling out, but as soon as the Holsteiner led the talk to their threatened attack, the king was laconic.

"At daybreak we shall betake ourselves back to Hadjash," said he. "Before then we can hardly secure a third horse, so that each of us can ride comfortably in his own saddle."

After he had spoken in that strain, he went back into the dwelling-house.

The Holsteiner came down with a vehement stride to the ensign, and pointing at the king's door, he cried out, "Forgif me, ensign. We Germans don't mince words when a wount oozes after a rope, but I lay down my arms and gif you, sir, the victory, because I also could shed my bloot for the man. Do I lofe him! No one efer understands him that has not seen him. But, ensign, you cannot stay any longer out in the weather."

The ensign replied, "No cape has warmed me more sweetly than the one I now wear, and I lay all my cares on Christ. But in God's name, major, go back to the door and listen! The king might do himself some harm."

"His Majesty would not fall on his *own* sword, but longs for another's."

"Now I hear his steps even down here. They are getting still more violent and restless. He is so lonely. When I saw him in Hadjash bowing and bowing among the generals, I could only think, How lonely he is!"

"If the little Holsteiner slips away from here alife, he will always remember the steps we heard to-night and always call this refuge Fort Garten."

The ensign nodded his approval and answered, "Go to the stable, major, and seek rest and shelter awhile between the horses. And there through the walls you can better hear the king and watch over him."

Thereupon the ensign began to sing with resonant voice:

O Father, to Thy loving grace . . .

The Holsteiner went back across the court into the stable and, his voice quavering with cold, intoned with the other:

In every time and every place
My poor weak soul would I commend.
O Lord, receive it and defend.

"Oohaho! Oohaho!" answered the Cossacks in the storm, and it was already night.

The Holsteiner squeezed himself in between the two horses, and listened till weariness and sleep bowed his head. Only at dawn was he wakened by a clamor. He sprang out into the open air, and beheld the king already standing in the court looking at the sword that had been set up as a sun-dial.

By the gate the Cossacks had collected but when they saw the motionless sentry they shrank back in superstitious fear and thought of the rumors concerning the magic of the Swedish soldiers against blow and shot.

When the Holsteiner had gotten forward to the ensign, he grasped him hard by the arm.

"What now?" he asked. "Brandy?"

At the same instant he let go his grip.

The ensign stood frozen to death with his back against the wall of the gate, his hands on his sword-hilt, and wrapped in the king's cloak.

"Since we are now only two," the king remarked, drawing his weapon out of the snow, "we can at once betake ourselves each to his horse, as it was arranged."

The Holsteiner stared him right in the eyes with reawakened hate and remained standing, as if he had heard nothing. Finally, however, he led out the horses, but his hands trembled and clenched themselves, so that he could hardly draw the saddle-girths.

The Cossacks swung their sabres and pikes, but the sentry stood at his post.

Then the king sprang carelessly into the saddle, and set his horse to a gallop. His forehead was clear, his cheeks were rosy, and his broadsword glimmered like a sunbeam.

The Holsteiner looked after him. His bitter expression relaxed, and he murmured between his teeth, while he too mounted to the saddle and with hand lifted to his hat raced by the sentry: "It is only the joy of a hero in seeing a hero's noble death.—Thanks, comrade!"

A Clean White Shirt

Private Bengt Geting had got a Cossack's pike through his breast, and his comrades laid him on a heap of twigs in a copse, where Pastor Rabenius gave him the Holy Communion. This was on the icy ground before the walls of Veperik, and a whistling norther tore the dry leafage from the bushes.

"The Lord be with thee!" whispered Rabenius softly and paternally. "Are you prepared now to depart hence after a good day's work?"

Bengt Geting lay with his hands knotted, bleeding to death. The hard eyes stood wide open, and the obstinate and scraggy face was so tanned by sun and frost that the bluish pallor of death shone out only over his lips.

"No," he said.

"That is the first time I have heard a word from your mouth, Bengt Geting."

The dying man knotted his hands all the harder, and chewed with his lips, which opened themselves for the words against his will.

"For once," he said slowly, "even the meanest and raggedest of soldiers may speak out."

He raised himself painfully on his elbow, and ejaculated such a piercing cry of anguish that Rabenius did not know whether it came from torment of soul or of body.

He set down the chalice on the ground, and spread a handkerchief over it, so that the leaves which were tumbling about should not fall into the brandy.

"And this," he stammered, pressing his hands to his forehead, "this I, who am a servant of Christ, shall be constrained to witness, morning after morning, evening after evening."

Soldiers crowded forward from all sides between the bushes to see and hear the fallen man, but their captain came in a wrathful mood with sword drawn.

"Tie a cloth over the fellow's mouth!" he shouted. "He has always been the most obstinate man in the battalion. I am no more inhuman than another, but I must do my duty, and I have a mass of new and untrained folk that have come with Lewenhaupt. These have got scared by his wailing, and refuse to go forward. Why don't you obey? I command here."

Rabenius took a step forward. On his curled white peruke he had a whole garland of yellow leaves.

"Captain," he said, "beside the dying the servant of God alone commands, but in glad humility he delivers his authority to the dying man himself. For three years I have seen Bengt Geting march in the line, but never yet have I seen him speak with any one. Now on the threshold of God's judgment-seat may no one further impose silence upon him."

"With whom should I have spoken?" asked the bleeding trooper bitterly. "My tongue is as if tied and lame. Weeks would go by without my saying a word. No one has ever asked me about anything. It was only the ear that had to be on guard so that I did not fail to obey. 'Go,' they have said, 'go through marsh and snow.' To that there was nothing to answer."

Rabenius knelt and softly took his hands in his.

"But now you shall speak, Bengt Geting. Speak, speak, now that all are gathered to hear you. You are now the only one of us all who has the right to speak. Is there a wife or perhaps an aged mother at home to whom you want me to send a message?"

"My mother starved me and sent me to the troops, and never since then has a woman had anything else to say to me than the same, 'Get away, Bengt Geting, go, go! What do you want with us?' "

"Have you then anything to repent?"

"I repent that as a child I did not jump into the mill-race, and that, when you stood before the regiment on Sunday and admonished us to go patiently on and on, I didn't step forward and strike you down with my musket.—But do you want to know what causes me dread? Have you never heard the wagon-drivers and outposts tell how in the moonlight they have seen their comrades that were shot limp in crowds after the army and hop about on their mangled legs and cry, 'Greetings to mother!'—They call them the Black Battalion. It's into the Black Battalion that I'm to go now. But the worst is that I shall be buried in my ragged coat and my bloody shirt. That's the thing I can't get out of my mind. A plain trooper doesn't want to be taken home like the dead General Liewen, but I'm thinking of the fallen comrades at Dorfsniki, where the king had a coffin of a couple of boards and a clean white shirt given to each man. Why should they be treated so much better than I? Now in this year of misfortune a man is laid out as he falls. I'm so deeply sunk in misery that the only thing in the world that I can be envious of is their clean white shirts."

"My poor friend," answered Rabenius quietly, "in the Black Battalion—if you believe in it now—you will have great company. Gyldenstolpe and Sperling and Lieutenant-Colonel Mörner already lie shot on the field. And do you recall the thousand others? Do you remember the friendly Lieutenant-Colonel Wattrang, who came riding to our regiment and gave an apple to every soldier, and who now lies among the Royal Dragoons, and all our comrades under the meadow at Holofzin? And do you remember my predecessor, Nicholas Uppendich, a mighty proclaimer of the Word, who fell at Kalisch in his priestly array? Grass has grown and snow fallen over his mould, and no one can point out with his foot the sod where he sleeps."

Rabenius bowed yet deper, and felt the man's forehead and hands.

"In ten or at most fifteen minutes you will have ceased to live. Perhaps these minutes might replace the past three years, if you sanctify them rightly. You are no longer one of us. Don't you see that your spiritual guide is lying on his knees by you with head uncovered? Speak now and tell me your last wish; no, your last command. Consider but one thing. The regiment is disorganized on your account, and meanwhile the others go forward with glory or stand already on the storming-ladders. You have frightened the younger fellows with your death-wound and your wailing, and you alone can make it good again. Now they listen only to you, and you alone have it in your power to make them go against the enemy. Consider that your last words will be last forgotten, and perhaps sometime will be repeated for those at home, who sit and roast their potatoes behind the oven."

Bengt Geting lay motionless, and a

shadow of perplexity passed over his glance. Then he gently raised his arms as if for an invocation and whispered, "Lord, help me to do even so!"

He gave a sign that now he was able only to whisper, and Rabenius laid his face to his so as to be able to hear his words. Then Rabenius motioned to the soldiers, but his voice trembled so that he could hardly make himself heard.

"Now Bengt Geting has spoken," he said. "This is his last wish, that you should take him between you on your muskets and carry him with you in his old place in the line, where he has stubbornly marched day after day and year after year."

The drums now struck up, the music began, and with his cheek on the shoulder of one of the soldiers Bengt Geting was carried forward step by step over the field toward the foe. Around him followed the whole regiment, and ever with bared head Rabenius went behind him, and did not notice that he was already dead.

"I shall see to it," he whispered, "that you get a clean white shirt. You know that the king does not regard himself as more than the humblest soldier, and it is so that he himself wishes sometime to lie."

Poltava

On the first of May Field Marshal Rehnskiöld gave an evening dinner, and Colonel Appelgren became heated about the forehead and inquisitive; he rolled breadcrumbs with his fingers and looked cross-eyed.

"Can Your Excellency say why Poltava has to be besieged?"

"His Majesty wants to have amusement till the Poles and Tartars come with reinforcements."

"And nevertheless we know that neither of them is coming. Europe begins to forget our court *à la* Diogenes with riding ministers of state, fighting chancellor's clerks, chamberlains falling in battle, seats of honor on tree stumps . . . and with palaces of tent-cloth, and pancakes and small beer on the royal table."

"His Majesty wishes to practise fortifications now, and is getting the habit of camping out for the rest of his life. So we have time ahead of us. Poltava is a little flea fortress, which will probably surrender when the first shot cracks."

The field marshal became abruptly silent, and dropped his fork.

"I believe those fellows in the town have gone crazy, and are going to defend themselves."

He sprang out and threw himself into the saddle. All arose and heard a continuous firing.

The Russian sentries around the walls had the custom of shouting long and noisily in the darkness, "Good bread, good drink!" During this screaming, Colonel Gyllenkrook, without any one being able to hear his approach, had begun to open trenches, and had set up a cover, but at that moment the king ran over the field, and shouted aloud something to his adjutant-general. The fact that he held his drawn broadsword prevented him from looking ridiculous as he ran. Gyllenkrook asked him not to cry out so loud so as not to alarm the enemy, but even while he was speaking, the outposts were silent, and began instead to light their port-fires and shoot. Fire-balls that rose aloft threw their light over the hills and meadow-land, and were reflected in the hurrying waters of the Vorskla. Gyllenkrook's laboring Zaporogeans then sprang back from their spades and gabions, and the Swedish soldiers, who thumped on their leather coats with the flat of the sword, at last began themselves to flee or to lie down on the ground.

In that way the shooting had begun.

"Look there!" said Gyllenkrook, who

stood behind a tree with the king and the Little Prince. "A small cause may bring about such a big confusion, and for the last time I dare propose that the whole siege be given up. In my prayers unite the tired troops and all the unhappy subjects at home. Why were we not commanded hither in the winter, when the town might have been easily taken? Now the garrison is strengthened every day, and the enemy's whole army is on the advance. We have barely thirty cannon left, and the powder, which has many times been wet and dried again, only casts the shot a little way from their muzzles."

"Nonsense, nonsense! Why, we've shot away many a log thicker than a scaling-post."

"But here we need to shoot away many hundreds."

"If we can shoot away one, we can shoot away hundreds. We must perform just what is extraordinary, so that we get reputation and honor from it. Now we shall let the Zaporogeans see that they can work here without the least danger."

The king stuck his broadsword under his arm, and went out into the rain of shot on the field. Behind him followed the Little Prince, pale, erect, festal as a youth in an ancient procession to a sacrifice at the temple.

Two thick logs were driven down like two gateposts close to the open trench, and there the king took his stand behind a fallen fire-ball, whose daylight brilliance exposed him to the enemy. The Little Prince gave him a hesitating side-look, and felt up and down his sword-hilt with his hand, which trembled a little. After that he climbed upon one of the logs and took a position with his arms at his side. Then a junior officer, who was called Morten Preacher, stepped up on the other log. He had a face brown as leather, black hair, and brass rings in his ears. Motionless as two painted wooden statues in some Catholic country district, the two guards stood in this way behind their king, and the furious Russians directed their catapults and field-pieces and muskets at the remarkable spectacle. No one wished to humble himself and descend first, and for that reason they had to stay. There was whistling and swishing as of whips and rods, as of storm-gusts and pipes, while cannon-balls, striking near, threw gravel and clods on high. It lightened and thundered, the ground trembled like a frightened horse, and splinters and bits of stone whirled by.

"The king is there! Now he'll be shot!" cried the soldiers, rushing forward and driving the Zaporogeans among them. Again they seized the spades, and again the Zaporogeans tore up the turf and opened the earth, so that they could lie down and get shelter.

In the light of the burning pitch stood the monarch of the generals and dignitaries, the comrade of the soldiers, at once knight errant, king, and philosopher. All day long dark memories had slunk in his footsteps. He recalled Axel Hård, whom he himself had killed by accident, and Klinckowström, the friend of his youth, shot dead. He felt the loss of neither, but he could not forget their bloody clothes. All the heaven-storming gayety of boyhood, however, awoke to life and silenced the heavy thoughts, when one heard the bullets. He had drained the cup of warlike adventure to the bottom, and the drink needed to be spiced more strongly every day to have relish. He began to see the great clamorous victories in a colder light as they became rarer. To be sure he could still sometimes talk about ruling great states, but that was mostly so that these should provide him daily with a hundred more gallant guardsmen. He never forgot that any moment might be his last, but the years of misfortune were come. How sweet would not repose be after a glorious death! To will, to know he had the power, ut yet to fail and become a mockery, ecause the others could no longer fol- ɔw—that was the breath of frost from he autumn of life. He wished to prove, e wished to show, that he was still the xceptional man under God's protection. f he were not that, then he wished to fall ke the plainest soldier.

Morten Preacher meanwhile grew so xcited that he could not hold himself notionless on the pillar, but shifted the nusket from his back. Who did not know Morten Preacher, the sharpshooter, who ould make even the king clap his hands? Either an infantryman or a cavalryman e could bring down in full career. He nuttered and laughed, laid the weapon o his eye, and shot at a shadow that limbed in the farthest cherry-tree. Struck y the ball, it tumbled down among the lossoming twigs like a bird. Then a hunt- r's enthusiasm came over Morten Preach- r, and he hopped down and sprang to the pot.

There lay an old man, shot dead, and eside him stood a little girl of nine years.

"That's father," she said without cry- ng, and looked at Morten Preacher. "We vere out picking nettles, and on the way ome—"

"Well, on the way home—?"

"We heard shooting, and then father limbed up to look around. That is fa- her's cherry-tree."

Morten Preacher shook his head, took ff his hat and tore at his hair, and sat lown.

"God forgive me—the old man has ever done me any harm. Dear child— ou cannot understand this. But I have a lucat in my pocket. Take it! You see, my hild, I'm a hunter, you understand, a egular old expert hunter. Formerly I ad my cottage and my sweetheart, who uarrelled and struck at me because I ever moved my spade—you know what spade is?—but only sat in the woods nd listened to the blackcock's song. Hearken now! Then one morning I took my musketoon and my dog and went my way out into the world."

The girl turned over the ducat in the light of the fire, but he drew her to his knee, and stroked her softly on the cheeks.

"When I had gone along so the first day, I shot the dog. When I had gone another day, I gave the gun to a forester who showed me the way. After that I had nothing."

"Can one buy coppers for it?"

"Surely, surely. So when I joined the army like that and got me a war musket, then, as you may believe, I became a hunter again. But Heaven have pity!— You shall come here every evening in the dusk, and then you shall get half of my day's rations and all I can pick up."

She stared at the musket in the grass, so he rose and went, leaving it there.

"The girl can't know that it was I who fired the shot, and she shall never get to know it.—You are a Judas, who has robbed an innocent man of life.—Thou shalt not kill! Thou shalt not kill!"

He held his forehead and tottered away over the field. Then he came to d'Albe- dyhll's Dragoons, who lay around a log fire and read prayer-books, and there he sat down to read, until finally he began to pray aloud and preach.

"What news?" the soldiers asked next morning of Brakel's red-haired sutler, a little knowing West Gotlander, who stood in his gray blouse among the pots and hung-up clothes.

"News? Morten Preacher must have had a sunstroke in the middle of the night and become ripe for the fool's locker. He goes bare-headed down to the river and shouts. When the preacher's fever sets in on him, he always says he has been out and shot somebody."

In gloomy silence the soldiers received tin bowls hardly half full.

"Bread or dead. Why don't we go

ahead and storm before it's too late?"

"The king is working with ditches, and Gyllenkrook has to stand by the work night and day. Just listen to Morten Preacher now down by the water! Here has been praying and psalm-singing lately so that it makes one warm at heart to hear the field marshal go on the rampage."

At dusk Morten Preacher slunk away to the cherry-tree, where the little nine-year-old stood already waiting with her smooth flaxen, almost white hair and her serious face.

He had with him his day's rations, and he gave her his last kopek for the promise that he might kiss her on both cheeks.

"Is your mother living?"

She shook her head.

"What's your name?"

"Dunya."

He wanted to kiss her again on the cheeks, but she moved away.

"Give me a kopek first!"

He went back to the camp—and begged kopek pieces of all whom he met.

"I will watch over her when there is a storming. She is like a little, little princess. I will lay by from my pay, so that one day she will have something to get married on.—Why should she not get married?—Surely, surely! I have, to be sure, my wife at home, and I have a sweetheart in the baggage-train, too. And it seems I'm a murderer. Surely a little princess shall marry!"

He had made a copy of St. John's Gospel and, sitting down, he read aloud from it to d'Albedyhll's Dragoons.

All the plants of spring flamed up over the hilly meads down to the yellowish banks of the Vorskla, but the soldiers looked only toward Poltava, which shone out through clumps of forest with its white cloister walls, its wooden towers, palisades, and ramparts, on which young and old men, women, and children had thrown up a breastwork of sacks filled with earth, of wagons, bundles of twigs and barrels.

"What's the news? Will they never lead us against the foe?" the soldiers inquired of the sutler.

"The foe is so kind as to come to us instead," he answered, and dried his forehead with his blouse. "In the night I heard how he rolled his field-pieces. The heavy firing is not from the Swedes, for we have no other cannon-balls left than those which the Zaporogeans pick up out of the ground. It's the czar's whole army that's already standing on the other side of the river."

Then came Major-General Lagercrona spurring his horse and shouting that the king was wounded in the foot. Beside the royal litter the field marshal pointed out the situation of the seventeen redoubts which the enemy had already begun to throw up at the village of Pietruska.

"What's the news?" muttered the soldiers daily around the sutler.

"If there's nothing else that any one offers, then I'm the richer," answered he and pointed with his ladle around the verdant landscape. "The king has got mortification in his wound. The brandy is done. The bread is done. I've a little porridge for you today—but then that's done. The enemy has barred us in and disputes our retreat. Oh, the devil, the devil! It's only the Swedes that can stand such bitter days."

He stamped on the turf, put the ladle to his eye, and aimed like an assassin at the king's battered cabin, but the heroic, frost-bitten heads around him lowered their eyes.

"Thou shalt not kill!" whispered Morten Preacher with upraised arms.

So passed the month of May, and the heat of June shone in through the tent-cloths. The soldiers sat in a row and twined wreaths for midsummer-poles, but did not talk. They thought of the pastures at home, of the cottages, of the wide, wide moors.

On Sunday, a little before evensong, Morten Preacher slipped to the grove, where little Dunya, in return for some kopeks, handed him a basket with the first half-ripened cherries. He ate them along with her, patted her small hands, and played with her, carrying her like a child, but he could not get her to smile. For his last kopek he was allowed to kiss her three times on the cheeks.

When he came back there was clamor and unrest. Officers inspected the soldiers' equipment and thumped on their swords, which here and there were so ground that they were like worn scythes. Brakel's sutler pulled together his empty pans. The king had resolved to deliver battle.

On the grassy banks outside the king's window the generals and colonels were already sitting to receive their divisions and written instructions. There sat the melancholy Lewenhaupt with his great clear eyes and a little Latin pocket lexicon stuck between the buttons of his coat. There sat the gallant Creutz with hands crossed over the pommel of his sword, and Sparre and Lagercrona carried on a noisy conversation in loud tones. Colonel Gyllenkrona stood by the table, bent over his fortification drawings, with which he appeared to be so fascinated that he did not notice the others in the least, but occupied himself instead with carefully and slowly flicking the grains of sand from his beloved sketches. Leaning back a little by the door, in the worst of tempers, stood the field marshal himself with his pointed, somewhat turned-up nose and his puckered, purple-red girl's mouth.

In the dusk began the march with furled banners and without music, and the king's litter was set down for a while in a grove in advance of the lifeguards. From the field were heard sounds of the enemy knocking and hammering on their palisades as upon waiting scaffolds. The band of Charles men, once so proud, had now so little shot and powder that they could not bring along to the encounter more than four poor field-pieces, and now when they heard hammer-blows so near, many among the scarred warriors were seized with corporal fear and vainly offered a ducat for a swallow of brandy. It was the wane of the moon. The horses stood saddled, and the men had their muskets or carbines at their side. From one of the infantry regiments was heard murmuring and whispering, as the chaplain distributed the Communion, and he had to grope with his left hand in the darkness to put the chalice to the mouths of the kneeling soldiers. Around the litter, beside which the king had stuck his broadsword into the earth, the generals had lain down for a moment in their cloaks, and Piper sat on a drum with his back against a tree. To break the force of gloomy thoughts and avoid one another, they began a philosophic discourse with the king. He sat in a circle of ponderers and taught like a master in his school, and Lewenhaupt, the honest old Latinist colonel, recited Roman verses.

When he ceased, he took a burning torch from the attendants and threw the light on the king, whose head had slid to one side. Piper and all the generals arose and forgot their spite, so beautiful appeared to them the aspect of the sleeper. His hat lay on his knee, and the coverlet was folded about the hurt and bandaged foot. The emaciated and fever-wasted countenance with the frost-bites on nose and cheek had become even smaller than before, and harder and more set. Yellowish and humid, it was already shadowed by a premature old age, but there was a drawing and twitching of the lips. It looked as though he was dreaming.

The king of the Charles men dreamed that he saw an endless line of giggling and tittering folk, who went hurriedly past and held their hands before their faces to hide how they laughed at him. Sometimes they were bright green or blue, and they shone like lighted lanterns. Finally, on a sweating bay, there came a tall man who was completely clad in dusty silk taffeta. "Begone! you bald and lame Swede," he cried, guffawing from the back of his horse. "In this very place, three hundred years ago, the hordes of Tamerlane cut down the united armies of the West. What would you do to me and my ocean of men with your last thinned-out regiments and your four field-pieces? My men are thieves and drunken miscreants, and are of less use to me than nails in a plank, but I make good use of such nails. I am building at a great ship to sail the centuries, and I myself am still the same to-day as when I stood at my trade, a simple carpenter in Saardam. Millions upon millions shall bless my work."

The king would have answered, but he found that his tongue was paralyzed.

Lewenhaupt knelt with bared head, and touched him on the shoulder. "My most gracious lord, day is dawning, and I call down God's protection over your noble person and actions."

The glow of morning already burned between the tree trunks, and the king opened his eyes. Straight-way he grasped his broadsword. As soon as he noted the many men who stood around him and the bearded cavalry chaplain Norberg and all the attendants, his expression changed, and he nodded with his usual chilly friendliness—but the dream still stood out clear in his thoughts. It seemed to him that the others, too, must have seen it.

"What is a kingdom?" he said. "An accident, a far-stretching estate with fortresses at the outlying farms. Battles and negotiations move the boundaries. And yet, czar, supposing you have power over millions but not over yourself? The Lord God may so ordain that men shall one day inquire less concerning states, but all the more concerning individuals. If I conquer you, your whole ship takes fire and becomes ashes, but if you cut down me and my men, you only fulfil thereby the victory of my achievements."

Lewenhaupt gripped Creutz by the arm, and whispered mournfully: "Dear brother, dark forebodings will not slip from my mind. Shall we all ever again stand together under God's free heaven? Hark how the field marshal swears and curses behind the Upplanders. Gyllenkrook won't even go forward to him and ask for orders. You are holding back, too. And look how haughtily Piper is glowering after us!"

"The Swedes always look haughtily at one another. For that reason they will some day be undone, and their name erased among peoples. Our children in the tenth or twentieth generation will see the time. To-day is only the beginning."

"The Lord pardon your words! Never did I see more glorious champions of God than the Swedes, and never a people so wholly free from the self-assurance and rough hands of a despotic will. The king is now too ill to hold us together longer, though he pretends to be as confident as a young cornet. He was given at birth the recklessness which the gods lend their favorites, but now—"

"Now?"

"Now he has got the impenetrable and overmastering delusion to which the favorite's recklessness hardens when the gods abandon him."

Lewenhaupt pressed his hat on his head and drew his sword, but turned yet again to Creutz and whispered: "Perhaps men such as I with my care for the rank and file, and Gyllenkrook with his compass-case and all his redoubts adorned with palisades, have never all this time understood him rightly. You with your broadsword have blindly obeyed. May it be granted us all to-day to fulfil his mission ith him, for I foresee that he who survives the evening will envy the brothers ho by then have entered into eternal lessedness."

The riders now sprang into the saddle. ewenhaupt went to his foot-regiments, nd in the light of daybreak they saw bere them the expectant field. It was lack. It was already burnt. It was a heap f ashes, which without flower or grasslade vanished between clumps of trees nto the barren steppes. It was so level nat a cannon-carriage could easily be riven back and forth.

Out in front of the largest Russian reoubt came a red-clad rider, who fired off is pistol. Then the enemy let all their rums beat behind the outworks, on hich appeared innumerable troops of oldiers and standards and catapults and eld-pieces. Immediately the Swedish muic answered throughout all the regiments.

The indomitable Axel Sparre and Karl iustaf Roos rushed in front of the army ith their battalions, and stormed the eld redoubts. Horses snorted, harness reaked, swords and carbines clattered, nd ashes and dust fell over the clumps of rees so that the green was quenched on he leafage.

The king sent Creutz with the left wing fter the conquering Sparre, and behind he captured entrenchments the enemy's avalry rushed in flight toward the wampy meadows by the Vorskla. On the ther side Lewenhaupt advanced with his nfantry, occupied two redoubts, and disosed himself to attack the enemy's camp rom the south with the bayonet. There he confusion was so great that women egan to harness horses to the baggage vagons, but the czarina, a tall woman of ome twenty years with a high bosom, vhite forehead, and deeply colored heeks, still stood out by the wounded mong her bandage-strips and water-flasks vith an almost haughty tranquillity.

Meanwhile the generals collected around the Swedish king's litter, which was borne along not far from the East Gotland infantry regiment and set down by a bog. Here a halt was commanded, and a crowd with deep bowing and taking off of hats began already to congratulate His Majesty and wish for further progress. While the lackey Hultman was filtering water and catching it in a silver goblet, the king said: "Major-General Roos has been surrounded, and the field marshal has therefore checked the other troops, but Lagercrona and Sparre have been sent back to help Roos on, and he is likely to come here soon."

Thus the army remained standing there awhile, but soon Sparre came up, sprinkled with drops of blood, and related that he could not get through on account of the enemy's superior numbers. The troops now marched back and forth for a long time without the officers' knowing where they should lead them, and during the wasted time the Russians got fresh courage. Then Lewenhaupt suddenly put himself in motion, marched to the stretch of woods where Creutz' squadrons had taken position, and there drew up the infantry in line against the enemy. No one knew from where the command for this had been given out, and, beside himself with wrath, the field marshal galloped forward to the king's litter, which went beside the Guards.

"Is it Your Majesty who commanded Lewenhaupt with the infantry to draw himself up against the enemy?"

The disrespectful tones took the king aback, and as if by the light of a dark lantern that has been suddenly opened, he saw how wearily and coldly even his closest favorites in the circle were staring at him.

"No," he answered reluctantly, but became blushing red, and all understood that he lied.

Then in the furiously raging field marshal every last glimmer of respect and trust was quenched. He gave voice to the spite and despair which all had nourished for days and months. The king, acclaimed for his love of veracity, had all at once been humiliated to the level of a wounded soldier, had behaved himself churlishly, and tried to exculpate himself with rude prevarications. Rehnskiöld did not reflect. The moment of retribution had come. He lost control of himself. He wanted to take revenge and punish and humiliate. He could not pretend that he believed in the lying. He could not even use the customary form of address.

"Yes, yes," he shouted from his horse, "that's what you always do. Would that you would leave it to me!"

With that he turned his back on him.

The king sat motionless on the litter. He had been shamed before the whole troop, and his diffidence and disinclination for bickering had befooled him into an unpremeditated and pitiful trick. His own men had heard him lie like an interrogated baggage-driver. He could not take back his words without still more exposing his shame. The degradation he had brought upon himself as man was for him harder to endure than if he had lost his crown. He wanted to spring up, throw himself on a horse, and take along with him the deep ranks, *his* men, who still believed that he was the chosen of God. But the pain in his foot and a great lassitude restrained him. His cheeks still glowed, but it was the heat of fever, and for the first time the broadsword trembled in the hand which he was now barely able to raise.

"Take the litter before the front!" he shouted. "Take the litter before the front!"

"The cavalry have not got forward yet," burst out Gyllenkrook with vehemence. "Is it possible that the battle shall begin so soon?"

"They are marching now," answered the king with vexation, "and the enemy is coming out of his lines with the infantry."

Then Gyllenkrook commended th king to God's protection, and seated him self on his horse beside the Guards, wh straightway advanced and gave the firs volley.

The battle-token was a straw fastene on the hat, and through the noise of shot and trumpets and oboes and drums an cavalry kettle drums sounded the battle cry of the troops: "God with us! Go with us!" In the throng and farther ou on the field old war-comrades and nea relatives, who had aforetime sat merril together at home at wedding and christening, met and shouted to one another last greeting. Where there was more space captains and lieutenants and ensign marched before the battalions, pale a corpses, in time with the music, as if the had filed up to a parade in the citade square by the old Three Crowns; but th soldiers clenched hands over their empt cartridge-boxes. Through the midst of th fire from the redoubts the Life Guard went in a stubborn line with muskets o shoulder, but when they came to clos quarters with the enemy, they shook thei clicking weapons savagely and graspe their bayonets. Dust and dirt soon begrimed them all, so that the green coat of the enemy could no longer be distinguished from the blue, and Swedes lifte musket butt against Swedes. In front o Kruse's dragoons Cornet Queckfelt tumbled from his horse with a bullet in hi body and the banner against his breast Major Ridderborg, who in the mornin had seen his gray-haired father fall amon the troopers by the king's litter, wa dragged unconscious from the hand-to-hand struggle. In front of the Nyland regiment fell Colonel Torstenson, and Lieutenant Gyllenbögel stood with shot wounds in both cheeks, so that one coul see the daylight through them. In a thicke behind the Scanian Gentleman-Dragoon reeled Captain Horn, badly wounded i the right leg, and his faithful servant, Daniel Lidbom, held him around the body and dried his forehead. Cavalryman Per Windropp sat dead on his horse, in his hand the tatters of a company flag that had been torn to pieces, and Lieutenant Pauli, who believed him only wounded, offered him his canteen. In front of the Kalmar regiment dropped Colonel Rank, struck in the heart; Major Lejonhjelm lay with his leg shot off; and by the corpse of Lieutenant-Colonel Silversparre Ensign Djurklo fought with broken sword to save the banner, until he sank down dying. Around him lay half the non-commissioned officers and half the men as a hero's watch. The Jönköping regiment, which was nearest the redoubts, carried along their wounded colonel, and after Lieutenant-Colonel Night-and-Day and Major Oxe had fallen in their blood, Captain Mörner took command. Beside him lay prostrate in the ashes on the ground Ensign Tigerskiöld with his face hidden in his hands, propped on his elbows and bleeding from five wounds. Scarcely a fourth of the regiment could still bear arms.

At this moment the field marshal came riding, and cried out to Mörner with untimely warmth: "Where the deuce have the regiment's officers gone off to?"

"They are lying wounded or dead."

"Why the thousand devils aren't you lying there with them?"

"No, my old mother's supplications have called down God's protection over me, and therefore I'm alive and have the honor of commanding this regiment, which has done and will do its duty as true warriors.—Stand, boys, stand!"

Colonel Wrangel lay already dead and unrecognizable, and his recruits sought in vain to prop him up under the arms. Colonel Ulfsparre, who went before the West Gotlanders, fell with his hands pressed to his heart, and his major, the dauntless Sven Lagerberg, was struck down backwards by a musket-ball. The whole hostile army went over him. He heard the horses and the cannon-carriages. He was trampled and kicked and rolled in ashes and dirt among stiffening corpses and moaning wounded, till a wounded dragoon finally took him on his horse, and mercifully conducted him to the baggage-train.

The beloved old banners, shot into strips, were still fluttering in goodly numbers over the human sea, but they wavered and tottered, they were torn and snapped, and at last they sank and vanished one by one. The Uppland regiment, which drew most of its men from the heart of Sweden, from the ancient home of the Svea at Mälardale, was annihilated. Flags with the cross-surmounted apple in the corner were twisted from the clenched hands of the fallen, and amid Cossack pikes and butts and sabres Colonel Stjernhöök was stretched on the ground, as he stammered: "Now is the time when we may cry: Father, it is finished!" Lieutenant-Colonel von Post and Major Anrep fell almost side by side. Captains Gripenberg and Hjulhammar, and Lieutenant Essen, and the three boyishly slender and beardless Ensigns Flygare, Brinck, and Düben already lay in the throes of death. "Stand, boys, stand!" shouted officers and soldiers, and fell over one another, so that of corpses and rags, of clothing and sod and sand, was built a mound which served the living for a breastwork. Whistling grapeshot and musket-balls, grenades and exploding canister, rained over the fighting and the dead, and the air was so saturated with dirt and smoke that men could see only a horse's length ahead.

Then the troops began to waver. Lewenhaupt drew a pisol from the holster and pointed it at his own men. He threatened and struck. "Stand, boys, in Jesus' holy name! I see the king's litter." "If the king is here, we'll stand," answered the soldiers. "Stand, boys! halt, stand! God with us!" they shouted to themselves, as if to control their limbs, that trembled and dripped with sweat and blood. But step by step they yielded, and the riders reined in their horses, until, with slashed faces and hands, they finally wheeled about in wild flight, man after man, and trampled one another down. Under the rising clouds of smoke they saw the king, who amid fallen troopers, bearers, and attendants lay on the ground without a hat, supported on his elbow, with the injured foot propped on the crushed litter, over which had been spread the clay-spotted cloak of the slain trooper Oxehufvud. The stiffened face was raven-black with grime, but the eyes kindled, and he stammered: "Swedes! Swedes!"

In the yielding ranks many stood still when they recognized the voice, because it seemed to them that even if they could save themselves now, they must sometime on their death-bed hear across the pillow that timid and lonely voice. He had not the strength to raise himself, but they lifted him on their crossed pikes like a doomed and helpless invalid. Again and again, though, the bearers were shot down, and yet in that instant, when the bleeding men succumbed, they stretched up their arms to support him so that he should not be hurt in the fall. Then Major Wolffelt lifted him on his horse, and afterwards fell himself under the weapons of the pursuing Cossacks. The foot, which was laid over the horse's neck, bled violently, and the bandage dragged in the dust. A cannon-ball from the entrenchments struck off the horse's leg, but Trooper Gierta lifted the king upon his charger and, himself wounded, mounted on the three-legged and bleeding horse. The cavalrymen who had made a ring about the king could hardly hold back the pursuers.

Meanwhile Gyllenkrook rushed over the field, and exhorted the straggling soldiers to rally, but they answered him: "We are all wounded and our officers dead." He then met the field marshal, and now upon the day of retribution there was no longer any deference.

Gyllenkrook shouted to him offensively, "Does Your Excellency hear that the volleys are still sounding on our left wing! Here are a mass of squadrons that have sat down. Order them to go somewhere!"

"Here everything is mad! Here to be sure some obey me with their haunches, but few with their hearts," answered the field marshal, and rode further and further to the left. At the same time Gyllenkrook saw Piper with his men of the chancellery ride off to the right. Had the two Excellencies spoken together? He shouted after them that they were betaking themselves straight toward the enemy, but they did not turn about. Then he struck his hand on the pommel of his saddle, and understood that now the wine of patience was drunk, that now there remained only captivity or death.

There lay behind him no longer a field. There grew from the earth a boundless wood, but the trunks were men and the boughs weapons. It broadened out. It filled the whole landscape, and constantly, constantly spread forward over the bleeding and dying. It was the czar's army, that marched on to take possession of its land and dedicate its empire to future times. Ever nearer and nearer was heard an uncanny and dull-sounding religious hymn. Slowly, step by step, as in a funeral procession, between swinging thuribles and high over the heads of thousands upon thousands, was borne the giant standard. On the cloth appeared the czar's ancestral tree, surrounded by saints, and above, under the Trinity, was his own likeness.

The Swedish fugitives gathered around the king by the baggage, where the Swedish Nobleman-Guards and some other regiments kept watch. Having bound up

his foot and tolerably wiped off the grime, he now sat in a blue wagon beside the wounded Colonel Hård.

"Where is Adlerfeldt, the chamberlain?" he asked.

Those who stood around him answered, "He fell by a cannon-shot close to Your Majesty's litter."

At that moment the Dalecarlian regiment came past, shattered and in great disorder.

"Dalecarlians," inquired the king, "where is Siegeroth, your Colonel, and Major Svinhufvud, and where is the merry Drake, who is said to have fought so valiantly at the redoubt that he shall get a regiment?"

"They are shot, all of them."

"Where, then, are the Little Prince, and Piper, and the field marshal?"

Those around him shook their heads and looked at one another. Should they once for all tell him the whole truth? Should they on that day of judgment expose all his loneliness? Should they tell him, too, that Hedwig Sofia, his favorite sister, had lain for half a year in her coffin—unburied? There was none who dared to do that.

"Captured," they answered reluctantly.

"Captured? Captured among the Muscovites? Better go among the Turks, then. Forward!"

He paled, but he spoke calmly and almost triumphantly with the unalterable smile on his lips.

A grizzled soldier among the Dalecarlians whispered to the comrades, "Truly I have never seen him so youthful and happy since the day at Narva, when he went with Stenbock. This is a day of victory to him."

The wagon rolled away, and the king of the Charles men, in front of his disordered, fleeing army of haughty ragamuffins, swearing baggage crones, cripples moaning loudly, and limping horses, marched with flying banners and resounding music as from his greatest victory.

By two o'clock the last volleys were fired, and then stillness had spread itself over the battle-field, where Mazeppa's last Cossacks and countless Zaporogeans were impaled alive on stakes. Homesteads and mills stood burned, trees shot asunder, and the fallen heroes lay with dust and ashes blown over them, all with eyes wide open, as if they had stared back from another world on the past years and on the living. A few captured priests and soldiers roamed about, seeking for their countrymen and sometimes opening a shallow grave, over which the words of burial in the speech of their far-off homeland were softly whispered out into the dusk of the June evening. After that the grave was again shut, to be overgrown with sedge grass and rough thistles. For centuries after, they have rustled to the winds of the steppes on the gloomy bogland to which the Russians gave the name of the Swedes' Cemetery.

When one of the priests found Lieutenant-Colonel Wetzel, who had fallen, together with his two sons, he picked up the empty covers of the prayerbook which lay beside him, adorned with the family crest.

"You are the last of your family," he said; "and how many a stock has been extinguished on this field! Galle, Siegeroth, Mannersvärd, Rosenskiöld, von Borgen. As I now tear apart the crest on this cover and strew it to the winds, I also in the name of my afflicted, my annihilated father-folk, shatter the coats-of-arms above you all."

A multitude of bodies were thrown together in a heap outside of the field entrenchment where the day's conflict had been hottest, but the others remained strewn about. The air was filled almost at once with a stale vapor and with countless flapping crows. But darkness descended silently with all the more solemnity over the wide city of graves, though the wounded still cried for water. Those most pitiably mangled prayed that some one in mercy would finish them with a sword-thrust, or they dragged themselves to a horse that had been shot, pulled the pistols from the holsters, and took themselves from the light of day, after they had on tremulous knees called down a blessing over all at home and recited the Lord's Prayer. Then a mortally wounded dragoon began to speak words of power and to thank God for his glorious death-wounds. Over himself and his comrades he uttered the burial words and thrice took earth with his hands and cast it upon his breast. "Out of earth are we come, to earth we shall return." After that he preached with ecstasy of the Resurrection, and finally with a loud voice took up a funeral hymn, and twenty or thirty voices answered far off in the dark under the star-bright heavens.

Morten Preacher, who stole around on the plain without feeling any terror of the fallen, continued the psalm when the dragoon was silent. Then he caught sight of an old woman, who came with a torch. After her followed a line of peasants with long, rude carts, on which they loaded clothing and all manner of plunder. A fallen cornet, who was not yet dead, defended himself with his hand and would not let go from him a necklace with a little silver cross, but they thrust him down with a hay-fork.

Then Morten Preacher sprang forward. "Thou shalt not kill! Thou shalt not kill!" he whispered. Among the plundering women he recognized his nine-year-old Dunya, his little princess. His whole countenance changed, and he stretched out both hands to her, half like a father, half like a bashful lover. She stared at him, and burst into a silly laugh.

"That's the wicked Swede," she cried, "who bribed me so as to get cherries and kiss me on the cheeks."

She sprang upon him like a cat and tore the earrings from him, so that the blood ran down the sides of his neck. He fell backwards, and the women seized him and struck him and tore his clothes from him. They came upon his transcript of St. John's Gospel, and strewed the leaves around like feathers from a plucked fowl. They pulled off his flap-boots and ragged stockings, but when he saw his little Dunya clutch at a hay-fork, he wrenched himself loose with the strength of upflaming hate and fled in his shirt over wounded and dead.

"Not even trust in a guileless heart is left us more," he muttered, and clambered up on a lame horse which had attached itself to him in the darkness. "God has abandoned us. This is the judgment. All is over, and the whole world is dark."

He rode for two nights and two days, and wounded stragglers pointed out the road. He found the fleeing Swedes on a peninsula between the Vorskla and the bright Dnieper, which spread itself out like a lake between banks overgrown with reeds, underbrush, and bushes. The Russians were close behind them on the landward side, but when the outposts saw Morten Preacher in his bloody shirt, riding bare-back on the lame horse, they sprang to one side in terror and only shot after him when he was already past.

The sun burned hot as fire. The wounded and those with camp-fever were bedded under bushes by the water. The generals stood in conversation, and Lewenhaupt turned mournfully to Creutz.

"If the king is taken, the men of Sweden will abandon their houses and leave their last wisp of hay for his ransom. The responsibility is ours. This war is a game of chess, where everything is decided by taking the kings. On my knees I have prayed him to have himself rowed across the river, but he pushed me away, and said he had serious matters to consider."

"My dear brother, you talk to him as to a gouty statesman. You should never talk to him as to a man, but as to a youth who is proud of being challenged to show his manhood."

Creutz went forward to the king's wagon and swung the gloves in his hand with such violence that it seemed as if he meant to strike Charles on the forehead, but he was at once confounded by his radiant glance.

"Your Majesty is in perplexity?"

"I fight ill with the pen—that's what I'm thinking of. I wish to draw up my will and arrange for the succession. Then we'll set the guns cracking! If I'm left on the field, I wish to be buried in my shirt like a common soldier on the place where I fall."

Creutz twisted and squeezed the gloves; he was cowed and lowered his head, like the others.

"Most gracious lord, I am not of those who pray God to spare their life, because full well do I understand the highest longing of a hero. If Your Majesty should get your bullet . . . well, so be it, in Jesus' name! But to-day Your Majesty can no longer stay in the saddle. God forgive my words, but Your Majesty has got to the point of being carried around helpless, and when the last of us has lost his life, there will be left only Your Majesty—a prisoner!"

"A man should not only stand one against five, he should also be able to stand one against all."

"True, true. But—devil take me!—we common fellows in uniform are not fit for that. One against all? That means one against the whole world. For that are needed men of quite a different sort, for we are such pitiful wretches that we have nothing to defend ourselves with but our blades. Now that I have described the situation plainly, I therefore beseech Your Majesty to stay with us and not cross the river, because then Your Majesty would set yourself one against all. Then it would be: What an Alexander to run away and leave his troops to the Russians! What a heartless, disgraceful dolt; Look, look! And he took the plate and money-barrels from Saxony along instead of leaving everything to the Russians. Oho, yes, hahaha!—We poor honest subjects can never allow that Your Majesty should set yourself as one against the whole world in that way, to expose your high person to the mud-flinging that ignorance and stupidity will not spare either to the field marshal or Piper or Lewenhaupt or the rest of us. When did stupidity ever learn to understand misfortune? Your Majesty wants to die, and therefore it is no sacrifice and no achievement to die—that we old war-dogs know; but pride, pride, Your Majesty, to offer up that for your subjects is a sacrifice that the subjects cannot consent to. That the men cannot be taken over is clear. We have no barges, no anchors, no spikes, not enough logs, no carpenters. Therefore I require that Your Majesty remain and do not defy the world."

"Get the boats ready!" ordered the king.

Mazeppa, the gallant landed proprietor, had collected his trunks and his two barrels of ducats, and was already sitting on his wagon far out in the water. Zaporogeans and swarms of soldiers tied their clothes on their backs, took wagon-lids and branches of trees under their arms, and sprang into the waves. At midnight the king's wagon also was lifted on two boats tied together, and Gyllenkrook, who stood at his feet, dumbly surrendered to Lewenhaupt the battle-plan, pasted on a board. No one spoke. The night was starry and quiet, and the oar-strokes of the troopers died away on the shining river.

"We two shall never see him again,"

muttered Creutz to Lewenhaupt. "His eyes were so wonderful just now! There is still oil in the lamp, but I am gazing curiously at his future. How will he be when he is conquered, ridiculed, old?"

Lewenhaupt answered, "The wreath he twined for himself slid off upon his subjects instead. It will lie forever on the forgotten graves up there in the marshes. —So we must thank him for all he has made of us."

Far off through the darkness of the night was heard the lamenting voice of Morten Preacher: " 'And men have made of me a by-word before the world,' saith Job. 'And I am become a mockery, and mine eyes are wasted with grief, and my limbs are all a shadow. Unto corruption I say: thou art my father, and unto worms: ye are my mother and sister. And where then is my hope? It goeth down to the gate of death, when I and it shall rest in the earth.' "

Day came on, and Morten Preacher in his bloody shirt rode from group to group, examining the men in the Catechism and Biblical knowledge. The soldiers stood in silence by the empty tent of the king, but when the shout was raised that they must surrender, and when the Russian general Bauer, tanned by the sun, ascended the hill to receive the trophies, Morten Preacher stepped down and wrung his hands.

Round about, with their brazen helmets and pikes, sat the Cossacks on their tired and panting horses, and before them on the ground were laid kettledrums and bass-drums and horns and muskets whose thunder had rolled over battalions, and the well-known flags to which once mothers and wives had waved farewell from door and stairway and window. There was gleaming and sparkling on the heather. Sullen old under-officers embraced each other sobbing. Some cut off their bandages and let the blood run, and two battle-brothers quenched each other's lives with their swords at the same time that they threw them down before the conquerors. Dumb and threatening, the cripples advanced. There came youths with frost-bitten cheeks, and without noses and ears, so that they were like dead men. Ensign Piper, not yet full-grown, who had lost his heels, stumbled up on crutches. There came the courtier Gunterfelt, who lacked both hands, and had got in France two others of wood, black and shining, which fingered up and down on his coat. There rattled wooden legs and canes and litters and ambulance-wagons.

Morten Preacher stood with hands clasped. Sparks leaped before his eyes. There was a roaring and moaning within, and the old preaching-spirit came so violently over him that he himself heard how his voice at one time was choked and hoarse, but the next grew so strong that it seemed to him as if he were borne away on the wings of it and were changed to a flame of fire.

He reeled forward to the arms that had been laid down and pointed to the empty tent of the king.

"*He* alone is the offender. You, mother or widow, clad in mourning, turn his picture to the wall! Forbid the little ones to mention his name! You, little Dunya, who with your playmates will soon be picking flowers on the graves, build his monument with skulls and horses' heads! You, cripple, knock with your crutch on the hollow earth and summon him to a meeting there below, where thousands whom he sacrificed await him!—And yet I know that one day before the judgment seat of righteousness we shall all limp forward on our wooden legs and crutches, and say: 'Forgive him, Father, as we have forgiven him, because our love was both his victory and his destruction.' "

When no one replied, but all stood bent forward and dumb as if they had answered the same, his despair was yet more vehement. He covered his angular face with his hands.

"Tell me by the Grace of God that he lives!" cried he. "Say that he lives!"

With his black wooden fingers Gunterfelt raised his hat from his head and answered, "His Majesty is saved."

Then Morten Preacher bowed his knee, and trembled, and recovered himself.

"Praised be the Lord of Hosts!" he stammered. "If the king is saved, then I will bear whatever burden fate shall lay upon me."

"Yes, yes, praised be the Lord of Hosts!" repeated the Swedes mumbling, and all slowly lifted their hats from their heads.

Behold My Children!

Corporal Anders Groberg stood with his canteen on Saracen's Heath. Around him reeled and marched the last band of fleeing Swedes and Zaporogeans, and on wagons lay those who had been wounded at Poltava. The whole night and morning Anders Groberg had endured thirst so as to spare the last drops of water to the utmost, and the torture had now become overpowering. But in the very moment he lifted the canteen to his lips, he lowered it again.

"My God, my God!" he stammered, "why should I alone drink, when all the others are thirsting? If Thou hast led us forth into the wilderness and the steppes, it is that Thou shouldst sometime be able to say: 'From your poverty-stricken country of snow I let you go forth into the world with musket on shoulder to be hailed as heroes and conquerors, but when I read your hearts and saw that they remained pure, that ye were my children, then I tore your clothes in pieces and set crutches in your hands and wooden legs under your bodies, so that ye should no more hanker after domination over men, but should be gathered among my saints. Such greatness did I grant unto you.' "

Anders Groberg stood awhile longer with the canteen before him. Then he went on, and handed it to the king, who lay in burning fever among the sacks of hay on his wagon. The king's lips adhered to his teeth; they split and bled when he opened them.

"No, no," he whispered, "give the water to the wounded! I have just had a glass."

Anders Groberg knew well that the king had had no water. He himself was the only man who had taken thought for the morrow and saved it up, and neither spring nor bog had they found for many a mile. But now, as he turned away from the wagon, weakness and temptation once more came over him. He hung the canteen back at his side and continued to march and march without handing it to the wounded. He squeezed the stopper and strove in his soul, but every time he raised the canteen to his mouth, he let it fall again and had not the heart to drink of the water.

"Perhaps," he thought, "I might refresh myself with a clearer conscience, if as an offset I should humiliate myself in something else."

At noon, when the sun burned most hotly, he saw a gray-haired subaltern who went almost naked with unbandaged wounds on his shoulder. Thereupon he tore up his shirt, bound the other's wounds, and gave him his coat; but as soon as he shut his hand on his canteen again, his unrest of conscience woke anew. Then he gave his boots to a sick driver lad, who limped along with bare and bleeding feet, but when he still could not swallow the water with an easy mind in the midst of all the other thirsty men, he became embittered and hard. He pointed with derisive curses at the money-barrels which, full of gold and silver, clattered as they were taken along on two of the wagons, but which could not provide the unfortunate soldiers with a spoonful of brackish bog-water.

"Whip the horses!" he shouted, "whip the horses, so that the money-barrels shall not be left behind! Whip the men, too!"

The soldiers answered nothing, because now they recognized him again as he used to be formerly, when in the years of success he had gone in front of the line, bitter and abusive. They did not notice that he had hardly heard his own voice before he bent his head and began again to cudgel his brains and whisper to himself.

"Must I then of necessity offer up just the one thing that has now any worth for me?" he thought. "Haha! May we also some day roll the money-barrels on the grass and nevermore touch them with our fingers! My God, my God! Once at Veperik I heard the dying soldier Bengt Geting speak with envy of the fallen who had received a clean white shirt. My longing dares not rise so high. I desire so little . . . ah, only this, not to be left lying behind the others on the heath, only to be laid in the ground, to have earth and grass over me—and a couple of words on the muster-roll. Now it will stand: Anders Groberg, his fate unknown."

Towards dusk a halt was made to bury those who had died during the day, and a couple of Zaporogeans had already stuck their spades in the ground. In the reedy grass grew a few low bushes with cherries which, meanwhile, officers and soldiers picked and divided among them as a bounty bestowed from God's own hands. Anders Groberg slunk behind the bushes to drink the water unseen by the others. But just then the trumpets began to blow as a sign that the pursuing Russians had again become visible against the heaven on the farthest waves of the parched desert of grass.

Anders Groberg opened the tin stopper, but the longer he inhaled the moist smell, the harder beat his heart, and in the nea est wagon the dying Börje Köve, a soldi in charge of the silver, raised himself an stared at him.

Anders Groberg tried to meet his loo but could not, and yet again he pushe the draught of refreshment from him.

"Blessed are those that hunger an thirst after righteousness," he said.

Like an acolyte who gives the sacr ment, he bore the canteen in front of hi and held it to the mouth of the soldie and the dying man drank the water to th last drop.

Anders Groberg held on tight to th tail-board, but when the wheel rolled o again, his hand slipped off, and he tottere to his knees on the grass.

"There is no place for me on the wag ons," he said, and pulled a spade to him "Though I'm hardly thirty years old, am as weary and infirm as a man o ninety. But leave me one of the spades, s that, if my strength stays by me, I may a least be able to open the earth and lay m down in my last abode. All my unrest ha now fallen sweetly to sleep, and a voic calls at my ear: 'Behold my children!'

Once more the soldiers around th shaking wagons began their wandering and the trumpeters turned in the saddle Flocks of storks with outspread wing hovered in the dusk over the darkenin tracts, and out on the steppe Anders Gro berg still knelt with the spade in his hands

Since then no one has learned anythin of his fate.

At the Council Table

In the ante-room of the Council Chambe already stood the secretary, Schmedeman with the address to the chiefs of the prov inces, which was now to be signed, and i which new levies were required from im poverished Sweden.

The lords began to assemble, and old Frölich, who with crossed hands was groaning and snoring in a corner beside the sick Falkenberg, suddenly awoke.

"We must hand over to the king the whole bank with the money and the patents," he said without lifting his reddened eyelids.

Then Arvid Horn started forward with such vehemence that his chair fell back on the floor, and shouted with his arms lifted toward the ceiling: "Keep yourself to your heavenly revelations and seasons of prayer with sister Eva-Greta and do not make thieves of us out of mere good intentions toward His Royal Majesty!"

"Satan, Satan!" retorted Falkenberg, and rapped with his colorless fingers on the arm of the chair. "Here is blackguarding and maligning from day to day. No Swede any longer respects the honor of another, but no one has the courage for an honest word against him who alone is responsible for it all. Yes, don't you sit down again, you Horn, for people are most of all incensed about your yacht in the Mälar, and assert that with the powder smoke from your salutes you want to win the same gallant favor with Princess Ulrika Eleonora which Creutz had with Princess Hedwig Sofia of most blessed memory.—Yes, yes, yes, don't talk any more about the person of the king, Read his letter instead! Do that! Is there a single line of it that is worthy of the leader of an unfortunate people?"

"Bah! Don't talk about the letter either!" answered Horn, picking up his chair and sitting down. "A little prattle for women, evasions, and indifferent matters! Don't ask that a person who never exposes himself in a conversation shall set himself down in a tent and pour out his soul on a sheet of paper! But I may well admit that sometime an after-reckoning will follow on all this misery."

"Sometime, say you!" continued the invalid Falkenberg, and raised himself on his trembling arms. "Sometime! Have the Swedes then become cringers and hypocrites? Neither Christian the Tyrant nor Erik XIV has done us so much harm as this man, and therefore he belongs to the devil. Since our men have fallen in the field, only old-woman souls are left alive, and those are they that now begin to propagate the Swedish people."

The venerable Fabian Wrede stood up among the speakers, and his voice was wondrously faint and quiet.

"The session is beginning," he said, and pointed to the open doors. "I'm no cringer. I was never of those who jostled around the young master to make him of age, and I am in disfavor. My native land, that is everything to me—father and mother, home, memory, all, all! I know that now my native land is bleeding to death. I know, too, that sometime retribution will follow. But the present is not the time to waste thought upon that. When God sets on us the crown of thorns, that man is not greatest who most conveniently puts it off, but he who himself presses it on all the tighter and says: 'Father, here stand I to serve Thee.'—And I say to you that never, never amid the victory-banners in former years has our little people come nearer to imperishable greatness than to-day."

Horn went into the assembly hall, but on the way he turned to Falkenberg with lowered voice: "My mother had many sons besides me. They have got their bullets. Shall I be worse than they? You talk about the king. If a single man can lure a whole people to so many sacrifices, must not that man be superior to other men?"

Wrede took Falkenberg gently by the shoulders, and added in an undertone: "And the people who have borne so much—would you to-day forbid that people to press fast the crown of martyrdom?"

The lords entered the hall, but, propped on his stick, Falkenberg continued to wander back and forth in the ante-room.

When he at length sat down at the Council table, the secretary had already read out the long address, and the signatures were desired.

No one asked leave to speak. Falkenberg sat huddled together in his armchair. His eyes were moist and dim. Forgetful of precedent, he fumbled with his hands on all sides and whispered, "A pen, a pen!"

In the Church Square

Broad-shouldered Jöns Snare of Mora was eating porridge with his peasant neighbors, Mons and Mathias. He was so stingy that he lay and slept all winter in a shutter-bed to save lighting. His large, flat, beardless face, which glowed in the light from the round window, was uglier and more wrinkled than a troll's, and he talked slowly with a hollow and rumbling voice.

"I predict," said he, striking his hand on the table, "that days of bark-bread are coming. To-morrow I kill my last cow. Every year brings new levies and conscriptions, and now they want to take from us the church bell, the money for the Communion wine, and the grain in the church storehouse.

"It's truly spoken, that," said Mons.

He scratched his gray cheeks and took another pinch of salt on his porridge-spoon, because it was the Sabbath. At other times Mons was so stingy that he went around among the neighbors and counted the pinches of salt on the porridge and the sticks of wood under the pot.

Mathias, on the contrary, leaned forward over the table, shrivelled and ugly, with black teeth and two small shining gray vipers for eyes. He was, however, the stingiest of the three. A more covetous peasant never lived in the parish. He was so stingy that he went into the sacristy to the priest and ordered him on week day to wear wooden shoes like the commo folk.

"My opinion simply is," he drone "that God set us peasants to keep ou thumbs on the nation's purse. Not a cop per will I lay in the bailiff's fist."

"But steal my fish-net," answered Jön Snare, "that you could."

"It's truly spoken, that," said Mons.

Mathias sneered, and broke a loaf wit the back of an axe: "What's a man to d when he's starving?"

Jöns Snare shook his long and strag gling yellow hair and got up, and hi speech could be heard far outside th cabin.

"Ay, sluggard, then do you take you father's old blunderbuss from the wall pick off the bailiff and the tax assessor and hide them in the hayloft. And befor you are done for or come to the gallows you shall go with me to Stockholm t teach the great gentlemen peasant wit Peace we demand, and peace it shall be."

"It's truly spoken, that. We'll go with you," said Mons and got up, swaying i the knees.

Even Mathias got up and gave Jön Snare a hand-shake.

"To begin with, let's go on to th church and talk to the common folk," h said, with his whining voice. "We mus hold by our ancient rights and liberties!"

"I'll talk, sure enough I will," answere Jöns Snare; "and peace it shall be. W demand it."

They went out of the cabin, and on th way talked with wives and servant-maid and old men and boys. When they cam to the church square, they had a goo twenty or thirty following with them.

The autumn sun shone cold and clea over woody ridges and lakes and on th long white church. On the square in fron of the stable-building the people murmured between wagons and carts, but th children of the confirmation class, wh had sat by the altar, had as yet got no further than the threshold of the church porch. The shaggiest old men, who came down from the woods and who had already put on their fur coats, began to cry out and make a racket when they recognized Jöns Snare, because they all regarded him as the most stiff-necked and powerful peasant in the parish. The other Dalecarlians, as well, with bright, open features and white shirts that gleamed out between leather breeches and vests, turned toward him, for it seemed to them that nothing in the world had more weight than his slow and obstinate words.

"You are great church-goers, you," he shouted to them. "I suppose it's to learn the new church prayer about the subject's duty of patience."

No one gave himself leisure to answer. All thronged about him.

"The king is taken!" they shouted. "The king is taken! The king is taken!"

"Is the king taken?" Jöns Snare stood with his hands clenched and looked inquiringly from one to another.

"It's truly spoken, that," said Mons.

"Be still, you fellow! What do you know about it?" roared Jöns Snare, and lifted his clenched hands half up so that all edged away and left him space.

He sat down on a bench before the stables, but the Dalecarlians would not leave him, and the circle around him became closer. No one wanted to lose a single word.

"Is the king taken?" he asked afresh.

"So it's being told from one to another. A smith from Falun has said that the king is taken among the heathens."

Mathias moved up nearer and bent himself and stretched out his long fingers.

"What do you think about these tidings, Jöns Snare, I simply ask?"

Jöns Snare sat with hands on knees, and the sun shone upon his wooden, motionless forehead and hard lips. He looked down at the ground.

"What do you say?" murmured the Dalecarlians. "In Stockholm one of the councillors is giving his own money to the Crown, another his plate, and the third proposes that every well-to-do subject shall give all he has and hereafter possess no more than the poor man. There is only the Queen Dowager who wants her allowance undiminished, the stingy trollop, and people on the street are breaking the windows of Piper's countess."

"And we," said Mathias, "we ought to take the blunderbuss from the wall, Jöns Snare says."

"It's truly spoken, that," confirmed Mons.

Jöns Snare was still silent, and it now became so still around him that nothing else was heard than the ringing of the bell.

"Yes," he answered after a time, and his voice rumbled more deeply and bitterly than ever before, "we ought to take the blunderbuss from the wall and leave the house. By God! you good men of the Dale, if the king is taken, then we demand that they should lead us against the foe, so that we may get him home."

Mathias remained in thought, but his brow became bright, and his gray eyes twinkled slyly.

"Look you, that is a demand that belongs to our ancient rights and liberties."

"It's truly spoken, that," said Mons.

"Yes, yes, that's a demand that belongs to our ancient rights and liberties," murmured the Dalecarlians, and lifted their hands in affirmation. Then there was such a clamor and uproar that the bells could no more be heard.

Captured

Far out in the wastes of Småland and Finnved wondrous portents appeared in the air, and since work lost all worth and the morrow all hope, people either went hungry or ate and drank with riot and revel amid half-stifled curses. At every farm sat a mother or a widow in mourning. During the day's occupation she talked of the fallen or the captives, and at night she started from her sleep, and thought she was still hearing the thunder of the hideous wagons on which teamsters in black oil-cloth cloaks carried away those who had died of the plague.

In the church of Riddarholm the body of the Princess Hedwig Sofia had lain unburied for seven years from lack of money, and now a new coffin had been laid out for the old Queen Dowager Hedwig Eleonora, the mother of the Charleses. Several sleepy ladies-in-waiting were keeping the death-watch, and wax-lights burned mistily around the dead, who lay wrapped in a simple covering of linen.

The youngest lady-in-waiting arose, yawning, went to the window, and drew back the black broadcloth to see if dawn had not appeared.

Limping steps were heard from the ante-room, and a little man of a gnarled and rugged figure, who in every way tried to subdue the thump of his wooden leg, advanced to the coffin and with signs of deep reverence lifted aside the drapery. His fair, almost white hair lay close along his head and extended down his neck as far as his collar. From a flask he poured embalming liquid into a funnel, which was set in the royal corpse between the kirtle and the bodice. But the liquid was absorbed very slowly, and, waiting, he set down the flask on the funeral carpet and went to the lady at the window.

"Is it not seven o'clock yet, Blomberg!" she whispered.

"It has just struck six. It's an awful weather outside, and I feel in the stump of my leg that we're going to have a snowstorm. But then it's a long while since one could foretell anything good in Sweden. Trust me, not this time either will there be enough money for a decent funeral. It was only the beginning when the sainted Ekerot prophesied misery and conflagration. And perhaps the fire didn't go on over the island in front of the castle! Over the plain of Uppsala it threw its light from cathedral and citadel. In Vasterås and Linköping the tempest sweeps the ashes around the blackened spaces devastated by fire—and now there's burning in all quarters of the kingdom. Forgive my freedom, gracious mistress, but to tell the truth is in the long run less dangerous than to lie. That's my old maxim that saved my life once down there by the Dnieper River."

"Saved your life? You were then a surgeon in your regiment. You must sit down by me here and tell the story. The time is so long."

Blomberg spoke resignedly and a trifle like a priest, from time to time lifting his dexter and middle fingers with the other fingers closed.

Both cast a glance at the corpse, which slept in its coffin with gracefully disposed locks, and wax and rouge in the deepest of the wrinkles. Thereupon they sat themselves on a bench in the window-nook outside the hanging broadcloth, and Blomberg began whispering his narrative.

I was lying unconscious in the marshy wilderness at Poltava. I had stumbled along on my wooden leg and got a blow from a horse's hoof, and when I came to, it was night. I felt a cold, strange hand fumble under my coat and pull at the buttons. An abomination before the Lord are the devices of the wicked, I thought; but gentle words are pure. Without becoming frightened, I seized the corpse-plunderer very silently by the breast, and by his stammered words of terror I perceived that he was one of the Zaporogeans who had made an alliance with the Swedes and followed the army. As surgeon I had tended many of these men, as well as captured Poles and Muscovites, and could make myself tolerably understood in their various languages.

"Many devices are in the heart of man," said I meekly; "but the counsel of the Lord, that shall abide. No evil can befall the righteous, but the ungodly shall be filled with misfortunes."

"Forgive me, pious sir," whispered the Zaporogean. "The Swedish czar has left us poor Zaporogeans to our fate, and the Muscovite czar, whom we faithlessly deserted, is coming to maim and slay us. I only wanted to get me a Swedish coat so that in a moment of need I could give myself out as one of you. Do not be angry, godly sir!"

To see if he had any knife, I searched out flint and steel while he was speaking and made a fire with dry thistles and twigs which lay at my feet. I noted then that I had before me a little frightened old man with a sly face and two empty hands. He raised himself as vehemently as a hungry animal that has found its prey, and bent in the light over a Swedish ensign who lay dead in the grass. Thinking that a dead man might willingly grant a helpless ally his coat, I did nothing to hinder the Zaporogean; but as he drew the coat from the fallen one, a letter slipped from the pocket. I saw by the address that Falkenberg was the name of the boy who had bled to death. He lay now as fairly and peacefully stretched out as if he had slept in the meadow by the house where he was born. The letter was from his sister, and I had only time to spell out the words which from that hour became my favorite maxim: "To tell the truth is in the long run less dangerous than to lie." At that moment the Zaporogean put out my light.

"With your wise consent, sir," he whispered; "do not draw the corpse-plunderers hither."

I paid little attention to his talk, but repeated time after time: "To tell the truth is in the long run less dangerous than to lie. That is a big saying, my old fellow, and you shall see that I get further with it than you do with your disguise."

"We may try it," answered the Zaporogean, "but we must promise this, that the one of us who survives the other shall offer a prayer for the other's soul."

"That is agreed," I said, and gave him my hand, for it seemed as if through misfortune I had found in this shaggy-bearded barbarian a friend and a brother.

He helped me up, and at daybreak we fell into the long line of stragglers and wounded that silently tottered into Poltava to give themselves up as prisoners. They willingly tried to conceal the Zaporogean among the rest. His big boots with their flaps reached up to his hips, and his coat tails hung down to his spurs. As soon as a Cossack looked at him, he turned to one of us and cried with raised voice the only Swedish words he had learned in the campaign: "I Shwede. Devil-damn!"

My Zaporogean and I, with eight of my comrades, were assigned quarters in the upper story of a big stone house. As we two had come up there first, we picked out for ourselves a little separate cubby-hole with a window on an alley. There was nothing else than a little straw to lie on, but I had in my coat a tin flute, which I had taken from a fallen Kalmuck at Starodub, and on which I had taught myself to play a few pretty hymns. With that I shortened the time, and soon we noticed that, as often as I played, a young woman came to the window on the other side of the alley. Possibly for that reason I played more than I should have otherwise cared to, and I know not rightly whether she was fairer and more seemly than all other women, or whether long sojourn among men had made my eye less accustomed, but I had great joy in beholding her. However, I never looked at her when she turned her face toward our window, because I have always been bashful before women-folk, and have never rightly understood how to conduct myself in that which pertains to them. Nor have I ever sought fellowship with men who go with their heads full of wenches and do nothing but hanker after gallant intrigues. "Let every one keep his vessel in holiness," Paul saith, "and not in the lust of desire as do the heathen, which know not God; also let no one in this matter dishonor and wrong his brother, because the Lord is a powerful avenger in all such things."

I recognized, however, that a man should at all times bear himself courteously and fittingly, and as one sleeve of my coat was in tatters, I always turned that side inward when I played.

She usually sat with arms crossed above the window-sill, and her hands were round and white, though large. She had a scarlet-colored bodice with silver buttons and many chains. An old witch who often stood beneath her window with a wheelbarrow and sold bread covered with jam called her Feodosova.

When it grew dusk, she lighted a lamp, and since neither she nor we had any shutters, we could follow her with our glance when she blew on the fire, but I found it more proper that we should turn away, and I therefore set myself with my Zaporogean on the straw in the corner.

Besides the prayer-book, I had a few torn-out leaves of Müller's Sermons, and I read and translated many passages for my Zaporogean. But when I noticed that he did not listen, I gave it over for more worldly objects, and asked him of our neighbor on the other side of the alley. He said that she was not unmarried, because maidens in that country always wore a long plait tied with ribbons and a little red tuft of silk. More likely she was a widow, because her hair hung loose as a token of sorrow.

When it became wholly dark, and we lay down on the straw, I discovered that the Zaporogean had stolen my silver snuff-spoon, but after I had taken it back and reproached him for his fault, we slept beside each other as friends.

I was almost ashamed, when it was morning again, at feeling myself happier than for a long time, but as soon as I had held prayers with the Zaporogean and had washed and arranged myself sufficiently, I went to the window and played one of my most beautiful hymns.

Feodosova was already sitting in the sunlight. To show her how different the Swedes were from her fellow countrymen, I instructed my Zaporogean to clean our room, and after a couple of hours the whitewashed walls were shining white and free from cobwebs. All this helped me to drive away my thoughts, but as soon as I set myself again to rest, my torments of conscience awakened that I could be happy in such misery. In the hall outside, my comrades sat on floor and benches, sighing heavily and whispering about their dear ones at home. In due turn, two of us every day were allowed to go out into the open air to the ramparts, but when I laid myself on my straw in the evening, I was ashamed to pray God that the lot next morning should fall upon me. I knew very well within myself that, if I longed for an hour's freedom, it was only to invent an errand to the house opposite. And yet I felt that, if the lot really fell upon me without my prayer, I should still never venture to go up there.

When I came to the window in the morning, Feodosova lay sleeping in her clothes on the floor with a cushion under her neck. It was still early and cool, and I did not have the heart to set the tin flute to my mouth. But as I stood there and waited, she may have apprehended in her sleep that I was gazing at her, for she looked up and laughed and stretched her arms out, and all that so suddenly that I did not manage to draw back unnoticed. My brow became hot, I laid aside my lute, and behaved myself in every way so lumsily and unskilfully that I never was o displeased with myself. I pulled and traightened my belt, took my flute again rom the window, inspected it, and pre-ended I was blowing dust out of it. When inally the Russian subaltern who had harge over us unfortunates informed my aporogean that he was one of the two vho were to go out into the city that day, drew the Zaporogean aside into a corner nd enjoined him with many words to ick a bunch of yellow stellaria such as I ad seen around the burned houses by he ramparts. At a suitable opportunity ve should then give them to Feodosova, said. She appeared to be a good and vorthy woman, who perchance in return night give us poor fellows some fruit or nuts, I said. The miserable bite of bread hat the czar allowed us daily did not even quiet our worst hunger, I said.

He was afraid to show himself out in the sunlight, but neither did he dare to arouse mistrust by staying in, and therefore he obeyed and went.

Scarcely was he out of the door, though, when I began to regret that I had not held him back, because now in solitude my embarrassment grew much greater. I sat down on the bed in the corner, where I was invisible, and stayed there obstinately.

Still the time was not long, for thoughts were many. After a while I heard the Zaporogean's voice. Without reflecting, I went to the window and saw him standing by Feodosova with a great, splendid bouquet of stellaria, which reminded one of irises. First she didn't want to take them, but answered that they were impure, since they had been given by a heathen. He pretended that he understood nothing and that he knew only a few words of her speech, but with winkings and gestures and nods he made it intelligible that I had sent the flowers, and then at last she took them.

Beside myself with bashfulness, I went back into the corner, and when the Zaporogean returned, I seized him behind the shoulders, shook him, and stood him against the wall.

But scarcely had I let go my grasp when he with his thoughtless vivacity stood at the window again, made signs with his hands, and threw kisses on all five of his fingers. Then I came forward, pushed him aside, and bowed. Feodosova sat picking the flowers apart, pulling off the leaves and letting them fall one by one to the ground. Vehemence helped me so that I took courage and began to speak without stopping to consider how it would be most polite to begin a conversation.

"The lady will not take amiss my comrade's pranks and unseemly gestures," I stammered.

She plucked still more eagerly at the flowers and answered after a time, "My husband, when he was alive, often used to say that from heel to head such well-made soldiers as the Swedes were not to be found. He had seen Swedish prisoners undressed and whipped by women, and had seen that the women at last were so moved because of their beauty that they stuck the rods under their arms and sobbed, themselves, instead of those they tormented. Therefore have I become very curious these days. . . . And the love songs which you play sound so wonderful."

Her speech pleased me not altogether, and I found it little seemly to answer in the same spirit by praising her figure and white arms. Instead I took my flute and played my favorite hymn: "E'en from the bottom of my heart I call Thee in my need."

After that we conversed of many things, and though my store of words was small, we soon understood each other so well that never did any day seem to me shorter.

At mid-day, after she had clattered

about with jugs and plates and swung a palm-leaf fan over the embers in the fireplace, she lifted down from the ceiling a landing-net with which formerly her husband had caught small fish in the river. In the net she put a pan with steaming cabbage and a wooden flask with kvass, and the handle was so long that she could hand us the meal across the street. When I drank to her, she nodded and smiled and said that she did not regard it as wrong to feel pity for captured heathens. Toward evening she moved her spinning-wheel to the window, and we kept on conversing when it was dusk. I no longer felt it as a sin to be happy in the midst of the sorrow that surrounded us, because my intent was innocent and pure. Just as I had seen the stellaria shining over heaps of ashes among the burned and desolate houses by the ramparts as a song of praise to God's goodness, so seemed to me now the joy of my heart.

When it became night, and I had held prayer with my Zaporogean and yet once more reproached him that he had stolen my snuff-spoon, the garrulous man began to talk to me in an undertone and say: "I see clearly, little father, that you are in love with Feodosova, and in truth she is a good and pure woman whom you may take to wife. That you never would enter upon any love-dealing of another sort I have understood from the first."

"Such stuff!" answered I, "such stuff!"

"Truth is in the long run less dangerous than lying, you used to say."

When he struck me with my own maxim-staff, I became confounded, and he proceeded.

"The czar has promised good employment and wages to every one of you Swedes who will become his subject and be converted to the true faith."

"You are out of your wits. But if I could steal off and take her home with me on horseback, I would do it."

Next morning, when I had played my hymn, I learned that to-day it was my turn to go out under the open heavens.

I became warm and restless. I combed and fixed myself up even more carefully than at other times, and changed to the Zaporogean's ensign coat, so as not to wear my torn one. Meanwhile I deliberated with myself. Should I go up to her? What should I say then? Perhaps, though that would be the only time in my life when I could get to speak with her, and how should I not repent thereafter even to my gray old age, if out of awkwardness I had missed that one chance! My heart beat more violently than at any affair with the enemy, when I had stood with my bandages among the bullets and the fallen. I stuck the flute into my pocket and went out.

When I came down on the street, she sat at the window without seeing me. I would not go to her without first asking leave, and I did not know rightly how I should conduct myself. Pondering, I took a couple of steps forward.

Then she heard me and looked out.

I lifted my hand to my hat, but with a long, ringing burst of laughter she sprang up and cried, "Haha! Look, look, he has a wooden leg!"

I stood with my hand raised, and stared and stared, and I had neither thought nor feeling. It was as if my heart had swelled out and filled all my breast, so that it was near to bursting. I believe I stammered something. I only remember that I did not know whither I should turn, that I heard her still laughing, that everything in the world was indifferent to me, that freedom would have frightened me as much as my captivity and my wretchedness, that of a sudden I had become a broken man.

I remember vaguely a long and steep lane without stone pavement, where I was accosted by other Swedish prisoners.

Perhaps, even, I answered them, asked after their health, and took some puffs out of the tobacco pipes they lent me.

I believe I disturbed myself over the fact that it was so long till night, so that I had to return the same way and pass her window in brightest daylight. By every means I prolonged the time, speaking now to one man, now to another, but shortly the Russian dragoons came and ordered me to turn about to my place.

As I went up the lane, I persuaded myself that I would not betray myself, but would salute in a quite friendly manner before the window. Was it her fault that so many of the Swedish soldiers, of whom she had had such fine dreams, were now pitiful cripples on wooden legs?

"Hurry up there!" thundered the dragoons, and I hastened my steps, so that the thumping of my wooden leg echoed between the walls of the houses.

"Dear Heavenly Father," I muttered, "faithfully have I served my earthly master. Is this the reward Thou givest me, that Thou makest of me in my youth a defenceless captive, at whom women laugh? Yea, this is Thy recompense, and Thou wilt abase me into yet deeper humiliation, that thereby I may at length become worthy of the crown of blessedness."

When I came under the window and carried my hand to my hat, I saw that Feodosova was away. That gave me no longer any relief. I stumbled up to my prison, and at every step heard the thumping of my wooden leg.

"I have talked with Feodosova," whispered the Zaporogean.

I gave him no reply. My happiness, my flower, that had grown up over the heaps of ashes, lay consumed; and if it had again shone out, I myself, in alarm, would have trampled it to death with my wooden leg. What signified to me the Zaporogean's whisperings?

"Ah!" he went on, "when you were gone, I reproached Feodosova and said to her that you were fonder of her than she realized, and that, if you were not a stranger and a heathen, you would ask her to be your wife."

In silence I clenched my hands and bit my lips together, to lock up my vexation and embarrassment, and I thanked God that He abased me every moment more deeply in shame and ridicule before men.

I opened the door to the outer hall and began to talk to the other prisoners:

"As wild asses in the desert we go painfully to seek our food. On a field that we do not own we must go as husbandmen, and harvest in the vineyard of the ungodly. We lie naked the whole night from lack of garments, and are without covering against the cold. We are overwhelmed by the deluge from the mountains, and from lack of shelter we embrace the cliffs. But we beg Thee not for mitigation, Almighty God. We pray only: Lead us, be nigh unto us! Behold, Thou hast turned away Thy countenance from our people and stuck thorns in our shoes, that we may become Thy servants and Thy children. In the mould of the battle-field our brothers sleep, and a fairer song of victory than that of the conquerors by the sword Thou dost offer to Thy chosen ones."

"Yea, Lord, lead us, be nigh unto us!" echoed all the prisoners murmuringly.

Then out of the darkest corner rose a lonely, trembling voice, which cried: "Oh, that I were as in former months, as in the days when God protected me, when His lamp shone upon my head, when with His light I went into the darkness! As I was in my autumn days, when God's friendship was over my tent, while yet the Almighty was with me, and my children were about me! Thus my heart cries out with Job, but I hear it no longer, and I stammer forth no longer: Take away my trials! With the ear I have heard tell of Thee, O God, but now hath mine eye beheld Thee."

"Quiet, quiet!" whispered the Zaporogean, taking hold of me, and his hands were cold and trembling. "It can be no one else than the czar who is coming below in the lane."

The lane had become filled with people, with beggars and boys and old women and soldiers. In the middle of the throng the czar, tall and lean, walked very calmly, without a guard. A swarm of hopping and shrieking dwarfs were his only retinue. Now and then, turning, he embraced and kissed the smallest dwarf on the forehead in a fatherly way. Here and there he stood still before a house, and was offered a glass of brandy, which he jestingly emptied at a single gulp. It could be nobody but the czar, because one saw directly that he alone ruled over both people and city. He came so close under my window that I could have touched his green cloth cap and the half-torn-off brass buttons on his brown coat. On the skirt he had a great silver button with an artificial stone and on his legs rough woollen stockings. His brown eyes gleamed and flashed, and the small black moustaches stood straight up from his shining lips.

When he caught sight of Feodosova, he seemed as if smitten with madness. When she came down on the street and knelt with a cup, he pinched her ear, then took her under the chin and lifted up her head, so that he could look her in the eyes.

"Tell me, child," he inquired, "where is there a comfortable room in which I can eat? May there be one at your house?"

The czar had seldom with him on his excursions any master of ceremonies or other courtier. He took along neither bed nor bed-clothes nor cooking utensils; no, not even a cooking or eating vessel; but everything had to be provided in the turn of a hand wherever it occurred to him to take lodging. It was for this reason that there was now running and clattering at all the gates and stairs. From this direction came a man with a pan, from that another with an earthen platter, from yonder a third with a ladle and drinking utensils. Up in Feodosova's room the floor was strewn deeply with straw. The czar helped with the work like a common servant, and the chief direction was carried on by a hunchbacked dwarf, who was called the Patriarch. The dwarf every once in a while put his thumb to his nose and blew it in the air straight in front of the czar's face, or invented rascal tricks of which I cannot relate before a lady of quality.

Once when the czar turned with crossed arms to the window, he noticed me and the Zaporogean, and nodded like a comrade. The Zaporogean threw himself prostrate on the floor and stammered his "I Shwede. Devil-damn!" But I pushed him aside with my foot and told him once for all to be silent and get up, because no Swede conducted himself in that fashion. To cover him as much as possible, I stepped in front of him and took my position there.

"Dat is nit übel," said the czar, but at once fell back into his mother speech, and asked who I was.

"Blomberg, surgeon with the Uppland regiment," I answered.

The czar scanned me with a narrowing gaze, so penetrating that I have never seen a more all-discerning look.

"Your regiment exists no longer," he said, "and here you see Rehnskiöld's sword." He lifted the sword with its scabbard from his belt and threw it on the table, so that the plates hopped. "But for certain you are a rogue, for you wear a captain's or ensign's uniform."

I answered, " 'That is a hard saying,' saith John the Evangelist. The coat I borrowed after my own fell in rags, and if that be ill done, I will yet hope for grace, because this is my maxim: To tell the truth is in the long run less dangerous than to lie."

"Good. If that is your motto, you shall take your servant with you and come over here, so that we may prove it."

The Zaporogean trembled and tottered, as he followed behind me, but as soon as we entered, the czar pointed me to a chair among the others at the table, as if I had been his equal, and said, "Sit, Wooden-Leg!"

He had Feodosova on his knee, without the least consideration of what could be said about it, and round them stamped and whistled the dwarfs and a crowd of Boyars who now began to collect. A dwarf who was called Judas, because he carried a likeness of that arch-villain on the chain around his neck, seized a handful of shrimps from the nearest plate and threw them to the ceiling, so that they fell in a rain over dishes and people. When in that way he had made the others turn toward him, he pointed at the czar with many grimaces and called quite coolly to him: "You amuse yourself, you Peter Alexievitch. Even outside of the city I have heard tell of the pretty Feodosova of Poltava, I have; but you always scrape together the best things for yourself, you little father."

"That you do," chimed in the other dwarfs in a ring around the czar. "You are an arch-thief, you Peter Alexievitch."

Sometimes the czar laughed or answered, sometimes he did not hear them, but sat serious and meditative, and his eyes moved meanwhile like two green-glinting insects in the sunlight.

I called to mind how I had once seen the most blessed Charles the Eleventh converse with Rudbeck, and how it then came over me that Rudbeck, for all his bowings, amounted to far more than the king. Here it was the other way about. Although the czar himself went around and did the waiting, and let himself be treated worse than a knave, I saw only him—and Feodosova. I read his purpose in the smallest things. I recognized it in the forcibly curtailed caftans and shaven chins at the city gate.

There was a buzzing in my head, and I knelt humbly on the straw and stammered: "Imperial Majesty! To tell the truth is in the long run less dangerous than to lie, and the Lord said to Moses: 'Thou shalt not hold with the great ones in that which is evil.' Therefore I beseech that I may forego further drinking. For behold, I am soon done with the game, and my gracious lord—who is both like and unlike Your Imperial Majesty—has in the last year turned me to drinking filtered marsh water."

A twitching and trembling began in the czar's right cheek near the eye.

"Yes, by Saint Andreas!" said he. "I am unlike my brother Charles, for he hates women like a woman and wine like a woman, and offers up his people's riches as a woman her husband's, and abuses me like a woman; but I respect him like a man. His health, Wooden-Leg! Drink, drink!"

The czar sprang forward, seized me by the hair, and held the goblet to my mouth, so that the Astrakan ale foamed over my chin and collar. As we drank the prescribed health, two soldiers entered in brownish yellow uniforms with blue collars and discharged their pistols, so that the hot room, which was already filled with tobacco clouds and onion smell, was now also enveloped in powder smoke.

The czar sat down again at the table. Even in all that noise he wanted to sit and think, but he never allowed any one else to shirk the duty of drinking and become serious like himself. He drew Feodosova afresh to his knee. Poor, poor Feodosova! She sat there, a bit sunk together, with arms hanging and mouth impotently half-open, as if she waited cuffs and blows amid the caresses. Why had she not courage to pull the sword to her from the table, press her wrist against the edge, and save her honor, before it was too late? Over and over she might have laughed at my wooden leg and my disgrace, if with my life I could have preserved her honor. Nor had I ever before been so near her and seen so clearly to what a wondrous work she had been formed in the Heavenly Creator's hands. Poor, poor Feodosova, if you had but felt in your heart with what a pure intent a friend regarded you in your humiliation, and how he prayed for your well-being!

Hour after hour the banquet continued. Those of the Boyars and dwarfs who were most completely overcome already lay relaxed in the straw and vomited or made water, but the czar himself always rose up and leaned out through the window. "Drink, Wooden-Leg, drink!" he commanded, and hunted me around the room with the glass, making the Boyars hold me till I had emptied every drop. The twitching in his face became ever more uncanny, and when we were finally together at the table again, he moved three brimful earthen bowls in front of me and said: "Now, Wooden-Leg, you shall propose a health to be drunk all round and teach us to understand its meaning with your maxim."

I raised myself again as well as I could.

"Your health, czar!" I shouted, "for you are assuredly born to command."

"Why," he asked, "should the soldiers present arms and salute me if any other was worthier to command! Where is there anything more pitiful than an incompetent ruler? The day I find my own son unworthy to inherit my great, beloved realm, that day shall he die. Your first truth, Wooden-Leg, requires no bowl."

The pistols cracked, and all drank but the czar.

Then I gathered the fragments of my understanding as a miser his coins, for I believed that, if I could catch the czar in a gracious and mild humor, I might perhaps save my Feodosova.

"Well, then, Imperial Majesty," I continued, therefore, lifting one of the bowls on high, "this is Astrakan ale, brewed of mead and brandy with pepper and tobacco. It burns much before it delights, and when it delights, it puts one to sleep."

With that I threw the bowl to the grounds so that it broke in a thousand pieces. Then I lifted the next bowl.

"This is Hungarian wine. 'Drink no more only water,' writes the Apostle Paul to Timothy, 'but use a little wine for thy stomach's sake, and because thou art so often sick.' So speaks a holy one to weakly men and stay-at-homes. But go out on the battle-field amid frost and wailing and tell me, to how many of the groaning would this bowl of sweetish wine give relief from pain and a softer death?"

Therewith I threw that bowl also to the ground so that it broke. Then I lifted the third bowl.

"This is brandy. It is despised by the fortunate and the rich, because they thirst not after refreshment as the desert for coolness, but would only gibe at the pleasure it gives. But brandy assumes power in the very moment it glides over the tongue, like a despot in the moment he steps across a threshold, and the bleeding and dying draw comfort from a few drops. Therefore I call brandy the best, for I speak as a warrior, and to tell the truth is in the long run less dangerous than to lie."

"Right, right!" acclaimed the czar, and took the bowl and drank, at the same time that he handed me two gold-pieces, while the pistols cracked. "You shall have a pass and a horse to go your way, and wherever you come, you shall tell about Poltava."

Then I knelt yet again in the straw and stammered: "Imperial Majesty—in my pettiness and weakness—beside you sits a—a pure and good woman."

"Haha!" screamed the dwarfs and Boyars, who tottered to their feet. "Haha! haha!"

The czar got up and led Feodosova toward me.

"I understand. He who limps on a wooden leg may fall in love, too. Good. I present her to you just as she is, and you shall have a good situation with me. I have promised every Swede who enters into my service and is baptized in our faith that he shall become one of our people."

Feodosova stood like a sleep-walker and stretched her hands towards me. What did it matter that she had laughed at me? I should soon have forgotten that, and she would soon not have seen my wooden leg, for I should have cared for her and worked for her and prayed with her and made her home bright and tranquil. I should have lifted her up to my bosom as a child and asked her if an honest and faithful heart could not make another heart throb. Mayhap she already bore the answer on her tongue, for slowly she beamed up and became flushed, and her whole face became transfigured. Far away in a corner house on Prästgatan in Stockholm a lonely old woman sat with her sermon-book and listened and wondered whether a letter would not be left for her through the door, whether no disabled man would step in with a greeting from the remote wilderness, whether I never should come or whether I lay already dead and buried. I had prayed for her every night. I had thought of her in the tumult in the midst of stretchers and wailing wounded. But at that moment I thought of her no longer; I saw and heard nothing else but Feodosova. And yet I was angry and strove against something heavy which weighed upon my heart and which I did not understand, but was only slowly and gradually able to make out.

I bent to Feodosova to kiss her hand, but she whispered, "The czar's hand, the czar's hand."

Then I stretched myself toward the czar and kissed his hand.

"My faith," I whispered equally softly, "and my royal lord I may not desert."

The czar's cheek still twitched, and the dwarfs in their terror pulled forth the Zaporogean from his nook to make the czar laugh at his ridiculous figure. But then the czar's arms began to move convulsively. His face grew gray and he trembled in one of his dreaded fits. He went toward the Zaporogean and struck him in the face with clenched fist so that the blood streamed from his nose and mouth, and with such a hoarse and altered voice that it could no longer be recognized he hissed: "I have seen through you, liar, from the moment you came into the room. You are a Zaporogean, a renegade, who have hidden yourself in Swedish clothes.—To the wheel with him, to the wheel!"

All, even the drunken men, began to tremble and feel toward the doors, and in his terror one of the Boyars whispered: "Bring forward the woman! Shove her forward! As soon as he gets to see pretty faces and woman's limbs, he grows quiet."

They seized her, her bodice was cut over the bosom, and, softly wailing, she was supported forward step by step to the czar.

It grew black around me, and I staggered backward out of the room. I remained standing on the street under the stars, and I heard the clamor grow muffled and the dwarfs begin to sing.

Then I clenched my hands and remembered a promise on the field of battle to pray for a poor sinner's soul. But the more fervently I spoke with my God, the further went my thoughts, and my invocation became a prayer for a yet greater sinner who with his last faithful followers wandered about on the desolate steppes. The surgeon ceased with an anxious glance toward the coffin, and the lady-in-waiting followed him forward to th catafalque.

"Amen!" said she, and the two agai spread the covering over the wax-pal Queen Dowager, mother of the Charleses

END OF PART I

THE LIFE AND WORKS OF VERNER VON HEIDENSTAM

By STEFFAN BJÖRCK

About 1860, a number of writers were born in Sweden who were destined to join Strindberg, several years their elder, in making the late nineteenth and early twentieth centuries into a particular brilliant chapter in the history of Swedish literature. Selma Lagerlöf, the teller of legends, and the lyric poet Gustaf Fröding both belong to the group, and for many years Verner von Heidenstam was its unchallenged leader.

Heidenstam was in his time the greatest lyric interpreter of Swedish patriotism and he enriched his country's literature with some of the finest historical stories ever written in the language. At the end of his career his poetry achieved a serene grandeur of universal significance and figures among the imperishable treasures of Swedish poetry.

The man behind the work in many ways stands apart from his time, and the distance between Heidenstam and his public was often an obstacle to a clear understanding of his writing. Even if it were only through the aristocratic, landed culture from which he came, Heidenstam could be said to have greater affinity for the old ideals of Enlightenment than for those of a democratic society, where a writer is a professional among other professionals. His rather British sense of humor and his weakness for spectacular effects sometimes exasperated even his contemporaries—which, indeed, was precisely his intention. He was given to extravagant behavior, as is shown by his second marriage in 1896, solemnized by torchlight on a very inaccessible Baltic island. The guests—a few fellow writers and journalists—were dressed for the occasion in a kind of toga improvised from bedsheets.

Both as a youth and in his maturity, an extraordinary, captivating, and adventurous aura seemed to radiate from Heidenstam, giving him a foreign quality, as if he were not really Swedish at all. Fröding, also a poet, wrote a physical description of him, beginning with his aquiline profile, which suggested a kinship with the eagle or the vulture. Fröding also revealed certain equine traits in his friend and amused himself by asking whether these characteristics were to be attributed to the Heidenstam family's German origins. "Does this vulture come from some Rhine fortress? Is this steed descended from some thoroughbread sire on the plains of Holstein or Schleswig, where crossbreeding and selection have ennobled the race during the campaigns of the Swedish cavalry?" What is the origin, he asks, of this olive darkness of complexion that could let Heidenstam pass for an Arab?

Verner von Heidenstam was born on July 4, 1859, at the estate of his grandmother, Olshammar, north of Lake Vättern. His father was an army engineering officer and a famous builder of lighthouses. The family lived in Stockholm in the winter but left each summer for Olshammar. There the boy, an only child, was surrounded by old people, mostly women, all of them excellent and enthusiastic storytellers. The region, close both to the primitive forest of Tiveden and to a civilization dating from the time of St. Bridget, was to play a role of prime importance in the development of the poet's imagination. The family lost Olshammar about 1890 as Swedish economic life, which until then had been exposed to few hazards, was revolutionized by the new techniques introduced into metallurgy and by the vast increase in international trade. Many provincial families, unable to adapt to the new conditions, were ruined, and a good number of first-rate writers in the 1890s came from distinguished families dispossessed of their ancestral estates. This painful break with the past, this feeling of being rootless, provided fertile soil for the sentimental exaltation of the soil and the fatherland flourishing at that time.

A frail youth, Heidenstam was forced to interrupt his schooling. From 1876 to 1878 he traveled to Italy, Greece, and the Orient. Later he wrote, "To me fell the privilege of being exposed, at the age of greatest receptivity, to the cosmopolitan atmosphere of the southern countries. Instead of studying antiquity in the lecture halls of the provincial university town of Uppsala, at the threshold of manhood I was treading the soil of the Athenian acropolis. Instead of taking root definitively in modern Christian culture, I got to know the Orient."

Ten years were to pass before he would give final form to his impressions of the Orient in a feverish, glowing burst of poetry. The drawings and watercolors Heidenstam made on the spot are quite lacking in distinction, but they reveal the artistic ambitions that the writer was nursing at the time. For years he had aspired to becoming a painter and had even contemplated studies toward that end. In 1880, newly married to Emily Uggla, he quarreled with his father, who frowned upon his plans to be an artist. The young couple then left Sweden and lived for a time in Rome and Paris, on the Côte d'Azur, in Switzerland, and several other places. Heidenstam worked regularly at his painting in Rome and Paris, where he studied with Jean-Léon Gérôme. He was lacking in discipline, however, and was quite unable to settle down to the detailed naturalistic studies required by the curriculum of the day and too eager to start painting huge decorative canvases. Among the better of the paintings is a self-portrait dated 1886, in which he painted himself in an autumnal landscape with a retinue of skeleton knights of death. He was attracted to Symbolists like Böcklin and Klinger, and in his later literary work there are scenes that reveal the influence of their style.

His friendship with Strindberg was an important element in his gradual evolution toward maturity. He had taken the initiative in the fall of 1874, when both were living abroad. Strindberg, Heidenstam's senior, had been famous for years, in spite of going against the current of public opinion in Sweden. Strindberg immediately saw Heidenstam's great promise. Their correspondence is marked by frankness and mutual esteem. Both were brilliant letter writers—Strindberg as the master of the striking word, the flashing phrase, Heidenstam as the witty thinker, capable of turning his irony against himself. Their correspondence is one of the jewels of Swedish literature. At various times the two families lived near each other and were intimate friends. They spent the summer of 1886 at the Brunegg castle in Argau, and it was there that Heidenstam met the Wedekind brothers. Strindberg's Utopian socialism made a deep impression on the younger man, but Heidenstam's attitude in turn had its influence on Strindberg and was doubtless a factor in the latter's acceptance of Nietzcheanism.

It was in 1888 that Heidenstam made his literary debut when he published a volume of poems entitled *Vallfart och vandringsår* (*Pilgrimage: The Wander Years*). In choosing his title, the poet, mindful of Goethe's *Wilhelm Meister,* wished to show that his book was a summing-up of his experiences as a young man. Here his criticism of contemporary authority, of the taste then in vogue, of establishment morals and faith was identical to that of the political and literary left, but it was presented in the guise of stories, fables, and Oriental scenes whose sensuous, seductive colors were the feature most appealing to his public. His daring images were painted in tones far more brilliant than the watercolors he had brought home from his travels.

Heidenstam sang the praises of the Orient, homeland of a lazy, carefree *joie de vivre* that has been smothered in the West by the demands of duty and work. True, there were also certain melancholy reserves expressed in regards to this gospel of the easy life, but his contemporaries turned a deaf ear to this part of Heidenstam's message. Few first books have caused such resounding echoes as Heidenstam's. One immediate effect of this was to free the powers of his lyric imagination, which had been fettered by a confining naturalism. Heidenstam himself continued to develop his literary talent in several fields at once—travel books, essays, novels.

At the end of the nineteenth century, people throughout Europe were turning away from socially oriented naturalism and turning toward everything remote and exciting to the imagination, toward historical and regional themes with a sense of mystery, toward a taste for complex esthetic effects and the connections which link music, painting, and poetry. It was, in general, a search for a civilization richer in artistic expression that inspired the new writers. Heidenstam fired off esthetic manifestoes against naturalism. One of them, written in collaboration with Oscar Levertin, the poet and literary historian, publicized the new directions taken by French literature and the tumult provoked by Zola.

All of these new trends find their greatest expression in Heidenstam's great prose-poem *Hans Alienus* (1892). The book opens with a fairly pedestrian love story set in Rome, where the hero held a low-level job in the Vatican. Discouraged after the failure of his attempts to achieve a life of beauty, Hans Alienus descends to hell, where he journeys from civilization to civilization in search of the one most successful in achieving the "aspirations of life." He tries the way of life of a Roman Emperor and of a god, and finds both unsatisfactory. He tarries at the court of Sardanopolis to enjoy the decadent transports of a life of pleasure. Heidenstam's style is filled with morbid splendor, reminding us that he is a contemporary of Gustave Moreau, and one of the followers of Baudelaire, Oscar Wilde, and Aubrey Beardsley. What comes closest to the hero's "aspirations of life" is barely revealed as it passes—an ancient statue embodying the unfinished dream of man who would be God. The final part of *Hans Alienus* is of a different flavor. The action takes place in Sweden, in the region where Heidenstam lived as a child, and Hans Alienus returns to his native land, clad in his pilgrim's dress, with shell ornaments that rustle at every movement.

Heidenstam's next work, *Dikter*

(Poems, 1895), was, in the opinion of many readers, his best. It is certainly the work that best brings out the richness of his poetic gifts. His lyric imagination exalts the feeling for life, and many of these poems constitute richly sculptured tales built around themes taken from Greece during the Trojan War, from the aristocratic society of Sweden, the Italian Renaissance of the Malatesta, and the Icelandic Sagas. Heidenstam also uses Biblical subjects, sometimes inverting them and changing them for his own purposes: he ascribes a longing for death to the resurrected daughter of Jairus, and he shows us Jesus tempting the devil by offering him oblivion, poverty, and solitude.

Heidenstam's poems established the author as the unchallenged leader of Swedish literature. He was to implement this role in several ways, the chief of which was perhaps his encouragement of the founders of the newspaper *Svenska Dagbladet,* established in 1897, with its policy of opening its columns to current ideas in every field. The leading literary critic was his collaborator, Oscar Levertin, and on the political level the newspaper supported a kind of progressive liberalism based on a thoroughly national sentiment expressed in the slogan "National defense and reform." During the next few years practically every poet, artist, and composer in Sweden was to rally to this program—an affirmation, on the eve of World War I, of a coherent and liberal cultural idea. In the group of poems entitled *Ett folk* (One People, 1902), Heidenstam is, himself, the interpreter of the national aspirations in terms still quoted today. After a brilliant review of all of Sweden's history, the poet vigorously calls for complete and universal democratic suffrage and he invokes for his country a period of trials to arouse the people from their torpor. Here we find the expression of that passionate insistence that was a common theme of nearly all European nationalistic documents of that period. The passage that best succeeds in reaching the hearts of readers is his poetic homage to Sweden, with its lines of an imperishable longing:

> O fatherland, where our sons live,
> and where our fathers lie
> in peace beneath the sacred stone.

The composer Stenhammer set it to music as an elegy, and in this form the poem has become the unofficial national anthem of Sweden.

Several years earlier Heidenstam had developed, in a historical perspective, the nationalist doctrine of the beneficent effects of suffering in *Karolinerna* (*The Charles Men,* 1897–1898), which is, of all the writer's works, the best known abroad. The men of the title, "Carlists," are the soldiers of Charles XII, as well as, in a broader sense, all the subjects who experienced with him the high-point of Swedish mastery of the Baltic and its downfall at the beginning of the eighteenth century. It is not so much the first phase of dominance and the hopes thereof that fascinated the poet as it was the defeat and heroism inspired by it—the individual sacrifices, the ability it had to force everyone to give of his best. Such is the master idea behind most of his narrative and the development of his central character, the enigmatic King Charles who, in spite of a certain stiffness that isolates him, exerts an irresistible attraction over all who are near him. Instead of that Corneillian *éclat* with which Voltaire endows Charles XII in his famous drama, Heidenstam substitutes a heavy penumbra of unrelieved melancholy.

In his conception of Charles XII as the exceptional man dedicated to solitude, a prisoner of his own imagination, the poet surely included something of himself. As much can be said for the historical study the author then wrote on Saint Bridget, *Heliga Birgittas pilgrimsfärd* (The Pilgrimage of Saint Bridget, 1901). He shows the saint deprived of her normal human happiness as wife and mother, leaving her instead to be driven by her religious vocation to an anguished isolation. Heidenstam went even further back into history to write the *Folkunga Trädet* (*The Tree of the Folkungs*) and *Bjälboarvet* (*The Bjälbo Inheritance,* 1905–1907). In these novels he used all the resources of his imagination to relate the ascension of the celebrated line of the Folkungars, starting with a coarse peasant girl, and moving through the family history to the end of the thirteenth century, ending with the two kingly brothers, Valdemar and Magnus. The treatment is very modern, but at the same time there is a remarkable impression of history as something vital, alive and breathing.

At the beginning of the twentieth century, Heidenstam set up his household at Naddö on the estate of Östergoland, where he virtually lived the life of a lord, gradually abandoning his social and political radicalism. Finally, in 1910, a storm broke, with repercussions that were not to die out in Swedish literary life for years. Heidenstam and Strindberg, who for twenty years had been following totally different roads, clashed suddenly in the press, in a battle instigated by Strindberg. The great playwright suffered from a persecution mania, even while his creative genius was otherwise still intact. In this verbal battle, the left and the worker's movement rallied behind Strindberg, who had taken his place in the ranks of the common people as early as 1886 with the publication of his autobiographical book, *Tjänstekvinnans son* (*The Son of a Bondswoman*). Heidenstam's enemies called him "the Junkers bard," and he was finally forced back into the ranks of the right wing. At the beginning of 1914 he took an active part in the militaristic propaganda of the conservative party.

In the last book Heidenstam published during his lifetime, *Nya dikter* (New Poems, 1915), there was no trace of all this. The poems are dominated by an atmosphere of relaxation and serenity, a mood that is also reflected in the prosody. The brilliant, sumptuous versification of the earlier works gives way to a simple and unaffected style. The new work was welcomed with a deep and widespread gratitude, and a year later, in 1916, the book won the Nobel Prize for its author. Heidenstam lived on for almost a quarter of a century, but the rest of his life was simply a long twilight. *När kastanjerna blommade* (When the Chestnuts Bloomed), written during this period, was published posthumously in 1941, together with a collection of finely introspective thoughts and maxims.

In the 1920s Heidenstam had gone to live on a hill overlooking the magnificent landscape of the Lake Vättern region. The house, built to his own design, is of a severe, dense style, succeeding in combining the styles of old Sweden and of Italy. It was there that he died on May 20, 1940, an aged, weary poet who had given the world an abundance of prose and verse that today are still fresh with the vigor of youth.

Steffan Björck is a professor at the University of Lund in Sweden.
Translated by Dale McAdoo.

THE 1916 PRIZE

By GUNNAR AHLSTRÖM

"THE Nobel Prizes are a good thing for the laureates, but they have the added useful function of bringing to the attention of an unaware public certain names which deserve to be remembered," wrote Paul Ginisty in the *Petit Marseillais* in 1908. "Although our curiosity now extends beyond our frontiers," he continued, "a bit of confusion has recently served to remind us that we hardly know the men whom the Swedish Academy has selected in its capacity as judge of the intellectual world, as stipulated by Alfred Nobel in his testament. This is an important function of the Nobel Prizes, since it makes us ask who this writer or that scientist may be whenever these men whose existence we never suspected are brought to our attention."

In other words, the Nobel Prize became an instrument for the literary education of the world. When the world learned that Selma Lagerlöf had won the award, this point of view had already been formulated. In 1916, it was repeated; it experienced a reprise of current interest when the decision was announced. At the same time, a year later, it was announced that Romain Rolland had received the Prize for 1915. Rolland's name was almost *too* well known in those bitter war years; but Verner von Heidenstam—who might he be?

On November 20, the Paris paper, *le Temps,* made the point, while recognizing the total public unawareness of the matter: "Although Mr. von Heidenstam had warm admirers in his own country, we must say that outside Sweden he was quite unknown both to the public and to men of letters. The Swedish Academy had thus conferred worldwide celebrity upon him, as if with a magic wand—a gift far sweeter to a writer than any conceivable sum of money."

A few of Heidenstam's works were translated into French, but they had disappeared in the bustle of Parisian literary life. In 1911 there had been an edition of his book on the celebrated medieval Swedish saint, *The Pilgrimage of Saint Bridget,* and a decade before, in 1901, there had been an edition, soon out of print, of the stories inspired by the fate of Charles XII's loyalists, *The King's Epic,* better known in English as *The Charles Men.* The French translation had been signed "Jacques de Coussange," a pseudonym concealing the identity of a distinguished literary woman, Barbe de Quirielle. This translation of Heidenstam was among the first of her published works in the field of Scandinavian literature, which she was to interpret for many years in France. On the announcement of the 1916 awards she was called upon for her comments, and her article in the *Journal des Débats* was followed, a year later, by a significant essay published in the *Revue des Deux Mondes.*

In 1916 the *Correspondant* of Paris published two contrasting articles in connection with the Nobel Prize. Pierre de Quirielle had a piece entitled "A French Internationalist—Romain Rolland," matched by another entitled "Verner von Heidenstam, a Swedish Nationalist" and signed by Madame de Quirielle with her pseudonym, Jacques de Coussange. This husband-and-wife double commentary was playing on the contrast which was truly the contrast of the age, an inexhaustible source of the drama of conscience, squarely in the midst of the battle raging beyond the walls of the idealistic city of the Nobel awards. On the one side, the pained pacifist, the disciple of Tolstoi whose highly unrealistic banner was soon to be drenched in the blood of the trenches and soiled by the spatterings of adverse opinions; on the other, the flashing of the swords, the heroic parade, the literary rumblings of the eighteenth-century cannon, the crowned emblems of Charles XII: and behind it all, a writer who came with solemn tread, with neutral features, with uncalled-for daring—for the artillery of Verdun spoke quite a different language from that of the *beaux esprits* and their picturesque, pathetic visions.

Indeed, Heidenstam was a Swedish nationalist. The lady writing as Jacques de Coussange had studied his evolution carefully, but she still found it far from an easy task to explain the laureate's particular greatness to her readers. Was he a kind of Arctic Maurice Barrès, imbued with historical attitudes and inspired by reverse pro-German sympathies? Was he a kind of Edmond Rostand, full of gleaming rhymes and seductive rhythms, a man ranging beyond the norms of precision and reasonableness? And how was one to explain this book about the Carlists, this somber patriotic message centered on a royal hero who had been so disastrous fc his people, even while infusing them wit a feeling of national grandeur?

In 1915 Madame de Quirielle had vi ited Sweden, where she had been receive by Heidenstam at his country estate. Th poet proved likable, handsome, tho oughly disposed to exhibit the famou much-photographed profile which wa known to be so irresistible to women. was no secret that his political sympathie lay on the right bank of the Rhine. Late he was even to declare, in an ill-advise interview, that the ideal of the Carlis found its modern expression in the so diers of Kaiser Wilhelm II. She was n aware of this attitude, apparently, an gave free rein to her constructive attitud in her article, which she concluded wi the following typically French patrioti analysis:

> How I should like for Heidenstam t see France as it is today! He woul surely be struck by the moral similarit which exists between our people an the Swedish people whom he has d scribed in his books. Never has th union of the people for a noble caus nor the devotion to the fatherland bee greater, in no nation has the absor tion of the individual into the mass c the people been so complete, and neve has one seen so stout a courage n such great virtues. There are man characteristics which unite our soldie and those of our allies with the hero of Verner von Heidenstam. Whatev the differences which separate us, w feel very close to this great and nob poet, because—he in his country, we ours—we have the same conception what patriotism means, the same vie of everything which should inspire th lives of a people faced with those tim which are decisive to their existence, their greatness.

The award did not cause a great st

abroad that year. Candidates from countries which were at war were proposed almost exclusively by neutrals. Such was the case of Anatole France and Emile Verhaeren, both of whom were nominated by Norwegians. The nomination of Henry James came from Finland. (James died before the voting of the award.) Only Germany proposed a candidate of its own —Elisabeth Förster-Nietzsche.

The German philosopher Rudolf Eucken of Jena, the 1908 laureate, sent a general memorandum in which he declared that he sympathized with the difficulty which the Swedish Academy must find in trying to give its awards to the great men of the belligerent countries without giving rise to misunderstanding. He felt that it would be regrettable, however, if the awards were to be canceled for that reason. The Germans, he thought, would be glad if the prize were to go to a Swedish writer. He listed a few names, among them the name of the Gothemburg philosopher who had proposed Eucken himself almost a decade earlier. One of the names on Eucken's list was that of Verner von Heidenstam. Heidenstam's candidacy was well based; indeed it had already been put forward several times before. He thus enjoyed that veteran's status which was not without importance in making the award. But the principal argument in favor of giving the award to Heidenstam was the poet's tremendous prestige in his own country.

The final vote took place on November 9, and it was perfectly apparent that the award was a peculiarly Swedish matter. Instead of talking about worldwide aspirations, the citation pleads the cause of Swedish literature. Verner von Heidenstam was awarded the Nobel Prize "in recognition of his significance as the leading representative of a new era in Swedish literature."

Translated by Dale McAdoo.

Johannes V. Jensen

1944

"For the rare strength and fertility of his poetic imagination, with which is combined an intellectual curiosity of wide scope and a bold, freshly creative style"

Illustrated by ***LIMA DE FREITAS***

PRESENTATION ADDRESS

By ANDERS ÖSTERLING

PERMANENT SECRETARY
OF THE SWEDISH ACADEMY

TODAY JOHANNES V. JENSEN will receive in person the Nobel Prize for Literature for 1944, and we are happy to salute the great Danish writer who since the beginning of the century has been in the front rank, always active, for a long time controversial, but universally admired for his vitality. This child of the dry and windy moors of Jutland has, almost out of spite, astonished his contemporaries by a remarkably prolific production. He could well be considered one of the most fertile Scandinavian writers. He has constructed a vast and imposing literary work, comprising the most diverse genres: epic and lyric, imaginative and realistic works, as well as historical and philosophical essays, not to mention his scientific excursions in all directions.

This bold iconoclast and stylistic innovator has increasingly become a patriarchal classic, and in his heart he feels close to the poetry of the golden age and hopes that one day he will be counted among the life-giving tutelary spirits of his nation.

Johannes V. Jensen has been such a passionate student of biological and philosophical evolution that he should be amazed at the singular course of his own development. A conquering instinct forms the basis of his being. He was a native of Himmerland, a relatively dry region in western Jutland, and his impressions of men and things were engraved indelibly on his consciousness. Later he was to remember those resources that were hidden beneath the sensations of childhood, the ancient treasure of family memories. His father, the veterinarian of Farsö, came from that area, and through his paternal grandfather, the old weaver of Guldager, Jensen is directly descended from peasants. Characteristically enough, his first book dealt with the province of his origin. His incomparable *Himmerlandshistorier* offer an original portrait gallery of primitive and half-savage creatures who are still subject to ancient fears. The promised land of his childhood, powerful and alive with the past, is found again in his mature poetry.

The first books of Johannes V. Jensen reveal him as a young man from the provinces; a student of opposition, living in Copenhagen; an arduous and agitated youth, fighting passionately against intellectual banality and narrow-mindedness. This native of Jutland, self-conscious, difficult to approach, but sensitive, was soon to find his country too narrow. Stifled by the familiar climate of the Danish isles, he threw himself into exotic romanticism with the cool passion of a gambler. His travels across foreign continents for the first time opened to him the space needed by his restless, unchained imagination. During that period of his life he sang the praise of technology and mechanization. Just as his compatriot H. C. Andersen was perhaps the first to describe the charms of railway travel, Johannes V. Jensen was the prophet of the marvels of our age, of skyscrapers, motor cars, and cinemas, which he never tires of praising in his American novels, *Madame D'Ora* (1904) and *Hjulet* (The Wheel, 1905). But soon he entered into a new stage of his development; at the risk of simplifying matters we might say that, having satisfied his passion for distant travel, he began to look in time for what he had pursued in space. The same man who had sung the modern life, with its rapid pace and noisy machines, has become the spectator of ancient epochs and has devoted himself to the study of the long, slow periods during which man first sought adventure.

Thus we come to perhaps his most important creation, the six volumes combined under the title *Den lange rejse,* which leads us from the Ice Age to Christopher Columbus. The central theme or one of the central themes of this work is the universal mission of the Scandinavian people, from the great migrations and the Norman invasion to the discovery of America. Jensen considers Christopher Columbus a descendant of the Lombards, in short a Nordic man, if not a Jutlander like himself. In this monumental series appears a legendary figure, Nornagestr. He is not at all the same person who appears at the court of King Olaf Tryggvason to tell his stories and die there. According to the Icelandic saga he was three hundred years old; but Jensen makes him even older and turns him into a kind of Ahasuerus, ubiquitous, always behind his time, a stranger among the new generations, but nevertheless younger than they because he lived at a time when existence itself was young and mankind closer to its origins. The writer has followed tradition only as far as it was useful to him. Three prophetesses came to Nornagestr's mother to see the child and one of them predicted that he would die as soon as the candle could no longer burn. Gro, the mother, immediately extinguished the candle and gave it to the child as an amulet. In the work of Johannes V. Jensen, Nornagestr sometimes lights it in foreign lands and whenever he does so a deep abyss of time opens before him. When he comes to again, seized by the love of life, he is transported to his country, the fresh and green Zealand.

All legends exist because reason alone cannot clarify experience. What then is Nornagestr, who plays such an important role in the epic of the Danish master? Perhaps it is the spirit of the Nordic people rising from the night like a phantom or like an atavistic creature. One suspects that this unique globe-trotter with his harp is closely related to the author himself, who has given him many ideas about life and death, and about the close relation between the present and eternity—the precious fruits of experiences gathered from the lands and seas of the globe.

For Johannes V. Jensen, who grew up on a Jutland moor where the horizon is often indented by a line of tumuli, it was natural to divide his interests between facts and myths and to seek his way between the shadows of the past and the realities of the present. His example reveals to us both the attraction of the primitive for a sensitive man and the necessity of transforming brute force into tenderness. He has attained the summit of his art by means of these violent contrasts. A fresh, salty breeze blows through his work, which unfolds with vivid language, powerful expression, and singular energy. Precisely in the poets most deeply rooted in their country do we find this poetic genius for words. Jensen is the voice of Jutland and of Denmark. With his talents he deserves the title of the most eminent narrator of the victorious struggle of the Nordic people against nature, and of the continuity of the Nordic spirit throughout the ages.

Mr. Jensen—If you have listened to what I have just said you will certainly think that the few moments I had were much too short to accomplish the long voyage through your work, and that I have neglected important aspects of it. It is fortunate for us as well as for you that a proper presentation is hardly necessary at all in your case. You are a well-known member of our great family and as such you are now asked to receive from the hands of our King the distinction which the Swedish Academy has awarded you.

ACCEPTANCE SPEECH

By JOHANNES V. JENSEN

I THANK THE VENERABLE Swedish Academy and the Swedish nation for the honor they have bestowed upon me in awarding me the Nobel Prize for Literature. Present in all our thoughts today is the founder, Alfred Nobel, whose generosity has done so much good for science, literature, and peace throughout the world. This great Swedish scientist and humanist linked the name of Sweden with a broad vision that stretches far beyond the frontiers of one nation and serves to bring all nations closer to one another.

When one thinks of great Swedish minds of international fame, our thoughts turn to Alfred Nobel's forerunner, that great genius of natural science, Linnaeus, who gave animals their proper names and, long before anyone had ever dreamt of evolution, classified monkeys, apes, and man under the name of primates. Passion for nature, for all that stirred and breathed, was the driving force in Linnaeus' genius. Whenever one reads of the determination of the species, or opens a book on natural science and history, in whatever language, one inevitably comes across the name of Linnaeus. There is something of the freshness of mind, of the lightness of spirit in him which for centuries has been linked in people's minds with the mountains of Sweden and Swedish joy in nature.

I cannot talk of Linnaeus without being reminded of Charles Darwin, remembering him not only as a man of science who has drawn a line between two epochs, but also as the most lovable, the kindest of human beings, the best of fathers; his distinguished name is now carried by the third and fourth generation of his descendants. To him, evolution was not only the subject of a life's study but the very essence of life, proof of the inexhaustible richness and wonder of nature, revealed each day and taken to heart.

Were one to determine the degree of maturity of each nation according to its capacity for reasoning and comprehension, England would come out on top for her sense of realism, and the man who put forward these basically English ideas in a simple, unaffected manner was Charles Darwin.

Linneaus' designation of species was the foundation which subsequently enabled Darwin to form his conclusions on their origin. This Anglo-Swedish sense of reality, derived from our common Nordic background, has established for all time the place of mankind in nature.

I should like to mention on this occasion another name in Danish literature which is linked with Swedish tradition, that of Adam Oehlenschläger. You will remember that when he met Sweden's national poet, Esaias Tegnér, at Lund in 1829, he was hailed by him as the great poet and simple man that he was. A hundred years later, in 1929, it was my lot to receive in the same town a degree from the University of Lund. I am not Oehlenschläger's successor, but I do count myself among his followers and admirers.

It is with a feeling of Scandinavian fellowship that I now wish to thank the great and free Swedish nation which once crowned my countryman Adam Oehlenschläger with laurels, and has on two occasions judged my literary efforts worthy of distinction.

AT MEMPHIS STATION

By JOHANNES V. JENSEN

Translated by S. Damon Foster

Half-awake and half-dozing,
in an inward seawind of danaid dreams,
I stand and gnash my teeth
at Memphis Station, Tennessee.
It is raining.

The night is so barren, extinguished,
and the rain scourges the earth
with a dark, idiotic energy.
Everything is soggy and impassable.

Why are we held up, hour upon hour?
Why should my destiny be stopped here?
Have I fled rain and soul-corrosion
in Denmark, India, and Japan,
to be rain-bound, to rot, in Memphis,
Tennessee, U.S.A.?

And now it dawns. Drearily light oozes
down over this damp jail.
The day uncovers mercilessly
the frigid rails and all the black mud,
the waiting-room with the slot-machine,
orange peels, cigar- and match-stumps.
The day grins through with spewing roof-gutters,
and the infinite palings of rain,
rain, say I, from heaven and to earth.

How deaf the world is, and immovable!
How banal the Creator!
And why do I go on paying dues
at this plebeian sanatorium of an existence!

Stillness. See how the engine,
the enormous machine, stands calmly and seethes;
shrouding itself in smoke, it is patient.
Light your pipe on a fasting heart,
damn God, and swallow your sorrow!

Yet go and stay in Memphis!
Your life, after all, is nothing but
a sickening drift of rain, and your fate
was always to be belated
in some miserable waiting-room or other—
Stay in Memphis, Tennessee!

For within one of these bill-shouting houses,
happiness awaits you, happiness,
if you can only gulp down your impatience—
and here there is sleeping a buxom young girl
with one ear lost in her hair;
she will come to encounter you
some fine day on the street,
like a wave of fragrance,
looking as though she knew you.

Is it not spring?
Does the rain not fall richly?
Is there not the sound of an amorous murmur,
a long, subdued, conversation of love
mouth to mouth
between the rain and the earth?
The day began so sadly,
but now, see the rainfall brighten!
Do you not allow the day its right of battle?

AT MEMPHIS STATION

So now it is light. And there is a smell of mould
from between the rusting underpinning of the platform
mingled with the rain-dust's rank breath—
a suggestion of spring—
is that no consolation?

And now see, see how the Mississippi
in its bed of flooded forest
wakes against the day!
See how the titanic river revels in its twisting!
How royally it dashes through its bends, and swings the rafts
of trees and torn planks in its whirls!
See how it twirls a huge stern-wheeler
in its deluge-arms
like a dancer, master of the floor!
See the sunken headland—oh, what immense, primeval peace
over the landscape of drowned forests!
Do you not see how the current's dawn-waters
clothe themselves mile-broad in the day's cheap light,
and wander healthily under the teeming clouds!

Pull yourself together, irreconcilable man!
Will you never forget that you have been promised Eternity?
Will you grudge the earth its due, your poor gratitude?
What would you do, with your heart of love?

Pull yourself together, and stay in Memphis;
announce yourself in the market as a citizen;
go in and insure yourself among the others;
pay your premium of vulgarity,
so that they can know they are safe, as regards you,
and you will not be fired out of the club.
Court the damosel with roses and gold rings,
and begin your saw-mill, like other people.
Yank on your rubbers regularly . . .
Look about you, smoke your sapient pipe
in sphinx-deserted Memphis . . .

Ah! there comes that miserable freight-train
which has kept us waiting six hours.
It rolls in slowly—with smashed sides;
it pipes weakly; the cars limp on three wheels;
and the broken roof drips with clay and slime.
But in the tender, among the coals,
lie four still forms
covered with bloody coats.

Then our huge express-locomotive snorts;
advances a little; stops, sighing deeply;
and stands crouched for the leap. The track is clear.

And we travel onward
through the flooded forest
under the rain's gaping sluices.

CHRISTOPHER COLUMBUS

By JOHANNES V. JENSEN

Translated by A. G. Chater

PRELIMINARIES

Christopher Columbus came from Genoa, a Ligurian by birth, but we shall understand the roots of his nature if we regard him as a descendant of the Longobards, of people who had moved from Lombardy to the coast.

From what we know of Columbus he was of Northern type, fair-haired and freckled, with blue eyes, the stamp familiar in the North among skippers and farmers. The immediately preceding generations of his family were established in the mountains above Genoa, their last stage on the way to the sea; peasants who through handicraft and contact with the port became seafarers. The great Migrations had brought their ancestors from forgotten shores by the Baltic, straight through the countries of the Old World and all the turbulent centuries of the Middle Ages, as far as the Mediterranean—now Columbus was to carry the migration farther. The history of the Longobards, then, is the history of Columbus's past; in his blood, though the origin is forgotten, he inherits profound and powerful promptings from wandering forefathers.

But his spiritual garb is another. Christianity in the literal adaptation of the peasant had replaced the traditions of his race long before he was born, and had become a part of his race's nature. His father, an ordinary craftsman, named him after Saint Christopher, a common thing in those days with pious folk who looked to a patron they could understand, flesh of their flesh, and gladly committed their children to his protection. Everybody was called Christopher, but Columbus when at the summit of his responsibilities felt convinced of his successorship to the carrier of Christ. Therefore the legend of Saint Christopher in its natural interpretation, Christianity accepted in primitive fashion, belongs to the antecedents which went to form Columbus, it contains the taste of the race.

His feeling Columbus derived from early impressions of the Gothic, which is the form under which Northern peoples have adopted the spirit of Christianity. It was an intensity of thought, which was rooted in the Northerner's memories and extended them beyond the finite, that created the pagan-christian myth of God's mother. In its nature the myth is purely Northern; the name is all the Holy Virgin has left of her biblical origin. Christianity demanded soul, adoration, of the pagan, and he gave what he had to give, what to him was sacred, Woman as Virgin and Mother. He centred his religion upon a beautiful ancient devotion to Woman, and in her honour his imagination refashioned his Forest and his Ship into a Cathedral.

Columbus was a child of the Gothic; we must seek its genesis if we would know how his nature came about; we must go backward in the youth of the race to the prototype of the myth of God's Mother, the heart of the Gothic. Columbus inherited it in the form of universal longing: the eternal feminine; the Holy Virgin was the woman in his life. Santa Maria *was the name of his ship.*

Forces which point back to lost elements in his origin, but whose tendency was influenced from elsewhere, directed Columbus onward in search of a world he was never to find.

Deep-lying Northern instincts were crossed and dominated by surface currents from the world that had shaped his consciousness, the Southerner's world, the local stamp, the stamp of his time; he behaved now as an Italian, now as a Spaniard, always as a Christian; an inner illusory world stood between him and Nature, which he still regarded with the prejudiced eyes of his day, several realities one within another, like the heavens of that age, and all of them fairly independent of experience, in conformity with the contemporary imago mundi*—and yet Columbus went clean through all imaginary realities and came out with a new one.*

Pure and monumental was that quality in him which made this possible: courage, a complete dauntlessness which he had received as a heritage from ancestors who were conquerors and colonists and to generations of whom uncertainty and playing for high stakes had become the very form of their existence. Courage and endurance, the sailor's daring, inflexibility of purpose, are the clean line which runs through Columbus's character as a discoverer. He was a sportsman, and he was a man of genius, his motives rose superior to his age; where he regarded his voyage as a mission the elements were at work within him, he pressed on as though the whole of human nature had been pressing upon him.

Personally, on the other hand, as an individual, such as his bringing-up and his circumstances had made him, he gave proof of a mixture of qualities, magnificence and pettiness which are difficult to reconcile, prophetic vision and a weakness in direct judgment, a certain dizziness in his capabilities; in spite of the broad lines of his character he was not always magnanimous, even judged by his own age, but made moan when others stronger than himself treated him unjustly; he was not able to keep his name clear of querulousness. His plans were worthy of a king, but it seemed as if some never-redeemed inheritance held him bound to earth. He had land-hunger and an eye to business, but on a large scale, like the conquerors and freebooters of whose race he came; the Longobard would go far when it was a question of acquiring and retaining possessions. As a born founder of kingdoms Columbus approached the sovereigns in whose service he made his great land-take naturally, as an equal, with an empire in his hand and a dynasty in his head—and what other rank had they *but that of being the top-shoot of a race that had begun as conquerors and husbandmen? Later, of course, he proved no match for the crowned heads; his ancestry had no long line practised in holding what they had won. Like most sailors Columbus had a rather clumsy gait ashore; he was more himself as the free skipper on his deck than as the decorated Admiral at court. Who was there that could honour him? As colonist on the grand scale he had his own rank, but he submitted to that of others.*

Christopher Columbus, as by virtue of his nature and his surroundings he was compelled *to develop, may be taken as the type of that flaring up of the faculties and that profound bewilderment which mark the Northerner when he is transferred to the South.*

Viewed from the outside as a spectacle Columbus's career is a play which does not resemble any of the current forms of art but has features derived from them all—the romance, the drama, the comedy; it is at once fantastic, tragic and sometimes almost laughable, melodious and discordant at the same time. He begins as an everyday man, the most ordinary of epics, which in fact has remained unwritten; he then takes on prodigious dimensions, painfully true the whole of it and yet on a closer view theatrical, a stage-world of fable and delusion; and he ends as the disappointed man, with something of the pitiless Nemesis of comedy rattling about his ears. The very action of his great piece develops as a farce; he is let loose as in blindman's buff between two continents and actually blunders into one of them, but has no idea which it is and never finds out. And he dies off the stage, almost like a scene-shifter whose fall nobody notices, while the play goes on without him with new figures and mighty new acts upon the stage. The ill-treatment to which he is subjected belongs to his part as clown of the piece, although he is its author. Everybody is amused, without thinking that even the clown has his feelings; afterwards they reconstruct his sufferings and are severe on his tormentors, martyrdom and halo awarded by the same public; first cruel, then crawling before his name—hasn't the public always been the same? But such as Columbus was, with his fine craving, his failings, we love him as the great lost child he was, our brother.

It was only for posterity that the figure of Columbus rose again and became a myth. No authentic portrait of him has come down to us. The idealized picture that has been formed of the voyager, as we know it from the accepted type of his monuments, hits off some features correctly, a Northern head, but is weaker and more pompous than the essentially popular class he really represents. It is characteristic of Columbus's true portrait that he hides his face from history and is his race; a real description of him must deal with that race.

Only he in whom the past is stowed is freighted for the future. Columbus grows with the bearing of his exploit; we see, however, looking backward, that history passed through his heart. As he stands, he bears a bridge which joins widely separated worlds and epochs. He sets up a boundary between illusion and reality, not by what he thought but by what he was and what his passion gave an impulse to.

In a strange, tragic and grandiose way a magnificent error coincides in his destiny with total disillusionment, which nevertheless proves fruitful; he leads the way through to a new reality though he loses himself. He is the most disappointed man in history:

> *For when he found the saving isle*
> *Gone was his dream.*
> *A world arose to sever him*
> *From the uttermost stream.*
> *Then grew thy heart's great longing,*
> *Conqueror in defeat returning,*
> *And bore, like the billow's burden,*
> *The world's eternal yearning.*

Columbus completes the Northern migration and at the same time renders Christianity impossible as a terrestrial dream. The Kingdom of Heaven he sought was the Bible's mystical abode, Paradise; but then he sought it on earth. He knew not that it was rooted in his nature. He sails for the Indies, means Paradise, and finds the New World—doesn't it look as if the Almighty, or Somebody not so good, was playing a game with him? And yet he makes the discovery!

In the person of Columbus the pagan yearning for Nature unites with Christian-

ity's fata Morgana*—and they perish together! It might be said that Columbus, regarded as the hero of a tragedy of destiny in which the elements are too strong for him, is the first modern man, the first god-forsaken figure; he substitutes space and reality for the spiritual prison and the superstition of the Middle Ages. But the modern age is founded upon acquisitions which came after him; other brains with trained qualifications he did not possess shattered the* imago *he believed in and enlarged the world; he had brought it within range of vision but himself died unenlightened.*

We must therefore look on him as a man of his time, such as heredity and experience had made him; we must see what he saw with the eyes he had, as an adventurer, a visionary, a gambler and a victim, with his brief glory and long renown, as skipper of the caravel which bore him with the rest of its medieval cargo—and which stranded upon that coast where he knocked and knocked and was not to be admitted. But his achievement points to the ancestry behind him, and when it passes into other hands, and he is forgotten, it is nevertheless he who is its protagonist.

What remains, however, the real event in his life is the oldest and most universally human of all, what we all sail for and bring home, the loss of hope:

Christopher Columbus, thy silver hair,
Frosting thy poll,
Crowns the sea-chilled viking brow
And the wreck of thy soul.
Thou gav'st us back Earth and didst enter
Immortality's murmurous seeming.
Now covers thy mighty shadow
The ne'er-reached goal of thy dreaming.

The voyages of discovery, which were the work of many, are inevitably connected with Columbus as their central figure. And of all the discoverers he was in fact the one who was governed to the widest extent by the idea of discovery.

When the world had become known in its entirety, more or less, and America had been added as another continent, a conception grew up and spread among seamen, spontaneously and vaguely as is the way of popular legends, of a skipper who might be met with at sea, a phantom in a phantom ship: the Flying Dutchman.

It is as though the old Northern roving impulse, made homeless when all seas had been sailed, and the earth circumnavigated many times, had passed into a myth, a voyage which can never end, the skipper who cannot die. Right in substance but fortuitous in form, the tale of the spectral ship is connected with the name of a Dutch captain, or perhaps we may rather say it hangs in the air—ought it not in reality to be referred to Columbus? It belongs to his myth as its last act. For it is the Santa Maria *that is the phantom ship, Columbus is the restless skipper-soul who is condemned to sail the seas until the Day of Judgment.*

Unblest is he whose aching desire
Can never die.
The ocean swell so drear and waste
Goes heaving by.
There stands the fettered skipper, steering
His ship of spectres weary
Under the pallid moonbeams,
In the ocean swell so dreary.

This spectre is the heavily laden, nonexistent but terribly real phantom ship which we call history, the memory of mankind.

Of this ship Columbus is captain. A numerous crew sails with him, lesser and better men than he, seekers and strivers, who are all condemned to continue their lives in an image; as the one who lost most and gained most he is captain of the Dead.

In this vessel we are now to sail.

BOOK ONE: THE CATHEDRAL

I
UNDER YGDRASIL

Some time in the Iron Age it chanced that a hunter lost his way in the forest while pursuing a deer, and reached a tract where he had never been before.

When at last he had brought down the deer and was sitting on it to rest, still angry from the exertion the hunt had cost him, he noticed that the trees here were strikingly bigger and mightier than anywhere he knew—nothing but lofty stems and airy tops, with only a carpet of herbage below, neither brushwood nor swamp as in other places; the spot where they grew stood higher than the surrounding land, like a raised floor, lifting a grove of tall trees up above the roof of the forest like a dome; it seemed a Thing-stead where the giants of the forest had assembled to take counsel together.

The huge slender trunks united their foliage high high up to form a spreading tent of leaves which shut out the sky but not the light; green, cool, resonant halls where sound carried so that the twittering of a single finch made quite a din, as though its tone swelled here of itself. The slightest sound was repeated and multiplied under the leafy vaults: echo, the voice of solitude; here was perfect solitude.

It was many leagues within the forest; from the high place under the big trees you could look over endless silent stretches of wood, dense forest and glades about watercourses and lakes, and again woods and woods, as far as the eye could reach, on three sides; but on the fourth there was a view of a great river which swung in a long bend with one bank against the foot of the rise, as though it had a message to bring; it was a broad, rapid river with a deep bed, which hurried along and raised eddies on its surface as it went; on both banks it was enclosed by virgin forest; only an opening here and there in the sedges showed where the beasts had trampled paths to ancient watering-places along the river. It flowed through the woods from a distant region where blue outlines showed that there were mountains, and it ran on through the lowlands to the horizon on the other side. The hunter's practised eye noted ospreys above the eddies; there were good days to be had with a line, as a change from hunting, if one lived here.

In a cleft on the slope below the trees the weeds grew knee-high, there was a hidden spring; the hunter pressed the back of his hand down into the soaking cushion of moss till it filled with clear water, and slaked his thirst; then he returned to the deer he had brought down, cut his arrows out and began to flay the big, heavy beast, with his knife now in his hand, now in his mouth, working with his knuckles between hide and carcass first on one flank and then, as he took the beast by the horns and turned it over, on the other, till the hide was off. When this was done he quartered the carcass and hung the pieces up on the nearest tree. The frontal bone and antlers he cut out and set up on a bough, for that belonged to the spirits of the place. Then he straightened himself and wiped his greasy hands on the back of his breeches, unrolled a leather pouch and took out a scrap of tinder which he placed on his flint between thumb and forefinger, then drew the steel along the sharp edge of the flint; sparks flew out between his hands, brighter even than the daylight, and at once a glowing spot in the touchwood began to smoke; he knelt and blew gently upon the glow, raking dry leaves together with one hand and bending quite low with his face to the ground; smoke curled upward about his head, he made a nest of his hands and nursed it, until at last he rose and at the same instant a flame licked up the heap of leaves. Not long after he had a fire. Then he sharpened a stick with his hunting knife and roasted kidneys on it over the fire, ate and chewed and went to the spring for a sip of water, all in profound silence, which was nothing strange since he was alone.

In a tree close by there was a hole left by a fallen branch, and in it lived a starling; at intervals it came out of its door and flew away, and after a little while it returned with several worms packed together in its beak and flew in a straight line into its hole, like an arrow aimed from a distance at a mark; and when it had disappeared a feeble smothered cheeping could be heard from the hollow in the tree.

Now and then the hunter's eyes wandered as he absently ate, swallowing big lumps at a time; the wood was alive around him and he knew it, he was one with it, saw the squirrel steal into a tree spreading its legs out on the vertical bark with tail erect, now behind the trunk and now back again on a fork higher up; he saw it as the brisk little red creature it was, until it disappeared among the foliage and other things attracted his attention. The forest attended to its affairs, like a great calm business in which everything got done by all concerned, in silence and away from each other. Far off, as though behind many partitions, the woodpecker was heard beating his tattoo on a sonorous dead branch; high up, from the secret chambers of the sunny tree-tops, from the sweet green light itself, came the thick cooing of the wood-pigeons, a mother full to the throat with happiness. The finch called now and again, making a great noise for such a little creature and rousing echoes in the wood; it had its nest and was as happy as a horse, though it was so small that the least twig could support it. The flies buzzed and excited themselves, spinning wildly in a wheel in the midday fires, and one would fall on a leaf and whiz around on its back, quite dizzy; the sun made the thing bewildered.

The cry of a bird of prey was heard above the tree-tops; down below there was a sniffing under the bushes, and the hunter shrank together as he sat, stopped munching in the middle of a bite: it was the badger come out in the middle of the day with two half-grown young ones, striped in the face and powerful of body; she was out teaching her young to root; she turned the earth with her paw and sniffed, and the young ones turned the earth with their paws and sniffed; but the hunter began to chew again: it was not the time of year, their skins could stay on till another opportunity.

When the hunter had finished his meal he looked up at the sky and guessed what time of day it was—something after midday, ladders of haze leaned steeply down from the tree-tops into the shadow, the wood was very still, with only a busy hum of flies and the cry of a buzzard above the tree-tops. The hunter yawned and worked his jaw, shook his head; he had been on the trail since before sunrise and all the long forenoon, running almost uninterruptedly in a straight line the whole time, so who could tell where he was now? And now he would have to go all that long way back—how long he did not know. But the food and the strong smell of the fire had made him sleepy; he yawned again and shivered and lay down to take a nap on the grass by the side of the fire.

When he awoke it was late. He jumped up.

The wood had filled with dusk which poured in among the roots of the trees and rose nearly to their leaves, but the sunlight still came through. It had come on to blow a little, and the leaves above were in motion and shook blue glimpses of the sky and green and red and yellow patches of light together; in the west a purple glow behind the trunks showed how low the sun had sunk. Other birds than before were heard now, and they had made for the topmost twigs, where they mingled their long, flute-like, questioning notes with the vanishing twilight. Down in the depths of the wood all was dark and still.

The hunter knew that he would have to carry a big load of meat many leagues through pathless forest before reaching human habitations; he had overslept himself, and saw with uneasiness that he would have to spend the night in the open. He quickly decided to stay where he was, rather than halt at some other place down in the dense swampy woods, and while it was yet light he looked about among the big trees for a comfortable fork between two branches where he could ride out the night in safety, even if there was not much chance of sleep. When he had found what he wanted, he laid more fuel on the fire and collected dead wood, getting ready for the night as a man does on such occasions; but he was uneasy. He dragged up big fallen branches so as to have more than enough, sweating and making a noise; he made a sort of attempt to sing, but broke off again. And when he had made ready for the night he kept quite quiet. In the fading sky the moon came out and began to gain power; he dropped his eyes before it, the sky was over him, he could not hide from it.

And gradually as the sun sank, the forest became strangely sombre and stiff, cold blasts from it struck upon the hunter, making him shiver beside the fire, for there was a life in the draught which touched him to the marrow. The air grew thick with all kinds of dumb things that gathered therein. The fire and the darkness augmented each other—the more light the fire gave, the blacker looked the wood. Soon the hunter found himself in a sort of cave of light, where only the nearest tree-trunks stared in the gleam; beyond was thick darkness, the ancient black evil Night.

He looked up, and his soul received a shock, for there were the stars: he was, as it were, in the centre of an immense cave with starry walls, the big familiar constellations stood out over his head—the Great Bear wheeling upon its own length, Orion blustering in the sky, the Pleiads flickering in the wind of eternity, now clearing their stars, now shrouding them in luminous haze, the Milky Way above them all, whose soul is giddiness; radiant and dumb as ever were the stars, with a gaze not to be sustained, the sky full of eyes, all the stars blinking, and between them space with its solemn deep-blue voice; fearful was the starry heaven, and the hunter was abashed before it and bent his neck, shook himself, rubbing his numbed hands together; he was but a poor hunter.

His eyes dropped from one marvel to another, but with this one he was familiar—the world of fire. He looked into his fire and blinked his dazzled eyes, comforted as though by a caress; the fire licked and shot up a flame, it was his friend. And, without giving it a thought, he fetched the entrails of the deer and flung them on the fire. For a moment they almost overcame it: the fire turned black and gasped for breath, the clammy guts and their contents threatened to smother it; but soon the flames grew about them on every side and began to feed upon the entrails as they became charred; the fire puffed strangely and gave off fat worms of smoke, running over the shrivelled skin in many colours before the flame found a place where it could bite and fix itself.

Long and deliciously the fire gave off its fumes, with little cracks, scorching and blistering and feasting itself, and long the hunter sat with dazzled eyes which now saw nothing when he turned them from the fire, sunk in deep thought, fascinated by the fire and what was going on within it, where he divined an infinity before which he humbled himself in his heart.

Then the hunter heard footsteps. He seized his long ash bow, rose and turned a terrible face to the darkness—fear and a mortal challenge together. The footsteps ceased, and then he was aware of a sound of wailing close at hand, the very note of terror; he gave a violent start, and with a roar drew his bow to the arrow-tip; there was another wail, with more fear in it, and then his eye suddenly fell on a figure that had come into the light of the fire, a vision that had appeared out of nothing, a human figure, a woman; she sat down at once when she knew that he had seen her, and stayed sitting with her feet on the grass. The great arrow with its iron point would have gone clean through an ox at such short range, and she expected it; but then the hunter blew the breath violently from his nostrils, transferred bow and arrow to his left hand and went up to her, relieved of a nameless terror. She rolled over on her back with limbs in the air as he approached, exposed her stomach to ingratiate herself and made painful barking sounds as in a bad dream, whimpering appealingly, unable to defend herself or fly.

It was a woman, quite a young one, who also must have lost her way in the forest and had followed the light of the fire. They were unknown to each other; she belonged to another people and could not say much for herself, but it did not take many words to bring them together; and soon after the strange girl was sitting very confidingly and seriously by the fire, preparing venison for supper.

It was a good thing they had met. When people have lost their way and have to stay out at night it is a misfortune to to be alone. Now that they were two the hunter gave the starry sky a casual glance and let fall a remark about its being a clear evening, didn't she think? They turned their backs upon the world, except the hearth and the spit, made a hearty supper and then thought of going to rest, there was nothing to stay up for.

The forest is always the home of the accursed when it is dark, the owl hoots in a lofty tree so that the woods ring again; it goes to one's very marrow even if one knows it is the owl. "Grou, grou," says a beaky noise just above the tree-tops, and a strident beating of wings is heard, rising and dying away again in an instant: wild duck, or something much worse; why else should it give one such creeps down the back?

A ghastly white light begins to haunt the tree-tops; it is the moon, that spectre of the skies. Far away there are shrill cries and answering cries among the slopes from one knows not what horror; a bent bough on a tree near by broods like a black and twisted dragon against the nocturnal sky; every visible shape crouches to become a great monster with horns and snout.

Even the breeze from the dark woods is unbearable upon one's neck, one feels that there are great ringed eyes in the air behind one's back, and now the best thing to do is to hide, a couple of little humans chilled by the dew, who are heavy-hearted and hold each other by the neck; and that is what they did, these two—lay down and pulled the fresh deerskin right up over their heads with the raw side out for all the ghostly things to bite at. They were in their own cosy darkness now and lost themselves in it, while the fire burned down and the moon advanced over the tree-tops out into the floating nocturnal sky, across which it was to travel before day came again.

The finch's call and an airy chorus of rooks in the lofty trees waked them; the light, the day, a lovely sunny spring morning; the great shining trees stretched down green arms to them; she sat up and shook the deerskin from her head, awake at once, and uttered a joyful cry.

But as the hunter opened his eyes he looked straight into a marvel, the sunrise appearing at the roots of the woods between the trees like a mighty rose of light, leaves, sky and sun merged in a radiant ring of green, blue and purple, the world dissolved in colour! As a sea of blood he had seen the sun go down the evening before, on the other side of the forest, a rose of coloured fire as now, all the refracted colours of light in which the sun, the woods and the day were merged and sank—and now this vision! It was to be bound up for ever with an awakening, a dawn in his stern hunter's soul, which understood what a gift the night had given him and at the same time made it inconceivable, a glory in the soul of boundless dreams he had had and could not remember, the reflection of another existence which had been near to him. As though petrified in the middle of a gesture, seized by a thought which made all else stand still within him, he looked out into the dawn; his very breath was checked, so immersed was he in an inner world though without being able to realize it, a lost memory.

They stayed together, the two whom the night had joined. Neither of them ever took the homeward path; they settled on the spot as a free hunter's household in the midst of the kindly woods, and in summer their life was easy. Neither of them was aware of time.

For the winter they made themselves snug in an underground dwelling without ever once feeling the want of human society. The woods took the place of friends; they loved the grove with its tall friendly trees because there they had found each other. Beyond that she had no world at all but him, and he had his own.

Once in the course of the summer the hunter saw four ships on the river, long black craft with a multitude of oars which all moved together like a loom; slowly they fought their way up stream, in sight for a whole day before they vanished in a bend of the river towards the mountains; long-handled axes were raised with a backward lean along the ships, like vipers stretching their necks to strike, and the regular chunk of the oars against the timber was heard hour after hour as the crews obstinately worked their way against the stream. They had come up from the lower reaches of the river, no doubt from the sea, and whither were they bound? The hunter never saw them return.

Occasionally he saw men over on the other side of the river, people who came out of the woods shading their eyes with their hands from the southern sun; but they could not cross here and withdrew into the forest to find other ways.

With the exception of these signs of an outer world, the hunter and his woman lived undisturbed on the lonely wooded hill by the river.

But as early as the end of the summer there were unmistakable signs that the girl was to become a mother—from eating raspberries, as she supposed in her own mind. They had eaten raspberries together in the woods, and as the new being had made itself felt at the same time it was natural to conclude that that might be the cause; she ate herself quite big, and then it came, and big she remained. She gave birth to the child in the middle of winter and wrapped it in kid's skin against the cold.

It was a warm and wet, pink, naked little thing, which as soon as it was born chirped like a bird and had little closed hands, and nails like buds on trees, tiny little twisted ears and new-born hair like sunshine, eyes like the hazy blue sky and a sorrowful mouth which immediately sought and sought and fell to on Mother's breast.

A nasty storm had swept through the low dwelling in the ground, where the mother had screamed as though some unknown cruel beast had been there, but now all was still, the little boy's babbling sounded like the song of birds on the first warm night of spring, when the great storms that tear the ice from the shore and break the trees of the forest have blown themselves out.

And the first he saw of the world was the spring. She carried him out for the first time when the trees had burst into leaf, and in speechless joy showed his blue eyes to the sky and his hair to the sun and his hands to the new-born leaves on the blessed green beeches.

Without any doubt it was a splendid and wonderful child, a little baby god, a son of the sky and the sun and the woods, that the ecstatically happy mother had brought into the world.

But the hunter who had become a father was enraptured with his partner and his springtime child.

She sat out in the open, now that it was warm, on the slope under the big trees, which flamed like calm green fires in the sun of May, just where they had met a year before; and in her arms she held her son, a thirsty son who gurgled at his work and let the milk run out of his nose in two streams when he could not swallow it all at once. He lay on his mother's knee simply stiff with overnourishment, with his fat, bare feet, each with five rosy toes, pointing in different directions; and when his mouth ran over and he began to choke his mother lifted him with laughter and admiration high in the air and shook him to let the food settle down, so that there might be room for more. Sweet was the scent of the two, and delicious was the fragrance of the still wet leaves on the tall shining beeches. And with the baby in her arms and a dream of happiness on her sweet flushing face the mother followed the starling, that black glistening bird which slipped in and out of the hollow tree with worms in its beak for its nestlings within.

When the hunter was not in the woods or by the river supplying the needs of the family, he was at home, busily building a new, real house. He worked and chipped at the wood and was always beginning again on a grander scale, he had visions of something magnificent and well thought out: a speaking house, he imagined, with images on the posts, which should make manifest his joy and form a precious shrine for the mother and her little god.

Up on the mound among the trees the hunter had a secret, secluded place of prayer which he used to visit alone—nothing but a heap of stones on the ground, on which he made a fire for the Powers when he gave them a share of his quarry; here he cut up the deer and hung them on the trees, and it answered very well; here he left a bit on one side for the badger who had his hole on the slope and was no ordinary badger—he lived in the ground underneath one, and it was as well to be on good terms with him; and every year at the solstices the hunter made ceremonies for the Powers, quite privately between himself and them. He made burnt offerings for the return and perpetuity of all things, walking cautiously about and mumbling a good deal with his lips—prayers by the look of it, but some part was strong language he had learnt, which he hoped might work upon the Powers and bind them even against their will—for one's position was not altogether a comfortable one in dealing with beings so much stronger than one's self.

But latterly he had got out of the way of appealing to them in the open air; the hunter was more occupied with his house and what it was to shut out, and with the glory and perfection which it was to shelter like a little improved world.

The hunter was becoming more and more of a carpenter. He worked and built all through the summer, and in winter he pondered over his images and shaped them in wood, at times so absent that he might gaze long at his dear ones without seeing them, entirely lost in his visions.

But the two were always about him, giving food for his work; he heard their voices, and he heard the neighbouring spring and the song of birds in the trees as one and the same music, while his thoughts were budding and his hands were shaping. He heard the mother singing, a wordless cooing from the heart which she had learnt from the wood-pigeons; she took the child's feet in her mouth and pretended to eat them, making him laugh so that his little chest clucked; she called him by pet names of her own invention. "My morsel," she would say, with heartfelt emotion, as she played with him; "my sweetest little knucklebone; my darling, darling little dick!" This meant "bird" in the wonder's own language which he was beginning to invent for the wonders about him as he tried to catch them in his hands, stammering expressions for what he wanted, and they were the foundation of an entirely new little language in the forest.

And when his mother had got the wonder dressed she put him out on her knees as on a promontory so that the world might see him, and he it, and made a fortification around his little defenceless body with her sweet, big girlish hands. All the flowers stretched themselves on their stalks among the grass to make a show for him about the place where the two were sitting, the trees shed fragrance upon them, the birds came out on the farthest twigs and chanted a triumphal chorus over this forest picture of childhood. The mother herself sang songs of joy over her miracle, without words, inarticulate hymns of praise that gushed from her throat and woke echoes in the woods as of an enchanted source, a source with the voice of a girl. She was so loving and so full of laughter.

And tender songs of praise and great joy resounded from the hunter's house when at last he got it finished and lodged the two within. It was as though the house, standing by itself in the forest, gave out music; it sang in the midst of the wood, the whole house sang with the happiness concealed within it.

It was built with walls of upright timbers, like a palisade, very firm, which was the first consideration, but with a riot of decoration and with meaning in its plan and all its details. From the lofty gables dragons gaped towards the four quarters of the heavens; above them, still higher up, four more; for upon the roof over the smoke-hole rode a lofty, slender castle, and above it again was a spire which ended skywards in a pole with a vane, and here the cock crowed, always *against* the wind by which it turned; it stood on guard up in the airy regions, and the first gleam of sunrise fell upon its comb. The dragons on the roof were, of course, to keep evil spirits away from the house; besides them the skulls of deer and other game were set up on the sods of the roof, with the double intention of scaring and providing a good hunting memory. Above the door the hunter set up the antlers of the first deer he had brought down in this place; for it was the very entrance to his happiness, the deer had brought him here.

The door was at one end of the house, the plan of which was an oval, and the doorposts rose high above the eaves; they were two whole straight stems; each of them had meant the destruction of an oak, but they had risen again in a higher form, carved all over with the most beautiful sinuosities of oak-leaves and terminating above in a great ornamental acorn.

The door itself was a single oaken plank—an old tree had gone to make it; it had two round panels for the sun and moon, filled with carvings and circles in every conceivable pattern.

The whole exterior of the house was to be a symbol of night, terror and counter terror: the four cornerstones which supported the house were four crouching monsters which were here bound and made to do good much against their will; the dragons explained themselves, they were the personification of Nature's terrors. At a little distance the house really looked like a hideous nest of serpents with the heads of the whole brood raised in rapacity; it was a powerful outside to turn towards the night, for with evil must evil be expelled.

But the inside of the house represented the ash Ygdrasil. Of course, it was a room, and the meaning of all the carvings and embellishments was not apparent at first glance, and yet all the imagery of the forest and the ash Ygdrasil was present. From the middle of the floor rose the great pillar which supported the whole building and the topmost point of which formed the spire; it was a mast, an old fir, perfectly straight but twisted many times about itself in the wood, as though while growing it had turned to follow a heavenly body; it formed the stem, the carvings in the roof and round all the walls were the branches and foliage of the world-tree.

It was like being in a transformed forest, foliage above and below, and in the branching patterns the deer moved with his branching crown intermingled with the crowns of the trees, one could scarcely tell which was tree and which was deer high up in the top of the world-tree sat the eagle, the far-seeing one, and between its brows a hawk, one bird of prey crowning another; the squirrel hid and appeared downward among the branches like a weaver's shuttle, Ratatosk running with his news up and down the ash Ygdrasil between the eagle and Nidhug, the dragon of Time, who lay under the roots of Ygdrasil devouring them. Ginnungegap was there, below another root of the world-tree, a frozen hole in the earth wherein frost giants brooded with their heads between their knees; Mimir's well was shown, with Odin's eye which he gave as a pledge for a draught of wisdom; Urd's well, and the Norns taking water and mud from the spring to heal the world-tree of the gnawing in its root and top. If you looked up again, there was the rainbow overhead and great constellations, the eternal stars of heaven depicted; and again foliage, great plaited tents where the leaves were birds and the birds leaves. But at the top, in the middle of the roof, where the window was, the light fell in; you could not see the sky itself but the dim light that came through the smoke-hole, light from above met smoke and the gleam of the fire from below; the daylight above changed with the time of day, paled and took fire again, like a coloured, translucent and veiled halo over the room.

Such was the house of images the hunter-carpenter had raised, that he might give back his soul to what had produced it.

Most of it was still in the rough, not all carried out as he saw it in his mind; far from it, there was work enough for years to come—and already an entirely new plan was dawning in his head, to begin all over again, in a new, wider, still more eloquent style.

Then it chanced that one day the hunter was again pursuing a deer which would not let itself be taken, and which led him farther and farther away, until at last he no longer knew where he was.

The chase and the speed of it excited him so far beyond all bounds that he ceased to be human, he was nothing but passion; in his heat he took no note of anything, and nothing could stop him until he had overtaken the deer and brought it down. He was a hunter who had never suffered any game to beat him, either in endurance, sagacity or strength.

But this was a most extraordinarily powerful stag, it seemed. The hunter was used to finding stags swifter than he was, much swifter of course, to begin with, but not in the long run: their wind was broken before he was exhausted, they spent themselves in one terrified rush after another, while he followed the trail in a steady, persistent trot. The moment was bound to come, even if it took days, when the deer could no longer rise when he came up to it with his hunting-knife. This stag, however, showed not the slightest sign of weariness, it galloped as swiftly every time he started it, and every time it seemed to have grown, to be gliding away ahead of him as though on air, a mighty royal stag with antlers that seemed rather to lift it and bear it than to weigh it down. And as the hunter did not give up—for he had never yet turned back without his quarry—the stag went on soaring ahead with the hunter on its trail, as though he had never done anything but hunt that stag and was never destined to do anything else.

At night he slept on the ground without a fire, with his head in his arms, speechless from fatigue, and every morning he felt less rested, when again he took up the trail and followed it till he had started the stag, to run after it throughout the day.

And as he ran the forest behaved strangely; it was summer when the hunt began, but when he looked about him the trees were bare and he shivered with cold; and then again the woods were green and he was too hot, and this repeated itself he knew not how many times; but he did not let it trouble him.

At last the stag actually did stop. It was at night, for now the hunter was pursuing it in the dark as well as by day; it could not hide, for there was no more forest, they had come out into bare country beyond the inhabited world, a distant, gloomy region where skeletons of dead beasts were seen everywhere upon the ground, great piles of bones; it was evidently the place where all the beasts come when they go away to die. Over this ground the stag soared, and now it could be seen that it did not touch the earth in its flight; but the hunter himself had a sensation as though he was in the air and moved more by the power of his soul than by running.

The plain of the dead beasts ended in an immense cliff which extended on both sides as far as the eye could reach, and below the cliff yawned empty space, sheer black nothingness, the abyss or the place the night comes from; whatever it was, there was no going any farther. The stag stopped on the extreme brink of the abyss and stood against the sky in its full height with its mighty antlers raised, looking like a mountain, with its shoulder exposed. Now an arrow could reach it, and the hunter ground his teeth and shot.

Even while the arrow was in the air he saw the stag rise high above the earth and turn to fire; it galloped to the sky in a flash of flame, and as it mounted higher and higher its light waned and became a group of sparks, revolved once upon itself—and stood still in the firmament!

And then the hunter saw that what he

had shot at, believing it to be a stag, was a constellation. He knew it perfectly well, had always known it; seeing it made him feel a child again. But how cold he turned! The starry sky swung above him like a fearful wheel, and a jet of air from eternity struck him to the marrow. He perceived that he was at the world's end, and that it was Time itself he had been hunting. Then the awe of death came upon him.

His hunter's rage had left him, he remembered the mother and the child, turned and began to walk towards home.

A hundred years had passed when at last he came back to the place he had left. Light of foot, with a flying arrow to lead his yearning, he had run from home; he came back staff in hand and swaying like an old old man.

He found the place again where he had had his house, but it was greatly changed. There was the small knoll, but the wood was different, though aparently the same; there were only the rotten stumps left of the trees he had known, or nothing at all, and new ones which before had been young saplings in the undergrowth had become old trees. It was another forest; he was now a stranger in his own home.

The spring had dried up; a depression in the slope showed where it had been, to one who remembered it, but it had no water, it had run out long ago. Of the house with the carved posts in which the couple had had their nest and where fabulous beasts had crowed from the roof-beams, there was not the slightest trace—only a little grassy mound, like an old grave, showed the place. It was so still in the wood; the strange lofty trees raised their branches stiff and bare into the winter mist.

The old man sat down on the grave of his house and gathered dead leaves about him as though for a bed. The nest was cold. He found small fragments of charcoal in the grass, the remains of a vanished hearth-fire; they were covered with rime and seemed to wound his hands. The wood was lifeless, it did not even harbour fear, for what had he more to fear? —only loneliness.

The hunter had grown old, but so great a longing did he feel for those he had lost, so near were they to him, though he was never, never to see them again, that he could not die. The memory of his loss could not die, for that was now the only thing he had left; it was stronger than time, and it craved a form.

He built himself a hut in the forest, and when he had as much shelter as a solitary old man needs he began to model in his mind, trying shapes in the air with his hands and familiarizing himself with visions he had; they were to become an image, he would carve an image, it was to be the two as they lived for ever in his soul. And around them as a centre he began to build a house in his mind for eternity, which was to show forth Life and Time, and the forest and the beasts, and the sun, and the underworld, everything that existed, and all that he had possessed and lost and still possessed in memory. Such was the house his craft would build, and in it the Mother and the Child should dwell, risen again and made immortal in an image.

With them he began, they were to be represented in one, two souls in one shape; he imagined the two as they used to sit under the trees, the mother holding her little son before her on her knee so that the whole forest should see him; and he would show how his hair had borrowed its gold from the sun, and how the old trees bowed down before him with their branches.

Alas! when he had finished there was a block of wood which bore the marks of tools and of much labour; there was indeed a hint of a human image in it, but it was neither the two as he saw them in his mind nor the image of them he had intended. It would have to be made over again, from the very beginning. But until he could accomplish that he set up the image in his hut and fed his soul on it, in the memory of the two never-forgotten ones and in the hope of the real and perfect image, of which this only served as a poor outline.

He often sat before it, as he had sat on the grass before the young mother and her child; he sang to it, while the forest outside roared powerfully above his hut, as he had sung to the two, when the forest roared over them and made them small.

In the spring he moved the image out into the open and played before it on a bark flute; it sounded like new-born babes in the woods. And the beasts, with whom the former hunter had made peace, came sniffing up at the sound and stood quite near the hermit to listen.

On one of these spring days, when he had been playing to his memories under the beeches and was in rapture, his eyes closed.

The aged easily fall into a doze, and their slumbers are short. But one sleep is as long as another. The old hunter nodded; it might have been only an instant, or it might have been a thousand years. And in an enraptured absence such as this his being passed into Time.

II
THE FERRYMAN

Once more the oaks grew old after the hunter had dwelt by the river, and then another hermit settled there. Like the hunter he was nameless, but he was to acquire a surname by which he afterwards became known to all the world—Christophorus, the bearer of our Lord. He came from the country of the Goths and left his native land some time during the great Migrations and went out into the world, like so many others who were moving from North to South; but it was his fate to halt and to pursue his calling at a station half-way between the two.

From his birth Christophorus was of unusual stature, big beyond all measure and so strong that he had never reached the limit of his strength. But he was gentle, and that was fortunate, for otherwise he might have wrought mischief. No one had seen him angry; that was out of the question, there could be no occasion for it since nothing could avail to irritate him. Even while he was still serving the franklins he was never in a bad temper, as others might be when the cattle strayed or were unruly; if the oxen got out of hand he simply threw them with his bare hands and held them down till they were quiet again, and if a bull-calf was obstinate and would not be tethered he carried it home in his arms. It was said of him that he was slow, but a man with such mighty limbs cannot be expected to move them so quickly as the small and irascible; he was in no hurry, since anyhow he could get more done than the rest.

At first, when he had just come from the woods, he was perfectly stupid and had to learn everything—how to eat from a bowl and bring the spoon out whole when he had shot the food into his mouth; but he never needed to be shown a thing twice.

He was not deficient in judgment; he thought over his position and had an eye for what suited him. For this reason he did not stay at the farm where he served. The man there, quite a good ordinary franklin, set him to clear waste land, and he pulled up trees by the roots, one in each hand, knocking the mould out of the roots, and went off with stones as big as houses; if he had kept on with it he might have cleared enough land for a whole earldom.

But the giant thought it more and more strange that he should serve a weakling, when it ought rather to have been the other way about. He took an opportunity of finding out whether the man considered any one his superior, and discovered that the good man was ready to bow down to several—people he called his gods, Odin, Thor, and a good many besides, some of whom moreover were females. From other sources also the giant got to know that small or middle-sized people liked to pretend to more strength than they possessed by referring to powerful allies they were supposed to have somewhere or other—beings who, however, as they themselves admitted, were invisible to the naked eye. This kind of thing the giant could not take seriously. He did not believe in spirits, not having met any yet, either by night or by day. Once when something stung him and he thought it might be a spirit, such as the others used to talk about if they felt any pain, he caught it between his finger and thumb, but it turned out to be a sheep-tick. Since nothing in his experience pointed in the opposite direction the giant had come to believe exclusively in his own strength. If therefore he was to serve anybody and to be induced to remain in his service, it would have to be some one even mightier than himself.

Besides his gods the master spoke with reverence of the King, the mightiest of all franklins and an actually living person, not just a doubtful thing in the air; the giant's deliberations therefore led to his taking service with the King. However, he had not been there long before he found out that there were even greater kings than he in other realms; and thus it was that the giant went abroad, since his mind was made up that he would serve no lord but him who did not fear anybody or anything in the world.

Now we know from the legend of Christophorus, which is familiar to the whole of Christendom, that he left the mightiest of all kings because on an occasion this King made the sign of the Cross when the Devil was named. Christophorus asked him why he was writing with his finger in the air, and was told that he feared the Devil; and straightway the giant took his leave and entered the service of the Evil One.

But when one day the Prince of Darkness evinced a fear of the Cross and, when asked by the giant why he went out of his way to avoid what was nothing but two pieces of wood, had to confess that he feared him whose sign was a cross, the giant perceived that the Lord of the Cross was the strongest and went out into the world again to find him. As every one acquainted with the legend knows, he did not find the Kingdom of God immediately in so literal a sense as he was inclined to expect; but he was instructed by a hermit, of whom he sought counsel, how in the meantime his deeds might prove acceptable to the mightiest of all Lords. Ordinary Christian exercises the giant rejected as unfitting for him; he would undertake neither fasting nor watching, and prayers were never on his lips, since he was a man of few words. But he was willing to take upon himself a stout piece of man's work, if our Lord would be pleased with that. And then the hermit had found a suitable occupation for him. It consisted in ferrying wayfarers over a great river which otherwise was difficult to cross: one of the aims of this Lord's rule was to bring people nearer to each other; here was a chance for a strong man. And thus it came about that the giant established himself on the river in question and became a ferryman.

Christophorus had now entered upon a service which was to his liking. Although he could not see the Lord he served nor knew where he was, which he felt to be something lacking, he took the word of the man of God for his existence and appreciation of the work that was carried out in his name. This work was sufficiently heavy and seemed to him useful. He preferred to struggle with the great river rather than, as he had done before, with troops of armed men; for in truth the giant had always loathed war, since by the nature of things he had always been left in peace by his fellow-men and was incapable of comprehending the reason of *their* mutual hostility, except in so far as it could be put down to their frailty. On account of their wickedness it seemed to be necessary for all men to go about with stabbing and cutting implements on them; for his part he preferred to be content with a staff to keep unruly people at a distance when they became numerous; it had never given him any satisfaction to perforate or slice up the bodies even of wicked persons.

To conquer the elements, on the other hand, not on some single famous occasion but every day, unnoticed, merely for the sake of doing it, as fishers and husbandmen contend with the weather, was better suited to his inclination. Just as intangible things, emulation and verbosity, all kinds of wordiness, were foreign to this man's nature, so did he abhor renown. With whom should he seek favour? He travelled when there was a reason, but preferred quiet; it did him good to stay in one place, now that he had found employment, while in return the world passed by him from day to day and from year to year.

The river was always on a journey; it came in a great flowing sweep from the forests and the highlands on one side and swung in a broad and mighty curve into the forests and out of sight towards the lowlands and the sea on the other side. Currents and waves dashed together like a procession of wild bulls; whirlpools and great smooth floors of water, which mirrored the sky and the endless woods, passed silently round points of land; the osprey hung over the eddies and dropped like a plummet upon the salmon which shot like lightning in the depths.

In springtime the river was swollen with the thaw on the distant mountains and flooded the woods, plunging thick and muddy and full of green ice that had fallen from the glaciers about its source, and uprooted trees that floated out from the submerged forest; then it was hard to cross and Christophorus had need of all his strength, both when he waded over with a single traveller on his back and when he had more passengers and had to use the ferry-boat.

It was a clumsy great log-boat or raft, which the giant himself had built, mainly with an eye to durability; an uglier craft was not to be found, it looked as if the giant had used his teeth in building it, and so he had. The pole he used was equally unadorned, a tree whose branches he had scraped off. But both answered their purpose. Christophorus used to push the ferry-boat before him into the current while he himself walked behind on the bottom, and if ice or big trees drifted down upon the ferry he pushed them out of the way with his staff.

But if the teeming river was thus always on a journey—not to mention all the traffic of fishers and traders who went up and down it—there was likewise an endless stream of people travelling across it, for the ferry lay just at that point of its course where it cut the great highways upon which the Migrations had now been moving for centuries on the way from North to South, and on which they continued to pass in ever greater numbers; at first scouts and a few scattered bodies of men in ages long past, now whole tribes and hosts at once. It was like a cross-road of the ages, where the course of nature met that of men, one athwart the other.

The river travelled on, and the people travelled on, but Christophorus stayed on the ferry and carried them over. He came to love the place; if he did not understand the symbol of the Cross, he lived and worked after his fashion in the very midst of it, at a cross of which one arm was actually drawn by the inexhaustible sources of nature and the other by the wandering of mankind.

While he dwelt here in the name of a God unknown to him he assisted half the North across the river, one troop after another of Northern peasants on their journey towards the South. They came in families and clans, often the whole population of a district, who had quitted their homes with household goods and cattle, old and young, women and children, each one having a responsibility within the troop, like the ants; from rude warriors who grunted after a murder as if it were a joke and wiped their bloody swords between two fingers, to little girls carrying in their arms the puppies that had been entrusted to them. They came, one swarm, one tidal wave after another, whatever they might call themselves or come to be called later when they had founded kingdoms in the South and made themselves famous; big ruddy peasants all of them, like Christophorus himself and of the same blood, the same hairy freckled folk with eyes blue as the sea, whether they came from the dense inland forests, from the river countries of the Baltic, from its islands, or from the long harsh shores of the North Sea; and they all travelled with the same object, that which had sent as many more of them by the sea way in ships—*they* came overland, for every road must be tried—to get away from the cold marshes of the homeland, away to the South, to the lands of legend and the sun.

III
KING SNOW

Bad harvests it was that had driven these husbandmen from their homes in the North, where they belonged. The winters were always severe, but still they could be endured, otherwise nobody would ever have lived in these countries. It was the winters that had made them what they were; they came of Carl's blood, steeled by adversity, and they could stand much; but even hardy folk will revolt when they think the limit has been reached.

The same Power that had formed the root of their being was still over them, but at a distance; in the farthest North lay the ice-sheet, and at times it seemed again to be stretching a cold arm over the countries where once it had been supreme; then the winters were lengthened and the brief summers were barely able to take the frost out of the ground; icebergs were seen in the North Sea, fog and mist hid the sun for half the year. Already these countries were scarcely dry after the great thawing of the ice, with a net of water, lakes and streams in the lowlands among the damp woods and morasses where the arable land was to be found; the earth held the cold under its surface, great floods from the winter sometimes lay through the whole summer, the cornfield became a lake, or the little corn there was never came to maturity.

But if only one of the brief summers failed, it meant shortage in the winter; the crop did not go very far even in good years, and if several bad years succeeded one another there was famine, no corn at all and but little meat, since the cattle could not be kept alive either if the crops failed; the only thing left was hunting, and for that there were too many. That was it, they were too many, another burden; the homesteads overflowed with children who seemed in a moment to become great greedy swarms; what was to be done with them in time of famine?

King Snow rules in the countries on both sides of the Cattegat; he comes in a seven days' snowstorm and fills the sky, turns night into a grave, and day into a driving twilight with no bounds between morning and evening; the air is snow, the storm is snow and seems to come from every quarter at once, snow pours out of the sky, and snow stands in vertical showers straight up in the air, the earth is buried, snow begets snow and whirls together into drifts, the whole world is like a white fire, but with a disastrous darkness at bottom, and cold; death is in the air. Men turn pale from looking out into the whirling gloom, an all-powerful breathing can be felt, they think they can see him soaring on limbs of the storm, see how the snow comes from under his wings—Odin, King Snow, is abroad!

And when he has finished his game and sends a calm the lands lie buried under snow, snow half-way up the stems in the woods, the earth everywhere hidden, a single white snowfield as far as the land extends, white shores along the Cattegat, white over in Skoane, on both sides of the Sound, Kullen looking like a headland of snow running out into the sea, the isles like isles of snow; and between all the buried coast-lines the sea open and black, reeking with frost, like gall; until the sounds too are closed with ice a fathom thick and the snow smooths out all the countries in one.

The fisherman who is accustomed to sail has to go on his feet and do miner's work with an axe to get down to his water. In the black nights the ice roars from bank to bank, a vast submarine discharge of force; and men in their beds of skins under the ground and under the snow hear the booming and crawl deeper into their skins; it is the sea arching its back under the floor of ice and lifting it; but the sea is bound, and in the echoes from shore to shore Odin laughs with scorn.

The ice stayed till late in the summer, and it was a rainy summer; sometimes the Sound was still full of old ice-floes when autumn and a fresh frost arrived. In such years there was nothing in the cornfields, the cattle grew lean, and hunger began to drive people out of their villages with long hollow cheeks—there would have to be a change.

On the part of the leaders, the chiefs, the wise men who intervened between the people and the Powers, everything was done to get the bad years to stop. There were sacrifices without stint; first they offered cattle and more than they could spare, and when that did no good they offered men, thralls or prisoners they took and hanged up in the wind for the Wanderer, since he seemed to be gruesome enough to demand it; the summer was just as bad.

In one of the districts they then resolved on an unusual thing; here the king and priest himself was sacrificed, as expiator for all the rest, and at the same time the sacrifice was addressed directly to Odin as the Lord of Fire, for it was in that capacity he failed them. And possibly he had been neglected in this way; latterly people had gradually abandoned the funeral pyre and had been giving their dead to the earth in mounds; perhaps the Lord of Fire had felt aggrieved at being deprived of his due. Now they would try to make amends, and if any one was to be sent to him through the fire, the best ought not to be too good. The king himself raised no objection to the decision.

The sacrifice was appointed for the day of the midwinter solstice, as being the solemnity to which the ancients attributed the most importance, and many old customs that had dropped out of use were dug up again for the occasion, in case there might still be some power in them.

The need-fire was kindled with great ceremony after all fires had been extinguished on the hearths, so as to have fresh fire and to give the Powers an example for imitation as concerned the heavenly bodies; many other things were tried which some perhaps only half believed in, but if the world, with the wisdom they possessed, was in danger of collapsing, they could only go back and do over again what the ancients had done to keep the universe going.

The solemnity took place on rising ground within the forest, the oldest sanctified place of sacrifice, whose stones had not been moved since the people took possession of the country, and some of the oldest men with long memories were chosen to perform it. Almost the whole population of the district, all the clans, had collected, women of course excluded; all the men were there, the whole host, for they were all under arms; not that they were summoned to war, but the day was a solemn one. Armed franklins on horseback and on foot were mustered about the sacrificial mound and far into the woods.

The invocation of fire was performed in the dark winter morning before sunrise, at the right moment when the sun might be expected, and it was accompanied by all the proper forms. The initiates made fire by friction, and meanwhile the sacrificial animals were slaughtered. They were not good to look upon, the shaggy, bony beasts they had; the blunt men who had led them forward were short-spoken and looked as though they thought the cattle might have been better if certain masters had taken more thought for their grazing. When they had a flame and the new fire began to blaze the whole host set itself in motion at a signal sounded by lurs; the lurs brayed sharply in the cold forest, a harsh and joyless blast, and then came the tramp of the host; levy after levy marched in battle-array up over the mound past the sacrificial pyre, in silence, but as though demanding to be called to witness; the mounted men came up troop after troop on lean horses and dipped their lances to the fire, all in silence; only their tramp could be heard, and the dark troops were seen ascending the mound as though the earth brought them forth, one wave after another.

When all had thus appeared before the fire the king was sacrificed. He came forward of himself into the glare of the fire, swelling with contempt, and offered his forehead; he received the blow in the middle of his wrinkled brow and fell backwards into the fire. At the same instant all the men struck their shields with their drawn swords, in a single clash, and a shout of home rose from the whole army at once, a war-cry from a thousand throats that sounded in the forest like a supernaturally loud roar from some beast of prey.

While the act, which moved them all to wrath, was in progress, silence fell again, and in the stillness, only broken by the beating of the flames from the pyre, the old franklin who presided over the sacrifice stood forth and recited the hymn of the day:

Now mounts the sun
with brightest beams,
and Balder's bane
goes down in blood.
Hope has returned
to sea and sky.
See and behold!
Fair is the day!

Allfather promised
this to our fathers:
That the lean years
linger not with us.
Patient the greybeard
suffers the hardships
of wildest winters—
the sun shall return!

Chary of gold
were the Northern Gods,
but they gave yearly
a new-made sun.
Thus the Preserver
is Lord of the slain;
often the noble
went to the pyre.

Praying, the peasant
sows corn on the land;
chary of seed
ne'er reaped a crop.
Fair wind for mead,
and rain for malt!
Only the fool
gives without getting.

Midwinter's moon
gapes like Hel's mouth.
In a sack of darkness
the sun turns again.
Cheerless sing
the children of earth;
Father of fire,
accept our offering!

But the sun did not show itself. It was cloudy morning with a closed sky, the aylight had no power, and it snowed as he host broke up and returned home. acrificial banquet there was none, no-ody had the heart to eat. Before evening he embers were cold and all traces of the ffering were buried beneath deep snow n the ancient place of sacrifice in the voods.

Through the following summer they vaited the result, but when again it rought no crop they saw that it was use-ess any longer to expect the Powers to eep the covenant, and so they denounced t on their side. The gods of the weather vere given no more offerings. Frey's al-ars were bare. And when spring came gain and brought no kindness, they de-ounced the country and its spirits, broke lown the posts of their high seats, tamped out the hearth and sought other hores.

Many had already begun to doubt the power of the Powers—did any such exist at all? As for the sun, it turned whether you played tricks with fire for it or not, but it never came any nearer. You had to go nearer to it. Starved and pretty well godless they turned their backs upon a world that had grown old, ripe now to be filled with a new one.

IV

THE LONGOBARDS

The country was not entirely depopulated, it was only the able-bodied men who left, the younger ones with their women-folk and whatever else they wanted to take; there remained behind the oldest and the youngest, who were not fitted for new and adventurous undertakings. The country became quieter when the host was gone, nothing happened, the homesteads were extinguished; it was as though the men had taken Time with them.

Before the departure there had been disagreements as to who should quit the country. For a while the warriors considered that the best way of remedying the distress was to reduce the surplus population; the aged and infirm might let themselves be buried, and the superfluous children should be exposed; the remainder could then live in the country, even without gods. This counsel was opposed by the aged and the children, supported by their mothers, who advised the younger people to emigrate, and this advice was adopted. The host that emigrated and afterwards became famous was called the Longobards, from the long-handled axes the men carried.

The axe reflected their destiny: originally it was a forester's axe with which they felled trees and cleared land; afterwards it also served as a carpenter's axe, good for shipbuilding and the work of a wheelwright; but first and last it was a weapon, and it became one more and more.

They marched overland to the coast, built themselves ships and became seafarers, went ashore on other coasts and became husbandmen again, built ships once more and committed themselves to the sea; until they landed on the south shore of the Baltic whence the great trade routes ran inland into Europe, and then they pushed towards the South overland, lost their seafaring ways and became a caravan folk that trusted in the rolling wheel. It was not exactly a rapid-whirling wheel, but had its ups and downs, a creaking laborious wheel, but it carred them on. The journey was a slow one; the young generation that had left home with the thought of reaching the goal next day passed on this goal to a new one and stayed behind in the mounds that marked their track; in the end the journey was inherited through so many generations that its origin was almost forgotten and its purpose no longer remained the same.

Travelling, for an army which becomes a nation on the route, takes time and does not always pass in peaceable fashion; wherever you come there are other people in the world whom you have to make terms with or cut through, a life of difficulties; you have to live, and must stop in every place at least long enough for a crop to ripen, if you have a chance of sowing one; in winter no travelling can be done. Sometimes they stayed on, for a century or so, in some place where the pasture was good and the surrounding people amenable, and a number of them settled there for good, since land was what they came for, becoming absorbed in the population and using the axe again for clearing.

But soon there would be too many of them again; another army was formed which built itself waggons; the long slender axes turned their edge to the South, hope had burst forth again, they were o the march!

And it was while they were thus on th march from one station to another tha they struck the ferry where Christophoru lay and were assisted by him across th river.

They announced their coming as s many had done before them; Christo phorus knew them a long way off by th din they raised in the quiet woods, a bel lowing of cattle and shouts as at a fair, sound of neighing that dashed along wit the horsemen at full gallop; and when th column drew nearer it resolved itself int the roaring and crashing of a thousan throats and many thousand hoofs, whil a cloud of dust rose above the tree-top even before the swarm could be seen; the the first mounted outposts swung out o the wood on the other side of the rive stood still and began to wave and blov their cow's horns lustily to attract th ferryman's attention.

After them the first waggons came i sight—big, clumsily built covered carts i which women and children and whateve else the column carried with it were con veyed; round about them rode the arme warriors. The waggons were regular cas tles, and when a halt was called they wer drawn up in a circle and became a fortres within which the army encamped; on th march they swayed over the trackless tur and creaked loudly with their hug wheels, which were made in one piece lik the sun and turned as majestically.

The woods flashed with axes and lon spears round the waggons and their stoop ing horned teams. Behind them came th herd, immense motley crowds of cattl kept together by the thralls; and roun about the whole procession swarmed th young people, freckled overgrown strip lings who found something to do every where, girls who preferred walking to sit ting in the waggons; straight, big-limbe young women of seventeen with bare leg nder a hempen skirt and honey-yellow air like sunshine about their shoulders.

In the open fore part of the carts sat he matrons with spindles in their hands, nd children big and small with gleaming air, almost white like that of the aged, ooked out over them and beside them, vith the world showing in their clear, vide-open, childish eyes. From the back f the waggons projected house-timbers vith scarfed ends; they had been taken lown at their old home and were to be et up again when they found a new one; he plough, with mould from their old ields still on its board, showed its worn andles sticking out of the cart. But from he hindmost of all came smoke; here sat ged women with their wrinkles full of oot, tending a fire which was not allowed o go out; in the evening when the col-mn camped each housewife fetched a rand from it for her open-air kitchen.

All the waggons were decorated with reen boughs, for it was springtime. The voods had just burst into leaf and the ravellers had just taken the road; like reen woods on wheels the waggons went hrough the greenwood, like singing wag-ons, for song came from them, chirping oices of children, like a chorus of birds, nd the young girls walked beside them inging, their souls felt so new, the woods vere new, the world, the sun was new; he green young lads sang, with voices as ough and rusty as they could make them, nd many a stern warrior leaned back as e sat his horse and sang up to the leaves, he song he had sung as a boy coming ack to his throat. The matrons too sang s they span, rocking their heads gently, nd their voices could scarcely be heard; he same tones that lured the young into a vorld they did not know turned them in-vard and backward to a memory. Here nd there an old man, toiling beside the vaggon, setting his shoulder to it when it eaned and yelling and struggling with the hick-skulled oxen, had time to join in between the cuts of his whip, a growling hum that exposed blackened teeth, but his face grew brighter for it. It was the song of the wanderers:

Springtime sweet and green
Again on earth is seen.
The sun shoots beams aflare,
Mild is the air.
Southern wind,
Roaming mind!
Take up the staff, bring out the cart!
Come out, come out and let us start,
With creaking wheel and glad at heart—
To a far country!

The winter, weary jade,
Within her stall was stayed
Now she has foaled!
'Mid cobwebs by the cold—
Foal's foot,
Flying foot!
Up, lusty lads, mount and away!
Gallop in troop the livelong day,
As up and down your bodies sway—
To a far country!

And wilt thou go with me?
Till death I'll go with thee!
My fair young life,
My roving wife!
Girl and boy,
Lovers' joy!
Two together, day and night,
Double breathing, one delight!
Behind the dark, before the light—
To a far country!

The greenwood's freest glade
Invites us to its shade.
We know not where we go—
Swallows will show.
Swallow's wing,
Winds of spring!
Follow the springtime's call so free,
Southward, where the sun we see,
Follow, no bird so free as we—
To a far country!

The chorus filled the forest with one great, joyful human cry. And the children stretched their necks out of the waggons, like flowers turning their faces to the sun;

their young skin caught up the spring and the breeze from the forest like the first breath of morning in the world. Never before or after was the day so great a marvel. As they looked the woods opened out and the river swung into view as a new almighty wonder, a vast being in motion which lay about the world in a curve and flowed, bearing suns in its mirror and mingled with the sky in the distance. But just opposite were the woods again, on the other bank, swelling in their pride, like another entrance to another new world. Here was the ferry.

And here was hard work for the grown-ups and for the ferryman, work for many days. The waggons had to be taken across one by one, then the horses and men, and lastly all the cattle, a few at a time, as many as the ferry-boat would hold.

But when after much trouble the people had been taken across, and their leader, the man with the fate of the whole tribe in his fierce blue eyes, came forward with a pair of scales and a strip of silver to cut off the ferryman's fee, Christophorus shook his head and would take no payment.

The chief dropped his hand with the scales. What did he mean by that?

Christophorus then gave him to understand that he was not a ferryman on his own account, but had been put there to assist people over the river for nothing, in God's name.

Oh, that was the way of it. Then *which* god was it that the fare was due to?

Christophorus pointed with his thumb to the cross he had planted above his hut, and had to explain to the stranger that he did men a service in the name of the great King Christ; however, King Christ did not desire any reward either; out of friendship for men he had appointed people to act thus on his behalf.

The chief, a young man with wild eyes and red hair already tinged with grey, could not make him out. Travelling with his people in a continual state of war and accustomed either to take or to pay for what he required, he had never yet encountered anything but opposition on his way—murder, blood and treachery wherever he went. Here for the first time he came upon a gentler custom, and it startled him; he went on, saving his silver but could not understand it. And yet he was here at the boundary between the world he had left and the one he was entering. King Christ he would not forget.

Christophorus heard the column receding into the forests as it resumed its journey, the creaking waggons, the cattle and the loud, impetuous voices of the horsemen; they had now got their direction, the Alps awaited them; now they could try to cross them and see what they would find on the other side!

Christophorus shook his head and muttered in his beard: full of joy they travelled now, walking the earth as though they were the first and only men; the difficulties that had driven them out of their homes were forgotten and they saw the whole future in sunshine. But when these same strapping young women one day were reduced to cutting their children's and one another's throats, after their men the invincible, had been defeated in battle then it would be a different song; no one who had heard it would lightly forget that howl of a camp when a nation perishes no, no, and the old man shook his head again and again. Or suppose they were successful, the young warriors whose eyes shone with bloodshed and rapine, then they would become princes, their leader a king and their clans the nobility of the countries they would possess; but still they would have to pay the price in fratricide in centuries of treachery and violence, for power is dear and devours the soul, as it devours the race; such is the effect of power, but who has ever said "No" when it was offered him? When did one ever hear of husbandmen who stayed on the

soil? Christophorus talked to himself as to a whole congregation and admitted the truth of what he said, nodding and nodding again: ay, ay, ay, thus they had chosen their destiny. To travel and get rich, richer than their gaping minds could grasp, make nations subject to themselves, destroy and breed! Women! A kind of radiance and sweet perfume hung about the ferry after all the womanhood that had passed over; the old man blew and cleared his nose suspiciously—phew, new-married people, those Longobards! Couple after couple, hand in hand all of them! Their song echoed like a single great bridal chorus in a distant wooded valley—behind the dark, before the light! Ah yes, young people wear madness like a garland of light on their brows so long as they desire one another; afterwards they call the world to witness their torments in loud, offended birthplaints—ay, ay, ay, thus Life would live and multiply and die, thought the numbed old ferryman and saint, shaking his head in his celibate wisdom, cooled down by much water—but it has to be ferried across.

His own work was not finished; other swarms would come and want to cross. Christophorus continued to ferry people from the North over the river on their way to the South until it seemed that he had emptied all the countries up where he himself had come from, and sent them down towards the sun and the warmth; and to all of them he gave the lesson of an unselfish deed performed for the good of all. None of the fresh and vigorous nations he ferried over to the South ever came back.

But when Christophorus had stayed long enough by the river it was given to him to ferry the Christ Child in the opposite direction, to the North.

For a long long time he had served the strongest of all Lords without ever seeing him. But hope worked within him and desired to leave a trace; he began to build, having leisure enough from his ferrying, and what he built was to be a house for King Christ to lodge in, if he should ever vouchsafe him a visit. To his own house Christophorus could not invite him; it was half a hole in the ground, half a hut of faggots; something more was wanted. Not unpractised in carrying stones, Christophorus then collected all he could find and began to pile them one on another into a building. The ground-plan was a cross, as was befitting, and the walls took up almost more room than the space they enclosed, for they were to be durable; the sun and moon shone through, for the giant was no mason, but the whole bulk held well together, looking like a little mountain. How the building was to be finished off and roofed over had not yet been settled, it was not nearly high enough, Christophorus had thoughts of reaching the stars; at night when his cyclopean masonry towered up above the trees it seemed to him that the top was already quite near the moon.

The building never got any further, for in the meantime Christophorus really had a visit from his Lord. It happened very differently from his imaginings, as everybody knows from the legend. One evening he heard a child crying by the river and asking to be ferried across, but saw nothing when he went out; and this was repeated three times. The third time he became aware of a little male child standing on the river bank and imploring to be carried over the stream.

Christophorus then carried him over, but now for the first time found a burden which almost exceeded his powers. This little child was a marvellous child, it grew heavier and heavier, and the river swelled beneath him, the darkness closed before him and became doubly dark, it was as though the elements would swallow him. The child weighed him down, never had anything been so heavy. Such is the weight of Life's germ, Life's beginning and the time to come of which we have no knowledge. And yet it seemed that the burden itself sustained him, else he would never have come across without straining himself. When at last he reached the opposite bank it was as though he had carried the whole world upon his shoulders.

The Child looked upon Christophorus with a strange earnestness. "Let it not surprise thee," he said, "that I am so heavy. Know that thou hast not only carried the world upon thy shoulders but even Him who created the world. Behold, I am Christ thy King, whom until this day thou hast served in thy good work. And this shall be a sign unto thee: Strike thy staff into the ground. To-morrow it shall blossom and bear fruit." And when Christophorus awoke early next morning his pilgrim's and ferryman's staff had become a palm. Thus the South came to him.

He himself carried it into the North. But this belongs to another story, how the Kingdom of God penetrated northward and was received in the poor, harsh countries which had thrust out their young men, the stem, and which had only the roots and the young shoots left.

V

OUR LADY

When again the age of an oak had gone by since Christophorus had dwelt by the river, a city stood there.

The forest no longer existed; from the ferry as far as the eye could see was open, cultivated land; the woods began a long way off on either hand and on the other side of the river. The ferry had attracted all kinds of people, fairs had been held there, and then it became a town; the surrounding land was cleared by settlers and came under the plough. On every market-day the peasants now came in from the country with their produce and in exchange received from the town the things brought by vessels from many parts of the world, which found shelter under its walls; thus a city is made, no one remembering that it has ever been otherwise.

The city did not extend far, its height was almost greater than its breadth, it looked like a cake of houses with a thick crust about it, the walls with their roofs and towers running all the way round; on the river side the town wall plunged abruptly into deep water, and on the other side the river was led into a moat; a hoisted drawbridge gaped like open jaws with a roof of beams on the land side; here he who would reach the city had to swim, and be bitten if he came across. Within the walls the city lay closely packed, with steeply rising houses and many deep and twisting alleys between; the people went about at the bottom of a gutter and lived in many layers above one another.

But in the midst of the city rose the church hill, and on its summit rode the Cathedral, Our Lady's, like a mountain made by hands with peaks and carved-out flanks. It was so big that the shadows of clouds in the sky flecked it like a mountain as they glided over it; it lay here in sunshine and there in shadow with its forest of spires, flying buttresses, garlands of stone, ornamental cornices and thousand figures; at night it rose out of the earth as a mighty body with its foot in the gloom and its airy open towers up in the starry sky irradiated by the moon.

The city beneath it was full of all kinds of everyday life: a bustling in the houses and the alleys, a rumbling on the drawbridge of peasants' carts when they were allowed to enter, hammer-blows from the cordwainer's shop where sole-leather was eing beaten on the stone, little children olling about, tumbling and getting up gain, old women emptying their pails to e pigs in the street, crossbowmen pacing e walls on guard with morions on their eads. The city was a fortress: the beat of rums was heard in its narrow lanes and n the market-place a troop of horsemen araded disguised in blue-black steel from op to toe, each man a fortress with closed isor, his face concealed by bars and bolts, vith spikes and scales all over him. Carro- ades thundered from the walls on occa- ion, and the ships lying off the town, with igh curving poops, saluted astern with *heir* pieces, barking a brief while.

But the Cathedral reduced all to silence vhen it chose. Throughout the day it lumbered, reposing in its glory and in its roximity to heaven, merely accompany- ng the hours with a chime of bells, clear nelodies like a web of sound, a golden oliloquy of tones high in the air; in the norning it rang for sunrise with rousing, owerfully swelling strokes of the great ell, and at evening the same bell rang lown the sun, but then it had a lingering esonance and ended in a single stroke of he clapper, three times in succession, vith a pause between, like the last af- righted sigh of the dying day.

But on high festivals or when great natters were to be announced or exor- ised, war, fire or pestilence, the Cathe- lral spoke with all its bells, crying with mmense brazen tongues till its towers and valls swayed and resounded to their very oundations, the hill and the whole city esounded, and the sky far and wide and he country and the river winding through t, all this quivered and expanded in music vhen the Cathedral began to speak. At ast it seemed to rise and shake, it opened, not to the day but to Time, the bells welled as in a tempest and increased in one, one century after another was re- ealed, one abyss after another, the Cathedral roared, sweating sound with its whole body; it was the ages rising again and finding a voice, a mighty heart found utterance in it.

On this same spot the hunter had had his dwelling under the lofty trees on the knoll, deep in the forest solitude. On the river bank the otter had had its hiding-places, where afterwards the town walls came down into the water; the badger had had his hole on the hill, where lay the Cathedral crypt.

Instead of the lofty trees the Cathedral soared with its heaven-seeking spires; but at their accustomed height the rooks still flew in and out, filling the upper regions of the church with their resounding cries, in which the spirit of the great trees seemed to live again. Lower down, in cornices and niches behind the statues of holy men, doves brooded and cooed in the sunshine; they too had kept their nests. And at the very top, where the spire stood dizzily against the clouds and seemed to be sailing with them, the falcon lived under the vane, choosing as ever the highest point and the widest view. So old was the church that grass grew on it here and there, high up in some rift where mould had collected, as on a mountain side; the grass too was seeking to return. Up in an angle of the cornice where the wind had swept dust into a little layer of soil, moistened by rain and manured by birds, a rowan shoot grew, a real green tree at a dizzy height on the wall, calling to mind the forest. But from the gutters and galleries all manner of monsters and goblins looked down; they had been turned to stone, and spouted rainwater or made hideous grimaces over the city and the country, impotence perpetuated. They were the dragons from the hunter's house that reappeared in stone, banning night and terror. In the high and gloomy belfry a ticking went on at regular intervals, the pendulum of the church clock measuring time, a tardy ghost of Time that once was young—the woodpecker of the forest.

The hunter's woodland house and his image of Ygdrasil, his heart, the mighty expansion of memory, had passed into the Church; the *Ship* that carried so many yearning men towards the South had become its nave; Christophorus' cyclopean walls exceeding all human measure had passed into it together with his fidelity. He himself stood by the door of the church in everlasting stone, with the Child on his shoulders and a tree in his hand, wading trustfully through the deep; for the old ferryman was the patron saint of the river city.

And on passing through the door one came into a vast and lofty space with subdued light and coloured shadows, apparently boundless, the high, narrow nave of the church, supported by a forest of pillars. They stretched upward like bright and slender stems, one beside and behind the other, losing themselves in the background of pillars and arches and spreading out into vaults of stone ribs and foliage, high up where the air of the interior blended into a strange violet-blue smoke. Here was the rainbow wherever one turned, the high narrow windows through which the light came in every colour, deep blue gleams and sparkling green and red and yellow intermingled as when the sun penetrates the leafy roof of the forest. But there was more than light and colour; on looking closer it was figures not of this world that shone in a celestial eternity, crowned men and calm winged women that had come to rest here, and bright, many-coloured pictures. And at the end of the nave the light was refracted in a mighty checkered rose, a ring of colours that branched into quaint patterns as though all circles and orbits of the universe here ran together and came to rest in one sphere for all time; it was the sun's image depicted in and illumining creation, sunset and sunrise unite for eternity.

Up on the piers and in the half-light o alcoves within the walls stood the image of dead princes and warriors and hol men who here continued their existenc in stone long after they had become dus in the earth; they spoke in a mute language of the desire to live on in a form even when the flesh had bowed submissively to mortality. Here they were i their graves, the sarcophagi in the chapel on the top of which princely couples la at full length in stone, the dead captai with his sword on the coffin lid and ol captured banners hanging above in th mist of incense; here they were too in th worn reliefs of tombstones in the floo paintings black with age but with burnin eyes that follow you wherever you go Everywhere, in the church's pictures an statues, in its stained-glass windows, in it inscriptions and symbols, spoke the voic of a vanished time which is so powerful the voice of the dead who cannot die

The beasts of the forest were assemble here and turned to stone that they migh not perish: in the carved capitals, ami foliage and from corners murky with th dust of centuries they thrust out their wil visages, wolves and stags together, fo here they had finally made peace; the lived in the conventional blazonings o shields and armorial bearings which treasured old hunting joys, spread eagles, wil boars, the raven and the lion rampant i flourishes; fabulous animals here lived i stone a life reality had never seen, th dragon, the hippogriff and the indomitabl horse with a long twisted horn in th middle of its forehead. The horrors an spectres of Night, whose existence lose itself in the imagination, could be *see* here; in the crypt was the Underworld the bound serpent of Darkness supporte the base of its central pillar.

High up in the apse of the choir abov the altar, as though on the very wall o heaven, stood solitude and the sign of the Supreme Spirit, the sign one feels behind one's back, but whose sight is death, the Eye suspended in air.

The whole body of the church was like an enchanted forest. At the entrance stood the holy water in an ornamental marble basin; its water came from an ancient well under the foundations of the church, in pagan times a sacred spring.

The hunter was here, now become an obscure legendary figure whose head Time had encircled with the halo of transfiguration; he and the supernatural stag, the speedy, the unattainable, which transported him from the present to eternity.

His soul was in the body of the church, *echo,* the old voice of the forest which rolled among the pillars, in the corners, and haunted the vaulting, that was he. His soul and the soul of all was in the organ, the voice of the church coming from everywhere and nowhere; the very fabric swelled with it, the vaulting, the walls, the piers, the whole stone edifice made music, a soft coloured blast seemed to move within it, a many-coloured roaring, in which could be heard the voice of all the quarters of the heavens, and the deep tramp of the distant sea transmitting itself to the feet as well as to the ear, and the birds twittered in thin high notes, the beasts shrieked, or muttered in the bass, and whole hosts of human voices traversed the vault, clear children's voices, whole solid waves of purest melody, as though invisible flocks of maidens were soaring past in song, and a chorus of darkly brooding men still pondering in the grave over the brevity of life. The forester's long, clamouring night-songs when in fear of the moon, the hermit's simple piping in the first calm light evenings of spring, were here heard again. That which none can put into words, which speaks in the winds and the stars and the seasons and in our blood, that which yearns even when the dead are dead, this reverberated through the building in many tones and united into a single swelling note which was a breath of eternity.

And the fragrance within the smoke that spread, coloured like the Milky Way, as a heaven under the vaulting and dispersed a mist of distance and promise through the air—this was the heaven of all remembrance, the infinite inner world of our memory, the scent of all summers, the perfume of all memories, even memories of things we have never experienced, every secret thing the sun has fostered, from the time when the first fir tree scattered its brew of resin and dropped its cones on the crocodile's back, and the first apple tree blossomed and gave off perfume and hung full of bees in the first garden of the first human pair.

On the altar, just above that spot in the grove where the hunter had his cairn and made fire-offerings to his Powers, in the midst of this marvel of stone, colour, music and fragrance, stood the image of the Mother of God, Our Lady.

She was raised above all corruptibility upon a throne of ivory, for which a hundred elephants had given their tusks, and it was supported by chased and richly gilt clouds; she was robed in the most precious silks, to which hundreds of thousands of silkworms had devoted their blind lives; on her head she wore a great diadem of precious stones, a petrification of the ruttish fires of the South; each stone of them had cost human life and had witnessed lechery, whereby they had become so hard and flashed so immodestly, but upon her head they were the crown of innocence.

In her arms she held the Son of God, from whose childish head three golden rays broke out in the semblance of sunshine; in his hand he played with an apple, the symbol of the origin of all fruit and all spheres. For the rest this Son of

God was a boy like other boys, chubby-cheeked, with his fat little limbs in layers from exuberant health. God's Mother smiled upon him, the holy mother-smile that is Nature's most beautiful blooming, the young mother's mute reposing in the marvel that has befallen her.

Before the holy Virgin burned a lamp which had never been extinguished since the church was founded; it was an ancient flame, the cult that kept it alight was older than the Church, it went back to old forgotten fire-worshippers. Year in and year out it burned: in the daytime it stood in the midst of incense and the coloured twilight from the windows as an admonition of the night, a paled watch-light that had survived into the daytime; at night, when the Cathedral lay empty and still as a vast tomb, it burned like a yellow wheel in the midst of the immense darkness, like a spark left over from the day, a lonely drop of the eternal fire at the bottom of the well of the grave and of darkness.

Terrible was the church at night. Its fathomless space was full of darkness, region behind region of darkness; high up lingered a pale, ghostly, coloured gleam, like a lunar rainbow; and a long spectral ray descended and traced eyes on one of the piers, a hovering blind life in the midst of a world of darkness; but below on the floor of the church the gloom brooded all the blacker, with only the everlasting lamp deep down in its gulf like an eye surrounded by rings of mist. A strange coughing came from distant resonant corners, the body of the church sighing within itself, the night sinking deeper and deeper into itself. The organ was perfectly silent, with redoubled silence; but up under the hanging banners there was a noiseless fanning, and a fanning in the draught under the vaulting, a swiftly fleeting life, the beat of wings, and now and then a little black soul became visible in a moonbeam; bats flitting hither and thither on their little dragon's wings and feeling their way in rapid flight among the pillars and empty spaces of the church.

Far away and high up through many dividing walls and chambers a hooting screech was heard at intervals, the owl in the tower—but it kept outside, it was the church's dismal voice over the city at night. Then the Cathedral beetled above the roofs like a mountain of darkness clotted together with the night, and from the lofty intricate spaces of the belfry came the hooting of the owl, as though the tower itself was hooting and threatening far and wide with its terror of darkness.

Round the foot of the church brooded crosses and graves and darkness, shunned by all men; and no one who could avoid it would look into the churchyard; no, he shut his eye on that side and spied out his way as well as he could with the other. If any man had been shut up in the church and forced to spend the night there alone he would have died of fright or lost his wits, become a babbling idiot for the rest of his days; nay, the cries of the poor imprisoned maniac would have driven any one mad with terror who chanced to pass by and hear them. The figure of Death with his bare bones and his horrid grinning teeth, lurked here in the dark corners of the buttresses, among the tombs, behind door gratings; and vaguely connected with the church at nighttime was the idea of the Being of the Abyss, the Evil One, the repulsive male creature with a tail that was thought to be red as glowing iron, stinking of pitch and equipped with all the powerful and loathsome arts that are not to be spoken of.

Only the servants of the church were fortified to visit the Powers of the church by night as by day; these skirted henchmen sang vigils by torchlight in the crypt at midnight; a gleam of fire crept up hrough openings in the wall level with he ground, and a subterranean chorus vas heard; men knew it was the Mass, but houghts of the underworld haunted them; even such were the cries of those buried alive in Hell, the bloody howls of wolves below, the mad shrieks of distracted souls!

And to such terrors they delivered up their dead. Within the chapels where the dead lay buried, and the alcoves of the walls, gloomy even by day, the gloom condensed at night into the outer darkness; many times buried were the dead here. A sound as of withered leaves arose in the stillness of night and lost itself like trackless footsteps in the draught between the piers, unaccountably; it was a shifting of the bones in a coffin, muffled by boards and walls, one more whispered sign of life and death from what was slowly sinking to pieces through the centuries in the interior of the sarcophagus.

But again the church clothed itself in daylight, in its uplifting power over the eye. Every day it was itself a day above the day. But on Sunday it possessed an added rejuvenation. From early morning Sunday, the Sun's day, could be felt in the air; it set its mark upon everything throughout the day and preserved a greater beauty than all the other days of the week until the evening. The rooks called more clearly and with more of the dawn in their notes on Sunday morning from the roof of the church, the doves cooed and cooed as though there were bursting buds to coo over, and the people came up to the church in crowds as though to a grand migration; for the bells rang with a younger and stronger peal that day, rang out their welcome and the joy of Heaven over town and country, which lay so still and had adorned themselves because it was the day of rest.

Then it was the old world back again: in the church was a song as of waking birds, and the censers before the altar poured out cloud after cloud as they swung to and fro in a dizzy joy: the birth of the day, the young newborn clouds that the dawn brings forth and the sun turns red, and a fragrance of eternal summer spread within the church to its uttermost corners; not a beggar by the door outside of all but it brought him a message.

Up under the vaulting the smoke lay like the mist of fertility in a hothouse, and here, high up, could be descried as it were a web of swallows darting in and out; they had their nests at the very top among the ribs and scroll-work. But their faint *veet-veet* was not heard, for the organ rolled, clearer, vaster, fuller in its tone than on other days; it received the congregation as in an open embrace of sound. The church stood erect with its pillars and altars, Heaven was opened.

The organ pealed with full force, a choir of voices filled the church as though descending from the spheres:

Torches of the stars eternal
Burn before thy heart, O Mother,
Who hast freed the world's repining.

Round thy head the spheres of heaven,
In thy heart the living waters,
Wonder-working thou, God's Mother.

Depths of innocence we dream of,
Girt about with streams of gladness,
Well of goodness never empty!

Thou the one whose soul reposes
In itself; the world unheeding
Thou dost dwell in brightness, smiling.

As a tree from heaven moistened,
Clothed about with showers of summer,
Thou hast decked thee, green and gladdened.

Like the tree its dead leaves dropping
Thou hast bowed in deepest sorrow:
Dust is every creature's portion.

Thou wert stirring in Life's mourning.
As a rose by dew made fresher
Breathes Love's spirit from its chalice.

Roses blaze. Their thorns are cruel.
By the bier of short-lived summer
Bleeds the berry, with thy weeping.

Trembling dost thou tread, but dauntless,
On Life's pathways, mild and bleeding;
Bounteous art thou, Woman, bounteous!

For in thee has Life his dwelling.
From within thy secret chamber
Comes thy Child's voice, small and tender.

Here thy precious one thou lavest
And with mother-sources stillest,
Lifting, putting down, and tending.

Here when midnight's hour approaches
Softly sounds thy tender prattle
To thy nursling, warm and bonny.

With a song like flowery music
Gently rockst thou him to slumber,
Golden in the light thy tresses.

Newly kindled burn Life's torches!
He is born whom earth's unhappy
Kneel to when the earth is trembling:

Boy who shall the earth inherit,
Seed of man and Godhead's larva,
Hope that shall the future colour!

Wrathful wreaks the world destruction,
Sees itself with fear and loathing—
In thy nest are all things new-made.

Brutish lust would fain betray thee;
Sex's miserable riddle
In thy blood is turned to mercy.

In thy trouble's fiery torment,
When the shock of Nature casts thee
To the dust—then life thou givest!

Full of grace again thou buddest
In a young and lovely daughter,
Horror to sweet smiles transforming.

Miscreant's hand which thought to ruin
Answerest thou with double bounty,
Woman born again in bearing!

This is thy revenge, thou pure one:
Double fruit where first a single
Blushed defenceless 'mid the branches.

As a wave of sunshine chases
Shadows from a golden cornfield,
Even so thou smilest, fair one.

What in all the realm of Nature
Is like beauty, beauteous Maiden,
Eyes' delight, thou shining marvel!

Sunshine's fire and blood's warm billows,
Secret laws of Life pursuing,
Hide within thy maiden bosom.

All Life's sweetness, warmth of gladness,
We may see upon thy visage,
Youth eternal thou, Our lady!

Source of goodness and forgiveness!
Virgin! Mother! Gentle Woman!
Joy with thee to find vouchsafe us!

BOOK TWO: THE CARAVEL

DE MUY PEQUEÑA EDAD ENTRÉ
EN LA MAR NAVEGANDO, É LO HÉ CONTINUADO HASTA HOY.
LA MESMA ARTE INCLINA Á QUIEN LE PROSIGUE Á DESEAR
DE SABER LOS SECRETOS DESTE MUNDO.

Christofforo Colombo

I
THE "SANTA MARIA"

Lights were shining at midnight from St. George's Church at Palos, in the south of Spain; a service was being held for the crews of three ships that were to sail at daybreak; it was the third of August 1492.

The little port was as excited as any town could be. The voyage which had been in preparation for the past few months was one that attracted attention, and Palos itself had a vital share in it, for the owners and most of the crews were local men, even if they were not making the voyage entirely of their own free will, both ships and ships' companies having been pressed into it by the Government. The leader, however, was a foreigner, an Italian from God knows where, who gained the ear of the great for his quite obviously insane plans, nothing more nor less than sailing to blazes, down underneath the earth—altogether a fairly eccentric business and one quite calculated to upset Palos, both that part of it which was going to sail and the friends and relations who were staying behind. Not many of the grown-up people went to bed that night; the seamen who were leaving, more or less voluntarily, armed themselves against an uncertain fate as reasonably as they could by fortifying visits to church and to the taverns.

In the church there was great solemnity, the whole of the crews went to confession and communicated; but even later in the course of the night many a sinner dropped in again, when reminded by the bells, to repeat an *Ave* and cool his forehead against the stone pavement, until he felt drawn by the distant irresistible ring of goblets and stole out again. It was a difficult night, and many a worthy fellow swung like a pendulum between this world and the next.

Only one held out steadfastly in church to the last. This was the leader himself, Christopher Columbus. For hour after hour he knelt before the image of the Holy Virgin, with his huge and hairy skipper's hands clasped, himself an image of holy calm and self-communing, silent, with motionless features, weary with watching, absorbed in prayer and meditation. The glare of the candles fell upon the strong head with its reddish-grey mane and the strange blue eyes under eagle brows, which showed quite white against the flaming bright-red skin, weathered by a life in the open air, a picture of weather itself; the unusually tall and powerful frame reposed in itself, strength at rest. If this man was an adventurer he was in any case not one of the windy sort; there was a solidity about him as he knelt, his back and shoulders alone spoke for him, and many a roving eye seeking consolation in the sacred images of the church involuntarily came to rest upon him; it was well to be on good terms with Our Lady, but after all it was he who was to sail the ships! His lips moved like those of a man spelling out syllables, and the others nodded, nodded, mumbling to themselves; if only there might be power in his prayers—for if *he* were not in grace what would become of the rest?

What the Admiral felt, what was working in his soul, could not be read in his face. There was something hot about his eyes; but then it was warm in the church, the air in the confined space was thick with incense and the mawkish smoke of the candles, whose little flames had coloured rings like eyes that had watched overlong. The church was too crowded, the air like a hothouse or a lying-in room, saturated with music and incense; the priests said Mass and rang the altar bell, and the bells in the tower outside made the walls vibrate, the organ blared again and again, the Mass rose as in a wave culminating in loudly enunciated Latin conjurations, the holy images stared as though through a veil—and still Columbus was on his knees before the Virgin Mary's altar. The felted doors at the entrance to the church fell to now and then and let in air as the crews came and went; already a bluish gleam of daylight made its way in each time the door opened, day was breaking; even the priests yawned behind their hands and blinked their red and dried-up eyes. The body of the church stood out of the darkness, as though built up of dust and cobwebs, piers and walls came into being in a light from outside, and the candles grew dim, a wan meeting of day and night. The sailor who had hovered backwards and forwards so often in the course of the night fell asleep in the middle of an *Ave* and a hiccup, and woke again on hitting his forehead against the stone floor, with a groan; well, he would live or die, one or the other!

But a cold breath swept through the dawn outside, and a rich muddy smell arose from the river, hulls and masts came out of the darkness, the three ships lay ready for sea with sails half unfurled; their lights were extinguished, no longer wanted, and the ships' boats pulled to and fro in the stream between ship and shore, taking the last things on board.

In a tavern by the harbour some of the crew were swinging a final tankard and taking a last leave of their friends. Here the brothers Pinzon, who commanded two of the ships, collected a crowd about them and rehearsed once more the whole plan of this more than doubtful expedition. They were conscious of the attention they attracted, but not proud; on the other hand, of course, they had all the information and talked quietly like men who knew, so that every one had to crowd round to hear them; as men of experience and local men they spoke with weight. Martin Alonzo as the elder gave his opinion first, after him Vincente Yannez, who entirely agreed, but could put it in even stronger terms; everything that was obvious was said again and again. There was only one thing on which the brothers would express no opinion but kept their mouths tight-shut, and that was the possible outcome of the voyage. Martin Alonzo held his peace, and Vincente held his, but both were bursting with what was unsaid; and Martin Alonzo, standing in a noble attitude with his weight on one leg and the other advanced, shrugged his shoulders, buried his head in them as though bending to the elements, and showed both his palms—*Quien sabe?* And Vincente arched his back, and he too showed both palms—*Quien sabe?* The brothers wore sea boots reaching to the hips, for they might have a good deal to go through, but the upper part of their bodies was cased in iron, cuirass and helmet, with visor up; but in a little while they clapped it down, and then they were bolted and barred, ready to meet legions of unknown monsters and man-eaters.

It was a great rambling tavern with murky corners, and heads were not very clear; nobody knew exactly what was going on here and there in the background, female voices could be heard amid the clash of tankards, stringed instruments, singing and a rhythmical clapping of all hands in unison like a great raging heart, and above all their heads was a waving, sparkling, bewitching vision—for they had got a girl up on the table, where she was dancing a perilous dance on the very edge; so the Moors hadn't taken away all the dancing with them when they were chased out of Spain the other day, here was a creature as supple as if she had a bow for a backbone, with a stomach like an eel; and there was somebody who knew how to manipulate the flute with few holes and many repetitions. Rather African it was, the dance; the eel wriggled tenaciously on the table, she gave vent to a screech, and keeping her feet on the same spot she let herself go in a presto, the men yelled, *Brava!* and wall and ceiling showed the shadow of the dancer with raised arms and twisting hips, heeling over at the waist; she whinnied like a mare, the guitar-player stormed at his strings, the nasal trills of the flute came quicker and quicker, the audience stamped their feet as well as clapping, the castanets clattered, spurring her on, a teeth-chattering race, no longer an occasional shout but shouting all the time . . . for to-morrow they were to die, but *now, now* they had everything that life could give!

Yes, it had been a wild day in Palos—some of the men were hopping on one leg, the other lamed; others only saw with one eye and had a bloody bandage over its fellow—for this mad evening had begun with *letting the bull loose!* Of course, in a little place like Palos there was no bull-ring, but then they had a town bull and knew how to amuse themselves! Bull loose in the street! Hey! Jesus! Look at the bull, all by himself in the market-place, all powerful, waving his tail—and everybody scampering indoors and upstairs, headlong, on all fours—look at the bull trotting down the middle of the street with horns raised, quite alone, and all the doors are slammed, and a pair of heels vanish over a paling—hey, the whole street swept clean as if by magic, people hanging out of trap-doors and garrets to look on . . . and now the bullring is ready, it has arranged itself, out of the houses jump nimble young fellows and begin to tease the bull with their capes, horsemen dash into the street leaning over their mounts as they gallop round a corner, with long lances in rest; collision, crash, a cloud of dust and horses' legs in the air, riders on top of one another, a torrent of blood; the bull has got his horns into the first horse, the street yells, and now it's a mix-up, cracks, falls and hurly-burly, a hunt down the street and back again, till the bull is ready for the death-stroke—then the signal is given and all draw back, except one, a young desperado; he and the bull are left, absolutely alone, face to face in the middle of the street. He has no other weapon but a naked blade, like a spit, with a cloth wrapped round the end he holds. The killing is done in breathless silence. The raging beast, all body and horns, with a bloody gleam in his eye, and the slender, mortally determined man, the lurking spit . . . and then in a moment the street roars and becomes alive with the things people madly fling from windows and cocklofts, hats, clothes, flowerpots, some swing themselves down into the street—for he has done it, the spit lies buried in the bull's shoulder with the point in its heart, it collapses as if struck by lightning!

And now the desperado is sitting here in the tavern on a chair, nodding with his chin on his chest, drunk and sober and drunk again many times that day, sated with honour, worn-out, aged by a generation in a few hours . . . and to-morrow, no, *now, now* he is to sail; outside is the dawn, looking with a grey face upon the desperado and the dancer.

A person nobody paid any particular attention to moved about among the groups in the course of the night, now here, now there, chattering incessantly without any one grasping the connection of what he was saying, not that that mattered; now and then he gave vent to a burst of laughter which made people turn round to see what the joke was; but it was nothing, only that mountebank, the Babuino as they called him, who had once again said something he himself thought intensely amusing.

He was a little swarthy man with a big face, mauve about the mouth, and he looked like an old huckster; he had put in an appearance here to peddle his wares and had in fact done very good business among the seamen who were about to sail and were providing themselves for a long voyage. He was in a mad mood to-night, the Babuino, pretending to be drunk as nobody was sober, declaiming in a loud voice, putting on the airs of a Dionysus, and giving great lurches when he crossed the room; but he was only lame, not a drop of wine had passed his lips. He went up to one or another with his goods, sideways like a crab, with a confidential wagging, all grins and good nature; he stooped down, made himself still smaller than he was, a miserable thing, a dog in every respect, except his eyes, which shone like magic orbs, with a perfectly frank look of impudence, which, however, those present were too thick-skinned or too drunk to notice. When anybody made fun of the Babuino, or tried to shake him off with a threatening gesture, he retreated a step with quivering face, timorous, dazed, and his eyes disappeared altogether; he was then a sufferer, thrust out, infirm and palsied, into a cruel world; but at the same moment his lips drew back from his teeth, it was best to be on guard—only a grimace, and then he grinned again and crept near, fawning, almost lying on the ground, his limbs still quaking with fear, enough to move a stone, and in his forepaw he disclosed something that you had to look at, a brand-new amulet—and then there was a little bargain after all!

When attention flagged the Babuino raised his voice, of astonishing volume and timbre for so small a chest, and became a public crier, in a long and practised recitative, which he accompanied by remarks in a private undertone and emphasized now and then with one of his sudden bursts of laughter:

"Amulets! Amulets! Most excellent Santiago de Compostela! The apostle in silver-gilt, brass or lead, equally powerful, the protector of all seafaring men! Rosaries, imitation olive wood from the Garden of Gethsemane, rosaries that pray by themselves, rosaries! Crucifixes, in ivory or metal, for every passion! Relics, fragments of holy persons, every part of the body! Letters of indulgence, a selection in stock! Images of the Virgin, immaculate! Damaged at reduced price! Remedies! Salves! Rhinoceros-horn for love potions, genuine mummy from Egypt, stolen, with original smell! Prayer books, very effective! Books of magic! Secret books! Ha, ha, ha!"

The Babuino neighed and shook his lame leg; half of what he had uttered was enough to get him burnt alive, if anybody had been listening to his crowing; but all the rest were too busy crowing themselves, so he could play with fire as long as it amused him. The tavern was filled with a general roar, like a fire blazing at its highest.

But at last it burned itself out; after the fire comes the ash. The word went round that the Admiral had left the church at last and was about to take ship; the music died away, an uncanny daylight filled the corners of the tavern, all at once the guests broke up and streamed out to the boats in the river; a cannon shot from the *Santa Maria* announced with a loud boom that the tide was on the turn; it was the signal, the hour of sailing had struck.

Just as Christopher Columbus was stepping into the boat to go off to the ships he was detained a few minutes, though without its atracting much attention; it was only the huckster they called the Babuino who crawled up to the tall skipper's feet and addressed him. Few heard what he said, and nobody understood him, he seemed to be talking Latin. Columbus stood at his full height with a very serious air, still calm and with a cleansed look on his face such as men wear when they come from Communion, and when he had heard all the creature had to say he turned and got into the boat without having uttered a word in answer, nor could any one see what impression the stranger's speech had made on him.

The huckster addressed Columbus in a hurried tone, corrected himself and made light of what he had just been saying, it was all idle words; he made all kinds of absurd gestures, quivering and twitching his face before the tall man as though the sun was in his eyes, but tittering as he wrung his foolish hands in deference—and suddenly all the squirms and grins were smoothed away from his chops, he looked up with the face of a human being, as though through many masks, a strangely old look; still chattering he withdrew, with an empty laugh in his throat, while some incomprehensible reflex action made him take leave of himself; he actually put out one hand and shook it with the other, crouching to the ground in confusion and showing all his teeth, two rows of big molars like millstones, his whole body twitching with a thousand promptings . . . and he was gone! And what was it he had said?

"*Vale*—good wishes for the voyage from an old voyager! Allow me to add: your worship's idea of trying to find the Indies by sailing to the west, as I hear, when the Indies lie to the east, is not at all a bad one, since we know by experience that a problem can be solved by getting away from it in a diametrically opposite direction, he, he, he! A still quicker solution stares you in the face—why travel so far at all, when short cuts are so much pleasanter? The only proper voyage of discovery *has* been made, it is always the same: *a genibus ad genua* . . . and isn't that just where your worship comes from? Clack!"

He gave his sudden loud laugh, which sounded like the roar of a beast, but checked it at once and came a step nearer, with gleaming eyes, and dropped his voice confidentially, fleering with his tongue out:

"The greatest distance mankind can cover, isn't it a marking time on the same spot? Listen to a piece of advice; save yourself a costly, doubtful voyage and take up a study at home—this book that I have, for instance, *Itinerarium Amoris,* written by a connoisseur, a gynographer, a great rarity even as a volume, I may say, a unique copy, second century vellum, belonged once to the Library of Alexandria, from which I removed it, a dishonest thing to do, but it adds to its value as a curiosity; altogether an inestimable volume, isn't it? . . . But I'm talking nonsense, trying to sell voyages to a man with his foot on the gangway! The sea is calling! Won't you have an amulet to take with you? Or an innocent idol, a little woman, you're so lonely at sea; look here, no bigger than the palm of my hand, a bronze of Aphrodite, wonderful patina, the noblest Greek work, smoothed by the hands of centuries of connoisseurs, but intact in spite of all, Woman herself, in her ripe maiden bloom, ever young . . . no, not that either! The sea is calling! Well, I must leave too—and who knows which of us will go farthest, your worship with your big ships or I with my old seven-leagued boots? Our ways part. You go to the South, and I am bound for the North. Spain no longer offers an abiding place for an old wanderer, and he has no idea of taking the backward road to Africa again with the Arabs. Ah yes, the earth burns under him here, it's getting too hot for him, he must seek cooler pastures. If they prepare stake and faggots for the old man, he rises from the ashes like the phœnix, as everybody knows; but does everybody know what the fire tastes like . . . sssss! In proof that he can go he shakes the dust of Spain from his feet, ai, ai, ai!"

He raised first one foot and shook it thoroughly, then the other and shook that too; he looked all round him, hunted, desperate, like a rat in a trap; he sighed, and his distorted features were relaxed, giving way to a human expression, an old man's sorrow, but only for an instant, then he was twitching again, indomitably mocking:

"Well, good-bye! Until we meet again! As I say, your worship goes south and I north, though really it should be the other way. But perhaps we shall meet nevertheless . . ."

He came quite close, put his hand to his mouth and whispered: "Yes, now we're going each in his own direction . . . *but the earth is round!*"

After this stab he hurriedly made off: *"Vale!"*

At sunrise the field labourers who were up early saw a little man with staff in hand and pedlar's box on his back taking the northern road out of Palos, with halting steps, but covering the ground fast; at the same time they heard the firing of salutes and ringing of all the town's bells as Columbus sailed with his ships.

The sun lay as a huge red sphere on the horizon as the ships cast off and began to swing down with the tide, saluting with all their pieces. And the bells of Palos kept on: they were but small, those in St. George's Church and a few other chapels; the bells of La Rabida Convent sounded from their height, and in the distance all the bells of Huelva could be heard; all the parish bells out in the country round joined in, it sounded like a regular discussion between a fleet that was sailing and all the churches that stayed behind. It was not like the booming of the great cathedral bells inland in the river cities of Europe, but to make up for it the little bells of the coast went more rapidly, in a fussy tempo, reminding one of swarming bees and people running after them, beating brass mortars and anything that would make a noise, and the meaning seemed to be the same: Will you stop, will you stop! said the bells, chiming and tolling, but the ships would not stop, they fired astern with heavy guns that made the whole hull tremble, shrouded themselves in smoke and warped out of the mouth of the river with the ebb tide under their keels, one big clumsy caravel in front and two smaller and lighter ones behind with their poops towards Palos.

When well out in the bay they all set sail and began to heel over and make way, the Atlantic received them with a swell in which they rose and sank; from the land the three ships were seen nodding in the sea and slowly growing less as though carried away by an undercurrent out into the gently breathing ocean. At last, when they were far out, flags and pennants were seen to be hauled down, a white cloud shot out from the stern of the *Santa Maria* and lay upon the waves, a distant report was heard as though muffled by blankets, the farewell shot.

But those on board saw the Spanish coast unfold itself, turning about its headlands; sunbeams rose fan-like in the direction of Cadiz, the interior of the country extended and came in sight the farther they left it behind, but lost its sharpness; high up in the distance the airy snow-chain of the Sierra Nevada hovered like a cloud among the clouds, the land stretched out its arms to them on both sides of the bay. But as the coast grew vague and began to sink into the sea some of the crew went to the bulwarks and kissed both hands, stretching them out to land in an impassioned gesture, and their eyes moistened, they felt a stab in the breast, the parting was more than they could bear.

Only Columbus paced backwards and forwards on the highest part of the poop, a place he never left thenceforth, backwards and forwards, with his face intently turned in the direction of the ship's course, to the south-west; and, whether he was conscious of it or not, he never once turned to look back toward Spain. At a gesture from him the green wreaths, now withered, with which the ship had been decorated before sailing were thrown overboard. And now those of the crew who had had to be kept below, prisoners and pressed men, were let out; they ran round the deck like dogs, sniffing at the sea and towards the land—a league away—and towards the open sea head—*Madre de Dios!*—some of them, old pale-faced men, simply shook their heads, knew that it was all up with them, but the young ones threw themselves on the deck wringing their hands and burst into tears, as though the bottom had been knocked out of their existence and the whole of life was trying to weep itself out at once.

The gulls followed the ships, conversing among themselves in their parsimonious language, with an eye on the wake. With ships they were quite familiar—what? you so often saw an island of peculiar oblong shape break away from the land and drift off on its own account, possibly babies that were born of the land and went off to visit other shores. They were not the kind of island you settled or nested on, certainly not; there were men on them and it wouldn't do to come too near, but there was this about the islands that not unfrequently something fit to eat dropped off them, the gulls know that. *Meev,* they say to each other as they fly; that means that the day is blue, all is right with sea and sky.

But towards evening the gulls began nevertheless to have misgivings; they were accustomed to see travelling islands keep between coasts that could both be seen at once, at any rate from a height, but these three seemed to be going in a straight line away from all land and out to where there were no more coasts at all. That was too much even for the gulls, and the time came when *they* turned back.

For the first few days not many words were heard from the Admiral on board the *Santa Maria;* he walked the poop with closed lips and dark brows, not to be appeased, even by the fact that now they actually *had* got away, so furious had he been at one delay after another up to the very last.

For they were to have sailed in the spring, everything had been based upon that, a very important thing to have the summer in front of one, of course; now they were leaving when summer was gone and autumn coming on—it was significant of the whole plan, of his whole life. When he was young he was ready with his plan but met with every possible hindrance; now, when at last he was to have the chance of his life, he felt with insuperable bitterness that it was after the time; he had already reached the age when a man looks back. Fourteen years, fourteen long years, from the age of twenty-eight to forty-two, those years of a man's life in which his activity is at its highest, simply to get the vessels fitted out; and now that the voyage was to begin he was stiff and grey-headed, grown grey before his time from vexation at the time that was lost! Impatience, impatience, and nothing to show for it but his years! On then to death, in full sail, if death was all he had to seek!

Once more, for the last time, those fourteen years of adversity passed through his memory; he recalled all his humiliations, and the crew watched the Admiral quicken his pace on the poop, where he walked up and down like a lion; they saw his face swell and turn still redder, and they thought his black looks were meant for them and cast down their eyes, threw themselves eagerly upon some piece of work or other. But it was the years in Portugal that were in the Admiral's mind, the lost years, the insults, the impossibility of moving any one, until some back-handed advantage to themselves occurred to them: the King sending ships out into the Ocean behind Columbus's back, following the course he had laid down—leaving *him* in the lurch as a crazy person and stealing his idea! The great can do such things! That is why they own kingdoms! Of course. But when the King's men had been a couple of days out they got ocean sickness and turned back, reporting that the sea was too vast; they were quite benumbed, in a sort of delirium, and it was some time before they recovered themselves. Ho! A manly idea can always defend itself after all!

The Admiral stood still and raised his lion's head, embraced in a glance the ship below him, an absent glance, above the heads of all the crew; and they shrank from it, did not care to raise their eyes to the poop, any higher than half-way up the ladder. They knew well that they deserved a good deal of contempt, not all had the fear of God in them when they came aboard. It almost seemed that they had a taste for the rope's end, and the rope was busy the first few days; the officers had been catching it from above and passed it on. If Diego thought he was on a yachting cruise he had made a mistake; the chaotic state in which he had joined ship was converted with an iron hand into the strictest discipline. Boatswain and master may have had their own opinion about this fool's trip, but so long as they were at sea all would be ship-shape! Before they reached the Canary Isles Diego was a sober man, obedient, smart, tarry about the hands from stropping aloft and with clean toes from much wholesome swabbing decks before breakfast.

Every fifth man of the crew, as every other man in Spain, was called Diego, that is, James, after the Apostle and Saint. Diego had just as much of his namesake as the name suggested, a distant resemblance worn by time; the rest he made up for by a picture of the holy Santiago stamped on a medal which he wore strung on his bare chest. Ashore Diego was a desperado, a bully for all bulls, as a coast-dweller equally ready for adventure in a mercenary army, as trooper or musketeer, or as a sailor and halberdier on board a galley, the arm was as indifferent to him as the element; this time it was the sea, half involuntarily, but such was at times the way of Diego's destiny; this adventure looked like being the most incalculable in extent and the most uncertain he had yet *nolens volens* been involved in.

Like a seed that had floated out to sea, with its germ and its possibilities as a plant if it reached land, such was Diego torn away from his Spain and committed to the winds, with what there was in him, to take root—where?—or to die. And many things were concealed within that square Spanish head with its blue-shaven cheeks and its smouldering glance. What had not befallen the Andalusia from which he and his forefathers came? It had its name from the Vandals, a migratory Northern people, who had lost themselves in North Africa after having left their trace here. In return North Africa had pushed up into Spain for some centuries, the Moors with their Arab houses, the horse-shoe over their goings in and out, their cages for women, until they had recently been chased home to Africa again—several of the men on board had seen the banner of Castile hoisted on the towers of the Alhambra—but that did not mean that their ways were altogether driven out of Andalusia. Other foreigners had laid waste here and left their marks behind them, the Goths, the Romans, the Greeks; still farther back the ancient peoples of Africa, old Carthage; in the earliest ages the Phœnicians, those sea-rats from Asia Minor who had their noses everywhere—and Diego had a sprinkling of all of them in his blood, or was marked by their contact as one is by one's neighbours; he had inherited a turbulent destiny from his ancestors, was brave, covetous, blood-thirsty, a destroyer, but had the same godlike contempt of death as those Northern daredevils to whom fear was the only known crime; he was grandiose, with the Spanish bearing that had come down from the Romans together with the toga, the cloak with which to drape one's unwashedness, and he was untrustworthy as is sometimes the way in the Mediterranean countries, he had passion but came short in feeling, in love an Asiatic, violent, above all inconstant—and yet at bottom an Iberian, a primitive Spaniard, for ever reposing in his nature, contradictory and loosely connected as it was; all in all a human creature, very long-suffering, amiable, with a soul full of music—for among his mothers had been the mutest and most beautiful of all the women of earth.

Such was the Diego who was now at sea and who raised his eyes with a respect none too genuine to the quarter-deck, the holy of holies, where the Admiral paced his unresting watch—when all was said and done he was the strongest for the time being (the cursed Italian), the man whom it was best to look to, if one wanted to get out of this predicament. The powder-barrels in the *Santa Maria's* hold were charged with a soul like Diego's, sulphur, charcoal and saltpetre superficially mixed but with a hell imprisoned within them which could be released by a spark, and the spark was smouldering in Diego's Kabyle eyes.

The Admiral for his part kept an eye full of reservations on his crew; when he had walked off the rancour of his thoughts of Portugal he began to quicken his pace and turned yet more sharply in his walk up and down the narrow poop as he recalled what had befallen him in Spain, his nostrils snorted at the thought. Eight years' empty talk! All the shoes he had worn out in the pursuit of royal personages, in company with suppliants, lackeys and toadies; the smile that appeared on every silly face when he was seen or mentioned, Columbus, the eccentric, even the children hooting in the street when he passed by! The Council at Salamanca that was to test his scheme! Postponements, hopes and disappointments, up and down, poverty, homelessness, the fickleness and apathy of princes, a long long laborious pilgrimage which had taught him what beggars have to suffer. Day after day with his resolution blazing within him, ready for the leap, and day after day nothing but a fresh insight into human nature, year in, year out, all through the years! That last weary journey, when abandoning all hope he had quitted Cordova with his little boy, intending to leave Spain, and came to the convent by Palos, Santa Maria la Rabida, and begged bread in the name of God and for the first time felt with horror that he was an old man—ah, then his luck had changed, then it was that he was able to get away. But never could he forget and never would he forgive what he had felt that time, when with shaking hand he accepted the gift to himself and his boy—that old people's hands shook in just that way.

Again the Admiral stood still up on the poop, and Diego glancing up saw that he was terrible, the big, tall grey man was seeing visions and execrating spirits, how else could he have that frightful look? And Diego crept behind something, where the evil eye could not fall on him, crossing himself in great detail, on his forehead and over his chest, from shoulder to shoulder; *"Madre!"* he whispered, and turned quite grey in the face. A strong man, the one up there, and who could tell what Powers he was in league with?

But as the days went by before they reached the Canary Isles, where they put in for repairs, most of August and the early part of September, the feeling on board gradually became less strained. After all they were still within the known world, and the crew could not keep up the sense of their misfortune for weeks on end. Diego revived his forgotten songs, and poured out his soul in passionate chest-notes to the winds of heaven; he was full of sweet speech as a wooer, all his thousand bereavements; and at whiles when he had time—and the calm fine weather gave more than enough leisure, the sails stood for days and nights without having to be braced about—he got a game of dice on deck, shook the deceptive cubes out of the box and glared to see how many pips he had thrown, himself with a die for a head and a cinq in his face. They did not play for nothing; what money and valuables there were on board travelled by degrees from one Diego to another and back again, several times; now a man would be the owner of all the movable property in the ship, the object of cringing deference on the part of all the rest, now he would be reduced to beggary again, but whatever happened it stayed in the family. Play was hot, at times not without danger to life and limb, blood boiled up. Diego was stirred to the depths of his soul when luck went against him, he staked everything he possessed down to his shirt, and his lips could be seen moving as he made secret promises to the Virgin Mary; and when he lost in spite of that he tore his shirt to strips, and included the Mother of God in an oath which cannot be repeated, an exclamation which placed the Holy Virgin in the same class as the unclean creature on whose flesh in a smoked condition the crew lived daily, God's curse on it! At last Diego staked his amulet, and when that too was lost, and he was a naked heathen, he gambled for his hair, his life, his sweetheart, his share of heaven, everything, until at last his luck actually did turn.

Next day Diego might have won back all his possessions and a good deal of the others'. For a change they played cards, those who knew how; higher notions of numbers were required here and the illiterate contented themselves with looking on, a numerous and interested crowd around the few sorcerers who sat in a ring on deck with their naked feet under them, conjuring, each with a fan of the apocalyptically painted leaves in his hand. It was the book of fortune and its reading entailed excitement, the players disagreed and stabbed one another with their eyes, tapped the deck angrily with their fingers, nodded ferociously and shuffled the cards again; they smacked one card after another on to the deck like a blacksmith swinging his hammer: *espadilla, basta, punto,* and the adversary was smashed! They wrinkled their foreheads and thought, threw down all the cards at once and pushed across ducats from one pile to the other, the whole quite incomprehensible to the illiterates who looked on in wonder; how did they manage to keep it all in their heads? With the pictures on the cards they were familiar enough, there were knaves, kings and queens, lovely to look upon, the only ladies they had on board, sad to say; Diego pressed a card to his bosom, clasped it with both his arms in a storm of passion; it was the Queen of Hearts—oh, well, well!

What had come over Diego? He was seen to embrace the water-butt when he came near it, and poured tender words over it; his voice had a queer ring in it, he sang evening hymns and was ready to die of grief, he was gay, fantastic, witty, not exactly decorous, there were few things that didn't prompt his fancy in a particular way, the swelling sails, ho, hey! how they stretched, how they stretched, the mast seemed so straight, slender as a waist, and he had to embrace that too; he kissed his fingers and made declarations of love to the *Niña,* their sister, sailing a little way off; the *Pinta* didn't matter so much, that was a he-ship, but Sister was so sweet, she curtsied so sweetly in the waves, dipped her bow with a girlish air, with foam like a lace collar round her neck, and she had such tight little white sails, hey ho!

Even in the highest quarter there was a change of mood for the better during those sunny days before reaching the Canaries; the Admiral now and then opened his lips, occasionally indeed he came down from the poop and mixed with mortals in the waist of the ship, and Diego had an opportunity of finding out that this man of mystery had a warm and pleasant smile and was in certain respects the most unpretending of all on board.

At other times he was to be seen deeply engaged in his measurements and algebraic arts; every day he hung his astrolabe out in the sun and let it and the elements work upon one another, not without a shiver down Diego's back; properly speaking, no doubt, the magic disc with all its secret signs and the man who used it ought to have been burnt, except that of course the safety of the ship depended on his arts, but it was nasty to look at. At night the Admiral pointed up at the sky with a big pair of compasses straddling between the stars, presumptuously and with a lack of the deference due to one's Creator; necessary, may be, for the navigation of the ship, but Diego didn't like to see it.

And when it was Diego's turn at the helm they were serious hours for him; the actual steering was easy enough, but he could not get used to the presence of the compass, it gave him an uncanny feeling to watch the living, quivering needle in its glass house making for the north all the time with its nose, whichever way the ship was heading; it was what he had to steer by, but it made him uncomfortable all the same, like some kinds of worms and creeping things with feelers. At night Diego's hair was apt to stand on end when he watched the needle nosing about in the gleam of the little lamp; whatever Powers lay behind it, *he* had no compact with them, and Diego crossed himself time and again, he steered and he followed the compass, but beyond that it would have to be on the head of the skipper.

As regards the Admiral, he was calm, with a deep and powerful breathing; at last he had put the years behind him and looked forward to what was to come. He was at sea, and sailing was his nature, he felt more and more at home with every day that passed.

Now they were going as they ought, southward; autumn was advancing, but it grew warmer every day! Ah, age had touched him, they had robbed him of his years, God forgive them, but now, every hour he grew older he was approaching—what was he approaching? Eternal summer, said the sun, the soft air, which every day was softer, the fair wind said it, the waves that leisurely advanced before him like great blue outriders, the stars said it, the stars!

With them Columbus consorted in the long refreshing nights, to them he raised his soul and accompanied them on their sure but inscrutable paths. Abaft the ship's course and high up in the sky stood the lodestars, the two stars in the Little Bear which the seaman steers by, near the North Star, round which in the course of a night they make a half compass, the great clock of heaven whose tilting always tells the seaman what time it is at night. Beneath it the Great Bear, the mighty constellation which takes up more space in the heavens than any other—and yet how immensely greater is the rest of the sky! Orion rises and flaunts himself in the sky like an eagle with spreading wings, the evening star shows its distant gleaming soul, advancing visibly day by day, the moon, that blind one, our friend by night, the beautiful great moon!

Never did he tire of the starry sky, of being under it and watching its movements from evening to morning; Columbus, the sleepless one, fed his soul on the march of time, saw the sun come up and break out of the sea, saw it take its sovereign course over the heavens, till it sank again red and mighty in the sea on the other side, and it was as though time and space left their mark on his inmost sense, he *felt* how long they had sailed and what was his position; an extraordinary cosmic second sight took possession of him, in the calm nights when he was alone on the poop and the stars swung above him it was as though he could hear the music of the seven spheres of heaven, one within the other, shrill but immensely distant; for brief ecstatic instants he caught the feeling of what the reason knows but cannot turn into an image: the heavens and their revolutions with all the heavenly bodies that lie in the same sphere. On rare occasions he thought he heard a crinkling sound, muffled by thousands of miles, and nodded: the axles of the spheres creaking against one another, and the night seemed to him so vast, how mighty was the mill of heaven! Almighty!

And then when he turned his eyes from the shining nails of the vault of heaven the ocean lay beneath him in a ring, colossal, and yet he knew how small a patch it was that could be seen at any time; the ocean stretched to infinity, it made a man dizzy—so enormous, so incomprehensibly wide was the earth!

There was one thing that could be felt. In this very thing Columbus's profoundest experience was wrapped up, an observation summed up through all his life at sea, in itself inconceivable and yet based on direct perception, or a kind of feeling: the earth was round! This had already been declared in ancient writings, though not in the Bible, but a man must have seen it himself, so to speak, to be clear about it. And it was the altitude of the stars, their angle with the horizon, that told it. When one had familiarized one's self with the position of the stars in the sky and had sailed sufficiently far north and south, between Iceland and Guinea, as Columbus had, and when one kept an estimate of distances the whole time, the log, which Columbus carried in his head more than any man had ever done, then one could perceive that the earth was round, nay, in a certain inexpressible sense one could feel how *big* it was.

It was this observation and his inner conviction that had given Columbus his idea of a circumnavigation. For if the earth was round up and down, from north to south, it must also be so from east to west, around the Equator; and if one sailed due west for sufficiently long one must end by going right round the earth. Nobody would believe it; now it should be proved!

Sailing from Spain as far south as the Canary Isles the difference in altitude was already conspicuous to one who was practised in watching it; indeed, to a certain extent the difference could be felt every day; one was conscious of sailing on an immensely extended spherical surface, from north to south, and not for a moment did one lose the sense of how far west one had come.

Now, when he was as far south as he thought of going, the course would be set due west, and then they would see!

In the clear starry nights when Columbus was alone with the universe he could *see* that he was right. How else were the sun and moon and all the fixed stars and planets, the spheres in short, able to swing about the earth, unless it was round and suspended freely in space?

II

ON THE OCEAN

From August 9 to September 6, almost a month, they were delayed at the Canary Isles: it was the *Pinta* that had lost her rudder, a sneakish trick of the two men who owned the ship and were taking part in the voyage but wanted to be left behind—treachery and delays to the last, a yet deeper insight into human nature; but the damage was repaired, and with the loss of a month the voyage was resumed, now due west into the Ocean, towards open sea where nobody had ever sailed before.

Tenerife was in eruption that year, and when Columbus sailed past it at nighttime the crew of the *Santa Maria* had a vision that took the marrow out of their bones, the whole sky full of blood-red fire, the immense cone in the midst of the sea, illumined from top to bottom by its own flame, smoke and red-hot stones shooting up from the summit which seemed split with veins of fire, lava streams reaching far down the mountain's sides. The deck of the ship was as light as by day, for miles on all sides the night was banished, but stood like a jet-black wall around the horizon. Lightnings came and went amid the smoke, and deep boomings arose as though from below the bottom of the sea. It was a foretaste of the end of the world that the sailors were given; and if the impression afterwards gave place to others it had nevertheless sunk in and did not make them any bolder for the voyage.

Nor had their stay in the Canary Isles been of a kind to harden them; a good deal of softness and self-will that had been fostered ashore on the enchanting islands had to be driven out again by the rope's end before they had a taste for plain seaman's work. Diego, who had come in contact with creatures of a strange native charm, some of the few Guanches left unmixed in the islands, had added a fresh influence to the many and various ones that had already contributed to form his character; he was out of humour the first few days on board, with something foreign about him, and seemed to be nursing memories that were only half his own, the other half distant; and Diego shaded his eyes with his hand and gazed back at the cone of Tenerife till it floated away in its own veil, like a woman shrouding her face in her hair; he was melancholy, little inclined for talk all day.

But next morning when Tenerife was no longer in sight he surprised his mates by breaking out into new songs, with wild melodies of their own and a text of which he only knew fragments, in a language of which he only understood a few words, the sweetest ones; they often came back to him on the voyage like an echo which made Diego sad; and when the *Niña* aired her white hangings alongside, the only reminder of anything sisterly left on the wide ocean, Diego shook his head bent down between his knees as he sat on deck, he was the poorest man that sailed the sea.

On September 8 they got a stiff north-easterly breeze, just what was wanted, and it held, it had come in earnest. One morning they looked around and could no longer spy a vestige of land, the desolate ring of Ocean all the way round, and they looked at each other: was that the idea? Their hearts sank. Yes, that was the idea; up on the poop walked the Admiral with a face there was no mistaking; he had them in his hand, and he would use them, to the end. They were dazed, their eyes sought help from the other ships which were in sight, now near at hand, now farther off, sailing the same course, due west; and from them no doubt eyes were turned to the *Santa Maria*. There were these three little ships sailing together and keeping each other company, and beyond them nothing but the wide and terrible Ocean. . . .

That first forenoon tears were shed in secret, men came upon each other with red eyes everywhere; deep down in the hold where he had been sent to fetch something a man met a friend in the dark who turned his face away; up aloft where a sail had to be cleared he found a comrade who had climbed up into solitude to weep; the cook in his galley had red eyes. But they could see by the man of iron up aft that there was no turning back. He paced up and down, like a lion, with his eyes on the west, those fathomless eyes, blue as the sea—was he then the sea itself? He was calm, as if he knew the way, as if he was only going home, with his cargo of innocents that he had lured on board—was it Death himself they had shipped with?

The *Santa Maria* pitched in the long, deep Atlantic seas with her curving hull, high fore and aft, like a cradle rocking in the sea, her timbers groaned, her yards and tackle swung, her bows stamped up a collar of green translucent water and foam; she was no good sailer, but now she had a fair wind, and she made headway.

The clumsy caravel—which is a word derived from crab—built half as a fortress, combined in herself the same elements that were found aboard of her. At core she was a viking ship, with a mainmast and a big squaresail, of a hundred tons burthen, like a middle-sized schooner of our days, overcrowded with her crew of fifty-two. In her build she must have been derived from the fleets of the Normans, who made their way into the Mediterranean and left their traces on its shipping, Genoa, Venice—the gondola!—Spain too, where they penetrated up the rivers, the Guadalquivir; but in the Mediterranean they had added to her the lateen sail aft on a mast of its own, and forward she had got another extra mast with a smaller squaresail, and before that on the bowsprit she carried a still smaller squaresail to steady her; above the main course a topsail was set; she was a ship on the way from one type to another. The castles fore and aft were excrescences based on experience of land warfare, floating towers. The oars of the Norman ship were gone; in place of them she had artillery, little cast cannons, falconets and lombards, she could make a noise and do mischief at long range. Gothic was the style of the rich carvings all over the woodwork. In board she carried the Middle Ages and the Mediterranean, a leader of Northern ancestry, seer, wanderer and ferryman, and a ship's company with the multifarious heritage and the dark fiery blood which the Mediterranean had mingled together from all its shores and all its ages.

And as the caravel was now rocking in the sea, with a rolling, laborious gallop in which she seemed to be pulling herself in, but keeping steadily on, all day long, towards the sunset—a gigantic red sun like a one-eyed cyclops burying himself alone in the lonely ocean and leaving a bloody sky and clotted seas behind—so she rocked on through the brief evening, into the night, heeling over a little with the wind on her quarter; she was a caravel with a mission, she would sail day and night until she reached what she would reach!

Behind her lay the Europe she had left, an ancient world of conflict, countries and peoples mutually involved in relations of conquest and dependence, the Europe of popes, emperors and kings, of proud chivalry and of peasants buried in hovels and obscurity; the all-powerful bishops, the hordes of monks, the burnings of heretics, the commonalty bound hand and foot by the powers above them; the ascending ladder of the feudal nobility; the princes with their arbitrary interchange of kingdoms, their policy of marriages and wars of succession; Europe like a string of great estates, which in fact were soon to be married into one hand, nearly all of them!

But down on the ground it was getting warm, like a fermenting hotbed. A certain Doctor Faust was perambulating Europe with his arts, Satan was abroad! A nine-year-old boy was in Mansfeld, having Christian doctrine instilled into him and getting birched, the same year that Columbus sailed from Palos—Martin Luther. Copernicus was nineteen and carried within him the germ of revolutions. The peasants of Europe were meeting in their miserable alehouses and clamouring like dogs; nobody noticed them, and yet more than one great lord, riding by with hawk on hand, would be cudgelled to death in his armour by the swarming mob.

The Europe of that day towered up as though built for eternity, its central pillar was carried down through the earth to the basic rock; but it was after all the shell of an old tortoise they had built upon, and one fine day it moved in its thousand years' sleep and pushed its lizard's head out of the slime. . . .

The *Santa Maria* then had chosen a good time for sailing; Europe's heaven had lasted long enough, it was time to knock a hole in it.

Whatever might be happening at home, *they* were shut out from it, who now felt imprisoned, ringed about by the sea; perhaps they would never see the Old World again. And no word would ever be brought home of what had become of them, they would not even win the fame of the ill-fated like other poor brave men who perish and have a tomb and a great name; they would simply disappear, and soon even their disappearance would be forgotten.

So hard he was, the man aft! They thought they could understand a good deal, those who were with him, but this they could not understand, that he could expose himself to a trackless, inglorious death, for the sake of an exploit the issue of which no man could tell—no, that they could not understand.

A mournful feeling prevailed on board on the second and third days; in the morning they came on deck and saw the ocean's desolate ring, no land either ahead or astern, the loathsome waves, the sun travelling naked and pitiless in the sky, casting a glaring light on their misery, sea and sea and the bare sky right in their faces!

Cheerlessly the sun went down, a faded sea on every side, then darkness; with loud creaking the *Santa Maria* laboured in the waves, plunging and plunging on her way into the uncertain gloom, towards the west.

That night Diego rolled himself up in a corner on deck, too hot to sleep down below. How hot it was getting! What would be the end of it? He shut his eyes tight, clenched his teeth upon his seething inside—impossible to sleep, impossible to lie awake. But a little while after he did fall asleep and twitched his limbs as he slept, with muffled groans from his troubled, racking dreams.

High on the poop a dark waking figure could be seen, the Admiral, with his everlasting rods and circles in his hand, sighting up at the moon, always busy with some celestial tricks—did he never sleep? Night and day he was to be seen on the poop—did he need no sleep at all? He couldn't even be human.

Oh yes, the Admiral slept, a nap now and then, when it could not be avoided, but he never went regularly to bed. He could not do that, for he had the log in his head and dared not lose his estimate of the distance sailed. When he slept it was for a short spell, just such and such a time; he had himself called when the fixed time was up and was thus able to retain his sense of the passing of the hours in conjunction with the headway they were making. And as an old sailor he knew no difference between night and day.

There was another figure moving on the forecastle, the look-out on watch; to-night it was young Pedro Gutierrez; he walked up and down and seemed much engrossed by the moon; he could be heard singing pious songs—evidently a queer fellow.

Young Pedro had joined as a volunteer; he was the son of decent people, but had no means and lent an ear to the siren voices which promised rapid fortunes at sea. On board he had made himself remarked by his innocence and nice behaviour; he would have been an easy butt, if he had not also proved himself a swordsman not to be meddled with. He was very taciturn, his thoughts were fixed on other things than those of the rest, and finally he was allowed to go about unnoticed.

To-night he was singing, standing still by the rail and looking out over the sea where the moon was about to set, thoughtful, with slender, soft features, manly enough but so handsome that it seemed a lovely young girl was buried in them, his mother, who was now so far away. He raised his eyes in the starlight, sighed and sang:

Now comes the sea's fell darkness,
The moon sinks fast and hides;
And coldly blows the porpoise
Against the ship's thin sides.
With oily cry a seagull
Bodes ill for us to-night.
But I must keep my watch here,
Until the sun brings light.

The Virgin's starry garment
Is spread across the sky.
We men can be hopeful
And pray to those on high.
We cannot, if we wished it,
Foresee what still shall be—
O vouch, our Lord's sweet Mother,
That land again we see!

With many a tear at parting,
But with courageous mind,
We waved a tender farewell
To those we left behind.
When shall I see my father?
Where is my sweetheart gone?
The ocean's ways affright me.
Am I to die so soon?

Within my father's garden
There grows an apple tree,
A joyful gift from Heaven,
Where many a bird can be.
In springtime when the bee hums
It stands with blossom gay;
And when the birds are silent
It flings its fruit away.

Behind the ancient hedgerow
We used to hide, we two;
'Twas there, my only loved one,
You promised to be true.
Ah, shall I ever see it,
That dear old apple tree?

Will you be there, my darling,
To share its shade with me?

No green leaves here can greet us,
The sea's as salt as tears.
A creature 'midst the billows
Lives lonely with his fears.
Who knows where ocean ceases?
Where shall our voyage end?
In thy hands are we, Mother.
A happy landfall send!

The distant lands of promise,
Where all is made of gold,
They give us dreams of riches,
Until we grow too old.
But what a seaman suffers
I'll tell from what I know—
There's many a time I'm longing
To a dry grave to go.

Beyond the seas and rivers
Lies Paradise, they say—
O merciful God's Mother,
Preserve our souls this day!
To thee in Heaven's glory
We raise our sinful hand—
Give us a peaceful mid-watch,
And bring us back to land!

It was thirty-five days before they sighted land, a long time for men with such crazy nerves as most of the ship's company; to the inflexible leader himself the longest time he had known. As was to be expected, he had great difficulties with his crew.

The deep despondency of the first few days after they had lost sight of land soon gave way to insubordination; there were scowling looks, some trial of strength was felt to be coming, it would have to be seen whether it was safe to treat Spaniards in this fashion; eyes that till now had kept to the deck or never gone higher than the ladder were now fixed with a sinister challenge upon the Admiral. It came to a kind of collision, not open warfare, only a trial, and it fell out in this way.

Among themselves the crew talked of nothing but turning back; they said not a word to the Admiral, but they began to steer badly. It happened more and more frequently that the helmsman was awkward enough to let her come up into the wind, with a northerly course; they were trying it on, those that took the helm, gave the Admiral a stiff look and fell off their course, like naughty children seeing how far they could go. They were corrected and the course was resumed; the Admiral seemed to have no suspicion of what they were up to, or pretended with angelic patience not to see it.

But one morning the game was up on both sides. Contrary to his custom, the Admiral had left the quarter-deck for a short time, and when he came up again, and looked round, the course had been laid as near north as the ship would lie. . . . A couple of seconds later he was at the helm himself, laid his fists over the helmsman's and turned the ship back into a westerly course, turned the tiller with the man and all, and he was no wisp of straw either, a very stalwart man that same helmsman, but his legs trailed under him like a doll's, the Admiral just took a sweep with him and the tiller and the ship herself; she lay right over with the hard helm, heeled around into her new course, and the horizon danced a quarter of the way round. It was just as if the Admiral had lifted the whole vessel and put her down again!

And he was not out of breath after it, hadn't changed colour, was scarcely angry; he only smiled with amusement and a trifle ominously at Sancho Ruiz, the chief mate, who had allowed the thing to happen.

It did not happen again. The helmsman looked at his hands, which were all crumpled, and afterwards soaked them in a bucket of water—they had been badly crushed. The rest of the crew went about their work with pale lips. Had any one imagined that he was so strong! That he was as big as an ox could be seen, but that he was so quick! He was *invisible* for the second it took him to dash to the helm, he leapt like a heavy cat, and those big freckled spades of hands, with their red bristles, why they were blacksmith's tongs and not human hands at all. Unfair!

After that there was nothing wrong with the steering. The dark smouldering eyes the Admiral found turned upon him wherever he went had now a look of suffering, but the spite in them was concealed for the time being. The temper of the ship was dull for a few days, while the open sea still stretched as open before them, and the feeling of how far they were from land grew more and more dismal. And now the sea began to change its character; they still had the finest weather, but somehow the sea was more hollow, it ran in an ugly swell which lifted the *Santa Maria* as high as a house up and down besides making her roll and pitch; it took away the breath of many of them and was an unmistakable warning that they were beginning to sail out of the world and were approaching zones where there was perhaps no world at all. What made the ocean rock in such an abysmal way?

A mast which they saw one day drifting in the sea, a big piece of mast from a ship that must have been bigger than the *Santa Maria,* seemed to answer their anxious question. The ship had been wrecked somewhere in these waters, and if such a big ship could not live, what would become of smaller ones? The Admiral, whom they approached on this serious subject, took a different, cynical view and made light of the whole matter: that a ship had gone down here seemed to him a proof that the sea was just like any other sea—such things happened. Beyond the world there were no ships at all, they might be sure. For that matter nobody could tell how far or from what direction the mast had drifted. With this consolation the crew went to their quarters and wept. The sad piece of wreckage had made them so sorrowful, it had such a mournful look.

It rolled so forsakenly in the sea with its splintered top, green with slime, waterlogged and lying under the surface, always awash, and when the wave sank from it the end of the mast hung with dripping seaweed and studded with barnacles on its under side; and once it had been shaped by human hands, a tree once in the forest, and now the corpse of a mast in the sea's desolate wet churchyard, a thing rocking in the waves, floating with the current, abandoned to a drift unknown, lonely, lonely, travelling out of one horizon into another, a thing without a face and yet like a living creature, it broke one's heart to see it, as the waves carried it away and dashed over it in their sport; as long as it was in sight they gazed after it, and when it could no more be seen they turned away with tearful eyes.

The Admiral observed it too, long and carefully; the rate at which they left it astern was to him a welcome clue for the day's log and for estimating their leeway.

The thirteenth of September was an unlucky day. Not immediately so far as the crew was concerned, they only heard of it afterwards, but that day their fate hung in the balance, as also did several of the heavenly bodies, apparently, racing the compass-needle! Well, a layman forms his own interpretation of matters he is not conversant with but which reach him by way of rumour; perhaps indeed he sees into the heart of things in his own way, even if he is not an astronomer. It was reported that the compass had been deceptive that day, so grossly deceptive that even the man at the helm had noticed it, pointing a good way to one side of north, where it should have been. A serious business, which of course the Admiral tried to hush up, until the sailing master and the mate discovered it for themselves and called the Admiral's attention to it a day or two later. With them, of course, the Admiral could make no secret of what had happened, the magnetic needle *had* deviated considerably from north to west; but was it necessarily the compass that was wrong, might it not be the North Star that had fallen a few degrees out of its orbit?

And it actually appeared that he had succeeded in convincing the other navigators of this, for nothing more came of the affair—they went on sailing as before. Properly speaking, wasn't it a much worse thing that the North Star was toppling? An omen, one would imagine, a clear hint from above. How was it with this foreigner's Christianity if he disregarded such a warning?

More probably, though, it was the compass that pointed wrongly, and that was in reality a terrible thing; it could mean nothing else but that they were nearing the magnet mountain, which, of course, was situated somewhere out here at the world's end; and if once you came within range of its attraction you were lost, the nails and everything of iron would fly out of the ship, going clean through the woodwork, timbers and planks would fall asunder, the ship would part and become a mass of wreckage in the water all in an instant! They had hopes the Admiral would be in full armour when it happened—to see him fly through the air, imagine him smacking against the magnet mountain and sticking to it, rotting against its wall head downwards! Joking apart, was it *justifiable* to keep the course they were on when the magnetic needle had pointed its silent warning? If so, what did they have this invention of the devil for?

The crew were choking with tears and grimaces. But the Admiral continued to pace the poop, calm as ever. Was he though? To tell the truth, this phenomenon of the variation of the compass, now observed for the first time, disturbed him not a little; in reality, he could imagine no explanation—except perhaps just the same as the crew's, that they were approaching some stronger magnetic force, since the needle turned. However, they were out to venture something after all. So long as the nails stayed in the ship they would go on sailing.

But two days after the unlucky Thirteenth something happened which for a while converted the *Santa Maria* into a madhouse, although in itself it was a far less ominous thing than the affair of the compass. A terrible great meteor fell from heaven—in broad daylight, so to speak, towards evening when it was still light. It came straight down from heaven, everybody saw it, like a mighty blazing tail of fire lashing down from on high and disappearing in the sea—with a boiling sound which many thought they had heard, a whistling up in space. The whole ship was one shriek after the fiery portent had gone out. Half the crew lay howling on deck with their hands over their eyes, the rest ran about wailing and wringing their hands; those who kept their senses best fell on their knees and loudly invoked the Virgin Mary, repeating Ave after Ave. One hid himself under the water-butt, another bored his head into a coiled hawser like a worm, wriggling his body and legs outside; even the officers, Juan de la Cosa, Sancho Ruiz, Alonzo de Moguer, the ship's doctor, who ought to have known better, lost their presence of mind and raised an alarm. God's blood! they were all done for. . . .

And then nothing more happened. The mortal terror passed off; but this time the Admiral came right down from his lofty castle and mixed among the crew to calm them and explain the thing. How could they be so terrified of a big shooting star?

Shooting star! Scandalized exclamations, genuine indignation, hands left their faces and weeping eyes were riveted on the Admiral, chests heaving like bellows. What is the blasphemer saying? A portent, a holy portent, that was what it was.

Well, well, a portent if you like—the Admiral was conciliatory and ignored the smack of mutiny in their words—but it had shown itself beneficent, hadn't it? It didn't set fire to the ship but fell quite a long way off. For his part he had seen such falls of fire from heaven before. Perhaps it hurt their feelings to call them shooting stars, but still they were certainly phenomena which were to be explained in the same way, stars or other celestial lights which had come loose from the vault above and dropped down—a very common thing. Naturally there was a meaning in it, as in everything that came from heaven, but to call it a portent. . . .

It *was* a portent! the seamen sobbed. The softer among them obstinately persisted in their grief, weeping and drying their eyes, sniffling inconsolably; but others went about in little knots with clenched teeth, looked at each other, and their eyes grew savage. It was pretty strong what that Italian had the face to offer them! To explain away God's obvious warning written in letters of fire! Had it happened astern of the ship as a warning against turning back? No, ahead, due west—could there be any doubt? Stars, celestial light—when the fire that fell was bigger than sun, moon and all the stars together! A natural explanation indeed! It was unwholesome to have so many heretics aboard of a ship—that and all the rest!

Scornful and insolent snorts were heard blended with the Admiral's kindly, restraining and reassuring voice. And the discussion was long. Darkness fell, and still they were disputing about the alarming occurrence; several were quite unnerved and spoke in the dying, tearful voice of men stunned by a disaster, while in others hate blazed up again and again. But at last their feelings calmed down. The Admiral talked and talked, and in the end the mere sound of his monotonous voice had a soothing effect.

And meanwhile they were sailing on since nobody had thought of actually stopping the ship. The wind was fair they were long past the place where the meteor had fallen. Mentally the Admiral calculated what distance they had covered, making up his log while the talk was going on. And that was until everybody turned in for the night, weary and dull with sorrow, many of them quite sick with emotion; here and there long-drawn sighs and chest-shaking sobs could still be heard from dark corners.

The Admiral went quietly back to his post, took observations and wrote for the rest of the night by the light of a little horn lantern. There was a special piece of work which he preferred to do at night the log-book, which with provident foresight and knowledge of human nature he kept in two versions: one, the correct one for his own use, and one to be shown to his officers, who were then free to pass on the information; in this the distance sailed were shortened every day by as many miles as he dared; it was no use scaring the crew by telling them they were farther out in the ocean than was strictly necessary.

In the course of the night there was a milder panic, which however soon subsided: a man screamed out in terror and woke the others; he had happened to look over the side and had seen that they were sailing through nothing but fire, flame and gleaming waves all round the ship. Everybody flocked to the ship's side; wail and lamentations, they were sailing in sheer fire! The Admiral was down among them at once. Hadn't they ever seen phosphorescence before? Weren't they sailors some of them at any rate? In the Mediterranean it was sometimes just as bright. Oh well, they were sleepy and sore and al lowed themselves to be talked round. Some of them *had* seen it before and had only shouted because the others did. But others nodded and nodded, convinced in dead earnest. Of course, it was the fire that had fallen from heaven in the evening and they were sailing straight into it! Then the Admiral could not help laughing. How was it then that it hadn't set fire to the ship long ago? And he had a bucket of water drawn up and asked any one who liked to put his hand in it—it was quite cold. . . .

Well—cold; lukewarm, they would call it. And what was it then that shone down below in the water? That the Admiral could easily explain: it was simply the sunlight which the water had absorbed by day and gave off again at night. This explanation was received with hiccups—they knew what they knew. A reflection from *down below,* Purgatory with the hatches off, may be . . . ! Growling and bitterness; some were not ashamed to turn their backs on the Admiral. Soon after the ship was asleep again.

But from now on the Admiral was more and more often on the main deck. He no longer considered his dignity so strictly, and it was remarkable how this man, hitherto so taciturn, developed eloquence; he would often discuss things with the simplest of the hands for hours at a time, things which he might easily have said were no concern of theirs. It did no harm to the distance which ought to be kept between commander and crew. In one respect he possessed a quality which nothing he said or did could add to or take away from—his size.

Its effect was sure, even if nobody, not even himself, was quite aware of it. But not only did he keep his direct power over the men's minds, he even began to make friends among them. Many of them had not really paid much attention to the Admiral before now, and discovered that this giant, who bore the stamp of courage and indomitable resolution, who at the same time was capable, as he had shown, of unexampled violence, that this man was good-natured at heart. The big head with its reddish-grey mane, and the beard, which was now allowed to grow and was also mottled red and white, would sometimes beam with human feeling, a warmth which reached him from creation in spite of all, and which he gave back again. He had a pleasant smile, which showed two great rows of worn teeth; the blue eyes, usually so distant, might turn with a look of their own upon any one he was talking to, he had quick intelligence and sympathy for everybody. They were curious eyes, quite light and small with white surroundings and pink at the corners, something like what one sees in pigs, rather sore, for he scarcely slept at all. His voice was singular, rather small and weak for such an unusually big man, cautious, penetrated with loneliness and kindness towards men, even those who opposed him.

But it was felt that, whether silent or eloquent, he never disclosed his inmost thought, and to that no one ever succeeded in penetrating.

There was endless talking in the days that followed, on all kinds of subjects. The Admiral was almost always down on deck among the crew, all the time he could spare from his observations.

The *Santa Maria* seemed like a sort of floating school, with grown-up boys and a schoolmaster who towered above them all and was regarded with very diverse feelings, who gave lessons all day long, received complaints and gave instruction, over and over again—a providence that was never tired of leading its souls, not the way they would go but the way they should.

III

IN THE TRADE WIND

The Sargasso Sea, hundreds of leagues from land; three little ships lost on the boundless ocean, and their crews in despair.

The worst of their fright over this threatening new phenomenon, the masses of seaweed floating mile after mile in the ocean, had subsided; but it had been a hard trial. The first floating island of weed was taken for firm ground, land; it looked like a very low stretch of meadow lying flush with the water, and for a moment the idea that it might be land raised a flicker of hope, which was only to give way to deep disappointment and uneasiness—if it was not land, what could it be?

Soon the islands became so numerous that they formed a continuous carpet of weed over the whole surface of the sea as far as the eye could reach, and the Admiral kept straight ahead, while the crew cried out, in God's holy name, and implored the helmsman to fall off. Too late, they were already in the midst of the green, and look! she could sail through it without losing so very much of her way—for the present. But supposing the masses of weed got denser and they ended by sticking fast in them? That it was a sort of seaweed the Admiral convinced them all by having some of it fished up; but not any known kind of weed, and how could it grow here, how did it come here, many many leagues from land?

They need not be too sure that they were so very far from land, suggested the Admiral, sanguine of course as usual, and putting on a bold face just when the others looked blackest. But where could this land be? At any rate it was not to be seen for miles ahead or on either side, only a boundless pale-green expanse of tufted water with a false promise of meadows—so deceptive indeed that many believed in them. Might it not be supposed that sunken countries or submarine realms lay underneath here, from which all this grass had come loose and floated up? In that case it was dangerous; there must be shoals, at any moment they might run aground, and stranding so far from any coast would mean death. The Admiral's only reply to these complaints was to have soundings taken, and the lead ran out for hundreds of fathoms, all the line they had, and no bottom! If the pastures they were talking about lay below, then he must say they were a long way down; and the Admiral was cruel enough to add that *now* nobody would be likely to expect a cow to stick its head out of the sea from the meadows below or to see a church spire jutting out. Loud cries of pain drowned his words; the men were thrown from fright into terror. So deep! Why, there was no bottom at all here! So they *were* outside the world now and over the inconceivable abyss of Ocean. They had to prop each other up at the thought, and their eyes nearly dropped out of their heads. To be wrecked here, to sink and sink and sink. . . . But the Admiral asked them rather dryly if it wouldn't be all the same to them how much water they drowned in, a fathom or a mile, if it had to be: a heartless thing to say, and incautious. They roared—one man threw his cap at him. The Admiral turned his back on them, but came again and pointed with a great sweep of the arm out over the sea of weed that shone like gold in the dazzling rays of the sun: if they believed that all this splendour came from impossible submarine islands, then it was *his* belief that it was a presage of real islands, perhaps not so very far off, where the golden fields extended just as far as the seaweed here—floors of gold far and wide! And then they made a fuss like a pack of women over the trouble and risk of getting there—as if the islands wouldn't have been discovered and occupied long ago if there had been no danger in it!

Silence, not a sound; some of them were put to shame, others led into a new train of thought—it sounded wonderful, that about the gold. And the end of it was that they went on sailing; while bandying words they easily did a half-day's run. But the men stuck to their opinion. They passed through the weed right enough, but all the same it was an ominous sign that the sea was getting so thick. What if it thickened still more? They might sail in gruel, but in porridge any man would stick fast. And the Admiral's words had left a sting behind them: if he had more learning, it didn't give him the right to make fun of poor Christian men.

If, however, there were lamentations over the danger of getting stuck in the sea of weed, it was not long before the fact of their slipping so easily through it gave uneasiness. What would be the end of it? This everlasting breeze from the north-east! Why, it held for weeks, they never touched the sails, which stood day and night on the starboard tack, easy sailing, but what about it when they had to go the other way? How would they come home again? What kind of a wind was it anyhow? It had never been reported anywhere else that the wind held so long from one quarter; it could scarcely be interpreted otherwise than that there was a sucking from the opposite quarter, the one they were making for, like the wind that goes over a waterfall; it was from the *Abyss* the sucking came, they were in it now, and it was a desperate thing, it was tempting God and throwing away one's fair wind, which was of the kind the Evil One sends . . . etc., etc.

The Admiral shrugged his shoulders. Truth to tell, he did not understand himself why the wind held so long; it was a new thing in his experience, and every day he scanned the clouds and all other indications a seaman stores in his head and recognizes on later occasions; but these waters were strange to him, and nobody as yet could know how it was with this wind. There was every reason to be grateful for it though, if the crew had not been growing more anxious every day and scarcely to be managed in the long run.

Then it happened one day, the 23rd of September, that the wind changed, they had a head-sea, and the crew could no longer maintain that there were no other winds in these seas but from the north-east; Columbus was saved for another space, and he it was who clasped his hands that evening in deepest gratitude to the All-bountiful, in spite of the fact that they had made no headway that day.

In his private meditations, divided between the Bible and the log-book, he could not help thinking that evening of Moses, who led his refractory people through so many real dangers, but whose most difficult task was to preserve them from their own imagination and instinct of self-destruction.

But all the complaints returned with renewed force when the wind changed again; once more every one could clearly see that all the waves were hurrying to the west, the whole sea was flowing that way, straight into the Abyss!

They now passed out of the Sargasso Sea, out into clear deep waves again, and if lately they had eyed the hated weed with furtive looks of woe, they now cast back inconsolable glances after it. For all the signs of land the Admiral had fabricated with his ready tongue while it was there, were vanished now. That seaweed showed the proximity of a coast had sounded right enough; but now? That crabs which they had found in the weed were a good sign, that birds and fish they had seen, which found food in it, also pointed to the nearness of land, of course —but now it was days ago, and still there was no land!

The men's heads were beginning to get a little addled: they saw sea monsters in every wave that curled, and huddled together in groups at night, afraid of the dark; they wept over the increasing heat, which left no doubt that they were approaching the scorching regions in the immediate neighbourhood of the sun, where nothing can live, except salamanders; they would not escape with being turned as dark as the blackamoors in Africa, they would be completely charred, scorched up like flies, the whole ship would blaze up—in the name of the most merciful God, man, turn about before it is too late!

Other voices made themselves heard, and those of the soberest men on board, the officers themselves. The bottom could be seen of the ship's provisions, in a literal sense; in several places they had gone down through the cargo to the bottom of the ship; if they were to count on food for the same number of days back as they had sailed out, they would have to turn pretty soon. To this Columbus said nothing. In his own mind he looked forward to the hour when they no longer *could* turn back, when their food was exhausted to that extent; then there would be no other way than straight ahead, but he didn't say this.

The other complaints he took up, rather glad to be able to keep them alive, so that they might overshadow thoughts of the provisions; he went through them again with the crew, as often and as long as they liked, talking and talking, hollow-eyed, stiff with fatigue but indefatigable. It ended in a sort of permanent ship's parliament on board, where all, even the ordinary seamen, had a voice, and where the tone grew sharper and sharper. During these discussions all the theoretical side of the voyage was probed deeper and deeper, a kind of cross-examination which the Admiral accepted in good part, and which he spun out with a certain warmth, keeping an inner eye on the log the whole time.

All that Columbus had adduced again and again for fourteen years, before a commission of scholars in Portugal, and before a learned commission at Salamanca, had come up, and he had to listen to the same arguments against him and refute them again as well as he could. Now how did he think he would reach the Indies by this crazy route which took him farther and farther away from them every day he sailed?

To put it briefly, if the earth was round . . .

Yes, but the earth wasn't round! Everybody knew that, everybody could see it, and it was heresy to assert the contrary, high treason against the Church and against God. Juan de la Cosa, who was the owner of the vessel and accompanied the exposition in that capacity, here acted as spokesman and displayed no mean biblical knowledge. Neither the Pentateuch nor the Prophets nor the Apostles said anything about the earth being a globe; besides, ordinary common sense told you it was an error; take the Deluge, for instance, how would it have been possible if the earth was not flat? all the water would have run off if it had been curved . . .

Storms of applause from the whole crew for Juan de la Cosa, who modestly withdrew into the crowd, and a maliciou chorus of yelping at Columbus.

But now the Admiral took to both Latin and Greek against Juan de la Cosa, quoted utterances of St. Augustine and compared them with things Aristotle had said, Strabo, Seneca, Pythagoras, Erastos-thenes . . .

Aristotle . . . Juan de la Cosa nodded manfully, he had heard the name before and knew that it carried weight, but he was not sure of his ground and the Admiral was given a chance of quoting at length all the reasons that had induced the ancients to assume the spherical form of the earth, the shadow it cast on the moon in an eclipse, the weightiest of proofs, which passed over the heads of the crew like the wildest moonshine. Juan de la Cosa, however, had understood it and came forward with an objection:

How was it possible that the earth cast a shadow on the moon, *even* if it was round? In that case the sun would have to pass right round the earth, *under* it so to speak . . .

COLUMBUS: That is just what it does.

JUAN DE LA COSA: Oh, I see. But then the earth must rest upon something, whether it is flat or round, a foundation; how can a heavenly body pass under that?

COLUMBUS: The earth has no foundation; it is a globe hanging freely in space.

Sensation. Suppressed passion here and there. All eyes hung upon Juan de la Cosa, who was quite distressed and looked at the Admiral with genuine sorrow, as he asked in a faltering voice how . . . how . . . the earth, weighing many hundred thousand quintals . . . hang freely in space, how could that be?

What is impossible to Almighty God? answered the Admiral with force. He who has set the spheres in motion and keeps them going, with sun, moon and stars to give light and measure the day, should He not be able to keep the earth suspended in its place in space? *He* alone knows how!

Juan de la Cosa bowed his head and his forefinger went up to his breast, the sign of the cross made itself at the mention of the holy name of God. The crew followed his example, they felt as if they were in church, and the threatening conflict of opinion was resolved in a moment of solemn awe.

But the dispute blazed up again, and Juan de la Cosa obstinately insisted, on behalf of all, that *even* if the earth was round, which it was *not;* nay, even if hung freely in space, by the power of God, whose name be praised, then it was nevertheless an impossible thing they were trying to do. A globe *might* be so big that to us men it would appear to be flat in that part where one was situated, granted, and that must necessarily be the upper part; but if one left it, one would have to proceed along a slope which would get steeper and steeper, vertical at last, and then turn inward on the under side, always supposing that the spherical theory held, which, of course, was sheer nonsense, for how could water hang on a globe all the way round?

Applause. *Bravo! bravo!* they cried to Juan de la Cosa; and he was really brave, he looked the Admiral straight in the face as, with a bow to his superior, he resumed his place in the crowd.

The last question the Admiral left alone and seized on the first, pounced on it like a hawk:

We are sailing *downward* at this moment!

Pause, until his meaning dawned on them, then violent excitement; several men shrieked aloud and ran to the bulwarks to look, some instinctively laid hand on hilt. Juan de la Cosa turned pale, but pulled himself together and asked:

And how did the Admiral think of sailing upward again?

Everybody grasped at once the bearing of Juan de la Cosa's words, pictured the immense curve down which they were engaged in sailing, saw the impossibility of ever coming up it again and stood as though turned to stone . . .

In the midst of this consternation the Admiral was heard to laugh, a perfectly careless laugh at such a serious moment; he was making fun of them, the hell-hound, the cup was full, they wouldn't listen to him any more . . .

We are sailing *upward* also at this moment, said the Admiral mildly to Juan de la Cosa, and explained his meaning more precisely; if the earth was really round there could be neither up nor down at any given point, except in the direction that passed through the centre of the earth and the zenith . . . But Juan de la Cosa shook his head, gave the Admiral an honest look and shook his head, grieved for him, for his ship and for them all.

The Admiral then changed his tone, laughed with his cavernous eyes, and made as though he accepted the others' view, since they were in the majority; suppose they were right and the earth was flat. But in that case it could not be surrounded by an abyss down which the water plunged, for then the seas would long ago have run off the earth, the Deluge would have been impossible, as Juan de la Cosa very rightly pointed out. If on the other hand the Ocean lay about the earth in a ring, the common conception, it by no means precluded the idea of sailing westward to the Indies, round behind instead of straight ahead, not on a globe but on a circle, half-way round the earth's disc, if they preferred it that way . . .

Chorus of all hands that Juan de la Cosa was right, angry exclamation against the Admiral for evidently trying to obscure the heart of the matter and avoid Juan de la Cosa's direct question: how were you to sail up the curve of the earth again, when once you had had the mad idea of sailing down it? Out with it!

The Admiral: Now it was *they* who all believed that the earth was round!

Yells and bawling, cries of shame and general howls; and so the lesson came to an end.

In a succeeding one the Admiral had to produce all his reasons and proofs of the existence of land westward in the Ocean, apart from the cosmic ones; an argument they had heard before and that every man in Spain and Portugal had heard before, until they cried for help at the very sight of Columbus; an old trite lesson which he actually repeated for positively the last time, in fluent Spanish but with an accent that betrayed the Italian. In other circumstances than these, where their lives were at stake, they would have taken a wild delight in him, a glorious fool to have on board, all the more glorious as he was so big, so tall and so touched in the upper storey; had they not hated him as they did they might even have pitied him, alone against all, far out at sea, doubly alone as a stranger among strangers, this queer fish who was getting old and made himself a laughing-stock by repeating and repeating, explaining and dogmatizing about the same things over and over again—

Such as: From time immemorial ["Time immemorial . . ." Diego mimicked him, with Italian accent, discreet tone and all; aside, of course, but loud enough to amuse his neighbours]—from time immemorial there had been reports of a vanished land out in the Atlantic Ocean, Plato's Atlantis; opinions were divided as to whether it had been swallowed up by the sea or the way to it had been forgotten; the latter view was supported by rumours repeated through the ages of such lands or islands far to the west of Europe. Many were of the opinion that these were Paradise itself, the Lost Country, from which mankind had once been driven out and had never found the way back; the holy Brandanus had set out in search of them and had actually arrived at a happy isle in the Ocean, the abode of the Blest, as might be read in his legend but since then the way had been lost again, it was eight hundred years since St Brandan's voyage. The legend had afterwards been connected with the Canary Isles, wrongly of course; the islands must lie much farther out in the Ocean, at least twice as far as the Azores, which were also out of the question, and presumably more to the southward, possibly in the

ery direction in which they were now ailing.

Now it was to be remarked that in an- ther, more recent view the legend of nese mysterious islands or continents far ar to the west might be regarded as bscure but substantially correct reports f the east coast of India, which extended o far around the earth that perhaps there ad been contact with it now and then by ne other way, straight across the Atlantic. t was known that very large islands lay ff the coast of India, like Zipangu, of vhich Marco Polo had sufficiently trust- vorthy accounts; these must then be the ame as the Antilia or the Island of Bra- il which the latest geographers, in antici- ation of their discovery, had already narked on their maps, as for example the nost learned and famous Toscanelli "What kind of a fool was he?" from Di- go], and as the distance between the vest coast of Europe and the extremity of ndia was more or less known, the width f the Atlantic, that is, the distance to be educted from the whole circumference f the earth, could be approximately de- ermined; in the Admiral's opinion it was either more nor less than the distance hey had already sailed, so now the islands night appear any day [scornful snorts rom Diego and the rest of the audience; ow often they had heard this sanguine rresponsible tale!]

Well, well, if the geographical argu- nents were no more obvious to them than he cosmic, then they had the direct, tan- ible proofs, the missives to be taken up nd felt which from time to time had been rought by the Atlantic and which must oint to there being land on the other ide. In the first place there were the re- orts of many people who had *seen* the slands, on very clear days, out in the cean to the west of the Canary Isles "Long-sighted people, I must say"— Diego]; that was as it might be. Personal vidence: Columbus himself many years before in Madeira had given shelter to a ship-wrecked man who disclosed to him on his deathbed that he had been driven by a storm twenty-eight days out into the Atlantic on a voyage to England, and had there come upon islands the natives of which went about naked; afterwards he had got a fair wind back to Europe but was so worn out that he died in Madeira, the last of a crew of seventeen ["A nice story that! Why didn't he stay in the islands? Weren't they worth it?"]

There was Pedro Correa ["Oh, *that* fellow"] who was able to tell Columbus about a remarkable piece of driftwood that had come ashore at Porto Santo, a curiously dark wood and, be it noted, carved, though apparently not with iron tools. Still more remarkable: some big reeds had drifted up on the same shore, like a sort of grass on an extraordinarily large scale, almost as though they came from a country where everything was of supernatural size. ["Let's see them!"] Columbus himself might have had a chance of seeing them washed up with his own eyes; he had spent three years in Porto Santo and had himself observed many things there which indirectly pointed to lands in the west, curious cloud formations and appearances of the sky, on which, however, he would not lay stress. The reeds, on the other hand, had been sent to the King of Portugal, and there he had *seen* them. Martin Vincenti, a seaman worthy of credit ["I'd like to have him here"—Diego], had also found carved driftwood far to the west of Cape St. Vincent.

But the most remarkable of all proofs was that reported from the Azores: there after westerly winds they had found boats washed up on the beach, hollowed out of a single trunk, evidently the craft of savages; and on Flores, one of the Azores, two corpses had been washed up, possibly these same savages; they were broad in the face and did not resemble any known race of men. This one might almost call tangible proof of the existence of the Antipodes . . .

The Antipodes . . . here Juan de la Cosa coughed and ventured an observation. To a sober view the finding of the two corpses, if the account was to be relied upon, did not appear to him to convey any information about the Antipodes, since from what one knew about them they must have an entirely different appearance, scarcely confined to such a trifle as greater breadth of face. In the nature of things nothing definite could be known about the Antipodes, but it was obvious that beings who were to inhabit the under side of the earth, where the trees grew downward and the rain fell straight up in the air, must at any rate have suckers on their feet, like certain kinds of lizards, to stay where they were; in other respects also they were doubtless very different from Christians. It was not necessary indeed to go so far as the earth's poles or supports to find monsters; even in the heathen world, towards the outskirts of the earth, there was a great falling-off from the human form, if one might believe travellers and writings whose age entitled them to veneration. Not that he was himself a man of great reading, but still he had heard of the Arimaspians and of the Satyrs and knew that beyond Arabia there were people with only one leg, on which they hopped around, and that very swiftly; that there were Amazons and men without a head but with a face in their stomach was also known. From this it appeared that the farther one travelled from the Christian world, the more men ceased to be created in God's image, and there seemed to be good grounds for supposing that those who dwelt farthest down were created in the image of quite another Person, if indeed one might include the Devil in Creation; in which case they had wings and were to that extent capable of keeping on the under side of the earth. Instead of supposing Paradis to lie in that quarter it was more natur to imagine Hell there, even to an unenlightened view, since there was ever reason to presume that the earth rested o fire or had fire in its depths, as could b seen by volcanoes; the fact that it gre hotter and hotter the farther one sailed t the south was an indication in the sam direction, as all those present were in position to confirm. Thus the two corpse at the Azores, in Juan de la Cosa's humbl layman's opinion, did not tell them muc about the Antipodes. The mention c them, on the other hand, suggested quit other and horrible ideas to the mind.

An uncanny silence fell upon the cre at Juan de la Cosa's rational words. C course, the Admiral always made it appear to them that the only goal of thei desires was to sight land, but it depende a good deal on what awaited them whe they did reach land. Speechless resen ment against the Admiral was reflected i their features at the thought of what Jua de la Cosa had pictured; they could nc find words for their horror and abomination. Was it possible that he intended an had been intending all the time to sa them straight into Hell? Were they to los their salvation as well as their lives? Ha he sold their souls? Then let the Dev take him . . . The oath stuck in thei throats, for if he was the foul fiend himself . . .

Ugly pause. Even Jorge, the wholly inarticulate, who sat on deck poking bits c salt pork into his mouth with his knif and audibly pulling the blade out agai between his teeth, an old galley slave wit scars on his ankles from the shackles an bare places on his scalp like an old hors chafed by the harness—even he gave a *Ouf!* and raised his pock-marked face shaking a little with age, blinked an cocked his ear: What now, what made th men so quiet? Unwholesome air, he ha always found, when abuse died away o men's lips! Could there be worse things in store for him than he had already gone through, in his long, precarious life?

But Jorge was quickly reassured and shoved in another mouthful that had been checked in the air on the point of his knife, for the Admiral was evidently saying things that restored the men's breath and gave them back the use of speech: the Admiral crossed himself so frankly and feelingly for his own part at the mention of the Evil One and his abode that only the most grudging could doubt his piety; assuredly *he* was not in league with the Prince of Fire, far less was he that personage himself, so much would have to be admitted.

A protracted exchange of opinions ensued on difficult theological problems. The Admiral did not hold the view that the Underworld was a place which could be reached by any known route, at any rate not by sea; that was out of the question, since water was an element hostile and opposed to fire; the way thither was inaccessible to man, while alive; for such as died without grace it was easy to find. Paradise, on the other hand, which was commonly placed in Heaven, without more precise indication . . . well, they had no priest on board, but even in the absence of one the holy articles of faith and the revelation of the Scriptures should remain entirely undisturbed; however, even the Scriptures gave nothing that one might call a definite observation of the position of the Kingdom of Heaven; but as we were told that our first parents were driven from thence it was permissible to suppose that it had lain and still lay somewhere on earth. In contradistinction to the Underworld we had an example in Holy Writ that men might be taken up alive into Heaven, the prophet Elijah; although this happened a long time ago it could not therefore be regarded as absolutely impossible that it might take place again.

Shaking of heads among the Admiral's hearers, divided opinions and an uncomfortable feeling in their insides; as usual, the talk had an inconclusive, unsatisfied ending. To many whose sole unhappy thought was their abandonment in the midst of Ocean, the future appeared in a doubtful, hopeless light; in truth, with all the various prospects suggested by the officers, the cry of *Land* could not come soon enough!

When at last it came, however, it swept aside all other thoughts . . .

Land, land!

It was from Martin Alonzo Pinzon the blessed cry came. He had just closed the flagship in the *Pinta,* a comparison had been made of logs and charts, apparently of a disquieting nature, when Martin Alonzo noticed something like a low cloud or indication of land ahead to the westward, right in the sunset, a long way off, but with so unmistakably the character of a long, broken coast-line that Martin Alonzo was not in doubt for a moment:

Land! land!

They all saw it, the Admiral saw it and immediately fell on his knees on the quarter-deck and began to thank God with hands raised high. Immense sensation, all troubles forgotten, wild joy all over the ship at the sight of the distant blessed streak of land; the men ran up the masts and down again, fell into each other's arms, were quite beside themselves.

Ay, a mad scene of confusion, until the Admiral in a powerful, solemn voice which penetrated from one end of the ship to the other, ordered all hands to be called on deck for divine service.

A gun was fired, and the *Niña* sailed up; the three ships sailed abreast in the falling darkness, and as the streak of land vanished in the great glow of the sunset, and the afterglow paled away and gave place to the first tiny twinkling stars, the hymn arose from the *Santa Maria,* from the *Pinta* and the *Niña,* three choirs of men's voices which united in one and cried out upon the sea and to the stars:

Salve Regina, Mater misericordiæ, vita, dulcedo, et spes nostra, salve.
Ad te clamamus exsules, filii Hevæ.
Ad te suspiramus, gementes, et flentes in hoc lacrymarum valle.
Eia ergo advocata nostra, illos tuos misericordes oculos ad nos converte.
Et Jesum benedictum fructum ventris tui, nobis post hoc exsilium ostende.
O clemens, o pia, o dulcis Virgo Maria.

IV

SAN SALVADOR

Never had any night been so long, never any expectation so tense. Course was altered to south-west, the direction in which land had been sighted, and was kept all night in the fresh breeze.

But when the sun rose astern of them it exposed an ocean entirely bare as far as the eye could see; ahead, where the land had been sighted, there was only the sharp line where the distant empty sky met the distant edge of the sea and the waves ran together like snakes, a blue wilderness above and below, on every side!

The disappointment was hardly to be borne. With sinking hearts they realized that what they had taken for land had only been a mirage, a cruel sport with the hopes of poor hard-tried men. Could there be more trials in store?

A voice was heard, after some time of deathlike silence; a man went about among the hopeless ones trying to talk, to talk up his spirits, hopeless himself—the Admiral. Nobody listened to him, he scarcely had the heart to believe his own words, but something had to be said.

Speaking half to himself he explained dejectedly that what they had seen could be nothing else but St. Brandan's Isle, for it was known from his legend to be a movable island, which changed its place in the sea, a wandering isle, so to speak. St. Brandan had sailed after it for days without being able to overtake it; it continued to move on before him in the sea, just like an airy vision; but he had reached it at last, and in reality it was a mercy they had sighted it, a proof that it existed, and with God's help they too would reach it . . .

They turned from him in disgust, with forlorn looks, turned eyes like blazing coals on him, malice and impotence in one, like captive cats, they looked him up and down, this chattering old map-maker and impostor, Admiral of the Moon, with his Saints and his fine connections and his worn-out shoes; they gazed after him, curling their upper lips and baring their teeth, hating his back, the hair on his neck, his huge size, an advantage which of course the vagabond must have stolen. And the Admiral went up alone to his quarter-deck and stayed there, while the ship beneath him sank into the dull despair of a fasting morning.

It was on the 25th of September that they made the false landfall; its result was to impair the spirits both of the commander and of the crew. And there was still two weeks' sailing before them.

How did he get them to do it? How was it possible after they had suffered this collapse of all hope? It even repeated itself: once more there was a cry of land, and they believed it; another disappointment. He got them to do it.

The situation on board had changed greatly for the worse; for a time all communication between the poop and the main deck was broken off. The school on deck and the Admiral's long, kindly explanations were things of the past; he stayed aft and paced his watch, night and ay, no wonder his shoes were worn out; nd down on the deck the crew behaved s though there was nobody in command t all, so far as their part of the ship was oncerned.

They were still sailing, the westerly ourse was resumed, but the crew held neetings on their own account, put their eads together in groups here and there, roups which at first were not altogether n agreement, with many opinions and roposals, though none in the Admiral's avour. Diego could be seen, lively and ctive, with his black head showing up ow in one group, now in another, with iolent gestures and a programme which e hammered in with bated breath, point y point, one hand striking the other.

It was mutiny that had at last begun to ake shape. Diego saw blood and felt the ingling stiffness in his legs that precedes spring; the Admiral appeared to his nagination like a bull in a cloud of dust, is nerves egged him on to get at it, hough he was only a pygmy compared vith the monster—to jump over it, literlly, right in front of its horns, stick blazng darts into it, tease it by twisting its ail, and finally drive a yard of steel hrough its shoulder right down to the eart.

Thus it was with Diego, who always vanted the theatrical, a show for the eye; thers looked at the matter more soberly. The Admiral was to be got out of the way, vithout too much exposure or obvious uilt on the part of those who were the neans of doing it. Accidents may always appen, man overboard; the Admiral was p at night measuring the stars with his yes on the sky, right against the low rail; e might lose his footing and go head first nto the sea, nobody could tell how, and e himself would never be required to explain it. Then they would sorrowfully eturn home without an admiral . . .

Here, however, was a point which aused a fairly sharp difference of opinion, the groups nearly came to loggerheads over it: would they be able to find the way home without him? Those passably skilled in seamanship thought there would be no trouble about it, a long beat against the wind, several weeks, months perhaps, tacking to north and south, seeing how badly the ships worked to windward; but how else could the Admiral himself have thought of getting back when the time came? Others wrinkled their foreheads and made no attempt to conceal what could not be concealed, that the Admiral, in spite of all his intolerable idiosyncrasies, undoubtedly possessed remarkable powers, supernatural powers one might even call them; something more than ordinary knowledge of the sea was wanted, he had secrets which he would take with him to the grave, and perhaps it was as well to be wary of getting in one's own way by removing him.

A few men flatly refused to conspire against the Admiral—Pedro Gutierrez, whose hands were too white; Juan de la Cosa too, to the general regret, he would have been a good man to have on their side. But Juan de la Cosa, who had never for an instant believed in the voyage and was now more incredulous than ever, declared that in spite of all he would lay his bones where Columbus laid his; this was such a mad enterprise that life would seem poor to him if he did not see it out—something to be said for that, but it was not a comrade's point of view.

Thus opinions were divided until one of them gained the upper hand and sentence of death was passed.

The explosion came, but it was the Admiral himself who brought it about, just as the plan was ripe. He had long seen what was in the wind, and one day when all hands were on deck, groups and meetings in the greatest excitement, he came down from the poop right amongst them, unarmed, determined to have a talk with them.

Cries of rage greeted him as he came down the ladder; in an instant the deck was in an uproar, every man of one mind, no mercy for him, and if he came of his own accord to meet his death so much the better! A cat-like spring, and a blade caught the light, it was Diego at the head of mob; a scuffle, he and the Admiral hand to hand, a whirlwind nobody could follow . . .

But they saw the upshot. The Admiral had hold of Diego, however he had managed it, held him fast and broke the rapier in his hand, taking the pieces from him; and while holding him with one hand he grasped his forearm with the other and gave him two blows on the ear with his own hand, then swept him aside with his flat palm, with a twitch of the face as when one gets rid of a foul insect. And then Columbus rose and faced the mob . . .

Diego's imagination had not been altogether wrong in regarding him as a bull, for now in his anger there was something bull-like about him, the big head, the snorting nostrils, the attitude; he swelled, the blood went to his head till his eyes showed white against the blue skin, he hunched himself and struck out with his mighty arms as though he would jerk them out of his shoulders, snort after snort came from his nose and all his hair bristled and made him still more terrible, the thunderbolt was in his hand, his voice came in a huge roar. And then he gave them his mind:

Here he was to lead them into kingdoms their eyes had never seen, and by the living God, whether they liked it or not, they should see them! Never should the rabble say of him that he had failed his royal lord and master King Ferdinand of Spain and his Queen Isabella, in whose service he had sailed; never should any force hinder him in his duty! He was a seaman before God and Our Lady, appointed by Heaven to bring grace to the heathen, even if he had to sail to th
uttermost sea! So long as there were soul
in darkness who had not heard the gospe
and received the offer of grace, so lon
would he sail, to the world's end, a morta
only, but an instrument in the hand o
Almighty God for eternity. Who wa
strong enough to stop him on his way

He looked around with the eyes of
wild boar among hounds. But not one o
them made a sound.

His expression changed to one of sor
row, there was a quiver in his beard, an
the giant fell into terrible weeping, turne
and hid his face in his arm, staggering lik
a blind man towards the ladder. A broade
target for a crossbow-bolt than his back a
he went up to the poop could not hav
been desired, but now he went scot-free
the hands of all on deck hung limply b
their sides. They saw him go into the littl
cabin aft and close the door after him
like an unhappy man who wished to b
alone. And there were some among them
whose eyes blinked in their trouble; per
haps after all there had been *too* many o
them baiting the giant! Some saw that hi
hands were bleeding after the encounte
with Diego.

Not a word passed among those wh
stayed on deck. But the men who took
their turn at the helm that day steered s
carefully, with all their attention fixed o
the compass, the course due west.

Those who had noticed the Admiral'
worn-out shoes noticed again, in a day o
two, that they had been mended. Wh
could have done it? Was it one of th
crew perhaps who had taken upon him
self to sew them up early in the mornin
while the Admiral was asleep? Or had th
Admiral done it himself by the little chart
house lantern whose light always shon
from his cabin at night?

On they went, in the invariable, mysti
cal wind which seemed to have som
mysterious purpose with them; but ther

was no fair-wind feeling on board, their minds were dark and rankling like the doomed. Signs interpreted as showing the nearness of land came and went, awaking, after their bitter experience, a hope which had no strength and which left traces of a yet deeper affliction in their furrowed faces.

The crew began to lose the fixed notions about the world with which they had set out, they had forgotten Spain, forgotten almost who they were; the world appeared to them in an uncertain light as an enchantment which was already acting upon them, they were in other states of being, would not have been surprised if one day the roc had swooped down and carried off one of the ships in its claws; sea monsters lurked beneath them—that they saw none almost seemed an added unreality.

The quarrel between the crew and the Admiral blazed up again frequently, but was of a barren, disconsolate nature; the crew were too dull to plot together any more and had come to hate each other to an extent that made all common action impossible. It had gone with them as it goes with every collection of men confined in the same place, without women, without a chance of avoiding one another, a repulsion scarcely to be borne. They opened their mouths at each other in loathing, without uttering a word, gaped at each other like sick and sorry beasts of prey, even language was too heavy to lift; they turned their backs on each other as far as might be, got out of each other's way in the narrow ship, climbed out on the bowsprit and enjoyed a few fathoms' distance from the rest and a good long solitary cry, riding astride the spar with their arms round a thin rope; they hid out of sight among the cargo, up on the yard, hanging overboard by a line on the ship's side, like a man hung up for curing—anywhere if they could only escape the sight of one another. Ah, the voyage and the long companionship punished them by letting them see themselves as they were!

All discipline went to pieces, there was just enough of it left for navigating the ship, not that that was much trouble in the fine weather; the ship was like a kennel where you stumbled over meat bones, the men slept where they dropped, scratched themselves where they felt a bite, growled without opening their eyes when they were trodden on. On days when their spirits revived—when birds had been seen or other reminders of a world long ago abandoned and vanished which they had once known, or when the Admiral had been talking about land again like an automaton, the idiot above them, to whom they had grown accustomed as one does to a voice—on such occasions they took omens, a wearisome pastime during which the life ebbed out of them: if a certain cockroach, which they saw sitting still in a certain spot, ran a certain way when it did run, then they would sight land before evening. God help the man who prodded the cockroach and disturbed the divine judgment, or came near it; mad roars scared away any who wanted to approach the group where the trial was taking place; it might last for hours if it was a very sedate cockroach. If at last it ran, why then they would either sight land before evening, which would simply turn out a lie, or it ran the wrong way and all hope was gone, as it was anyhow.

Those of the crew who retained a remnant of humanity retired into themselves and became pious, clutched the crucifix, not now and then but continuously, had it in their hands night and day and moistened it with tears; pictures of the Virgin Mary were kissed as long as they would stand it, pious vows were made. All the pilgrimages they would undertake if they ever saw Spain again! In hair shirt, barefooted! No thought of expense in the matter of candles. Some promised the Virgin a stone of them, a whole stone! Could she hold out against that? Though innocent of any such intention, it gave a pretty good idea of what the giver was worth. But the whole was of no avail.

Away aft the Admiral paced his heavy beat like an ox in its stall, always the same weight, the heavy step that made the planks give under it and was felt all over the ship, a brutish, intolerable endurance. His shoes had burst again under his bull-like tread. The Admiral was all hair and beard, his face more inscrutable than ever before—couldn't he reckon his log by the amount of hair that grew on him?

This was just the sore point, the Admiral's own inner vexation, which of course he concealed from every one: there was something wrong with his calculations of distance. The length of the voyage to India as he had estimated it beforehand and the distance they had covered did not by any means agree, the Atlantic Ocean appeared to be a good deal wider than he had imagined—if it had any end. What was he to believe?

To begin with, the crew had been terrified that they might burst through the sky if they went on sailing, and have the pieces tumbling about them and fall into God knows what calamities outside, a superstition which they no longer entertained—oh no, it did not seem even that there *was* any world's end, it was nothing but sailing and sailing, without any actual catastrophe but at the same time without cessation, till Doomsday perhaps. Who could tell whether they were not already damned and would have to go on sailing, for having presumptuously tampered with the locks of the Ocean; perhaps they were already in eternity and could not die, but would see each other for ever, be shipmates together for all ages, ugh! and sail and sail and sail.

And the flesh would fall from their faces, and they would look upon one another as bare death's-heads but unable to die; and the *Santa Maria* would become an old ship, old as she was already, with splintered deck, sun-bleached sails and frayed ropes like prickly worms, the anchor scaly with rust; but she could not die either, the old tub would plough the infinite to all eternity and rock with her chafed spars and groan in her timbers and gather slimy seaweed at the waterline, and sail, ho, ho, ho, until some day Satan —if not God, who had forgotten her—took pity and opened a vent-hole down in Hell to receive the rotten old wreck!

And yet he pressed on, Columbus, persisted daily in romancing in his cautious voice about the signs of land, until they clasped their hands and begged the monster to stop, begged him to kick them and let them die; still he pottered about with his astrolabes and angles and hushed up to-day what he had expatiated on with criminal optimism yesterday, when it proved to be humbug.

If only they had thrown him overboard that time, when it was not too late and they had it in them to rise! He even grudged them their food now, for all his fatherly talk; they were on rations, the junk was eaten up or gone bad, vermin in what was left; at night the rats ran over them, some day they would have to eat *them,* like heathen dogs, unless it was the other way about; the water was rotten, might he but poison himself with it pretty soon so that they could be rid of his creaking about the deck and be able to lie in peace and close their eyes to the next man's disgusting dirty features, and die.

The heat increased, the heat increased. O dear! O dear!

And then, when they were at their lowest, an asylum in the extremity of moral dissolution, hope began to trickle in, for a long while against their will, for it only came in the shape of the old, hateful, torturing twaddle about signs of land, and the more they had of it the more it worried them. But at last they could not help beginning to see for themselves.

One morning early in October they heard the Admiral singing up on the poop, entirely alone with his God and the sunrise, and they understood that now he was confident, not with a world of hopefulness in his mouth and sick inside, as they had known him so long, for after all they had some sense—his conviction was genuine now. And soon they could do nothing but share it. In the course of that day and the succeeding ones, up to the 11th, the evidences of the proximity of land increased so fast that nobody could be in doubt any longer. They recovered as the sick recover, without any vital strength at first, but rich in the soul; quiet tears ran down their cheeks—no, now there was no doubt!

On the 7th of October the Admiral altered course to the south-west. For several days before they had seen birds, pelicans, but that day they saw great flocks of birds flying from north to south-west. Columbus knew that the Portuguese had found land by sailing after the flight of birds, and he followed their example. His supposition was that they had now passed the islands he expected to find in the Ocean, or had sailed through them without sighting them. He therefore thought he would sail straight on to the mainland; the islands they could always come back to. On the 11th the signs of land were certain: the crew of the *Pinta* fished up a carved log from the water; from the *Niña* they even saw a fresh bough with berries on it in the sea, and were reminded of the dove with the olive leaf in its beak which returned to Noah's Ark after the Deluge; stormy petrels were seen, and that day they sailed in a rising wind and a fairly rough sea, answering to the strength of the conviction that drove them on and the uneasiness which accompanied the thought that very soon, a question of hours, they would see land.

But so late as the day before the Admiral had had to go through a final tussle with his men, impending mutiny, now, now, just as uncertainty was giving way to infallible signs. It was the probability of the approach of land, and nothing else, that raised the crew; they had recovered their strength with surprising rapidity when the world began to be like itself again, and now a flood of misgivings rushed in upon them. Without a doubt they were reaching land, but what sort of land? At the best, if it was India, it would be a gross piece of foolhardiness to fall upon the back-door of the Great Cham's realms with three wretched little ships and scarcely a hundred men; if the Admiral hadn't thought of it before it was time to think of it now and turn back; anyhow the situation had been determined and they could come again with a fleet and an army. They had agreed to join him in the reconnaissance and had borne the indescribable sufferings that pioneers have to undergo in new and unknown seas, but to cut the matter short they would now go home for reinforcements—no question of exposing themselves to be massacred on a hostile shore and wasting the whole voyage if not a single one of them returned to tell of it . . .

Only a hundred men, the Admiral interposed, but *Spaniards* . . .

Proud looks, chests thrown out, the Admiral was courteous, knew how to strike the right note. *But* . . . and then it all came over again, not without hints of who was in the majority and had the power and meant to use it. Shouts, Diego jumping out of the crowd like a leopard out of the jungle, beating the air with all his limbs, a chorus of roars behind him: *thus* far they had sailed the Admiral and made his fortune, now not a mile more!

It ended in the Admiral declaring in so many words that for his part he would continue the voyage until he had found India, according to his plan. He did not get excited this time, did not thunder over their heads; on the other hand, he let them have a taste of his scorn, which had a bitter smack to some at least among the crew; moreover there was a determination in his demeanour which made them see that they would have to cross his dead body ere there was any chance of turning back.

Thus he succeeded once more in dividing them: cries of revenge, threats and much harmless swearing in one quarter, silence and brooding in another; postponement, tension, troubled waves inboard and out, but sailing and good progress all the while. And the next day they were in a different humour. The absolutely certain signs of land carried all with them. The day's work on the 11th of October was a triumphal progress; the sun went down that evening in a waste of water, as it had done for thirty-five evenings before, but with a great red glow of mighty expectation to mark its setting.

The night of the 11th was a dark night; the moon, which was in its last quarter, would rise at eleven. It was about ten o'clock when the Admiral saw from the poop the first direct sign of land, a light ahead in the darkness which moved up and down. Fire was the first sign of welcome that greeted him from the unknown shore, a gleam borne by a man's hand and swaying up and down with his walk. Columbus called Pedro Gutierrez, whom he trusted, up to him and asked if he saw the light, and when he had confirmed it he sent for Rodrigo Sanchez, the King's representative on board, that he might be a witness.

At two o'clock in the morning, when the moon was up, a sailor with good eyes on board the *Pinta* made out the coast-line ahead, Rodrigo de Triana was his name the *Pinta* fired a gun as a salute, and as the other ships came up they could all distinguish the line of coast, a low-lying land ahead. Sails were taken in, the worn sails stiff as boards in their clews from standing so long; only a few stitches of canvas were left set, enough to keep the ships moving up and down, more or less where they were; they had only to wait for morning.

What a night! Never before had men's minds been so wrought up by tension, triumph, fear of the unknown, curiosity, the sense of immense and fateful things. And no wonder; the time was now ripe for two worlds to meet here, with all that there was in them, to spread their fires one to the other and brand each other anew; hosts were to be let loose, and men's souls would not remain what they were, therefore the heart pumped so uproariously in every man's breast. All this they could not see, but it was in their veins as a great necessity: jubilation and festival spirit all through the long, sleepless, expectant night.

The night did not pass in idleness, a fever of preparation was everywhere. Some washed themselves in the waning moonlight against going ashore in the morning, others had their hair cut as well as could be managed, even the Admiral himself, whose hair and beard Pedro Gutierrez cropped: it was strange what a comparatively small head he had when his mane was off. The grindstone shrieked under the forecastle, splashing in its trough: the crew were sharpening their swords in expectation of what the morrow might bring, running a sensitive thumb along the edge; they spat between hand and hilt and tried their grip, swung the blade till it whined in the air.

And their tongues went, volubly; loquacity did them good, giving vent to much that was in them; and thoughts were numbed that would have cramped their spirits, after all things had turned out as they should. The Admiral, he was now peerless, the man of the day, and they had shown it too in that mad hour when land was sighted and everyone lost his head in a feeling of humanity and gratitude. Some had gone so far as to crawl to his feet along the deck on hands and knees and kiss the hem of his mantle, they had humbled themselves before him as before a deity, as was only fair on the part of those who had been the most impudent in opposing him during the voyage; others kept somewhat in the background, not wishing to recall their existence too prominently. For his own part the Admiral had been greatly moved and had clasped his hands in long speechless gratitude to his Creator, but apart from that it was remarkable how calmly he took his deliverance, really as though he had been quite certain all the time that it must come in this way.

And in this the men had to acknowledge that he was right; the thing was easy enough, nothing startling about it in reality, anybody could have done the same. Straight ahead, straight ahead, that was all, a course drawn with a ruler, with a turn at the end of it, neither storms, rocks, nor winding channels; straight across the ocean, thirty-five days' sail, what do you say to that? From the morrow he *would* actually be Admiral, and Viceroy into the bargain, ts, ts—and when he came out in all his glory it would be seen where *those* were who after all had done the whole of the work on board, built the vessel, so to speak, and trimmed the sails and taken the helm, and had borne all the anxiety on the top of it! For *he* had shown practically no fear at all.

Many were the eyes as the night wore on which were fixed from time to time on the distant indistinct line of coast, rather low-lying, it seemed, not forbidding with lofty mountains or abrupt cliffs, easily mastered . . . now it remained to be seen who lived there. Oh, if they had neither sailed into the Abyss, nor had the sky falling about them, nor been drawn to the Magnet Mountain, nor burnt up by the sun, nor swallowed by sea monsters, it would turn out sure enough that the inhabitants were just ordinary human beings; in that case there would be no concealing the fact that here again the Admiral had solved a problem quite simple from the start.

Among those who gazed landward from the *Santa Maria* was a man with a thick lip; he had been so wanting in tact as to remind a shipmate of all the candles he had promised the Virgin Mary; like a flash he had got one on the mouth. . . . Was *he* the one to claim the candles? Scrimmage, and a black eye for his messmate; and thus it was that one of them gazed at the land with only one eye open.

Diego was singing somewhere in the darkness, up in his highest falsetto, crowing to himself like a lonely cock quail on a spring night. Who would there be for him among the sleepers over there, with her ear hot from dreaming? He would soon find that out; but even now, *now* she was there, sleeping beneath the same moon, longing perhaps, like him, for what was to come—could she but know how near it was!

Up on the poop the Admiral walked with his diminished head and his great new dignity, which on the morrow he would bear ashore in fullest armour, with the banners of Castile. What were his thoughts? A deep surge of emotion filled him at the goodness and mercy of God. Great thoughts, possible and impossible, possessed him as the ship washed up and down, with the waves caressing her bow and her mastheads tracing letters among the stars; each time the ship went about the whole starry sky swung round upon itself; thus in the Admiral's head the world and all his thoughts revolved. What awaited him yonder?

The night was so mild and wonderful, the breeze had dropped and a land-air brought a warm scent out to seaward—many strange, spicy, obscure, powerful odours, of fire, mud, plants, the heavy night-sweat of the tropics that hangs out like a garment from land to sea, the ancient rank and pregnant scent of life.

What a life? The Admiral's head was swimming. For the last few days, which had carried them farther south, there had been a sort of forgotten and yet familiar soul in the air, a growing sense of summer, an atmosphere of rejuvenation, full of vanished summers, childhood's springtime, an eternal May, sky, air and sea reposing as it were perpetually in the Virgin's month . . . *could* it be imagined, was it possible that when day came he would be able to sail with his three ships into Paradise, the land of eternal summer, the land of youth, the abode of the Virgin Mary? *Would he see her?*

His breath failed him, he stood still, pulled himself together. It was not impossible. But it was not to be thought of until it came about, that was not lawful for a man. In the course of the night the thought recurred, but he kept it down, forced himself to think of what was more reasonable and actual, that it was the coast of India he saw there dimly in the moonlight, or the islands off the mainland, probably Antilia, the Spice Islands, from which all precious things came, for the scent wafted out on the night proclaimed it to be an island full of spices and sweet-smelling things; for that matter it might well be the Abode of the Blest. But then surely it would show a greater light than the solitary torch he had seen?

And yet, was the perpetual lamp that burned before the image of the Virgin in the cathedral a great light? Did it not burn as a solitary spark in the midst of an ocean of darkness? How great was the light the shepherds saw shining from the inn that Christmas night when God's Mother wrapped her First-born in swaddling clothes and laid him in a manger? The scent that was now wafted to him on the night airs from the island, the hearths ashore, of perfumed wood, it was the incense, the cathedral, and all it promised! He dared not follow his thoughts, their immensity inflamed him—was the Garden of Eden at hand? With an effort he forced them back into a human train.

By force he held himself to the conviction that it was Antilia he lay off, and thought over all that might be expected, and all that he would have to do.

In passing his thoughts turned back to Spain: the incredulous there, all the crooked smiles he remembered, and his human side came uppermost—down on deck they heard the Admiral snorting, as a horse snorts violently in his bridle—he was getting fiery up there, the Admiral and Viceroy.

But up on the forecastle walked young Pedro Gutierrez, on watch again to-night. He was silent, scanning the moon, scanning the land. The book of fate was dark for him, dark as that night, with only a red initial letter to be seen in it, the blood-red moon. What forebodings had he? Little he knew it, but he was not of those who were to see again the brown Spanish shores. Never more would he look upon the Guadalquivir!

Sunrise on the 12th of October, the long low green island ahead in full daylight, a good league away. Sails hoisted, creaking tackles and joyful chanties from the crew, a festal sailing in!

First the *Pinta,* that dashing sailer, stiff in the breeze and cleaving the waves with a short decided nod. After her the *Niña,* graceful as ever, spreading a fringe of foam about her like the border of a gown, meeting the seas with girlish curtsies. Last of all plunged the *Santa Maria* with her rounded hull like a segment of a wheel, swinging her nose down and ploughing the seas overmuch; but she too kept up, and nothing could be done till she came.

It was a blue day, blue sea, blue sky; in front of the ships flying-fish darted up from the deep clear waves like the vanguard of the seas's wet silvery souls, and between the ships sported a friendly school of porpoises, like mermaids, in a landward gallop, they too on the top of the galloping waves, the whole making a picture, the apotheosis of Ocean and of the fortunate discoverers.

Soon they saw smoke ashore, the mark of human habitation, trees and green plains opened up as the eye slowly took bearings; it was a good, tangible island, with surf about it, veritable, excellent.

The Admiral stood high on the poop, in full dress from early morning, iron all over and a scarlet cloak besides—pretty warm, just think of it, full armour! The crew puffed the sweat from their upper lips and thought they had too much on with a pair of linen hose and a cuirass over their bare skin. Finery was not all clover; one had to suffer for it! Besides being clad in steel, blue plates and scales, with trappings, the Admiral wore a helmet with feathers of a bird called the ostrich, doubtless some salvage from his African voyages. All this finery he had brought with him and laid by till the time arrived, so confident had he been! On his legs he wore brand-new sea-boots of tanned deerskin—imagine it, sea-boots, in his size, a unique pair of boots, each of them fit to hold a sack of flour! And people went abroad in search of curiosities, when they had such strange sights as this at home! Something different from the Admiral's old pointed shoes with the splits in them—what had happened to them, by the way? Ought they not to be preserved, even as cast-offs? they were a sort of relic. To return to the boots, wasn't it a funny thing that all through the voyage the Admiral had gone about in shoes, and now he was to go ashore he put on sea-boots? [Diego's licensed tongue.]

The Admiral heard the laughter and merriment below him on deck but was himself very serious. Was he not *too* serious for so blissful a day, when all the others were singing and the world smiled upon him in his glory?

If any one had observed the Admiral early that morning, when the sun rose and the outline of the island was disclosed beneath its rays, he would have seen as it were a shadow pass over his face; the clearer the view became the darker *he* seemed to grow. And since then he had been serious.

But now they saw him draw himself up and throw out his chest, as he called his officers aft. To them the Admiral announced that the island was to be named before they landed, after the Saviour; it was to be called *San Salvador*.

Juan de la Cosa looked up, in surprise—ought not the first land they sighted be called after the Mother of God, in whose name the voyage had been undertaken? But the Admiral held his peace, which meant that it was to be as he had said.

High on the poop he stood against the blue sky, looking in towards land, blinking his eyes, swollen with sleeplessness; he saw the surf rising against the shore like white figures leaping up from the sea, checking themselves and sinking back again, a noiseless distant play the seaman knows, the spirits of the sea ever seeking the land; the ocean's organ was about him as it had been now for so many weeks, and for most of his life, a note that was a part of himself; the wind plucked its dull harp-chords in ropes and tackle, another part of himself; a roaring, billowing, singing within him and around him, the blue day breathed in its strength, by the bowsprit a bright-coloured soul leaped into the light and vanished again, the rainbow in the flying spray; behind him the morning sun climbed in the sky, and before him lay the day.

And as he stood there under the flying banners and pennants and the ships saluted each other over the surface of the water, fire leaping from the throats of the pieces and the sharp report deadened by sea and wind, the drifting smoke, while the seabirds wavered in their flight and rose high, scared by the shots, and the crews raised a cheer, the ships in chorus —as he stood there looking towards the new land he thrilled and saw his life before him; the life behind his was as nothing, now at last his voyage was to begin!

But it was ended. Many, many things came after—harder years than those he had left behind, petty triumphs and an abyss of toil, the deepest-cut inscription on the tablets of history.

The shadow that had passed across his face that morning would give way to hope, and come again, until hope was driven out and there was nothing left of his face but a mask, the dumb form lent by death.

Labour, a human lot, awaited him, but his achievement as the instrument of the age was concluded. Through the power that was in his heart he had carried the age beyond itself; now it would sweep in his wake, after him and over him; the way was open.

Behind him, in the Europe he had left, it was as though men's souls were pressing each other onward to the coasts; now they would push each other out to sea and over it, the Ferryman had shown the way. The instinct in his fathers' blood had brought them as far as the South; now, he opened up the way to the other side of the world to those who followed after him.

Conquest and settlement were to be the work of others; the theme would be developed without him. For yet a little while he himself pursued the goals of mortals, but from the moment when he saw the light in the night and had thrown a bridge across the Atlantic his being passed over into Time.

V

QUETZALCOATL

The light Columbus had seen from out at sea was a burning branch which a man carried aloft on his way from one palmleaf hut to another on the island.

When one is out so late and alone and the evening is dark, one must carry fire, not exactly to find the way, it is only a short distance through the forest and across open ground, the path is known, but who would dare to walk by himself beyond the abodes of men without fire?

The man was perfectly naked, had always been so; the air, even at night as now, lay about his limbs like a bath at blood-heat, the same heat that he felt in the waters of the lagoon when he plunged into them, the same that surrounded him in his hut and radiated from women and children, natural warmth, the only clothing he and his ancestors had ever known. But he was painted, roughly smeared with greasy ashes and charcoal all over his body in rude figures; in his nose he wore a ring of mussel-shell and an ample string of cachalot teeth about his neck. His hair reached to his shoulders, but had been chafed off between two stones over the forehead and decorated with feathers; in his free hand he carried a spear hardened at the point with fire, and in a cord round his waist was stuck a bamboo-splinter fashioned into a knife.

The fire from the burning branch he held aloft shone upon his eyes, which were black and witless, curiously skewed, like false mirrors; they seemed not so much to see as to give expression to a wild inner imagination; and yet everything, without exception everything that took place around him was brought to his consciousness; with scared eyes he saw every leaf that moved in the forest within the circle of light he carried with him, which continually brought out the trees in front, while behind the darkness closed again upon his heels—parrots dropping noiselessly from the branch they sat on, sweeping down in a curve and up again into another tree, or sitting still and turning an eye towards the light, hopping sideways a step or two along the branch, without meaning to fly off, let's see first . . . he saw the iguana appear as the light suddenly fell upon it, with its thousand scales, its prickly spine, twisted legs, nostrils, little frightened eyes and all—but he was most apt to see what was not there, horrors and forebodings that leaped into life about him at the slightest sound of which he could not guess the cause; he showed the whites of his eyes and clutched the burning branch convulsively, raised it higher above his head and threw the light before him, towards the lofty slumbering Powers, the palms, towards the bamboo thicket, dense and grim, towards the white nocturnal mist, which filled the bushes and was a terrifying thing with a bush in its embrace, until the light made it powerless.

And when he came out of the forest into the open country he went more cautiously, he was a changed man with the different world that here met his senses; nothing but darkness in the air before him where the light ended, grass and stones entering the light as he covered the ground, a wide air here, breezy and open, with a message from afar. Now there fell upon his ears the long, rising thunder that ended in a crash, the seas running upon the reef around the island, just so long between each, he knew them, sensed the island all the way round, caught the sea air, his big, wide-open nostrils worked, the shore was in them, the living smell of coral mud and all that moved within it, the lagoon and all its life was in his nose, his soul was as it were mapped out with all he sniffed up, one with the island, and yet filled with a fear which only the possession of fire could keep under.

A few minutes' walk brought him to a copse and in its depths a hut, like his own, the hut of a friend, a man like himself, who sat on his heels by the fire and received him with a grunt. And all he had come for was to squat on his heels likewise, in company with his friend, and converse with him in a wide-mouthed speech, docked sentences—about what? The fishing, the state of the lagoon, upon which they exchanged opinions, all-wise and marvelling; very good canoe, such and such a one; a misfortune—a man they knew had got a splinter in his foot and was dying, for such a little thing, sorcery without doubt; foreign canoes seen, news from other islands?

In the background of the hut there was a glimpse of a bunch of women and children, asleep; now and then one of them awoke and lay down again with extreme caution . . . oh, if they should happen to disturb the men! Outside the entrance to the hut, in the half-light of the fire, prowled a couple of dogs; a strange kind of dog that had no bark, wise enough about the muzzle and with a wag in the tail, talking with the ears, but with no voice; thin-coated and fat they looked, they were here domestic animals and were fattened up to the right pitch, taking the place of pigs. They showed much attention when the men inside fell to eating: roast crabs, which they opened with a stone implement, and a handful of maize, looking like so many yellow teeth; a part of the crab's fat inside was smeared on the mouth of the god which stood under the roof of palm leaves grinning in coral-rag at the fire; manioc bread, tasting of the women's sweat, took off the edge of their appetite; of all they ate a small portion was offered to the fire and a fire prayer was mumbled between the lips; then big draughts of the calabash and the men had done, after duly belching to get rid of the spirits that might have entered with the food. Their talk naturally ran upon feasting, and their voices sank to a religious whisper: such and such an island, so many suns ago, much man food, good man, fat, big man, num, num!

And then a smoke to the night! Leaves of the good, the best plant were laid on the fire, and the men leaned over the smoke, breathed it in and drank with nose and mouth, coughed and moaned with pleasure, their eyes running and mouths watering, but happy and stifling themselves with smoke, until a god seemed to rise in it above their heads right up to the palm-leaf roof, an almighty being, the sombre narcotic spirit, friend of all poor mortals, whose name is Tobacco. Then they turned dizzy, with a glorious disquiet in their veins, a splendid headache, and they went to rest, laying themselves down where they sat, the guest as much at home here as anywhere else.

And when it was quite certain that they were asleep, shadows stole up to the fire, women and children and the dumb dogs, to share what was left. They were not sorry for it, as with hot whispering they made themselves a lovely late supper in the middle of the night, left off chewing with mouths full to listen—yes, they were asleep—and put fresh things on the fire to brown. The women whispered, loose-lipped and with little pigs' eyes, scarcely able to suppress a giggling gaiety, though most of them were still bleeding or had ugly unhealed wounds from the men's bamboo knives. And at last they came upon a leaf or two of the good weed, flicked the hair from their faces and glanced at the sleeping men; it was as much as their lives were worth, but they laid the leaves on the fire, breathed in the poison and moaned in ecstasy. An infant began to whine and was hurriedly gagged with a breast slung over its mother's shoulder to the inmate of the bag behind. The children quarrelled over the leavings and the little boys went for the little girls with little bamboo knives, a mimic attack all in the deepest silence, for fear of waking the divinities. Soon the whole hut was grunting in its sleep.

But when all were asleep yet another shadow crept up to the fire, an old mumbling, blind creature, the oldest in the hut who felt about among the embers and on the floor, eating charcoal and little burnt knuckle-bones and whatever else of a greasy nature it could find, and then stayed sitting by the fire, warming itself at the glow it could not see; its hands came upon the children's bamboo splinters and it scraped its dry bird's skin with them and fell into a reptile reverie: many, many dark ages since *she* had enjoyed man's cruelty! Among the things she found were some charred scraps of tobacco—and she knew well enough which way the good thing ought to go; no smoke for her, no, into the mouth with it; greedily she thrust ashes and tobacco on to her tongue, croaked and found consolation; at last she too crawled to her rest, with the good weed in her mouth.

Smoke from the tobacco fire, that was what had reached Columbus out at sea!

The men barked in their sleep and wriggled their limbs, as though they were all joints: gruesome dreams. Little did they guess that what awaited them next day would surpass even their most frightful and monstrous visions. What a sight they were to see!

The naked savage with a burning branch in his hand, surrounded by the horrors of night which he kept off by the fire—that was in brief the picture of his place in Nature and of his origin.

The terror of night which he felt had once been inspired in his primeval ancestors by fire; but this, the mightiest force in Nature, had been given into their hand, and with it they had subjected the beasts and the night and had even found in it a remedy for cold.

But not all of them had availed themselves of *that;* here mankind had parted, with a deep division between those who took up the battle against winter with the aid of fire, and those who gave way before it, farther and farther to the South, as conditions grew more and more severe in the North. The Ice Age set up the division. From the warm forests of the North, before that age, mankind had come, from the Lost Country; the man *Fyr* who first tamed fire and came down from the volcano with it, he carried it on a burning branch just as the savage of Guanahani went with his torch at night . . . so far then had mankind penetrated on its way to the South, in company with the warmth and the forest.

But because they had thus continually moved on in search of their own primitive surroundings, they had not changed; they were the same primitive men now as they had always been, the forest man with the few but powerful resources Fyr had once placed in his hands, the fire, the spear and the stone knife, to which the bow had been added. They still carried with them the ancient symbols, handed down from generation to generation through countless ages but practically unchanged; for the most part symbols of fear, a general foggy tradition of the Terrible One, whether it was the power of fire, *Gunung Api,* or the *Man,* the epitome of their own cruelty in the form of some particularly bloody destroyer, who crushed many and was long remembered —in any case, Terror, and a willingness to sacrifice if the terror would let itself be appeased. That was their idea of God, which they tried to make visible to the eye in stone or wood, and more hideous images did not exist. At the base of the idea lay ancient experience, crude forces in Nature, visible or invisible; all in all a Man, *that* Man, the spirit of One who had been and still was and would always haunt them. If you felt a pain inside, it was he; if a bough fell down in the forest where you were walking, it was he, stealthy as ever; if you knocked your big toe against a stone, it was he who put it in the way, you might know that; horrible dreams, there he was again; all this in the ordinary course. If hurricanes occurred, lightning and thunder and other great calamities, then he was angry, murderous or hungry for the sight of piles of corpses; and then men felt small, with no other means of grace but the sacrifice, and not at all sure whether it would be accepted.

When he allowed them to live they lived, avenging themselves below them for what they suffered, on the animals and whatever else was in their power, biting back when the louse bit them, putting into their mouths what was fit to eat, and finding at the same time the chief of their joys, hunting. For expanding their minds they had music, blissful thumping of drums; for prayer, an ancient ingrained predilection for caves, where such were to be found, in which they could shudder and rouse the echoes, play with lights and paint the Man on the wall, and where drums, singing and dancing had a particularly weird and supernatural effect; and as far as they dared they inspired themselves with the notion that *they* were the uncanny Powers who ruled Nature. Their greatest sin and at the same time in a mystical sense their atonement, was cannibalism.

And now for the first time the forest man was to meet his brother of half a geological period ago, the man of the Ice Age, that part of mankind which had remained in the North and had changed instead of leaving: the descendants of Carl. Would they know each other? How would the meeting go? That is just how the situation presented itself on the day Columbus landed on Guanahani.

But—it was *not* the first time. Some centuries before, there had been a man on these shores who had left deep traces in the life of the inhabitants, and had bequeathed to them an obscure but powerful memory, the legend of the *White God.* He was still worshipped by the name of *Quetzalcoatl.* Of him we shall now speak.

He came quite alone and in modest style, when he arrived rowing his single-handed craft of a hollowed tree-trunk, with no personal pomp, clad in the skins of beasts; but his appearance and nature and abilities, as they disclosed themselves, made the greatest stir and elevated him to the position he afterwards occupied in tradition as the White God.

He was fair, not like a human being according to their notion, the only one they had, since they were all dark; he was pale in the face, and all over his skin, almost terrifying to look at in the beginning, and his eyes were pale, like the air; his nose was not natural, flat and open like a human nose, but had its holes underneath and projected from the face like a beak. Strangest of all was his hair; it was light, like sunshine, and if you looked at him at a little distance it was as though he wore the sun on his shoulders. The sun! the sun! they cried when they saw him for the first time, and fell on their faces; his only difficulty in making friends with the people he met was that they dared not approach him. His beard too was light, big and long, not a couple of hairs such as ordinary men grew and pulled out, but a forest on his face and down over his chest; it was more white than yellow, he was not a young man. In the sunlight his head looked like the gold dust they found in the sands of the rivers, and gold was counted holy because it resembled his sunny head. He was tall of stature; his strength was never put to the test, nobody entertained such a thought. He himself brought them no evil, as they found out in time, and this again made him seem strange. When he stayed among them and began to show his inherent supernatural powers, not to the hurt, but, on the contrary, to the profit of all men, why, then they had him, and they showed him all the honour and solicitude that could be lavished upon a man who was the sun in person, came down to live and breathe among the children of earth.

If they asked him whence he came he pointed over the sea to east and north, the sunrise, and that was what they expected; but to one who made bold to inquire his name he replied, with a smile which might mean both that they were not to know it and that it was true, that he was a guest; later on, when he had left them again, they owned the truth of what he had said. Men who were children when he came grew old during the time he stayed, so long was it, but he himself did not seem to grow older; nor was it conceivable that he could die. They called him Quetzalcoatl, which means bird and serpent, referring to the wind and the lightning, over which he was presumed to rule; in the arts of fire he was more versed than many people cared for, but he never misused his power. They erected a temple to him and a high seat, and adorned his head with a glory of green feathers, a whole spacious and beautiful building on his head, the greenest that had ever been seen, and a splendour reserved for the gods.

Now the man who was thus raised on high was none other than Norna Gest, who, to his other experiences, had added that of sitting on a divine throne and wearing a crown of birds' feathers on his red hair, no heavy burden and a thing which need not get about, seeing what an out-of-the-way part of the world he was in; when they prayed that he would deign to wear it he had not the heart to refuse.

On the other hand he declined offerings that they wished to make to him of a bloody and fearful kind, and would only accept flowers and fruit, which occasioned the institution of a sacrifice till then unknown in the land, and drew a sharp dividing line in their religious ideas; of which more later.

First it must be briefly explained how Norna Gest had come here. A long journey, but not very remarkable in itself for a man who had time at his disposal, and no other business than sailing, like Norna Gest. It was at that period of his life when he had survived his dear ones, and sought them in vain in the most distant countries, the shores of the Dead, which he hoped to find in order if possible to meet them there. For he himself could not die, so long as the candle his mother Gro had given him was not burnt out, but the shores of the Dead he had not yet found. After searching for them in the South, as is related in his Book, he tried in the West, towards the sunset, perhaps a hint that the realm of the Dead lay just there. He could see beforehand that there was no hope of crossing the great ocean beyond Europe in the little single-handed canoe he disposed of; but as an old and tried coaster he had experience of how far one could go if one took time and followed the outline of the land, or went up the rivers, which had taken him all round the known countries of Europe and far into the unknown before; and this form of voyaging he essayed.

First, then, he made for the North, up along the coast of Norway, paddling and fishing his way as was his wont, the life he knew of old, without hurry, staying on for a few years when a place attracted him, and covering long distances at a stretch when there was occasion for it, but keeping the far-off goal of his journey before him the whole time. From the coast of Norway on a clear day he saw islands in the ocean far to the westward, the Shetlands, and risked the passage one summer in calm weather. From there he reached the Faroes, following the flight of birds, and then Iceland; perilous voyages, and black, bitter seas in those parts, a long time to be out of sight of land, but plenty of food for a patient fisherman, broad-jawed cod in the deeps; and he was not lonely, far from it, those waters were populous with great families of whales in the current and thousands upon thousands of seabirds on the rocks ashore. Much delight had the old man in birds' eggs and a fire on a desolate ocean isle, followed by a sleep on the turf and a song to himself in the morning; he rubbed his hands with pleasure and stepped into his boat to feel the sea stirring under him, and to commit himself once more to the waves.

From Iceland he reached Greenland, more by chance than otherwise, and not without distress and loss, since a storm drove him out into the open sea in that direction and ended by casting him on the cold shore. He lay senseless at the bottom of the boat when he reached land; fishing had failed him on the passage, and he happened to get no rain in the bottom of the canoe, his usual drink on long voyages; the seas were tremendous, and eternal night came on, icebergs towered about the hollowed chip with a man in it among the yawning waves. But he rode out the gale in a swoon, and came to himself on Greenland's coast, turned walrus-hunter and clothed himself in the skin of the polar bear, lost himself in endless fjords and wastes, stayed here for ages and worked his way farther and farther north, hibernated in the snow, short of fuel for his solitary fire, nothing but driftwood; but what he got he examined and inferred that there was land to the westward from which it came; and over he went, to the northernmost cold islands on the other side.

So he was across, and then went south

along the coast, in and out of fjords, for many ages, on many shores, till he reached milder climes again; still farther down, till he was in the warmth, and then the old man shook his shoulders and let the days go by, living on fish and solitude, among lovely islands; tasted the flying-fish, which came on board of itself, and found it good; and here at last he met with men without avoiding their company.

This was on the mainland, inside the great gulf with all the islands lying beyond it in the ocean; from the coast he came up to the high country where a great nation lived, gathered about the foot of the fiery mountain Popocatepetl, at once the symbol of their origin, their fire-giver and their greatest foe. To them he attached himself; if he had not found the shores of the Dead he had yet found mortals, whose lot in their blindness moved him to stay, if thereby he could alleviate their destinies. And here it fell out that, through no particular merit of his own, he was included among their gods and protected the people, so long as he had their support, against those of their deities who were at any rate worse than himself.

The first thing he did for them was to free them from their dependence on the fiery mountain. For they were still no further advanced than the primitive folk they were descended from, who had dwelt around Gunung Api, in the Lost Country; they knew the use of fire but could not themselves produce it, and had to get it from the mountain, the lightning or the forest fire, if their fire went out. Norna Gest taught them the holy need-fire, produced by drilling, the Ice Folk's greatest acquisition and possession; nothing of an art when you knew it, but to the poor primitive people of an importance scarcely to be measured.

With the difference in intelligence that separated them it was no wonder they connected the stranger with the sky and thought he was son of the Sun, perhaps the Sun himself, the first time they saw him conjure up fire between his hands from two pieces of wood.

It weakened the high, cruel Powers of Fire in whose proximity they dwelt and from whose terrors they had derived the conceptions of their gods—the lightning-god Tezcatlipoca, the bloody war-god Huitzilopochtli, to whom they offered human hearts. Quetzalcoatl showed displeasure when they were named, and utterly refused to accept sacrifices of the kinds that were offered to them. In this way a sort of conflict of gods arose, to which the people were witness, greatly desiring that Quetzalcoatl might have the victory; but as it fell out, the decision was postponed to the future, after the departure of Quetzalcoatl.

Besides the art of fire Norna Gest taught them agriculture. Maize, a very good cereal, grew in these countries, but the natives as yet knew nothing of cultivating it; they only gathered what grew wild, ranging all day for a few handfuls of grain. Norna Gest taught them to plant it, made a hole like a mouth in the ground and put a grain in it, feeding the earth and bidding them see what it would do in return. To be sure, they had a long time to wait, most of them forgot all about it; but when the plant came up, and Norna Gest had made the experiment often enough, the connection actually became clear to some of them; little maize gardens outside the villages came to gladden the eyes of Norna Gest and convince him that now they knew the art of giving in order to get back, before he left them. A proof that the hearts of the poor savages were good at bottom was that they repaid this simple service with boundless gratitude and devotion, and raised his chair on an additional foundation that he might sit more loftily.

By degrees he was raised quite on high, with many steps up. In the working of flint he also taught them things of importance and received their excessive thanks. They had positively superstitious ideas of him as a carpenter. The rudiments of the use of metals too he conveyed to them. On the other hand the country possessed no animals that could be tamed. But he taught them to keep birds for the delight they gave. Nay, so unbounded was the skill they attributed to Quetzalcoatl that many things they themselves produced or developed later were credited to him: architecture, social order, the calendar, the construction of canals, acquirements which came much later, after Quetzalcoatl had departed; all blessings were referred to the White God. Even the children's best games were said to have been learnt from him. Not only the people here but other peoples inland and far down the coast had the same tradition of this teacher and benefactor who had first shown them the way to a better mode of existence and had then gone back to his home in the sun or the morning star. From such a depth did they look up to an ordinary human being.

They did everything for Quetzalcoatl while he was with them, offered him flowers and fruit continually, wove him marvels of robes of humming-bird feathers, made him suns of raw gold in the semblance of his face to adorn his temple, showed him every mark of honour, except blood-offerings, which were distasteful to him. As yet, though, these could not altogether be abolished. Huitzilopochtli demanded his food and got it, but for their wars and human slaughterings Quetzalcoatl showed no sympathy; on the contrary, he turned away or stopped his ears when such things were talked of in his presence.

But in order that no living sacrifice might be left untried, they brought him women, bands of the country's choicest maidens, who would otherwise have been slaughtered and whose hearts would have been given to the god, hot, freshly torn out and still beating, while Huitzilopochtli's priests would have eaten the rest, the young, childishly sweet limbs.

Quetzalcoatl let them come to him, kept them and had them maintained as his property. They should surely not die; oh no, quite the reverse, they should taste of life. He let his eye rest upon them and found them fine and beautiful brown buds, with eyes like the tropical night with a firefly in them, limbs like honey, some of them; they were not to be disdained, a wrong that no woman deserves. But there was something not quite right about their joy at being allowed to live and being given to this sun; they could not be brought to raise their eyes to Grandfather, it was as though they froze in their nakedness amid the warmth of his beams.

So, when he considered them ripe, he gave them to young men of their own year, ho, ho, ho, and it was strange to see how they could shine, now it was they whose faces almost looked like little suns!

And afterwards the young people sent kisses up into the air to Quetzalcoatl, as before they had been wont to send kisses up to the sun; and when he was no longer among them they and their descendants scattered kisses to the winds that they might reach him.

For his part the old man had memories which kept him alone for ever.

The longer he lived among these people, who had so much worship in them, the more layers of their sense of distance did they put under him, more and more steps up to him; soon he was sitting high up in the air at the top of a pyramid, and at last he began to feel rather lonely up there.

The time came when Norna Gest longed for home. Those he bore in his heart and carried with him about the world wherever he went, they were dead, and it would be a long time ere he found the land where they had gone; but at home in northern dales dwelt a people of peasants whose ancestor he was; he wanted to walk beneath rowan trees again and meet blunt young swains upon the roads who would greet an old stranger courteously and in whose features he might see that they had blood in them of her who once, many generations ago, had been so dear to him.

Great was the dismay in Tenochtitlan when Quetzalcoatl announced that he would have to depart, and deep the sorrow of those who accompanied him down to the coast. Yet they understood that he wished to return to his bright abodes in the East beyond the ocean. And he had promised them to come again!

Yes, Quetzalcoatl bade them remember that if he did not come, others of his kind would come; they were not to doubt that, even if, perchance, it might be long.

Thereupon Quetzalcoatl stepped into his old tried canoe, poor enough for a god, but so much the more marvellous since he traversed the seas in it, said farewell to his priesthood and dipped his oar; they saw his back as he paddled out, with long considerate strokes. Ah, kindly even to the waves, thought those who stood ashore with tear-dimmed eyes and were never to see Quetzalcoatl again.

And Norna Gest rowed back the immensely long way in the opposite direction.

But the priesthood of Tenochtitlan raised images to him in stone, wherein he could be seen with his curved nose and his beard, with feathers on his head and surrounded by his symbols as the bringer of Light.

Ages passed, and he became a myth. The worship of Huitzilopochtli overshadowed him again, with all its horror, but stronger and stronger lived the tradition that the White God would come again.

VI
THE WHITE GOD'S RETURN

And thus things stood when Columbus opened up the way from Europe to the new countries in the West, which he believed to be India, but which, without *his* ever finding it out, proved to be an entirely new continent, with yet another ocean beyond separating it from India.

It took a century to make out merely the outline of the immense continent, which was given the name of America, centuries more to penetrate the interior of these countries, which extend for the whole length of the earth, through all the zones from one Pole down towards the other. The islands Columbus found came to be called the West Indies, the natives Indians, to the ineradicable memory of the error which formed the basis of his discovery. In the track of Columbus followed a string of other discoverers, whose luck it was to have the way made easier for them; on their heels came adventurers and conquerors, the Conquistadores; Europe had sprung a leak, its expansion was rapid, by leaps and bounds. But to the natives the whole of this invasion from the East seemed at the outset a movement which could be summed up in one and the same strongly agitated point of view: the return of the White God.

What a difference between the time when Quetzalcoatl left them and when he came again! It was the measure of the change wrought by the intervening centuries in him and his race, the variable ones.

The primitive people themselves were not the same, in many respects they had advanced, and in a very different degree in different parts; but in the main they were still living at the beginning of life, with the same primeval power above them, in the terrible likeness of Popocatepetl, fire and judgment. We are acquainted with their existence down to its details through the accounts preserved by history of their encounters with the Whites, for the most part seen from *their* side and furnishing at the same time the history of the destruction of these American nations as nations; it is best to prepare the meeting of these two widely severed cultures, whose roots were nevertheless in contact, by placing ourselves at the natives' point of view before the meeting took place.

The heart of the native American culture, which the Conquistadores thrust at and pierced wherever they came, lay in Mexico, the ancient empire of the Aztecs, in the interior and towards the centre of the two vast half-continents. The world Columbus found lay outside, a rampart of islands in the ocean fencing the great gulf that leads to Mexico, so far away that the report of Columbus was long in reaching Tenochtitlan, the Aztecs' capital. The tradition of Quetzalcoatl, on the other hand, had penetrated from there to the uttermost islands, so that Columbus was received as the White God as soon as he landed on Guanahani; the great tidings only reached Tenochtitlan in a tangible form with the first reports of the approaching Cortes. The description of the two meetings, different as the two men were, is merged in the same bird's-eye view.

Popocatepetl was in eruption during the years when the Europeans arrived in the new world, like Tenerife in the old world they had left; they seemed to be years of terror on both sides, foreboding great events.

In Tenochtitlan there was great alarm, the Lofty One yawned and sent forth fire, nights of horror with a sooty glow high up among the stars in the region of the mountain-top and a flickering gleam which came and went upon the mud walls of the pueblo. What had come over Popocatepetl, the Reeky, who in the memory of priests and other thinkers had continued peacefully smoking into the sky, from which he had his name? Now he gave off pulsing volumes of smoke by day, flashed lightnings and shrouded himself in fetid airs, and at night he smouldered with bursting bubbles of flame, so that even those down below, huddling in the houses of Tenochtitlan, saw a ghostlike gleam in the holes of the roof and could not sleep. A strange sport was witnessed; the mountain puffed out immense smoke-rings, shaped by his mouth, which rolled up slowly towards the summit of heaven, shining at night, and it looked as though Popocatepetl crowned himself with one halo of fire after another, hovering above his head, and a world of lightnings about his brow; was he angry with the stars? Were fearful fiery visions maturing in his mind? The more simple-minded ventured to suppose that the mountain had fallen out with Iztaccihuatl, Popocatepetl's wife with the white head of snow, the other great volcano of the plateau; that must have been the reason why he girt himself about with storms, thundered continually, rocked in his foundations and gave birth to all kinds of tempests; but the vulgar are ever apt to seek an explanation in their own narrow circle of experience. If they cast their eyes upon the priests they could not help noticing that *they* looked pale and shaken, and the turn given to public worship soon taught them that things were greatly amiss.

At the beginning the priests diligently practised their old and tried art of exorcism and conciliation: they smoked the pipe of peace with the mountain. A simple, an inevitable consistency formed the basis of this holy act, which was almost a legal form; you smoked together, and so long as you smoked quietly and moderately down on earth it was expected that the Great Spirit would smoke quietly and moderately up in Heaven, it was as good as an agreement, a covenant, and in fact the mountain had kept to it hitherto. They went up on high, to the top of the temples, so that he might see it, many men together to remind him of the covenant, the whole priesthood with the high priest at their head; they blew smoke up towards him, held up their stone pipes that he might see them: gentle smoking here, *here* they carried out their obligations! In vain. When the pipe of peace failed they saw that the treaty had been denounced. And then there was nothing for it but great blood-offerings. Popocatepetl blazed and was red, his many hundred altars in Tenochtitlan also blazed and were red.

The temples of the Aztecs were their country and their gods over again, in their very forms they were symbols of the worship; from the holy image the child of nature derives all his conceptions, as does the child. The Mexican dwelt on the roof of an immense temple Nature herself had erected, a plateau raised to the height of a mountain above the surrounding country, a land above the land, with its foot in the tropics and the ladder of the zones with its stages of vegetation climbing its sides; and up on the tableland in the rarefied air, the air of the condor, the home of the cactus and the aloe, mighty volcanoes towered yet higher, mountain crowning mountain, gods set on high, as the simple, wise child of nature thinks, and as he is one with almighty Nature and bows down to her, images leap from his soul and take shape in worship; in this way the Aztec temple had come about.

It was formed as a mound, with no interior, encased in masonry, with many terraces and platforms and steps the whole way up; the way the whole people had once ascended was now followed by the priests as a holy symbol. Above, the pyramid ended in a platform, upon which two towers were raised; within them stood the images of the gods. In front of the towers were two altars with fires that never went out, the eternal fire; more than six hundred of them could be seen burning night and day above the mud roofs of the pueblo of Tenochtitlan, and between them stood the stone of sacrifice. The whole arrangement of the temple an image of the mountain, and worship under the open sky, before the eyes of all, as though it was a worship of the mountain himself, Popocatepetl, the Great One, in an image adapted to human wit, but powerful, as is every likeness.

And now that Popocatepetl was disturbed, the disturbance grew more violent here. Evil portents had occurred before the unearthly terrors of the mountain began; some years previously the great lake in which Tenochtitlan was built had overflowed its banks, without any explicable cause, either tempest or earthquake, and had licked off a large piece of the pueblo; comets had been seen; one of the towers of the biggest temple took fire of itself, the finger of God; and finally, just lately, a heavenly portent had been seen, in the East, as it were a fiery pyramid bedecked with stars; not a doubt but great things were approaching from that quarter, or else the end of the world was at hand. So it was high time to appease the Powers and to sway their minds if possible with appropriate gifts.

No less than seventy thousand victims, prisoners of war and whatever else could be used to stock the pens, where they were kept and fattened up; processions two miles long, advancing slowly, step by step, up towards the temples as the head of the column was eaten off, so many at a time, apart from the daily scores and yearly thousands—such was the human contribution given to the gods. The obsidian knife, of volcanic glass taken from Popocatepetl's flanks and endowed with his nerve, was never at rest, and the priests, clad in red tunics, or with the flayed skin of a newly slaughtered victim drawn over them, grew weary, and so heavy with clotted gore from top to toe that they could scarcely keep going; still a god seemed to hold up their arms for yet another day, fresh strength was ever granted them for the few motions they had to perform; when others had stretched the victim on his back over the convex stone of sacrifice, tight across the stomach, they had only to plunge the flint knife in and tear out the throbbing heart with its roots, show it to the god and fling it into his sacrificial bucket. Then down the steps with the rest to those below, who did the quartering and roasting down in the smoking forecourts, where justice was done to the god's appetite, the holy mimicry—a sacrament, but interpreted so literally by many that they went about in a frenzy of slaughter, with eructations so violent that they nearly threw them down, eruptions which on a small scale were again a mimicry of the mountain. Children were sacrificed . . .

Ugh, no, enough! Things yet more repulsive were done, accounts are not lacking; but it almost seems that the abominations become worse in print, which is of a later day, and belongs to another order of imagination. Those who did the deeds were believers, naïve, when all is said and done there was a certain beauty in their thus devoting themselves to their Powers with blood and death; Nature was so immense, and they were innocent souls. Beautiful was primitive man in his submission to the mountain and the sun, the great marvels at which the enlightened stares in spiritual poverty; Nature was still within his heart, not outside it. Naturally the brute in him also asserted itself—has it even now died out altogether in the enlightened?

Meanwhile, for all their sacrifices and ceremonies, the evil omens did not show any signs of being warded off; and in fact they proved true enough, truer even than had been suspected. And in the presence of so much that presaged ill in Nature, and so much tension among the Aztecs themselves, they tried more and more to fortify themselves in the hope of Quetzalcoatl's return.

Besides the ancient sacred traditions which were kept alive by Quetzalcoatl's priests and by his images and temples—a great but distant tradition—new ones were gradually coming in, without any one knowing exactly where they came from, rumours in the air, such as occur among primitive people who breathe an image from one to another over great distances, short memories, but the rumour lives: Quetzalcoatl *had* been seen!

He was said to be already on the coast, out among the farthest islands, and it was only a question of time when they might expect him on the mainland. Well, well, let him come! Ah yes, all for the best, Huitzilopochtli was hard; even the most zealous in sacrificing to him, Montezuma himself, the high priest and war lord, could but sigh for his own part and feel loathing; he was eating everything up—would that a milder god might come!

It took a score of years before the report of the white man's coming reached the Tenochtitlan, just as the light reaches us from a star which no longer exists. Columbus was dead; and when at last Quetzalcoatl followed his rumour from the islands to the mainland it was not in the person of Columbus but of Cortes that he was received by the Aztecs.

The excitement occasioned by Columbus soon died away, like rings in the water when a stone has been thrown into it; he did not distinguish himself as some of his successors, nor were they the right people he had come in contact with. The first of all, as we have seen, out on the extreme coral islands and skerries facing the ocean, were nothing but poor crab-eaters, without power or possessions, scarcely even capable of great sensations; and yet the meeting was an overwhelming one, so much had they of a culture which was otherwise distant and had its centres on the mainland, that they knew it for the coming of Quetzalcoatl, that day when the strange many-voiced thunder was heard from the sea, lightnings in broad daylight, and the three winged wonders swept in round the north of the island and lay to under the lee of its western shore.

Emotional images, vast and vague, like dazzling mirrors in the soul, arose at once in those who saw anything at all; the majority turned their blind end and dashed headlong into the bush. The women's part was a distant flicker, like everything that happened in the world of men; some disaster, no doubt, this time, perhaps the sea had gone to pieces; what a frightful thing!

But there are those to whom curiosity is the most ungovernable of all forces, it would draw them into the very jaws of death, simply to look down his throat; this sort stayed upon the beach; nay, they even went to meet the god and his attendants when they came ashore. Gradually, as their heads cooled, they began to see properly and experienced the greatest expansion of the soul, as when one infers the unknown from the known and it tallies: why, they were *big canoes* these marvels, mighty huge canoes, too big to be true, but canoes all the same, not to be mistaken! There were trees growing out of them, and they had wings, which they were now folding; they were higher than a man could shoot with a bow, and all at once they had young, a baby marvel that pushed off from the mother and came paddling in to land. Of course, gods who came from the Ocean must live in big canoes, and naturally they carried thunder and lightning with them, for the god in heaven is known by these signs. And now they were to see him!

He seemed to have wings as he stepped ashore, great gloriously coloured things fluttering from his shoulders, and his face was that of Quetzalcoatl, as even the most foolish person could tell, big and fair, with a thick golden beard, not a doubt but it was he! His eyes were like the sky, but he was clothed like the sea, in a shining blue sheath, like a big beetle —God guard our tongues!—but is not the beetle a god too? In his hand he carried a long, long knife, nothing like bamboo, but what was it made of? A flame, a thing of air? The foremost and boldest of the natives was to find out how it felt, for when God held it out to him in greeting he grasped it and cut his fingers.

The great white strangers performed a curious dance; they knelt on the sand and seemed to address themselves to the heaven they had just come from, lifting up their voices in chorus, slow and powerful notes; and the tallest and whitest among them planted his wings in the sand, delivered a message and caused it to be traced on white tablets, a ceremony of which the savages understood nothing at all—least of all that it meant their own island did not belong to them any more.

Besides the wings, or whatever they were, they raised a tree on the beach, with a man on it hung up to die, only an image but very lifelike; and in the hands of the strangers the savages noticed smaller copies of the same stake bearing a tortured corpse.

?? Shaking of heads . . .

And he who shook his head wore a yellow ring in his nose; that did not escape the attention of the strangers . . .

Thus did they meet, these two whom the ages had parted; the one naked as he was born, still reposing with his child's soul in Nature's bed-chamber, the other clad in iron and bearing about him many deposits which *his* existence had taught him. One side saw in the other the messengers of Heaven and were to have their vision corrected before very long; the other side came with an equipment of factitious dreams which they were to exchange for a reality they did not care for. Such was the traffic that would take place between them, with many, many other consequences.

In all the islands at which Columbus afterwards touched he was taken for the White God, until he, and more particularly his men, took pains to make the natives better informed. Columbus did not treat them harshly, even when as Viceroy and Governor he had to keep order in the colonies he founded, no more than the rights of war according to the ideas of the time; but he had not much luck either. He sold the natives into slavery a little—the morality of the age; and that was not the worst thing, even as certain women prefer rape to missing their destiny—wherever he went he scraped the place clean for gold and reversed the natives' ideas of the yellow metal; it had been prized for its colour, because it reminded them of Quetzalcoatl; now they had a better understanding of its value, since the white men flew at each other's throats to get at it first; one might rather ask how much a red beard was worth in terms of the heavy yellow dust.

Reverence for the messengers of Heaven received a blow, and all the archangels Columbus left behind in a stockaded camp in Haiti, before returning home from his first voyage, were simply killed off—a lot of galley-slaves and swashbucklers, expert in tearing gold rings out of native ears and capable of surmounting the barrier of dirt, grease and stench which separated them from the natives' women—among them poor young Pedro Gutierrez, who had been put in command. Oh, they were very mortal, the white gods, and reeled just like other men, whether they got it with the bamboo knife, arrows from an ambush, or clubs on the head, twenty natives against one.

When Columbus returned he found them buried here and there, some of them, a nest of carrion full of ants; one of their heads he found in a basket in a native hut. Business was opened.

A trifling incident has been preserved about one of the savages from Guanahani whom Columbus met again later as he was sailing on among the islands and hauled up, for political reasons, in order to cover him with gifts and let him paddle on and make a good impression wherever he landed. He had in his canoe—the inventory is from Columbus's own papers—a piece of native bread as big as a fist, a calabash of water, a piece of red earth powdered and then kneaded into a dough, and some dried leaves, "which must be a thing they set great store by, since they have already brought me some of them as gifts in San Salvador" (tobacco); "and he carried with him a little basket of the native kind, in which he had a chain of small glass beads and two stivers" . . . which showed Columbus that the man came from San Salvador, where he had received these gifts from himself, in exchange for cotton, parrots and spears, which the natives brought of their own accord as offerings to the gods. We can imagine the naked savage in his canoe, far out at sea, paddling for dear life, hastening towards a distant island, where perhaps he has friends to whom before too many suns have set he *must* show his prodigious treasures and tell of the rich god from whose own hand he has received them!

For the untried savages were at first quite staggered with joy at all the wonders that came to them over the sea and of which they had a share. Even now, four hundred years after, our ears may be haunted by a faint tinkle of all the little bells with which Columbus and all the other discoverers after him enticed the natives; the old papers that tell the story of the discoveries simply ring with bells, a huge decoy performance, part of the same trick as the glass beads, red rags and the little mirrors, the backs of which the savages couldn't help clutching the first time they had them in their hands, to get hold of the mystical brother behind.

The little bells which had such a success are always referred to as hawk's bells; they were the kind hunting hawks had on their claws to ring in their flight when they swooped from the sky upon the heron, the primitive joy of the hunter; a bell of this kind is to be seen in Holbein's portrait of a nobleman with a hawk; sleighbells are descended from them, and little bells on the reins with which we played at horses as children are the last survivors of them. The medieval predilection for the sound of bells—people once wore them on their clothes—was now discarded to the savages and found a market among them; ah yes, the cannibal, already tricked out to advantage with a bone in his nose and pegs in his ears and nothing else, swaggered about happily with a bell tied in the towzle of his hair. You could lure them to you from a distance with the seductive music, they stood as though rooted to the ground and turned their ear: a little god, a bright thing with a mouth that sang in sweet tones—a smile spread on the face of the cannibal, so that you saw a head full of big, white, greedy teeth; but a hair was enough to bind him when he was moved, his hand came out: if he might but have it, if the little god might be his!

Then they put him to scraping gold dust out of the river sand for fourteen racking days, and he came with his bag, all bent and weighed down on one side from the load, heavy enough to bring a man to his knees, and got his bell, turned his back, went, and his shoulders showed how happy he was. Old hardened caciques with white hair on their legs hobbled long distances to listen to the speech of the bell, it was yet vouchsafed them in the evening of their life to catch a sound so lovely. Youth will always run after a new thing, but here old experience had to admit that it was no delusion, but a real, tangible, divine marvel!

This was the little tinkler; later came the big bell. The time was not far off when from the solid walls of churches it would peal out over coral beach and mangrove, startling birds and filling the sunrise and sunset, as in the old countries.

Ay . . . just as a few centuries before, when the first brave missionaries pressed into the dense forests of Northern Europe and tempted the rude natives in their cowhides with the prayer-bell. There too it had begun with a little bell and ended with the great doomsday peals of the cathedrals.

Was it then a discarded thing which had now grown too old for Europe and might suitably and with advantage be imposed upon the savages overseas?

In any case the bell which thus ingratiated itself with its lively note meant no harm; it was never the intention of a man like Columbus that the poor creatures who sat in darkness should be won to grace by other than gentle means.

The Conquistadores had other ideas. What did they have cannons for? The souls of the heathen . . . put them in harness first and then the sacrament! Nor were the natives of the mainland so harmless as the happy islanders out in the ocean; the first Whites who had anything to do with them got a taste of their *macquauitl,* a wooden sword with obsidian flakes fixed in both edges, a horrible weapon; the Mexicans were still living in the Stone Age but had not much to learn in the art of making holes in human skin, and they were a numerous, respectable enemy; no cosseting was wasted on them in the course of their conversion to Christianity.

The first news the Mexicans had of the great strangers was when Grijalva appeared off the coast with his ships. The conquest was undertaken from Cuba, where Diego Velasquez was Governor, one of the great family of the Diegos, who now began to get their foot in and spread themselves in the new world. Grijalva had been preceded by another hidalgo, Cordova, who had been in these parts rummaging for slaves, and had put in at Yucatan—which means, "What do you say?" a corruption of the natives' question, *tectetan,* when they did not understand the white men's language, and the country is called so to this day. He saw great permanent buildings there, not palm-leaf huts that would burn in a moment like those in the islands, and the natives were rude, indelicate, able-bodied men, and short of temper. Grijalva's experiences on the coast beyond the gulf came near to martyrdom, he got a dusting, and was chased out to sea again with the remnant of his men.

Among them was Bernal Diaz, who afterwards, when an old man in Guatemala, wrote his reminiscences, an incomparable work, and an incomparable man, eye-witness and participator in the whole conquest of Mexico, brave, simple, without guile, a true, noble Spaniard, and an honourable pen to boot; he it was who even in peace time could not sleep except in armour and on the floor; when he was out of the game a mighty clockwork in him, running down, caused him to write a book bulky as Homer, and as weighty in its contents.

Only the *Iliad* can be compared with the story of the conquest of Mexico, but we are so much nearer to it in time; the action is equally heroic, but the actors are men we almost know. Is that age so far from us? Only thirteen or fourteen generations separate us from it, a living tradition from grandfather to grandson would not have been repeated so very many times, and might have reached us orally, if written authorities had not rendered it superfluous. Here then is the voice of Bernal Diaz across the ages; it is meet to make obeisance to his book, and to refer those to it who would be witnesses of the conquest of Tenochtitlan. Here but a brief attempt will be made to bring out those features which throw light on the meeting between the child of nature and the white man.

The name of the Indian who saw Grijalva's ships and brought the news to Tenochtitlan has come down to us; he was called Pinotl, and was one of Montezuma's tax-gatherers down on the coast. To him came another Indian telling him that he had seen winged towers which moved hither and thither out at sea. Others who were sent as scouts reported that they had seen two such towers at sea, and from one of them a canoe had been put into the water with a kind of men in it; they were white in the face, and had big beards, and were cased in strange bright and shining sheaths. Then Pinotl himself hurried to the coast, and was lucky enough to meet the strangers, even went on board one of the towers, and had a conversation with them; much play of features, we may presume, and an abundance of finger language on the part of the strangers, from which it appeared that the business of the shining beings was to come and visit the great lord in the great city up beyond the mountains of which they had heard . . . he was very rich, wasn't he? how much gold? Arms spread out, and mimic invitations to Pinotl to spread out his arms and show how much gold his master had.

As soon as the towers had flown away to another part of the coast, where, as we have seen, Grijalva was half cut to pieces by the natives' flint swords and afterwards avoided the shore, Pinotl travelled night and day till he reached Tenochtitlan, where he presented himself to Montezuma and the whole Council, and declared that he had seen and talked with gods. Pinotl had caused descriptions of the gods and their sea-palaces to be drawn up on aloe-paper in picture-writing and Mexican hieroglyphics, and these were laid before the Council.

If we had them now! If only they existed as a marginal note to the sanguinary and moving tragedy which was soon to be enacted! They would have been evidence of how the Aztecs conceived and pictured the Spanish knights whom they took for gods; the scale was added by themselves. But no doubt they served with other combustibles to heat the pot in which some Spanish soldier cooked his supper, according to the habit of these descendants of the Vandals. They shared the fate of all the priceless golden works of art from Mexico which went into the melting-pot; the treasures of Peru, which Pizarro laid hands on, vases and wheels of gold, so many that they filled a room twenty-two feet long, and sixteen feet wide, to a height of nine feet from the floor, the ransom of Atahuallpa —which did not save his life—treasures whose value as works of art no European was ever to guess, and which Pizarro ran his bloated swashbuckler's eye over before having them beaten flat, so as not to take up too much room in the heap, and then melted down. The butcher did not know that their value as antiquities was more than their weight in gold, and they rose again in the form of the many four-fold inch-thick gold chains which grace the bull-necks in the portraits of all the sixteenth-century princes and grandees, the *Family,* the end of all estates and all gold: a superfluity of it in Europe and all the corpses, the overthrow of nations in mythical America! But that is the story of Pizarro, the exterminator of the Incas, a chapter by itself and a later one in the red book of the Conquistadores.

Courage is required to pronounce judgment on these terrible men, in whose hands more destiny was laid than Nature had designed captains of condottieri to deal with; for *they* were courageous, perfectly mad fellows as regards life and limb, and one would have to feel equal to a duel with them, even in retrospect, before putting them in their place. They placed themselves where they now stand, men of iron before the eyes of all; we must be content to regard them and leave judgment to self-destructive Nature, which produced them to the doom of many and to the assurance, in any case, of their own memory. Even bad men they can scarcely be called; when Pizarro as an old man died a violent death, stabbed by Almagro's gang who betrayed him on his own threshold, after fencing like an angel and reviling them entrancingly, he drew a cross of his own blood on the floor with his finger and kissed it before he breathed his last; that man was not solid all through, he had a little space inside in which he kept the image of his God. And with all he brought about Cortes captivates us by a certain extraordinary gaiety, the warrior's and sportsman's superfluous vitality, the propensity to outbursts of joviality among friends, for they were all young, a band of high-spirited boys let loose in a new world; in the face of a cruel death for themselves or for the overwhelming masses of their enemies they could not leave a trooper's jest unspoken or forbear to taste the fruits the country offered. Both Cortes and Pizarro were *Estremeños,* natives of Estremadura, where from of old the population had been a cross between Goths and Moors, without a doubt a very powerful mixture and a clue to the understanding of a character in which chivalry and contempt for human life, pomp and cruelty, imagination and absence of nerves, fortitude, faithlessness, pretty nearly all qualities except weakness, formed a whole of such vitality and frightfulness.

To give Cortes fair play we must in the first place not forget that with an army of six hundred and ten men he entered a country, by nature a fortress, with a population of millions, armies of hundreds of thousands of devils, after having burnt his ships, to conquer it or die. But he had ten cannons and sixteen horses! At his back his own people lay in wait, the Governor of Cuba, with the authority of the Spanish State, who was jealous of his enterprise; at a decisive moment he had to turn against a hostile Spanish army, the Narvaez episode, with all Mexico about his ears; but he beat him and diluted his own band with his men, forcing disasters to his own advantage, and ploughed his bloody way on, in the track of the guns, towards the fable city of Tenochtitlan.

Pinotl's report convinced Montezuma and all other initiates that Quetzalcoatl was in the country. And when in the following year Cortes arrived, he met with the reception due to the White God, though not entirely without reservation; there was a certain hesitation about it, for the interval had already added features to the traditional idea of the god of goodness which were somewhat at variance therewith: first Cortes' relentless war against the Tlascalans, the enemies of the Aztecs, and then his alliance with them, a step unlike Quetzalcoatl and one very dangerous to Tenochtitlan.

But otherwise there could be but little doubt that they were, if not Quetzalcoatl himself, his descendants, in any case *Teules,* supernatural beings. They were associated with fire and thunder, or were themselves thunder gods, that was granted, not rumour and vague talk but actual fact; a sufficient number of people had seen and heard the thunder-engine in their hands and seen the results; the frightful pipe from which fire and smoke leaped, just as from the mouth of Popocatepetl, and with the same deadly effect at a distance as the lightning: trees sent flying in splinters a long, long way from where the thunder was heard, and bloody lanes opened in the native army long before they came near to the ranks of the Teules, men torn to pieces wholesale; Popocatepetl could not have raged more furiously with his showers of stones and lightnings. Occasionally they had even found the thunderbolt lying cold on the ground, but a portent even when dead, heavy, round, of an unknown hardness and with a cold, blue lustre underneath its crust; evidently the same stuff as their thin swords, blue as the air, which gave off lightning while still far away and which they whirled so pitilessly in hand-to-hand fighting; the same stuff as the sheaths were made of which covered them from top to toe, with only little slits for the eyes to look out of, impenetrable to any weapon.

Ah, how poor were the Mexicans' little smoke tricks compared with the Teules'; at the beginning they advanced towards them with their incense-ladles full of smouldering copal, and smoked at them, an idea borrowed from the mountain and of presumed mystical effect, since he whom they smoked was thought, by virtue of similarity and in connection with perfume, to be brought under the influence of their gods. Alas, they needed a favourable wind if the smoke was to reach any one; and there was no heavy, round, murderous body with it to emphasize the enchantment and tear holes in the order of battle. No, they were only human, and the strangers were children of the Sun.

Xicotencatl, the leader of the Tlascalans, finally put the matter to the proof, while his people were still opposed to the Teules; if they were children of the Sun it was to be assumed that they only enjoyed their strength in the daytime when the sun was out; he was therefore advised to attack them at night—but what happened? He found them wide awake and fully aware of the secret plan before the attack took place; they knew everything, useless to strive any more with gods! The authors of the plan had their entrails taken out and pepper put in their place, by way of letting them feel remorse, and Xicotencatl then entered into an alliance with the sons of the Sun as the most sensible alternative, since he had to make a choice.

It was this Xicotencatl's aged blind father, a man of great influence in the country, who begged permission to feel Cortes' countenance, as he could not see him, after peace had been established; and what he felt was perhaps the best characterization of Cortes, if it could have been translated into language; but the old blind Indian took it into the grave with his finger-tips.

Other proofs presented themselves, both to the Tlascalans and to the Aztecs: Cortes sent men up Popocatepetl, and that while it was in full eruption, under the leadership of a certain Ordaz, not without the Christian name of Diego; a demented band who tramped up over Popocatepetl's brow, to the horror and profound distaste of everybody in Mexico, for if they were without fear they ought at least to have had modesty! But it was done, and the mountain allowed it, a fresh proof that they were gods, unpleasant ones, but gods. Cortes was even cool enough to have sulphur brought from Popocatepetl's crater for the production of powder: the identity was obvious, destroyers both!

Not only did they command thunder and lightning but bows with arrows like those of men, cross-bows—the wrath of God in their hands; they had a loud and evil clang, like a hurtling in the air; too late then to jump aside, the bolt was in you, and you had to put your hand behind you to feel it before you fell, it went right through. And these deadly things were tipped with the blue sky-metal, the same kind as the heavy round thunderbolts. Fire would not bite on it; on the contrary it did it good, a ball like this grew bright in the fire, dazzling at last like the very sun, of which of course it was a part; so there again they were face to face with the marvel.

But then the horses! Those who saw a horseman for the first time and naturally thought it was *one* creature, the heavy Spanish tilting chargers, in iron and trappings like their riders, and the trussed and clanking man on top, a single six-limbed, snorting creature charging along—oh, they raised a howl, fell down, crept on all fours to get away, hopelessly, but they couldn't move; they had been struck with a palsy, were like toads inside and out, sick axolotls out of their element; they lightened themselves in their fright, like certain birds when they take wing; the day they saw a horseman for the first time taught them panic. But what when the creature broke in two! For sometimes the man dismounted, and made two terrors out of one! If they had really been reptiles, the luckless ones who saw it, they would certainly have lost their tails; they would have been driven to the extremity of letting their tails go; but they were men and could only shudder until they collapsed, and there they lay.

Cortes took advantage of this, as Bernal Diaz tells us, the terror inspired by the horses at first, to make an impression on an embassy the natives sent to his camp. He had a mare concealed behind the place to which the ambassadors were shown, taking care that it was to windward, and at the right moment had a stallion led forward; it instantly reared and advanced on its hind-legs, with its shoed forefeet in the air, flying mane and fiery eyes, roaring loudly, straight at the spot where the ambassadors stood, while at the same time a cannon was fired! It had the desired moral effect.

If we had had pictorial representations by the Mexicans of their first impression of the horse, or could only realize their conception—a pity we cannot, for *that is how it looks!*

Cortes and his band of young hidalgos and desperadoes had some fun out of that incident! When the place where the messengers had stood was empty, the natives swept away from it as though by a waterspout, they must have burst into their loud peals of laughter. Cortes twirled his moustaches sky-high, one in each hand, and nearly fell backwards with swagger, cocking his legs and strutting. Oh, ho, ho, they knew the tricks! Alvarado, how he laughed! Alvarado, that great tall favourite of fortune, the darling of the expedition, the darling of the chroniclers ever since, and of all his fellows the one the Mexicans observed, feared and admired most; for he was quite fair, a giant with a head made up of gold and sunshine, of pure Gothic blood; they called him *Tonatiuh,* Son of the Sun, and were above all inclined to take him for Quetzalcoatl or his descendant, though he was not the actual leader. He was a mighty soldier and a fountain of mirth, the songster of the camp and the one who led the chorus of laughter when wit took fire, and be sure the jesting was of the strongest. Of Alvarado history has left us a long, exciting romance, tearing up and down, now bright-coloured, now clouded, but always heroic and stirring—his women a separate chapter; by his precipitancy he came near upsetting the whole conquest of Mexico, but he shines for all time through the personal bravery he displayed; he afterwards became the conqueror of Guatemala.

After the episode of the stallion, which happened not long after Cortes had landed on the coast, a personage came upon the stage who was to play a decisive part in the conquest of Mexico; a woman, Doña Marina, or, as she was generally called, Malina. She arrived among the Spaniards as one of the female slaves sent by the terrified embassy for the mollification of the strangers, but she was an Aztec by birth and therefore valuable as an interpreter and spy when the Spaniards came up on to the plateau and began to march against Tenochtitlan. She is reported to have been very beautiful and intelligent at the same time, was soon personally attached to Cortes as his secretary and had a son by him, proof that gods and mortals are capable of crossing; soon the country was overrun with demigods.

In contradistinction to other heroic women known to history—Judith, Ildico—who sacrificed themselves for the salvation of their people by delivering themselves into the power of the enemy, she indeed gave herself up, but only to betray the people she belonged to; clearly it was a new world that the strangers had come to.

We shall not judge her; only a woman is permitted to annihilate a whole population—she can produce a new one. Nature manifests itself in her deeds—keep her bound! Bound Malina had been, but the worm of chance had eaten through her bonds, and now she was free, let loose between two powers which were approaching each other as a lava-stream approaches a tidal wave; let loose indeed, a demon stretching its serpent's belly and throbbing with destruction, naked and drenched with love, in the bare glory of her tropical body, as though made of copper, and one or two parrot's feathers in her hair, delighting in her soul over slaughter—the obscure, self-destroying soul of her people.

She led Cortes into Tenochtitlan, interpreted to him what her countrymen said

—Spanish she had learnt from Cortes' lips—she mixed among the Aztecs and ferreted out their plans, disclosed them in good time to Cortes and thus gave him all the trumps in his hand. Woman's most astonishing talent, that of listening, of being everywhere with ear and mind and catching all that is in the air, this she had to an astonishing degree. What if she had used it to betray the speech of Cortes and his friends, for the good of those in Tenochtitlan, her own blood, her family and relations among them? No, all there is to be said is that that was not Malina's way, for such was her love of Cortes.

And so she nosed in and out, lovely and deadly, like the reinforced blending of the qualities of serpent and beast of prey which is peculiar to the weasel, the ferret and the ocelot. And every time Cortes clearly manifested the powers of a god by knowing beforehand all the plans of the Aztecs, their thoughts almost; it was she, their own flesh and blood, who was the power within his power! And it was part of her voluptuousness to lay her whole people at his feet, every man of them, torn and bleeding. How she must have loved him! Bernal Diaz says that Cortes was rather knock-kneed. Before setting out on this expedition he decked himself as leader with a plume in his helm and a medal on his breast, anticipated honours; many other things might be dug up to Cortes' disadvantage, but we are constrained to leave them alone and say that he had the love of Malina.

If the Aztecs were thus scared to their very souls by the firearms and horses of the Spaniards, not to mention their divine origin, there were also things on the side of the Mexicans which impressed Cortes. Not their numbers or their hideous warpaint and uncivilized weapons, the fact of being opposed by hosts of a thousand to one, the air full of obsidian-tipped arrows, an enemy that fought with broken glass, and howling, like a tidal wave of shrieking souls washed up from hell—none of these things got on Cortes' nerves. But they were cannibals!

Cortes was genuinely scandalized in his religious feelings. One of the first things that had happened on their march from the coast up into the hills was that a cacique, devout in his own way, had caused some fifty prisoners to be slaughtered, and offered the white gods cakes dipped in their blood; Cortes had been genuinely offended. An unchristian thing, the grossest of all sins, though not mentioned among the deadly sins of Holy Church—its possibility had never been imagined; Cortes positively developed theological skill on the question of anthropophagy and felt that he had an official mission to make an end of this abominable heresy, by all the force of arms if necessary (the symbol of the Host did not occur to him). From a purely personal point of view Cortes was repelled by this form of bloodshed, even to feeling ashamed of humanity; it gave the great strong man emotions he could scarcely control, of a purely nervous nature, like a woman when she sees a spider crawling; he got creeps, huh, huh, talked in falsetto and was a prey to fits of debility which only a refreshing day on the battlefield with stacks of Indians mown down by the guns was able to dispel.

This feeling remained fresh during the whole campaign, nay, it increased in strength the more examples of the Aztecs' gruesome degradation came to his knowledge. In the same proportion the Mexicans lost their awe of the white strangers. The glad tidings that this was the expected coming of Quetzalcoatl nobody could continue to take seriously—superstition that; whether they were Teules or not was doubtful; many had already come to the conclusion that they were quite ordinary, dirty, rapacious men. The horses that they had feared so much were the

first cause of their mortal nature being revealed; they managed to kill a few of them; the Spaniards buried the first ones, lest the truth should come out, but it came out.

Later, things were found on the Aztecs' altars which they had offered to their gods in the first days of the war, amongst them a horseshoe, a Flemish hat and a letter, things which in a strangely living way bring us near to both parties; it was not to remain at that.

But even after Cortes and his men had lost the advantage of being regarded as supernatural, they still had much in reserve, their frightfulness as men.

To Cortes' mission as an apostle of the Faith was added the overwhelming impression he gained of the wealth of Mexico, whereby we do not mean in the first instance its natural resources, but portable property. This came when Montezuma was civil enough to send him presents even as he was marching on the city; trifles scarce worthy of a god's acceptance, as the ambassadors politely expressed it, but in the eyes of the Spaniards fortunes in gold and precious stones, besides works of art, which were ordered to be beaten flat and melted down on the spot. But if *that* was a modest sample—what treasures of Golconda might they not expect to find in the city itself! And they were right.

The Aztecs' fate was sealed.

VII

THE EAGLE AND THE SERPENT

The most ancient symbol of the Aztecs, which was connected with the founding of Tenochtitlan, the place of the cactus rock, was a rock on which just enough mould had collected for the cactus to grow; on the cactus sat an eagle, and in its beak it held a serpent; the natural features of the Mexican plateau summed up in an image.

On the spot where the first Aztecs saw this sign they had built their pueblo. After the arrival of the Spaniards they might have extended this totem to signify their fate, in a dramatic sense, a duel to the death. To this day it is the national standard of Mexico: the Eagle and the Serpent united and combining their forces.

But the epoch of Cortes was typified by the eagle swooping down upon the rattlesnake with beak and claw.

The conquest of Mexico is known to all, in its several data: how Cortes advanced on to the plateau, the conspiracy of Cholula, Malina's service and the massacre, the entrance into Mexico and Montezuma's captivity in his own city, the parenthesis with Narvaez and Alvarado's doubtful conduct in Mexico during the absence of Cortes, the revolt, Montezuma's death and the disastrous retreat from Mexico, the return and the siege, the sacrifice of the Spanish prisoners, the famine among the natives, and finally their surrender. All this we have in lengthy descriptions, losing in rapidity of action the more they are detailed.

With due respect to the true sequence of events, our memory, our inner eye, pictures the conquest of Mexico in foreshortening, a free consideration of the characters as they develop in one place, no matter whether events chanced to come before or after, the law of the drama; we see these protagonists before us, Cortes and Montezuma, Malina, Alvarado, Sandoval and other heroes, Huitzilopochtli and his repulsive priests, the harrowing night when Spaniards and Mexicans fought together in the gloomy cannibal city floating on causeways in a salt lake like a Venice of the Underworld—the threescore naked, shivering Europeans who were sacrified up on Huitzilopochtli's teocalli, in full view of all the survivors—what a panopticon! Burning altars, burning houses, the whole scene shown up by fire, and in the background Popocatepetl in the burning sky, fire above fire!

And the piece may begin quite chronologically with the conspiracy, with Montezuma in the foreground, in person, not hiding in the wings, and the scene Tenochtitlan; the massacre we can lump together with Alvarado's massacre, and assign the butcheries, multipled by two, to the great spring festival, historically enough as regards the second; the rest, the great fight in the city, the storming of the temples, the retreat, the sacrifices, the investment and starvation, we can present in rapid acts succeeding or jostling one another.

Well then: the Spring Festival. It was celebrated with remarkable ancient rites, a young Aztec being chosen for his strength and beauty, proclaimed as a god and married to four of the most beautiful maidens in the country, whereafter the honeymoon was solemnized with all possible luxury and magnificence for twenty days, a symbol of fertility and of the return of spring with all its gifts. On the twenty-first day the festival took on a more general character; all the young men and maidens dressed themselves in holiday attire, gorgeous cloaks of quetzal-feathers with jewels and gold on their limbs, spring made visible, and in a great solemn procession, so sacred that no other public act, not even war, might take place on that day, they accompanied the young family, the god and his brides, across the great square in the centre of Tenochtitlan and up all the steps to the top of the great temple. Here all knelt and worshipped the young god, in whose form Tegcatlipoca himself was presumed to have taken up his abode. Thereupon he was handed over to the priests, sacrificed and slain; his heart was thrown into the golden incense-bowl before the image of the god, and his limbs were delivered to the congregation, to be devoured amid dancing and song.

But all is not as it should be at this festival, it is destined to be interrupted before it can be brought to a harmonious conclusion. The young caciques marching in the procession, the flower of the Aztec nobility, in precious garments of feathers, and with old hereditary emeralds, do they look as unconcerned and innocent as is fitting at a festival of joy? Put your hand on their hearts and perhaps you will feel something hard; for what purpose do they carry the macquauitl under the very raiment of innocence? Dark is the Mexican by nature, but if you look around in the teeming streets of the pueblo, you will notice perhaps that to-day they are more than usually dark, with lips drawn in and eyes like their own muddy lake.

There is one who reads all these faces like an open book, Cortes; for he knows the cipher, and it is Malina who has given it him. She has been quietly at work, at night, naked as a snake round all the holes and corners of the pueblo, using her ears here, playing the wide-mouthed native woman there, within hearing of a couple of distinguished old caciques; all the disguise she needs is to make herself suitably ugly, not an easy thing for this glaring flame of a woman, but she manages it; in the likeness of a perfectly doltish slave she carries water in and out of the inner sanctuaries of the highest priestly initiates; she is with Montezuma without his suspecting it, a meeting more secret than the abyss; therefore it is that Cortes is so all-knowing, and his lip curls so grimly under the moustache, inscrutable to all . . . what preparations has not *he* been making in the profoundest secrecy!

A notable trio indeed, as they stand

ıere in a mannerly group to watch the pring-time pass in gay and joyous proession—Cortes, Montezuma and Malina. ;ortes iron-clad from head to foot in onour of the feast, full dress, with his weaty soldier's nose sniffing out of his elmet; Montezuma plainly dressed with nly a few jewels; as the chief man of the ealm he has no need of magnificence, nd he is in mourning, for though, of ourse, he stands here as a free man, the bject of the deepest obeisances, he nows he is a prisoner; finally Malina, 'ith feathers on her head and a little pron of humming-bird feathers in open'ork. The three can only bestow courtly miles on one another, gracious and ıincing, as they stand there knowing 'hat the other knows; that is to say, ;ortes and Malina know what Monteuma knows, and look him in the face 'hen he speaks with an air of frankness –but *he* doesn't know that artillery is osted all round the square, and grimy unners match in hand, and that cavalry, ıen in the saddle, drawn swords and all, re waiting behind the doors, which are eady to swing open. . . .

Then it is that the three princely specators, around whom a courteous distance as hitherto been preserved, seem to beome the centre of a circle which draws ver closer, composed as it happens enirely of very tall Aztecs, warlike in apearance, but, of course, unarmed, only ı long, voluminous cloaks. . . .

How pleasant on a festal day like this ɔ be able to put away all thoughts of loodshed and abandon oneself entirely o the confidence one feels in an honourble prince, says Cortes with a bow, as he ɔoks Montezuma in the face, purring hrough his moustache. He puts his face o close to Montezuma's that the Emeror shrinks back a little as he nods conırming the truth of the remark.

But Cortes comes still closer with his big, sweaty face, and there is a glint of steel in those prominent, audacious blue eyes. He drops his voice and adds another sentence or two, which appear to have a deadly effect upon Montezuma. The life ebbs out of him, his eyes, his features, his frame; he is a dead man, as one is who has betrayed and failed, and is told it to his face by his enemy.

Yes, Cortes tells him in a few dry words that he knows all his schemes, the conspiracy against his life which is ripe for this very moment . . . and by his side Malina crouches, leaning forward so that Montezuma may see her face. He turns yet greyer, for now he knows her, by a gleam she puts into her eyes, so that he remembers her and the night, and how he disclosed all, and in an instant he sees the whole wretchedness of his situation.

Cortes still holds him as though spitted on his gaze, with his face close to his—Eagle and Serpent!—but then he gives over his features entirely to cruelty, draws himself up and throws his gloved hand in the air. A band of disguised Tlascalans, his allies, who have been spread about among the crowd, fall upon certain of the Aztecs, the conspiring caciques and high chieftains, eloquently disclosing the weapons concealed beneath their cloaks—within an hour they are burnt alive at the stake, with a fire of native arrows and spears, a very brisk blaze, under them.

But Cortes' raised hand is a sign for more than that—all at once the cannons thunder from every side, the houses open like yawning mouths, and slowly Alvarado rides out, like a shining tower of steel, man and horse in one, swaying rhythmically up and down, and behind him all the cavalry with closed visors and bright gleaming swords in the air. And now the soldier in Cortes takes fire, now the general is ready for action; with his left hand he closes his helm, and with his right he draws his long singing sword from its sheath, spitting between hand and hilt—*Iago!* A loud, piercing scream is heard at his side, like a leaping ocelot; it is Malina giving vent to her rapacious heart.

Alarum. Volleys of guns and muskets, the twang of cross-bows, cavalry charges, and all the daintily adorned spring procession, the pick of the country's youth, lies swimming in its blood; the god who was to be sacrified so prettily to himself is knocked down with his flowery wreaths about his head and trodden out of recognition under the horses' hoofs; bloody furrows are ploughed through the tightly packed crowds in the streets, so easily swept from the square; shrieks, curses and death.

And then an ominous pause, a hundred thousand souls hold their breath in horror at what has happened and what there may be to come.

The results: the revolt, the rising of the whole of Mexico, not the nobles this time but the people, whipped up by the priests, the holy war of extermination against this vermin that pretended to be gods and had seized upon the pueblo in order to snatch up all the gold and run away with it. Until now they had put up with all their shamelessness, their desecration of the gods' holy places where they had raised their own torture stake, for no other reason but that Montezuma in his indulgence had taken their part, he whom they had treated like an Indian, and in whose person they had for ever violated the ancient sacred royal house of the Aztecs root and branch, the dignity of the divine king; now there should be an end of that.

The gods were exasperated to the utmost, Huitzilopochtli sweated cold fire at night in his sanctuary, the priests said; he was phosphorescent, and the sacrificial blood on his flanks was alive; Popocatepetl himself, as every one could see, was moved and would soon destroy the world. The omens pointed to the last day bein at hand, a three-year-old child which ha been sacrificed had babbled prophecie before its death in a language nobody un derstood; in the stomach of another vic tim they had found a stone shaped lik many-branched lightning; a condor flyin from the east had dropped carrion o Huitzilopochtli's teocalli . . . was furthe evidence required? Mexico's fate was un certain—but these foreign impostors wh had stolen the thunder and in whon everything was false, even to the colou of their skins, should die, even if it cos a thousand Mexicans for every one of th palefaces they made an end of!

The rising came at dawn; notwith standing all other Powers, they woul now have the Sun himself in their com pany; before sunrise a sound as of cock chafers in a sack arose from Mexico, th ardent whispering of a whole populatio —and that day, when the sun had reache the zenith, a vast pillar of dust and roar ing seemed to rise up towards it, broa as the whole city of Mexico; all th countless hosts of the city attacked th palace, where the few whites had at onc barricaded themselves—a rain of stones obsidian arrows, fire-hardened stakes an spears, bare hands, teeth if they got nea enough; thousands dropped before th cannons and the tireless Toledo blades forming heaps in front of the palace, bu other thousands came on, and that wit a ceaseless shouting, roaring and howlin from a multitude of throats, from th moment the sun rose, without cessatio all through the day, calculated to scar the enemy—and it scared them.

The situation of the invested Spanis force, now with Narvaez' troops full 1200 men, 6000 Tlascalans and 80 horses was indeed desperate; the whole countr rose against them, it was as though th earth opened wherever they looked an gave forth Mexicans, in black waves, hos upon host of death-defying savage dressed like devils in the skins of beasts and feathers, rolling on towards the palace, howling, yelling and with a devilish ear-splitting noise behind them of terrifying instruments, drums, an inferno of pipes with four holes which screeched uninterruptedly hour after hour, grooved antelope-horns which were scraped with mussel-shells, a music invented by Satan.

Blood ran that day in rivers through the streets of Mexico. Flaming arrows penetrated the palace and set fire to the woodwork, many Spaniards fell, however many lives they took themselves. The howling and the infernal music exhausted the brain, not every one kept up his heroic spirit; the soldiers of Narvaez sat idly and began to ask why they should die to make Cortes' fortune—disorder even in their own lines.

When the position became untenable Cortes made a sally with his bravest,—Alvarado, Sandoval, Olid, all sportsmen to whom fighting was an art,—and together they stormed Huitzilopochtli's temple, an impossible thing, seeing that the pyramid was black from top to bottom, on all its hundred and fourteen terraces, with Mexican warriors, who flung down blazing timbers upon the attackers; they *took* the temple, after three hours of acrobatics and slaughter, set fire to the towers on the top, and—then Huitzilopochtli came!

The Mexicans saw him come out of his sanctuary like a toad out of its hole, but in a recumbent position, how now—the Spaniards were behind him, rolling him along; out he came in his square block over the edge of the topmost platform, and down he thundered squarely over all the steps, taking a dozen at a jump, knocking holes in the masonry and a corner off himself, smoking with a breath of thunder, and finally crushing a group of red-jerkined priests who stood howling at the foot of the pyramid!

A mighty exploit, the fall of Mexico underlined—but a piece of bravado; the Mexicans themselves were not dead yet, they came and continued to come, one black wave out of another like the smoke of a conflagration, shooting, stabbing, yelling, not a Spaniard but was wounded; what could be done?

An appeal to the people, through Montezuma himself, was attempted; he had power over them after all, and was induced to go out on the roof and get them to listen to reason. A great moment; the noise actually stopped for a few minutes and gave place to a stillness never known before, when Montezuma showed himself and the crowds saw him they had regarded as the highest and most dignified of all men. He spoke, a single thin human voice was heard amid the ocean of silence, with thousands of lowering eyes directed upon him.

But he had no answer. Stones answered him, arrows and stones; wounded and bleeding. Montezuma staggered and had to be led away.

No, he had no answer. For he was no longer Montezuma. They had torn him out of their hearts. The Council, the ancient power in the land, had met and declared his hereditary rights forfeit; he was a nobody now, and in his stead Guatemozin, the next-of-kin, had been proclaimed God's deputy and leader of the armies.

Then Cortes himself tried to appeal to the people. After the fall of the temple he went up on to the roof with Malina, his interpreter, obtained silence, a silence of death, and spoke to the people; no mild words of peace and conciliation, which was what he desired, but the cold anticipations of the general, designed for moral effect:

Now they could see for themselves, their temple destroyed, their gods reduced to dust, how could they think of resisting him? Amicably, such and such terms; with continued resistance, not one stone left upon another in Mexico!

And these harsh words were translated by Malina into flutelike tones; the ocelot had the ear of the human ocean all to herself, and mewed out the utterances of the man of iron to the thousands of warriors, above whose heads the dust of war hovered in a cloud. She twisted her body charmingly and licked her pink lips, in feathers for the occasion, but with the gleam of her copper limbs shining through like a lavish fire, a willing and voluptuous echo of Cortes' destroying words.

They gave him an answer, some old cacique or other acted as spokesman and spoke very plainly, to the effect that in a short time they would have no more food, that most of them were wounded and patched up—and moreover the bridges on the causeways were broken, they needn't think they could get away!

It was true.

After the pause, drums, pipes, antelope-horn rattles and a hundred thousand howling, yelling Aztecs: the burial chorus started again and would not stop until the funeral was over. And what graves to end in!

Meanwhile Montezuma died. A blow to Cortes, for even if he was now quite out of favour he must have a party and might have been used again. But they could not keep life in him; he tore off his bandages, would not eat, preserved an obstinate silence, with downcast eyes, from the time he was stoned by his own people until his death. The chronicler notes that he refused to kiss the crucifix!

If Columbus was the most disappointed man in history, Montezuma rivalled him in a way; both of them had a great and genuine hope of seeing God, and one of them found a cannibal, the other Cortes.

The night after Montezuma's death Cortes commenced the retreat.

It was the famous night of sorrow, indelicately referred to by Diaz as the night when they were thrown out of Mexico. On this occasion he had an experience he had never known before, and of which he had never imagined the possibility—he was *afraid*. Yes, he mentions the fact with surprise and in remarkable terms, almost as though fear were some kind of horrible creature outside himself with which he here became acquainted. So terrible was the night.

With scattered features and incidents brought together in foreshortening the night appears thus—Popocatepetl in the leading part:

He stands flickering in his heaven, lost in his own glowing dreams, with his own long time, and in one of his instants, when he shoots up fire and lays bare the whole plateau beneath him in the gleam, a land of lava with black shadows, and a salt lake with heavy, sluggish waters, in the lake a city, seemingly caked together with blood and lime—in such an instant it is that they fight and make history down there, Eagle and Serpent, a duel in the air, the bird of prey has the reptile in its claws, and the snake writhes and tries to get at its breast with its poison-fang.

Cortes waited for the darkest hour of midnight, as far as it could be dark in Tenochtitlan with its hundreds of flaming altars, before he set out, with artillery, horses and all, his whole train and all his men, a special detachment to carry the great wooden bridge they had built in all secrecy to lay across the gap in the causeway.

It was this gap of sorrow that separated them from the dry land; here was the fighting, and here they suffered their losses, with the burning city at their back and the Mexicans after them on the causeway, the lake black with their canoes; for they had word of the departure only too soon, and set fire to everything that would burn in the city to show the enemy the way home, came after him with yells and roars and sharp spears, a whole world of splintered glass; and once more the Spaniards had to cut into them and keep them off rank by rank, while everlastingly fresh ranks and more canoes flashed up.

A frightful night. Some got across, then the bridge gave way; a living mush of men struggled in the water, drowned, were slaughtered; the gap was filled up with the guns and the sinking baggage, high enough for a few more to make their way across, last of the rearguard Alvarado, who *jumped* over; impossible, declares the sober Bernal Diaz, but to this day everybody says he did it; over he came.

Yes, down in the muddy bottom of the lake lay all the good guns. The greater part of all Cortes' gold, in chests and boxes, found there a safe deposit for eternity; a terrible pity, the sun and moon in heavy chased gold, as big as wheels, bars enough to build a little house, cast from all the art treasures of Tenochtitlan; precious stones to an untold amount. Only the melancholy songs of the Spanish homeland were capable of giving utterance to such a grief. Yes, they lost all. Yet one long chest was saved of the baggage, it *had* to come through—Cortes had put it in charge of his most trusted porters and given it an escort of his keenest blades; in it Malina was concealed, packed away in feathers like a jewel, a fortune in quetzal-feathers at any rate; we may guess her dreams were warm ones if she slept through the trip.

Malina survived the horrors of the night. Apart from her the Spaniards lost all their slaves, male and female; Montezuma's children, who were with the baggage, were slain. All but twenty of the horses perished. Diaz drops a tear over Alvarado's sorrel mare; she must have been worth it. We hear of one other woman being saved, the only Castilian woman who was ever with the expedition, according to Diaz, by name Maria de Estrada—street? platform?—and a remarkable woman she was, fought like a man on the causeway with a two-handed sword, and came through alive. What a woman! Imagine her experiences!

Seven hundred Spaniards perished that night, drowned or slain, some taken prisoner, nameless most of them, and yet every single one had once been swung up to the ceiling by his mother, a cherub in swaddling-clothes, growing up into a vagabond and soldier of fortune, to end here like chopped straw. But there were also grandees and caballeros among the fallen, Cortes' best friends and supporters, never, never to be forgotten!

The sacrifices: the poor, hapless ones who fell alive into the hands of the Aztecs and were slaughtered to the gods; white men, Christians, ah, their eyes mirrored the greatest horror ever seen, Tenochtitlan's night; they alone of all men knew what it was to go with open eyes, with all their wits about them, straight into Hell!

Their fellows on the causeway saw them being led naked up all the terraces of the temple, round and round, the whole way up, in a glare as bright as daylight from burning altars, burning houses, while distant bursts of flame and lightning flashes from Popocatepetl flickered across the whole sky. Ay, up they had to go, the steep sacred way of the Mexicans, the symbol of the nation's wanderings from the tropics up the ladder of the zones to the roof of the world, into a rarer air; the doomed white men were forced to pace it, with lash and stab, pinioned like sheep, and from the causeway and the shores of the lake their white bodies could be seen shining among black and red devils, the red priests in their robes of office, sacrificial jerkins, flowing hair—the young white-skinned sons of Spain, with their blue blood, *sangre azul,* showing through the skin like a map of fair rose-pink river-valleys, the skin of their exquisite mothers, milk of their milk—and when they appeared on the platform they were forced to dance before the altar of jasper, Huitzilopochtli's stone sacrifice; he himself was absent for the moment, but represented by his priests!

Face to face with them, the priests of Huitzilopochtli, they were brought, aloft on the top of the pyramid, as though in the air, with night and fire below, night and fire above their heads, the mountain brooding over the world like an evil red eye, and around them a pack of joyful tormentors, in garments as of clotted blood, vultures with befouled drooping wings, their hair matted with blood, long nails, most of them earless, clucking like birds and clinking their obsidian knives together. A clatter of cauldrons, forks and huge ladles down in the forecourt; flutes, antelope-horn rattles—the drum!

The great death-drum! Ay, to-night it sounded, from the top of Huitzilopochtli's temple, the doomsday drum, made of the skins of anacondas and audible for miles over the country as a deep bellowing, a sluggish, fearful pulse in the night, boom—boom! Down in the city the women, alone on this night of conflict, came out of doors and smeared blood on the mouth of the serpent totem on the wall of the house, when they heard the snake-drum, conjuring up the oldest, profoundest symbols of Mexico.

To the booming of this voice from the Abyss the doomed Spaniards went to their death. And all the images of death were before their eyes, the place of skulls below the temple lighted up by the fire, the scaffolding of bones, the elaborately built-up mounds of death's-heads, dried mummy heads stuck on stakes, an abyss as though paved with upturned faces, the grinning, naked human form . . . truly this was the Underworld itself!

The young Spanish noble . . . now they had hold of him, came close to him wit the bestial warmth of their bodies, force their way into his soul with their grins the dogs; now they broke down his bear ing, stretched him in a ridiculous posture now they cut him open—ah well, tha only hurt—but then they laid hold of hi heart, then they laid hold of his heart

Boom—boom!

And when his ears rang in the las lulling, when he began to be alone in friendly darkness—why, then let the drun go on, let the rest be accomplished, hel for hell, let it bustle and boil over dow in the priests' kitchens, let the vulture scream from the gods' aviaries, where th great birds fan together darkness and fier gleam under their wings, let it snarl an hiss from the menageries, where pum and jaguar pad softly up and down an arch their backs, with yellow eyes watch ing for what their stinking keepers wil bring, the ocelot pit like a snake-pen ful of cats, marked like the boa and as noise less, with the same narrow vertical pu pil . . .

Splash, splash, sounded in the rattle snake pit, as the entrails were flung t them, the share of the deadly grey serpent and in the flickering light which crept i from a reflection in the sky, Popocate petl's distant fires, a gliding life could b seen, scarcely to be distinguished fron the dust underneath the fat, scaly reptiles they came out of holes and corners, dart ing a dry tongue from their mouths tasting the air, with scaly jaws and littl enamel eyes, giving a faint rattle in th gloom, the castanets in their tail . . .

Boom—boom!

On the other side of the lake Cortes sa and listened to the ceaseless throbbing o the death-drum, saw the awful scene recognized his friends in the distance. Ir the course of the night he had had heads flung at his feet by Aztecs infuriated tc madness, the heads of his comrades; he saw them make that terrible progress, saw them die—and then Cortes wept, with a boy's hard, abandoned weeping that hurts the throat and strangles the breath, over the sufferings of his boys and brothers.

A creature stroked her head against him, rubbed her ear on him, Malina, trying to console him, to make up to him for all his loss; but Cortes flicked her away like a grain of dust that had got into his tears; she could not help him.

No, there was only one thing that could help him, as time would show, that which he swore as he shook his fist at the flaming temples of Mexico—that he would see them razed to the ground, and all their foul butchers rotting corpses in the earth! Was that so strange an oath?

And it came to pass as he had sworn. With murder and manslaughter he was hunted out of Mexico, with siege and starvation he returned.

Better would it have been if Popocatepetl had buried Mexico and the whole plateau under a layer of ashes than that *that* should be seen which was seen in the streets of Mexico when it was at the last gasp and the mothers took back into themselves that to which they had given life, and Huitzilopochtli's priests in hunger delirium, when the last rattlesnake had been devoured, stole glances at each other —no hope left even if they ate each other, nothing left to eat on them, plucked living corpses of vultures, staggering with the last of their strength to the carrion-heap and falling dead on their faces in it.

To such extremes does one misdeed drive another.

At dawn one more last sacrifice took place up on the platform with the smoking ruins of its towers, after Huitzilopochtli's image, with immense toil, fury and triumph, had been dragged up all the steps, hundreds of men pulling at it, like a swarm of impassioned ants round a caterpillar, and set up in his place again somewhat battered, with a chip knocked out of his forehead and all the precious stones and ornaments broken or shaken out, but still Huitzilopochtli the ancient. They trembled before him, for the insult he had suffered, the revenge he might take—but had they not already avenged him pretty well? Mexico purified, the great and rare offerings he had received—and now he was to receive the last and best, if that was good enough, the white strangers' own god!

Just before sunrise this extraordinary sacrifice took place; the tall life-size crucifix, which the Spaniards had set up in the square before the palace where they had been lodged and from which they had been turned out, was borne in solemn procession round all the steps of the temple the whole way up to the platform.

Here the two gods were confronted with one another. They were left in each other's company a good while, even the priests withdrawing from the platform to the next step below, and thousands of Mexicans filled the remaining terraces, still mad with the night's orgy of slaughter, silent, glaring like wild cattle.

Well, then the gods had a chance of looking at each other and making some remarks; they might have a good deal to talk about, their passions, their impressions of mankind for a thousand years, and so on. But the gods were dumb.

It was as though they spoke in the language that was spread out before the eyes of all in the dawning, the earth hidden by corpses, half the pueblo fallen in like bakers' ovens after a shower of stones, black smoking logs all that was left of cedarwood timbers, whose perfume was changed to the sour smell of burning; the temple drenched in blood from the top step to the bottom and covered with dead bodies, like a mountain of corpses; the lake stained red far out from the shore, a vast raw scent of blood hanging over the earth as high as the top of the temple.

Underneath the huge drum the drummer lay dead, burst by his own fury, after having danced the whole night long like a devil about his doomsday drum, howling, in a hurricane of his hair, naked, with limbs like glowing copper; now he was cooled down, lying crumpled up on his drumstick like a man of ashes.

Sunrise! Silence! Far and wide the land and mountains stare out into the clear, light air of the plateau, the ring of heaven and earth uniting in the distance. Popocatepetl smokes up into the morning sky, and to-day his smoke is not black but white.

Silence! The gods stand face to face. They do not budge. Huitzilopochtli broad, short in the neck, with a piece chipped out of one eye, nose gone, a good deal knocked about, but still a black; the white god stiff and mute on his cross, in an everlasting agony: Man, after his own handling.

Then they set fire to the crucifix, and as the sun's eye appeared over the horizon it burned, with a pale fire rising straight up into the air.

But Huitzilopochtli was soon to travel down all those steps again, and this time he would be left standing on his head among ruins and rubble, until one day a later generation pulled him out and put him in a museum with a label on him, a piece of monstrous sculpture, for the ecstatic delight of those who recognize their own genius in Negro fetishes, to others only the hideous image of a nightmare from which mankind has awakened. Where his temple was, now stands the Cathedral of Mexico; if fear is no longer to be worked upon there are feelings to answer the purpose.

A gleaming white dome of snow fills the extinct crater of Popocatepetl.

VIII

THE NEW WORLD

We came to Portorico's shore
And fought with cannibals full sore.
Chek, chekkelek . . .
(Teeth-chattering, castenets.)
To all our saints we prayed,
And scrap-iron in our gun we laid,
And shot and stabbed and hit around galore.
Ha, ha, ha!
(Chorus of howls.)
And then we got an appetite;
A curly maiden came in sight.
Chek, chekkelek . . .
The pot's just on the boil,
And in she goes with spice and oil.
Deep water makes you ready for a bite.
Ha, ha, ha!

A curly maiden's not so bad,
With skin and hair and all, my lad!
Chek, chekkelek . . .
Each epicure his taste—
Give me a cut from near the waist—
There's chops and steaks and brisket to be had!
Ha, ha, ha!

Then you can take a lily-white bone
To pick your tooth, the hollow one.
Chek, chekkelek . . .
Strike up a dead men's dance,
With skull and crossbones, now's your chance!
Come on, come on, don't let me dance alone!
Ha, ha, ha!

Our Eldorado's found, I guess,
Since we've tobacco in our mess.
Chek, chekkelek . . .
Strike up a firemen's jig,
And puff the smoke about your wig!
Cheers for tobacco, that's the weed we bless!
Ha, ha, ha!

With whip and loaded gun stand we
And make the slaves work busily—
Chek, chekkelek . . .
The black man he is black;
He gets the sun right on his back—
And that's what keeps the white man white, you see!
Ha, ha, ha!

Like stallions we rushed around
And women, lots of them, we found.
Chek, chekkelek . . .
Old Huitzli we defied—
But strange diseases here betide;
And now some noseless ones are homeward bound.
Ha, ha, ha!

I've had enough of going to sea,
It's making an old man of me.
Chek, chekkelek . . .
I'll see my girl again,
She'll meet her boy from off the main—
And she'll have been, let's hope, as true as we . . .
Ha, ha, ha!

Comparatively pretty cannibal chanties such as this and others not so nice, in the savages' own gibberish, were sung by the crews of the slave-ships which brought home gold from the West Indies and carried back cargoes of slaves from the Guinea Coast to the islands, to take the place of the native population which was dying out in the mines. Two worlds had begun to infect one another.

Armies of men, whole populations, were ready to force their way over to the other side, now that an escape from Europe had been opened. A great liquidation was going on among prelates, princes and contentious theologians in Europe; the Church was going to pieces and losing its absolute power over men's souls, only to split up into several, equally intolerant; many whips in place of the great scourge. Crowned heads watched their opportunity and raked in estates which the Church could no longer keep hold of since it had become divided against itself. But two or three hundred years elapsed before this liquidation came to an end. And the common people, who found themselves in a tight place whatever happened, who got a Reformation but no reform; the peasants who were bound faster than ever after their flails had struck down one or two nobles and they had burnt a few castles; the surplus of the Middle Ages along the highways, beggars, discharged soldiers, an unthrifty but vigorous rabble—the common people could not wait, the discontented made for the coast and jumped at the bounty money, which men with raw gold on their fingers were offering in every port; the caravels put to sea loaded with men who had not yet become a class; but they were to become one.

Men like Rodrigo de Triana, the seaman who first saw land on board the *Pinta,* but did not get the promised annuity of 10,000 maravedis; he was discontented, furious, and his wrath lasted him his lifetime, however it was with his annuity. The Admiral got the money, he had seen the first light ashore that evening—ho, who was talking about seeing lights, it was land they were looking for! But the Admiral was within his rights, decided his own case, strict justice, first is first! Rodrigo was wild all the rest of the voyage, and beside himself when six months later they came home and dazzled Spain with the mighty news.

While the Admiral was being honoured like a prince in Seville, and invited to attend their majesties' court at Barcelona—now the ex-cartographer was mounting, he was ennobled, had *always* been noble—Rodrigo raged over in his Triana and ran amuck through all the wineshops, from which *he* derived his extraction, banged all their tables and threatened the lives of inoffensive men, without harming a hair of their heads, with a dry sob in his throat, drunken laughter and shaking his head at his glass:

First is first! The great can do these things! Muck to the mucky! Saw a light in the dark—light in my breeches! Puerca Madoña!

Drunk and with drawn knife Rodrigo then reeled through the streets of Seville talking to himself aloud, hiccupping and with many an empty laugh, making his way for himself with the edge of his hand, though he had the whole procession to himself—this was when he had heard the rumours of Columbus's triumphal progress through the whole of Spain, the mountebank shows with parrots and gold masks, the dyewoods, and bamboo, and the dozen poor savages with rings in their noses—a nice Spain *they* were shown, the whole of Christendom running after a handful of Indians!—and Columbus himself at the head, propped up aloft on a palfrey, which must have been rigged with a rudder aft so that he could steer it . . . for all this mummery and the honours and Columbus sitting on a chair with their majesties and his newly bought coat-of-arms and the gold chain on his neck and his going hunting with the King, for all this Rodrigo didn't give a blow! Even the wall of the church came in for a share of his contempt!

But when rumours came thick and fast of the Admiral's glory—now he must be eating from the same dish as the King, and be sure they each stirred the soup well to scoop up the dumplings!—then Rodrigo lost all appetite in his native land and emigrated, stormed across to Africa. There he turned Mohammedan; Columbus might take his share of salvation too; a dirty lot of Christians, not another breath would he draw among the dogs!

To the day of his death Rodrigo stayed over in Africa, praising Allah in burnoose and turban, only to be distinguished from other Mussulmans by his wrathful blue eyes. A seaman's calling—Rodrigo spat on it! He broke stones for the rest of his days, and between spitting on his hands and punishing big blocks he shook a clenched fist northward at Europe over the water and gave vent to his feelings in Arabic—might his tongue shrivel up in his throat if his native speech ever crossed *his* lips again!

Such was the wrath of Rodrigo.

It was not America in his particular case, but it was for thousands of others, who without regret turned their backs on Europe for good.

First it was the Conquistadores and all their troop, Cortes and Pizarro, Diego Almagro, who conquered Chile, another man of iron with an uncommon keenness of character which reminds one of the Estremeños, the worst and the best qualities of Arab and Goth, united; there were Ojeda, Alvarado; and with them the nameless armies that accompanied them. We may suppose that all Spain could show of old Northern descent, the seed of the Normans, the waggon-folk of the Migrations, the restless ones who at one time had thrust to the South, that these were the first to seize the opportunity of moving on again, now that a Farther-off had been found. It was like a great Magnet Mountain overseas acting at a distance and drawing the nails out of Spain.

But after the discoverers and adventurers came the settlers. This was a slower movement, it was the foundation itself that was transferred; but there was no hurry about it, it is not finished yet.

And this is the great book of the Emigrants. The emigration was divided into two main streams: one from southern Europe which was to settle Latin America, Norman at the top, the Migrations filtered through the South, and Romance at the bottom; but the other later stream came from the North of Europe, the very source of the Migrations, and from it have come the United States.

Once more peasants committed themselves to the waves, nameless unknown bands, once more the emigrant's waggon creaked in new trackless regions, with children's faces looking out ahead from under the awning and long, worn handles of farm implements projecting behind, the plough on its travels again. And once more peasants drew up their waggons in a ring at night, with the cattle inside, a camp-fire and a frugal supper under the open sky, while round about lay the strange and hostile wilderness and a stealthy, powerful and cruel native population: the romance of the Red Indian, with all its bloody and fanatical chapters, the arrow quivering in the awning of the emigrant waggon, the frontiersman's long rifle bringing down the feathered horsemen at impossible ranges, Daniel Boone and the Last of the Mohicans; California—a trumpet-call no longer ago than when our fathers were young! Klondike—our own fanfares!

A mighty, many-coloured, stirring book! What did they not see, the men who saw the vast young countries, coasts, prairies and mountains, immense rivers, cordilleras, tropical forests, pampas, for the first time! Overwhelmingly the thought forces itself upon us: never, never again will the world be so fresh! Not again will the world renew itself! Childhood lost! Manhood lost!

The poor "prairie schooner" that rocked its way west and made ruts for the first time on untrodden soil, with the elements of a home and of a population within; long-haired, wrinkled, resolute men on horseback surrounding it rifle in hand, and the outline of a mounted Indian far away by a steep pass—well, now the long trains are running there between the Atlantic and Pacific, and from the stern and silent emigrant has come America's robust farmer, the millions who feed millions.

Wide is the shade of Ygdrasil, the Tree of the Migrations, with its root in the North and fresh branches spreading over all the world!

Plants and animals move on and change their places, are given or deprived of a destiny; as though by some unexampled natural catastrophe the North American bison is wiped out from the continent and the ancient domestic cattle of Europe come in. The horse is put ashore, the first ones from the cramped caravels of the discoverers, where they have stood for months in a swinging stall, turning the whites of their eyes upon a desert of waves, kicked and banged at the woodwork, and foaled, long-legged shaggy foals that the waves throw down every time they try to stand up—but at last a gangway is put ashore for them, which the creatures refuse to go down; they throw up their heads and make a great to-do, have to be forced ashore, but then there they are! The prairie! Do they remember that they have been there before? Oh no, that is at least a geological period ago, they remember nothing; but how they shake their heads now that they feel soil under their hoofs, with flying manes, hindquarters in the air and lashing out with pleasure!

Thus they trot into the new world and put their muzzles to its pastures, stamping its soil with the mark of the heart from their feet, from the northernmost North America right round the curve of the globe to the southernmost Patagonia; galloping and neighing and turning back into wild horses, a whole continent bred full from a few pairs; the mustang's swift career, for a time free as the air, but lassoed again and bitted, bucking and kicking but spurred and broken, much ridden, petted and glorious!

The sheep comes over, even with Columbus, and trips ashore with its little hoofs, shakes its tail and drops its marks of habitation on the smallholder's field, has its spring lambs here again and shivers once a year when shorn for man's benefit, chews the cud sideways and stamps its forefoot with frightful peremptoriness when any one comes near its tether, just as in the old world—honour to simplicity! But here the sheep becomes a gregarious and mountain animal again, sharing the soil with the llama and alpaca on more highlands, stony prairies and borderlands than can be numbered.

Wheat comes over, in exchange for maize, which makes its way to Europe with its long straw and fertile cob; all the wheat in Mexico is said to come from two grains which a Negro found in a sack of rice, as early as the days of Cortes. From some pips Bernal Diaz planted behind a temple are descended all the orange trees of Mexico. Life and nourishment take up but little room and are so ready to replenish the earth, only asking to be lost in the soil and forgotten.

In some remote upland of Chile or Peru, no one has yet discovered where, there grew a nightshade which preserved its life in time of menace by stored-up nutriment in tubers at its root, the *potato!*

Another sallow nightshade, tobacco, acquired a power above all other plants on earth, although it is anything but nourishing, makes a man cowardly and shortens his life; man's inherent craving to multiply his being with poisons and widen his experience, by sickness if need be, holds a protecting hand over it. Chocolate, sweets came in; teeth went out. The barndoor fowl to the new world; the turkey to the old.

But how did things go with the natives? Not well. In countries where a population had spread to the limits it required, and where so many fresh millions came in, somebody had to give way. The natives gave way, they politely died out. Even the Conquistadores could see with their own eyes how places were emptying, and like good economists they replenished them with fresh hands, an island of exiled Africa, which spread and spread beyond the sea.

The weak people of the tropics went out first; they could not share the land with Spaniards, even shook their heads when referred to a life to come, if they were allowed to live here. It is related of a certain Hatuey, a cacique of Cuba, who was burnt alive, that when they wanted to force baptism and grace upon him before his death he inquired whether the Whites also went to Heaven; on hearing that they did he preferred fire to water and went unabsolved to the stake. The Indian farther north withdrew in sinister silence.

The cannibal went out. Of the happy islanders nothing was left but Famine, a lean shadow on the top of a pile of skulls, grinning at *Hope,* which was hanging opposite from a palm tree.

Nor did all the Conquistadores have the same luck; conscience, or Nemesis struck some of them, or they simply met with a brawler's end; most of them died a violent death.

A sigh of atonement reaches us from the brilliant and admired Alvarado. He met his death on an expedition to California, in an athletic style worthy of him. In scaling a mountain to capture a native stronghold the path was so steep that the horsemen fell from it, and Alvarado got one of them on his head, avoided horse and man but was hit by a piece of rock which they brought down and which broke every bone in his body. He lived for several days, and is said to have wept over all his transgressions, his acts of thoughtlessness and injustice against the natives. One day, when the crushed and contrite man was sighing with more resignation than usual, he replied to a friend who asked him where he felt most pain: *el alma,* in the soul; and in his last will he provided that all the savages he had branded and enslaved should be set free. Thus died Alvarado, in torment, a good lad.

But that did not bring back to life the hundreds of thousands whom other Spaniards in a bestial tropical frenzy had burnt, flayed, infected with Europe, flogged to death in the mines and destroyed.

But the trouble lay deeper than ordinary malignity and callousness; Nature had here brought together creatures incapable of mixing; of the same origin, but at a primitive stage on one side, the other changed beyond all return; they might meet, but could no longer be grafted on one another, one side had to eclipse the other.

Primitive and civilized man had come too far away from each other. The former's state of innocence was doubtful enough, already marked by the beginning of a culture, cruelty conscious and intensified; but how were they to overtake the Whites in the arts of destruction? They, the Christians, had plenty of soul, self-knowledge enough, a noble conception of God—were they the better for it? With the growth of civilization *all* qualities grow, including brutality; even fatuity, callousness and lack of judgment manifest themselves on a grand scale. No, simple savages and the lords of creation, who had parted with their natural disposition, could not understand one another.

Not everywhere was the barrier so insurmountable; in Mexico a crossing took place which has held its own. The incipient culture there! Malina's forces!

But farther north the white man took land for himself and himself alone, claiming latitudes which were his own at home. It was as though Columbus only opened up America at second-hand to those whose instinct had been at work in him, the Northerners; from a point in his rear these races set out to found the America which is *America,* the States.

Here, on new soil and for a long time unnoticed, liberty grew up, which had become homeless in Europe, the ancient independence of the peasant.

And when it was strong enough it was able to turn back to the old world and show its light there; when the Republic, the pristine national form of the West, was reintroduced in France, the infection came from the young American Union.

The yeomen transplanted, a new root for the race, generation after generation of nameless families hidden here on their sovereign farms, from the hereditary homesteads in the old country to the new free land in the West—that was the true line in Columbus's instinct as Ferryman. What was perverted in him avenged itself in his life and upon his successors.

If it came to the ears of Rodrigo de Triana it must have consoled him that Columbus's glory was so short-lived. For King Ferdinand soon elbowed the "Viceroy" out of all his rights in the newly discovered countries. To follow the course of Nemesis: four hundred years later America drove Spain out of her overseas possessions; Columbus avenged.

But the holy Christophorus, if he could have seen the fate of Columbus and his successors, would assuredly have pointed with his big numbed finger to the dynasty of the discoverer, which died out in a single generation, the race decaying almost at once in the atmosphere of power, pomp and vexation of spirit.

BOOK THREE: THE PHANTOM SHIP

I
PHILIPPA

But what of the country Christopher Columbus sought after, unofficially, for his fleets were always fitted out for *India;* but the country that was the source of all his passion, what of that?

Well, it is still to be found; the Admiral wants to get away, he is lying sick in Valladolid and has no time to be sick, he has to go to sea; tries to get up, but can only raise his head from the pillow; he must get up, he fumbles over the bedclothes with his big, feeble hands, has letters to write, looks about him and wipes his ailing eyes, to think that they should be bad again now! The room seems misty to him, he does not know that he is nearly blind. Movement is quite impossible, he is perfectly stiff, the sea salt that has got into his joints; bad luck to have such a poor day just when he has so much to see about. But still he has been worse before, he thinks, that time two years ago in Jamaica when he lay for weeks like a dead man.

Patience; and the Admiral has the Scriptures read to him, dictates with closed eyes, sends for people and has long conferences about what is to be done; though he speaks in a scarcely audible voice he keeps his servants busy, the room is like a highway where everybody is coming and going, very respectful gentlemen who shake their heads as they leave. But the Admiral is busy all day long, lying anchored in his bed with his long frame crippled with rheumatism, snow-white and with deep-sunk eyes, looking like a centenarian though he is still some way off sixty; he is busy all day long, muttering and muttering, the invincible mind flaming incessantly behind the drawn forehead and beneath the closed eyes, over which the brows already yawn with the hollow shadow of death.

Great difficulties at this time, disagreements with the King, always those rights they had taken from him and which he had not yet recovered; opposition, enemies on every hand, infringements of his proprietary rights, and on the top of that delays, delays, hindrances that had to be got rid of before he could come to the real business, a new voyage, God willing, the fifth . . . and when that was successfully accomplished, for now he must succeed, there was the raising of an army and the crusade against Constantinople! The Turk to be driven out of Europe! Christ's sepulchre restored to Christendom! The opening of the Millennium! Much to lay his hand to, when once he had surmounted a mass of worries, and found Eldorado in the meantime, and a vexatious thing to have his old sea trouble tormenting him again when time was so precious.

Thus worked his ever-busy brain, the only part of him spared by four long laborious voyages of discovery, twelve years of toil and disappointment, since the year he had found San Salvador, but had he always kept his brain clear, had he not rambled now and then, seeing how incomprehensible, enigmatical and tantalizing the world persisted in appearing to him?

Ah yes, they were twelve bitter years; it pained him not in his limbs alone to look back on them; years of suffering, full of fatigue, never an affliction was he spared, sleepless, long, hard, anxious, fruitless years! Ever since his first homeward voyage after the discovery, when he had to pay for the easy, untroubled outward passage, and was tossed about in the *Niña* in fearful storms, storms, storms, till all hope of seeing land again was abandoned; the Atlantic in its murky might, the *Niña* riding over mountains of water, from one abyss into another, incredible that the little craft could do it! Yes, there she was pounded and buffeted by the waves, and rolled and flung into such a depth that it seemed as if clouds and seas were flying straight into heaven; there they stood in dripping wet clothes day after day for weeks, watching till they simply could not close their eyes again. . . . Ah, yes, that was the pain he still felt.

Then the second voyage: the beautiful island of Jamaica, *Santa Gloria,* the airs of Paradise that haunted his nostrils there, the fruitless hunt for the mainland, the strain, eye trouble, headwinds home, distress and shortage of food in the ships; the failure of the colonies, the King's ill-humour, Spain full of enemies.

Third voyage: still the vain hunt for the passage to India, the private probing of the coasts for the Kingdom of Heaven; a more southerly route this time, Trinidad, the mouths of the Orinoco and the great freak of nature where the mighty freshwater stream meets the Equatorial Current.

This time Columbus was within an ace of it, he got into a whirlpool with his ships and turned a trifle giddy: here at last was eloquent proof of the proximity of the earthly Paradise, one of the great rivers that run from the source by the Tree of Life, the river from which the Deluge once came! The stars spun a little before his eyes, he felt he was under the sign of the Virgin, and interpreted his whole reckoning as a conjecture bordering on certainty that the earth in these zones must have an immense wart on it, like a sort of supplementary earth; it was round, no doubt, but like a pear, and up at the point of this supplementary earth lay Paradise; that explained why the current was so strong and the volume of water that came from there was so vast, making the sea fresh for miles out, with a smell of vegetation, full of mud and torn-up plants: no question about it, such a stream must come from the Garden of Eden!

Other observations pointed to the proximity of Paradise: in a bay Columbus caught sight at a distance of pink-winged creatures bathing, by all appearance angels. Seamen with undamaged eyes thought they were a kind of long-legged pink birds with long necks and a broken beak, flamingoes; but they did not contradict the Admiral in his hearing.

Columbus thought he had been nearer to Heaven, literally speaking, on this voyage than ever before; and his own deluded, rainbow-coloured letter should be read; a great soul speaks in it in spite of all, we can feel the beating of a heart like the very pulse of the world, the rivers had infected him, he had touched the earth like the Greek hero and had regained his hold of the marvellous—hope, hope will never die!

And the heart-breaking letter he wrote to the King after his fourth and last voyage should be read, when he had sailed as a private person and was not even allowed to land in his own colony, which was now administered by others. For he returned from the third voyage as a prisoner, deprived of all his dignities; that was the end of it, and the fetters he had worn were hanging at this moment above his bed. That they had done to him, and never after could he recall the injustice without weeping; that and a life of sleepless nights, salt of the sea and salt tears, that is what made his room seem so misty.

But then on this last voyage he lived to see Bobadilla's death! Yes, there is a God in Heaven. He would not even let Columbus put into harbour, this man who had thrown him into chains; and when Columbus predicted a gale, he knew better, was churlish and sailed out with his ships and his cargo of stolen gold, injustice, cruelty and lies—and was never heard of again! No, God may be long-suffering, but still a noxious beast may goad him into opening a hole in the sea.

Then Columbus felt his way along the coast of Honduras, Nicaragua, Costa Rica, new rich coasts all of them, but no way through; and then the unspeakable sufferings when he was stranded on Jamaica and lay there without ships for many, many months, sick, half-blind, without the slightest hope of rescue, starving, so that he had to juggle with an eclipse of the moon to get food from the savages; then the homeward voyage, against contrary currents and headwinds;

a complete wreck when he saw Spain again after a lapse of two and a half years.

Thus the twelve years had gone by, and they had since become fourteen. And now he would be off again. That river mouth was worth attempting. That Paradise lay where the river came from was beyond a doubt, but he had no great hope of being able to sail up against the stream. He would try it. Improved ships, perhaps with oars, nothing was impossible. And then the crusade to Constantinople was urgent, it wouldn't do to lie here any longer, he had to get up. . . .

And the Admiral tries again to raise himself but only gets his head a little way from the pillow, like an insect that has been trodden into the dust and moves a leg now and again, life that will live, when flight is over for ever.

At night the Admiral is alone, and in the long sleepless hours he hears the wind howling in the doorways, a being that finds a voice and calls, the Wanderer; and he sees the waves before him, as he lies there with closed eyes, he is on board his ship listening to the wind's harp, its strings are about him as they have been all his life: I'm coming, I'm coming, is the answer in his soul; and they two, the Wanderer without in the night, the excluded but ever calling, and he within who is anchored down, they blow together, sigh, roar and pass on their way through the long black night, through many nights, many nights and long.

But at last the song has a deeper note and comes from farther away, perhaps the Admiral does not know whether he is dreaming or awake or where he really is, *when* it is; the howling wind awakes a soul within his soul, old forgotten springs burst forth, and with the wind's mournful ballad in his ears, the most mournful of ballads, he sinks in a sea of melancholy:

The wind is sighing, O hear it wander!
A lost soul strays through the world out yonder.
Oh, ho, huh. . . .

Like children crying, alone and weary,
Till early morning—is aught so dreary?
Oh, ho, huh. . . .

As lonely children we wept full often,
'Mid howling blasts that a stone would soften.
Oh, ho, huh. . . .

Since then we slept in so many places,
With sighing bosoms and mournful faces.
Oh, ho, huh. . . .

Then infants filled all our house with crying.
Now we are left with the midnight sighing.
Oh, ho, huh. . . .

Ah, can it be that we still may hear them,
In howling wind can we still be near them?
Oh, ho, huh. . . .

Like childbed pangs or like childless mother,
Like tears of Fate that no time can smother.
Oh, ho, huh. . . .

To pain is turned all our gladness vanished,
'Tis gone, but ne'er from our memory banished.
Oh, ho, huh. . . .

We hate the cry of a sinful action,
But life unlived is a worse distraction.
Oh, ho, huh. . . .

The dead are witness in deep graves sleeping
That life has brought them but sighs and weeping.
Oh, ho, huh. . . .

Beneath the stars is there aught that's lasting?
The wind alone in eternal blasting.
Oh, ho, huh. . . .

A thousand years shall the wind still wander.
The ancient woe shall return out yonder.
Oh, ho, huh. . . .

And then it came upon him in his last hour, at last he received his sight when the light from without no longer made impression on his eyes, in a clear inner world he saw that he *had* been there, on the happy isle he had hunted for, the isle of youth, in the days when his children were little.

Philippa!

The far-off days in Lisbon when he was a young man, with a knowledge of the sea from the time when, as a big-limbed lad, he ran away from his father's weaver's workshop and disappeared in one of the ships lying in the port of Genoa, where it had been his boyish delight to hang about, until the sea claimed him; rough years which made a man of him. Then the book which absorbed him more and more, the cosmography that he studied whenever he was ashore, while his companions were out rioting, science and cartography—the convent at Lisbon where the young mate and cartographer entered to kneel and make his devotions among the holy images, surrounded by incense and the tones of the organ and the beautiful choir of women's voices—one voice more lovely than all the rest, which he could single out as a high, clear, silvery ray from earth to heaven amid the hum of sound: Philippa's voice!

Nor was it long before he spied out, eyes and ears helping each other, from whom the voice came, a slender young maiden with narrow cheeks, black and white, the more beautiful black hair and great, dark, warm eyes, looking like a seraph when she opened her throat and with delicate parted lips sent her wonderfully pure notes swelling out into space.

But when he made discreet inquiries and learned that she was nobly born, Philippa Moñez Perestrello, daughter of the distinguished navigator and Governor, a family far, far too high for a plain mate to raise his eyes to—ah, then he was unhappy, without even the boldness to look upon himself as crossed in love; then he was a giant brought low, who might be seen by himself on lonely walks outside the town, weary with thinking, with his eyes on God's birds up in the trees, gently shaking his head; a cartographer who neglected his rolls of paper but with a heavy heart put on his best clothes, striped hose of different colours, as was the mode, combed his hair, and never, never failed to appear in the Convent of All-Hallows when the choir sang there! a man with a fine ear for music and a pair of devout blue eyes turned towards the stalls where the choir were singing.

Could it be possible? . . . passionate incredulity, a hope, a resolve to die, violent weeping with cap before the eyes, wooing, days of emotion and disquiet, the dew of love all over him—the unbelievable, that *she, she would have him,* had seen him every day in the church and now told him impossible things of *her* thoughts! Philippa!

Lisbon and the blessed garden where they met and all was well and with a great sigh she gave herself into his hands, content that he was so ruddy and uncouth a giant.

Ah, she was like the damsel sung in every ballad, with a train about her feet, clad in samite and marten, trustful, with smiling eyes and her throat full of song, love all through!

And then came the happy years at Porto Santo, the island remote from the world, framed by the long, thundering, sun-illumined Atlantic rollers, clothed in the hum of solitude and roofed over at night with constellations vaunting in a sky of southern purple, full of great visions and mirages by day over the endless unknown ocean, the heavens a blaze of fire morning and evening when the sun came and went.

Here in a blissful solitude, all in all to each other, their little son was born and they were three, a new little whimper on a desert isle, a helpless life shaded by Philippa's black hair and protected by her long, tender hands.

How is it with man—is it that the greater his happiness, the more he demands from it, a fire that feeds our longing?

For we think that life is long; then looking back on it we see that a few sleeveless errands have devoured the years and that there is no turning back.

An unavoidable expedition to Guinea, to England, his head full of Perestrello's papers and charts, which Columbus had with his wife; plans of discoveries, voyages, the fourteen years of wandering, *all preparatory*—but gone was Porto Santo, Philippa resting eternally with crossed hands in the *Piedad* chapel of Carmelite convent at Lisbon; Diego, when he saw him one time, a tall, slight boy who was annoyed when given an apple, another time a page at the court of Isabella, already heavy about the eyelids, displeased when his father appeared with his ungainly walk; Diego Columbus, whose name the other pages and their friends underlined with tar.

But never had there been greater happiness than at Porto Santo when the little boy got on his feet and for the first time in high delight ventured a step from his father's arms to his mother's knee. Never had any wound left a deeper scar than when the boy, as they were tramping to Palos, his hand in his father's had said he was hungry, and he had to beg bread for him.

There is a sound in the room as of a dog barking; the blind dying man does not know that it is the heart in his throat.

II
SOUTH OF THE SOUTH

In the winter of 1832–33 a British brig, the *Beagle,* lay off Tierra del Fuego, trying for twenty-four days to round Cape Horn from east to west, but was obliged to give it up and sailed through one of the channels among the islands which now bears the name of the ship.

More than three hundred years before Magellan had found the passage here, a little to the north, the first man to sail from the Atlantic into the Pacific, the passage Columbus sought for in vain, and the first circumnavigation of the globe. Few dreamed that it was necessary to go so far to the south, right down towards the South Pole, to find a way through, across the Line and down into regions where the climate became raw again as in the North, but with the year turned round, opposite seasons, and with the "South," the warmth and fertility, to the northward; a world on the farther side of hope, new, but a strangely lifeless repetition of the old.

On board the *Beagle* was a young naturalist, Charles Darwin, then twenty-three; the cruise was undertaken with scientific objects and he was the zoologist of the expedition, a tall, rather lanky young gentleman, slow in his movements, beetle-browed, but with genial blue eyes, a bottle-nose which, as he tells us himself, was an annoyance to him and nearly got him rejected for the expedition—and yet it was the keenest nose aboard the *Beagle;* if the ship was the sleuth-hound of the century he was its inmost sense.

The final intellectual conclusion of the voyages of discovery, from Columbus to Cook, was drawn by him. Before becoming acquainted with primitive man, humanity had viewed itself from within in the light of sensibility, God's image; now it was forced to view itself from without, in the light of its origin; Darwin took the backward step. He was hated for it as the one who with a miscreant's hand dragged man down from his height; in reality his thoughts were directed by a profound philanthropy, he drew the despised "savage" up to the breast of civilization as the distant kinsman who stands between the white man and the beast.

When Darwin first had his great idea of the origin of species and their inner mutual kinship as different stages of the same manifestation of life, and what concrete impressions suggested it, he does not tell us, perhaps it was not clear to himself; an impulse of feeling may have been the first point of departure.

It may have come to him in an obscure form, the first subterranean subsidence in his mind, in Tierra del Fuego. Though he himself has nothing about it, his artless description of the Fuegians shows that he was deeply moved; here he was close to the animal and yet pity and sympathy bound him to these outcasts thrust into uttermost misery as to brothers who had fared badly, but still brothers; his heart bled for them, he went as far as he could to meet them, as a zoologist he voluntarily abandoned the old proud charter of humanity and came down into dangerous proximity with the quadruped, well, well, and at last he went the whole length. With his knowledge of apes and after seeing the Fuegians there was nothing else for him to do; they could not come to him, Darwin came to them.

An expansion of feeling and a recognition, the legitimation of mankind's poorest relations, not excluding those farther down either, tail and all, that was the fine step that was taken, from the voyages of discovery to the doctrine of evolution, in itself an evolution, by Darwin, whenever and in whatever connection the idea as an idea may have originated in his brain.

For those four-and-twenty days the *Beagle* lay off Cape Horn sawing backwards and forwards, a zigzag far to the south, till all land was out of sight, and back again towards the foggy, windswept promontory, without making way against the ceaselessly raging westerly gales, as it were a barrier of wind raised here to cut off access to the other ocean; during those days there was time for much thought and of many things.

A factor was not wanting to give exercise in humility and candour, a sufficiency of danger, isolation; here they lay in a lonely brig far outside the world's beaten track, totally forgotten by Europe, and who would ever have thought of them again, whom would it have concerned—a surveying vessel lost some time in the thirties—if they had not come home with their momentous cargo of knowledge and a new view of nature?

Nature did its best to wipe them out, fell upon the hard-pressed ship with violent squalls, washed her from stem to stern, broke seas over her on every side and weighed her down, dragged right under water, till every nail in her hull quivered and she only righted herself with the utmost difficulty, shook off the water and lay trembling and motionless like a creature struck to the very marrow by a jet. A world of semi-darkness it was down here, bitterly cold seas, rarely a gleam of sunshine through the ragged flying clouds; and when they were up under the land on their long vain beat there was the prospect of the steep and mournful antarctic coast of Tierra del Fuego, glaciers calving into the straits, wet, misty, sleety forests, foam flying from the breakers far into the inhospitable shore, and hail-showers scourging the barren mountains of the archipelago.

And here dwelt men! Now as in Magellan's time a gleam shone here and there ashore at night, a pillar of smoke in the daytime, man's ancient beacon, which told of the immeasurably rude, inhumanly hardened people who lived here in life's beginning, without hope of ever coming any farther, for they had entered one of Nature's blind alleys, they had come south of the South. Time itself was not the same here, lacking a calendar, the chilly light-forsaken mornings of the ages, the glimmering misery we know when we have watched all night and day dawns in a grey, unreal, hope-abandoned twilight.

In such an ebb-tide of the soul, half-light within and without, it befell the little company on board the *Beagle* to meet the Flying Dutchman.

Unhistorical this, no written accounts of it, either from the hand of Captain Fitzroy or Darwin, or any one else on board; such things are not even talked about, they are hushed up, or one doesn't trust one's own senses after the event, putting it down to fatigue, hallucination perhaps, after days and nights of sleep-lessness and hard work.

But even regarding it as improbable, a lie if you will, it gives one a cold shiver down the back to imagine the encounter. It is in the grey dawn, doubly gloomy in these latitudes which are always gloomy, and only the white foam on the crests of the waves shines with a cold light like phosphorus in a cellar. The *Beagle* is close-hauled with the wind on her star-board bow, heeling hard over, reefed al-most to the yards, thumping in the sea as though lashed to her course, the Horn looming ahead through the mist like a hoary head from which thin white hairs are flying in the westerly gale; a good deal of leeway again to-day, storm and current seem to keep the ship in the same spot in spite of all the distance sailed—then it is that they sight a ship astern to leeward, the first they have seen for many weeks; suddenly she appears within the narrow horizon which lies like a grey ring in the sea—but what's that? she's sailing *against* the wind!

In a few moments the ship had passed them, for an instant a collision seemed inevitable; the strange ship came sweep-ing along under full sail against the wind, like a thunderstorm, rocking from side to side like a ship running free and climbing up and down over the waves; she seemed to be sailing in her own gale, directly contrary to the one that was blowing; not a very big vessel when she came nearer, a kind of barque-rigged schooner—but what kind of a schooner, what a way for a ship to behave, what sort of a rig was that?

Rapidly the vessel came near in the grey, poor light, strangely clear though the air was within the ring of leaden water; her hull was clearly seen, a curi-ously short hull, high fore and aft like a swing, and she moved in the water like a segment of a wheel, rolling her bow down and ploughing up the sea in a collar round it as though trying to stand on her head, checking her way and rolling up again, advancing a little on her stern with the masts pointing aft and flapping sails, stick-ing her nose into it again, but on she came; and before the silent crew of the *Beagle* had time to recover themselves, before any one exchanged a word, they saw the sailer run past with her broadside towards them, two or three little open gun-ports, richly carved stanchions and rails around the lofty castles fore and aft; near and yet strangely indistinct, as though the sea showed through the whole vessel, she swept by, rocking her high and narrow stern, with its carvings and little windows whose panes were like flies' eyes, a great unlighted polygonal lantern high up aft; in flying foam, up and down be-tween the hollow waves, she was now visible, now lost again, till she ran beyond the narrow horizon on the other side up in the eye of the wind. The storm raised a squall, lashing salt drops from below and a scourge of hail from above; behind this curtain the stranger vanished, and nobody asked his companion whether it was a vision they had seen or a real vessel, whether they were living men or dead they had made out behind the taffrail of the rolling mist-grey vessel, or who was the tall man who stood on the poop with his great white head held high amid the squall. Nobody spoke of what he had seen, and afterwards it was buried in the secret chambers of the soul as a thing he kept to himself and could not communicate.

But the captain wore his ship round, gave up his obstinate attempt to force a passage south of Cape Horn, whether he had privately accepted the omen, or came to see that it was impossible.

Meeting the Phantom Ship is supposed to mean shipwreck, this did not hold good here in a literal sense; on the other hand it meant that the fatal hour had struck for the whole fundamental view of life on which the mental edifice of Europe rested.

But the *Santa Maria* continued her ghostly voyage south of Cape Horn, round the Cape of Good Hope, across the oceans, round the world, into every remote channel, past every island, as she must so long as the yearning lasts which once fitted her out to sail for the Lost Country.

A strange ship, more powerful as a memory than she ever was in reality. Of the old tub, built for trade, which was taken by chance for that memorable voyage, there may possibly be left even to-day some timbers or nails deeply buried in coral-rag on the West Indian coast where she stranded on Christmas night 1492 and broke up at once, incapable of sustaining her own weight without the water to hold her together; the coral grew about the wreck, Time's layer upon layer, and there the mortal remains of the *Santa Maria* are nobly preserved; but neither iron nor any other solid is imperishable as is the ship that passed into the ages.

A spacious ship, in all respects the image of a caravel but without bounds when seen from within, capacious and airy as our memories, our dreams, the yearning of the dead which reaches us, and our yearning which can never let them go.

And there they are, all the yearners and discoverers who craved to see the earth, the great names—nothing but vocal sounds, like an organ pealing in the soul, but true music—*Columbus, Vasco da Gama, Bartolomeu Diaz, Cabral, Balboa, Cabot, Magellan, Frobisher, Hudson, Cook!*

Storms, seas, vast new continents, mountain ranges, rivers and channels which they opened up have forever become one with their names; the discovery of America, the sea route to India, the circumnavigation of Africa, the discovery of Brazil, the Pacific seen for the first time by the eyes of a man and named, Labrador, the whole northern passage opened; the first circumnavigation of the globe, to the everlasting memory of the unswerving, indomitable Portuguese; the thrusts up north into Arctic waters locked by ice; the navigation of the South Seas and Australia.

There they are, all the later travellers, pioneers and map-makers who gave their names to rivers and mountains, the bridegrooms of the Mississippi, the Amazon, the revealer of Chimborazo, the man who saw Ruwenzori for the first time as a cloud in the sky and who scattered the darkness of Africa, Stanley, white-haired and worn-out before his time, a man without an equal; the scent and expanse of the earth, all the trees and beasts, the varied babble of colour, all the breath of the open air surrounds you when you live their lives over again in their company.

And there are the first nameless subduers of Nature, before the days of history, who began to pry about in their surroundings and to ponder over means of making themselves their masters, the first unknown leaders on mankind's long journey out of primeval darkness; the man who tamed fire and made movement possible, the inventor of the boat and the car, the first horseman; here are those who tamed beasts and sowed corn in the earth; here are the ravenous seafarers who opened up the world with their sharp sword, the Vikings on their sea-steeds; here they are, all the seekers and strivers.

The wind, *anima,* that first conception of the soul, the earliest of impulses, from the time the air first enters the lungs of the newborn babe with a scream till he gives up the ghost in a sigh: to taste the breeze of many lands between birth and death, that was their soul, that was the rhythm of their lives.

III
AT HOME

But now, is the phantom sailor, the flying skipper, never to find peace? Is there not some condition that sets him free, if he can see it and fulfil it?

There is. The condition provides that if he can acknowledge when he is himself, he shall be redeemed. Impossible, no man can do that. That is why he has already sailed for centuries, with the prospect of being at sea till Doomsday.

But supposing the terms are that if only he is able *afterwards,* when he has sailed for such and such a time and had occasion to look back and reflect, to recognize at what moment of his life and in what respect he came nearest to realizing himself as a man—even if during all the rest of his life his desires and conduct were other than properly accorded with his nature—he shall find peace. This comes about at the moment when he returns wholly and in truth to his own nature.

And when this acknowledgment comes to him, these things shall be seen, as it were a recurrence in his soul:

The storm, which the phantom skipper always carries along with him and always sails in, shall subside, a calm shall follow, clear weather, and with dazzled eyes the skipper shall find his altitude, the correct one at last; and then the old sea-worn vessel of eternity beneath him will spread out and become an island, securely moored in the sea, the deck will turn green and become a cool Northern plain giving off a scent of mould and grassy sweetness and covered with flowers, a cool and humble show, but here the nights are light and bees and flowers consort in the mild honeyed air of noon. Broad is the land, no mean island after all, a mighty continent, more than room enough; if the old salt-stained ocean-farer has had the elements for his world within his narrow hull, he will have room to expand and stretch himself on the firm land to which it is now transformed.

But the sails swell and become great domed clouds in the sky, roofing the summer day like a cool tent and casting slow-moving shadows upon the earth, smiling pastures, forests and lakes blended together.

The masts burst into leaf, from every knot a branch shoots out, the top expands like a banner of fresh foliage, yards and spars change into trees, there is a murmur as of a breeze of spring, a blaze of pale green and a fresh leafy scent, the wood is fully out and trembles in its cool bright garment beneath swelling white clouds and blue patches of sky, sun and shade blending like a refreshing draught among the slender Northern trees.

And behold, all the carvings and ornaments of the old ship have come to life, the stag steps out of his convolutions and stretches his legs, casts off his larva of artistry and wanders easily among the trees with rocking antlers, his muzzle nibbling at the sweet dewy leaves. The squirrel leaps out of his scroll-work, straightens his twisted limbs and flies into the colour of life, the reddest of reds, and up he darts like a flame, clutching the trunk with all his paws, rearing his lively tail and vanishing in the top of a birch. Out of the woodwork, from holes and corners of the carving, fly the birds, the hawk sailing in slow flight above the tree-tops and circling on the wing, the owl shunning the light and flapping noiselessly as a moth among the branches, losing itself in a shadow; song-birds whirring out and distributing themselves upon the hanging leafy twigs, puffing out their feathered throats in song.

But now comes the greatest marvel, the *Santa Maria*'s figurehead, the Mother of God with the Child, comes to life and seats herself on the grass beneath the fresh green trees, the young mother with her first-born in her lap, life over again from the beginning, under the open sky, springtime, the forest, childhood!

Yes, life begun over again, in the person of a young settler's wife, who leaves the log-hut on the first warm day to sun her baby and sits with her fair hair uncovered in the sunshine; the blows of an axe reach her ears from the forest hard by, the strong man, carpenter, tiller of the soil and hunter in one: the family founded again in a wild spot, Canada, the depths of Minnesota or Dakota, where Northern peasants find again their own weather and their seasons, and where the hard winters keep them strong of soul.

As she sits under a tree with hand to brow shading the sun, shy of the light and silent, alone in a great loneliness, but with her child in her arms and the rhythm of her husband's labour within hearing, so sat the young Longobard woman before her, on a clearing in Skoane, with her big legs in a hempen skirt, a homely shift and nothing else but a shock of yellow hair like sunlight in the forest. Behind the tree under which she sat with her plump golden son, her cow was grazing. And the settler's wife has hers where she can find them.

Thus an old world has moved over and become new. The ship has changed to fields and forest. All has turned to what it was in the beginning; every sailor has become an earthworm, and hurried into the ground.

But the tall white skipper becomes yet whiter, rises from the ground and dissolves into a shred of mist or sea fog that comes from the beach and drifts in under the trees, till it vanishes altogether in the sunshine; and in the place where he stood there is nothing but a little heap of dust and some withered last year's leaves.

The Long Journey is ended.

IV
AVE STELLA

In the hour between night and morning, when the last have gone home and the first are not yet up, the great city's brief hour of torpor when it seems as though all life is extinguished and the streets lie all gaunt and empty, like the veins of a body drained of its blood, an artificial, faded world of stone—in this hour a Being appears in heaven, leaning out over the world and looking; a Woman, formed of light upon light, almost invisible.

It is the earth she is watching, and she sees how the beautiful blue globe rolls in its æther and slowly turns its flanks to the sun, always night on one side and day on the other, wrapped the whole way round in a cloak of water, tense and refracting like an immense drop, and amid the blue shrivelled crusts of the continents and their green and motley land; the transparent atmosphere above, stirred by clouds and air currents, like a veil about the earth's blue nakedness—a lovely coloured ball in space, engaged for æons, with a monotony that knows no varying, in turning and lighting itself equally on every side while at the same time it goes in a great orbit round the mighty luminary in whose beams it bathes.

If the super-terrestrial Being descends lower she sees the immense extent of oceans and continents, countries and realms and all the life there is in them, ships moving over the seas all round the ball, trains hastening across the continents from coast to coast, great cities shrouded in smoke, arteries of traffic peppered full of people, in every zone, from both Poles to the Equator, all the Earth's motley, teeming, fantastic circle of countries, peoples, animals, plants and things, fixed and definite things, the sea blue, raw and wet the whole way round, the greensward green, and not a spot anywhere on earth but it is directly in contact with space, every blade of grass stretching straight out into the Universe as far as it can reach.

The great old river cities with their cathedrals and town walls, now only the trace of a narrow ring lost in the city's heart—and a widespread network of streets outside like great crystalline scars on the earth; not one but many, many bridges over the river, where once a single ferryboat splashed across from forest to forest; of the forest nothing left but a reconstruction in the form of parks—and from the whole monster a heavy grating rumble, the interminable note of the city, rising up towards heaven.

She above hears it and looks down, wondering, clutches at her heart; and not one of those below has an inkling of the sympathy felt for them in eternity, of th pain and deep pity with which a lovin heart, unable to help, follows their doings

Who is she? The rolling Earth, what i it? Why? What is this phantom ship i eternity, abandoned entirely to itsel among spheres it cannot reach, with a ter rible amount of lore about them, but n help from that, just as much alone; wha is it carrying, why, whither? At the ver moment when the chemist is busy with hi tubes and his mysterious rays, the inmos life of matter, Negroes are lying in wai for each other behind anthills with lon assegais; what is their object, what i working in them both, how did it all be gin, and how will it end?

Schoolboys ask questions; the rest g about their business and multiply, buil or pull down, and die.

But the cosmic Being that appears ove the earth as a Woman to those who ca see her, she is Life, the stem of Life be yond the æther, from which the germ have come to earth; true Life, the sourc of Love, of which we can know no mor than longing teaches us.

Have the creatures of Earth, through long process of life and change—approxi mate, faulty, abandoned and taken u again—been seeking a form for an eter nal, intrinsic, unknown type existing o other stars?

Ave Stella!

THE LIFE AND WORKS OF JOHANNES V. JENSEN

By TOM KRISTENSEN

When in one of Johannes V. Jensen's last novels, *The Temptations of Dr. Renault,* the doctor wakes up in purgatory after his death and signs a contract with Mr. Asbeste, the ruler of purgatory and hell, which would enable the doctor to return to life, he says first: "Existence outside the rules does not appeal to me in the least." He rejects the offer whereby he could be reborn as a younger man and scorns the inexhaustible purse that would make him an immensely wealthy man. Thus, as an old man, did Johannes V. Jensen himself consider his life and his work.

The Himmerland, in Jutland, where Johannes Vilhelm Jensen was born in the village of Farsødin on January 20, 1873, was at that time a forgotten corner of Denmark. During the 1870s, the people of the Himmerland truly lived outside the bounds of civilization. The culture that existed on the isolated farms was so primitive that it could, without exaggeration, be compared to that of the Iron Age.

Johannes V. Jensen was from a very old Himmerland family. His grandfather, Jens Jensen, who lived at Wolles Krog in the parish of Simested, was the first to make the difficult leap from proletarian to craftsman, choosing the weaving profession. He was a warm, peaceful man with a long beard, and when Johannes felt the need to look clearly into himself during the course of World War I, he conceived a novel, *Norne-Gaest* (1919), in which his grandfather plays the leading role.

Jens Jensen had three sons: the eldest, a miller in Aalestrup, was a brilliant teller of stories about the Himmerland; the second son, Hans Jensen, went to Copenhagen where he passed the veterinarian's examination, settled in Fars, and married the young Marie Kirstine, whom he had met during the course of his studies. Marie Kirstine's family was originally from Møen and Falster, and was of Wendish origin. Their son, Johannes, was the product of this fusion of blood. Although Johannes mentions his mother only rarely, his father had a great influence on him. A friend of animals and flowers and a cultivated man, the elder Jensen wrote a spiritualist book called *Spøgeri* (Apparitions of the Dead).

Hans and Marie Jensen had ten children, all characterized outwardly by "rapid and violent movements." Johannes was brusque, lacked moderation and had a great need to show off his strength. All these qualities he concealed beneath "a proud modesty." He led the hyperactive existence of a boy, jumping over every puddle, climbing the highest trees, hollowing out boats, and perfecting bows. With his "mole's paws," he was the tough guy of his band of boys. The books he read in grade school were like most schoolbooks, as he noted, but "the germ of my whole universe was contained in them and it is impossible to express what these little texts of prose and verse—and, first and foremost, the wood engravings of the period [1870–1879]—represented for me." There were passages of the sagas in these books, stories that were ultimately to hold the greatest importance for him (especially *The Gods of the North* by the classic Danish poet Oehlenschläger, of which "Thor's Voyage to Udgaard" is part. He spent his leisure time reading the Danish historian Carit Etlar, who was not such a bad teacher, and several of Etlar's nature descriptions in *Fangen paa Kalø* (The Prisoner of Kalø) seem to foreshadow Jensen. In any case, it is certain that Jensen avidly read Cook, the *Adventures of Hans Christian Andersen,* Poulsen's *Forces of Nature,* and that he drank up knowledge "like a sponge."

Jensen belonged to that Danish generation which after 1864 was seized with emigration fever. A good number of his schoolmates crossed the Atlantic, and he himself wrote of those who left home. Jensen directly treated the type of emigrant who leaves for America, feels homesick there, and returns home where he then finds himself permanently uprooted in one story in his *Himmerlandshistorier* (Himmerland Stories), *"Guldgraveren"* (The Gold Seeker, 1898–1910). And in the characters in the novel *Kongens Fald* (The King's Downfall, 1898–1899) and *Columbus* (1921) we find the man who, goaded by nostalgia and pain, takes off to conquer space and with each conquest only encounters a new disillusionment. Johannes V. Jensen owed this powerful desire for time and space to the Himmerland of his childhood.

Jensen's childhood came to an end the day, described in the story "Barndommens sig" (Twilight of Childhood), that his father took him to the Greenland priest J. P. N. Krag, with whom he was to learn Latin and prepare for his baccalaureate. But it was soon obvious that Jensen had more interest in tales about Eskimos than in a dead language, and it was decided to send him away to school. And so it was that, at the age of seventeen, he arrived at the school in Viborg where only gymnastics and the study of German were able to attract his attention. He discovered Heine and Goethe, and, apart from his studies, he read the Danish Catholic poet Johannes Jørgensen and Rudyard Kipling.

After completing his studies in Viborg, with twenty-four crowns in his pocket and without any hope of external help, Johannes Jensen went to Copenhagen in order to take the philosophy examination leading to a doctorate. His life was that of a peasant student, absorbed in his own intellectual curiosity. Several months later, he returned home, convinced that he could discover the philosophy of Høffding and the botany of Warming just as well in Farsø. Then in the following year he again left home to live the life of a poor student in Copenhagen. He debated at the student association, where he made the acquaintance of Georg Brandès, who was to become a great literary critic, and Edward Brandès and Peter Nansen, both of whom he absolutely could not tolerate, because of their pessimism and heartlessness.

We know little about how Jensen managed to exist during this period, although he did pass his examinations in philosophy during the following semester. Then on January 2, 1895, the weekly *Revuen,* edited by Louis de Moulin (Ludwig Møller), began to publish a serial adventure story called "Skutten fra Korsør" (Korsør's Treasure). Although the stories were signed by Ivar Lykke, Johannes V. Jensen had undertaken to write these pieces which were, according to his agreement with Møller, to contain at least one murder in each issue. That same year, a long story of Jensen's appeared in *Revuen,* but from a literary point of view the only other thing that brought him any attention was an article entitled *"Om spiritismen"* (On Spiritism), which bears the mark of a certain skepticism.

The following year, 1896, was a year of real writing. It began with the story *Blodfesterne i Arizona* (The Bloody Games of Arizona), published in *Revuen.* This story was based on Jensen's studies of Bernal Diaz's *The Discovery and Conquest of Mexico.* During the course of that year, he completed three novels.

One day Jensen visited Witzansky, the publisher of the daily paper *København* and offered him a serial. A week later he appeared with his first novel, *Danskere* (The Danes), and, to his great consternation, it was rejected. He then took it to the newly created periodical *Nordiske Forlag,* where, to his great surprise, it was accepted. At one stroke he had become a bit more than an uncelebrated author. With his royalties from this novel, Johannes Jensen left in the fall of 1896 for New York, returning home for Christmas. The years of travel had begun.

The result of his trip to America was a short prose sketch *En der kom underfor del hele* (Someone Has Got out of the Company), a treatise on the noise in New York, and a novel, published in *Revuen,* with the sonorous title *Milliontyvenes Høvding eller Dem rode Tiger, original, illustreret New Yorkerroman* (The Chief of Twenty Millions, or The Red Tiger, an Original, Illustrated Novel of New York), in which there is a clever detective who always gets his murderer. Beginning in April 1897, the *Illustreret Tidende* published, at rather lengthy intervals, several Jensen stories that indicate that the writer was beginning to sink his roots in the Himmerland of his childhood. The first of the Himmerland stories now began to appear. *"Oktobernat"* (October Night) has as its theme the story of youth's confidence in its own strength and the fear of an accidental death. *"I Mørket"* (In the Dark) is a serious and sad story about love, a theme that Johannes V. Jensen now took up. As for the story of *"Lindsbyskytten,"* the strange epileptic, it shows an aspect of the Danish character that had never before been described in its literature. On holiday in Norway in 1897 Jensen met the Norwegian writer Knut Hamsun whose novels *Hunger* and *Pan* had stirred up public opinion. Slowly Johannes V. Jensen was coming to grips with the novel form. The year 1898 marked the breakthrough with the novel *Einar Elkaer.*

In May of 1898, Viggo Hørup, of the newspaper *Politiken,* sent Johannes V. Jensen to Spain as a war correspondent, to cover the Spanish-American War. The Spanish reportage attracted great attention, and it is accurate to say that *Tyrefaegtningen* (The Bullfight, 1898) was the masterpiece that made Johannes V. Jensen famous. It contains a realistic and brutal description of this sport as it was practiced until the second decade of this century when the talented torero Juan Belmonte transformed a veritable butchery into a still more bloody ballet.

Jensen returned to Farsø in the winter of 1898–1899, and he now concentrated on the first part of his historical novel *Kongens Fald* (The King's Downfall)—the part called *Foraaret* (Springtime). Jensen worked without any documentary sources other than the *History of the Three Norwegian States* by C. F. Allen and Knackfuss's edition of the works of Dürer and Holbein. The second part of the novel appeared under the ironic title

Dan store Sommer (The Long Summer), and was completed in 1899 with the volume *Vintern* (Winter).

During the following months, Jensen continued to write a number of his Himmerland stories, among others the important "*Kirstens sidste Rejse*" (Kirsten's Last Voyage). Then in March of 1902, the writer was able to go on a trip around the world. He resolved not to touch a pen during the course of the trip.

He sailed for Singapore and remained a while in the independent Malaysian state of Trengganu, lost in the virgin forests. Both places were to assume great importance for him. He visited Hankow and Shanghai in China, and there experienced an adventure which he recounted in the story "*Vor Tidsalder*" (In Our Times, 1904).

It was the winter Jensen spent in Chicago, in 1902–1903, that proved decisive. He broke the promise that he had made to himself not tc write. In January and February a serialized novel, *Tigeren* (The Tiger), appeared in the local periodical *Danish Pioneer*. On February 1, 1903, a play of his was put on for Danish-American circles; it was called *Trods for trodsen* (Stubbornness for Stubbornness) and is set at the time when he was experiencing Chicago's struggle against the cold weather, a characteristic struggle that made a deep impression on him. This play foreshadowed a later novel, *Braeen* (The Glacier, 1908). At this time, he wrote the first act of a play entitled *Sangerinden* (The Singer, 1905). And finally, while there he published a separate reprint of the myth, "*Kirken i Farsø*" (The Church of Farsø), later published in his collection *Mytr* (Myths) (1907–1945).

After this burst of creativity, he felt the need for a rest; he traveled to Arkansas that icy spring, a visit whose memory he would preserve in the highly regarded hunting myth "*Potowatomis Datter*" (The Daughter of Potowatomi). He then continued his trip to Denmark by way of New York.

The following year, 1904, *Madame d'Ora* finally appeared. It was a disappointment to the public, for they could only see in this captivating and at the same time highly ironic detective novel a direct attack against spiritism. But this novel, according to Johannes V. Jensen's own explanation, is a version of *Faust* with new lighting, with characters whose evolution took place after Goethe. During the same year, Jensen continued to write his Himmerland stories and he added several masterpieces: "*Tordenkalven,*" the story of the Himmerland eccentric, "*Wombwell,*" "*Jens,*" and finally, "*Ane og Koen*" (The Grandfather and the Cow).

The year 1905 was dedicated primarily to the second great novel of America, *Hjulet* (The Wheel), which appeared in serial form in the Danish review *Politiken*. This novel is a sequal to *Madame d'Ora* and contains long translations of the poems of Walt Whitman. Although it is not a social novel, the basic Faust theme was replaced by social themes inspired by Frank Norris, by capitalism, and by strikes; also found in *Hjulet* is a certain disgust for literature, which was to last for several years. Jensen's journalistic instinct told him that it was more important to reach the large public through a newspaper than to spend time on subject matter only because it might eventually turn into a book. To support this rather American attitude, Jensen made a brief trip to New York that same year.

In July of 1906 Jensen took up the editorship of a daily paper in Denmark, *Pressen,* proof of his desire to be an editor. The need to reach the readers of his paper led him to write several series of myths and stories.

The year 1907 was marred by his attack on Herman Bang and his literary skirmish with Sophus Claussen, Sven Lange, and still others. His irascible, bitter polemic greatly isolated him.

It is possible that during the course of this solitude the idea of a novel on obstinacy, that typical quality of the inhabitant of Himmerland, again presented itself to him. The memories of his winter in Chicago and of a trip to the Jotunheim in Norway in 1907, where he "decided to catch his breath," combined with the reading of German anthropologists like Wilser, Reinhard, and Hoernes, gradually led Jensen to believe that man had been engaged for a long time in a struggle against the cold. Thus, his new novel, the first of six novels expounding his theories of evolution published in two volumes in 1938 as *Den lange rejse* (*The Long Journey*) (1908–1922), deals with the earth's Tertiary Epoch, when Scandinavia's tropical vegetation was destroyed by the southward advance of the glaciers.

Although the new novel was a popular success, Jensen devoted himself exclusively to short works in the following years. In 1912, however, he published the second volume of his epic of evolution, *Skibet* (The Boat). This novel, written in a youthful style, takes place at the time of the Vikings.

In November of 1912, Jensen left for Genoa, where he set sail for the Orient. The mission he wished to accomplish on this journey was to "reduce the spirituality of the ancients to phenomena of a known physiological nature: for it seemed to him that the passage in Exodus (24, 17) "And the sight of the glory of the Lord was like devouring fire on the top of the mount in the eyes of the children of Israel," alluded to an actual volcanic eruption of Mt. Sinai which Moses, a cool and collected man, had utilized to give his people a new faith, enabling him to smash the golden calf and the idols while at the same time reinforcing his own power. This theory of the volcano was the basis for his belief that man's discovery of gods was due to the fear created in him by forces of nature.

Jensen's second adventure on this particular trip was China, which on his other trip around the world had left him strangely cold. With his usual happy knack for comparisons, Jensen remarked how much the Chinese resembled the peasants of the Himmerland and the Europeans of the Middle Ages, and from this comparison he arrived at the conclusion that humanity should not be divided into races but into degrees or stages. Thus he returned from this trip hoping to dispel the racial theories that soon were to fall like a plague over the world. From Peking he returned to Denmark via Siberia, Russia, and Sweden, bringing back a volume of exotic stories completed during the trip, *Olivia Marianne* (1915), as well as his remarkable *"Introduktion til vor Tidsalder"* (Introduction to Our Time).

In March of 1914, Jensen took himself and his papers to New York to settle. Meanwhile, the horror of World War I was unleashed, and Jensen was to think frequently with tender nostalgia of his gentle grandfather of Wolles Krøg. From him he took the inspiration for the beautiful portrait of *Norne-Gaest* (1919) in the more extended form of a saga of Norne-Gaest, the little saga of a boy who is warned of his impending death by a vision.

Det Tabte Land (The Lost Country), another volume of *The Long Journey,* appeared in the same year, 1919. The volcano was the focal point this time, but the volcano is situated in Kullen, for during this time there were volcanos in Scandinavia. The vegetation is subtropical, and Scandinavia appears as a sunken forest. Jensen makes us see how this period has persisted in the race and awakened the nostalgia for the warmth of the South to be finally transformed into the dream of the celestial paradise.

During this time, Jensen made an effort to complete *The Long Journey*, and he published another volume, *Columbus*, in 1921, and another, *Cimbrernes Tog* (The Cimbrian Expedition) in 1922, both of which must have been written at a rapid pace, with zest and delight.

The essential aspect of his later work was his defense of the great idea of *The Long Journey: Aestetik og Udvikling* (Aesthetics and Evolution, 1923), *Evolution og Moral* (Evolution and Morality, 1925), *Dyrenes Forvandling* (The Metamorphosis of Animals, 1927), *Aandens Stadiens* (The Aims of the Spirit, 1928), *Det Blivende* (The Immutable, 1934), and *Vor Oprindelse* (Our Origin, 1941). Some of these books are very cheerful, due no doubt to Jensen's trip to Egypt and Palestine during the winter of 1925–1926.

Finally in 1943, there appeared a volume of poems by Jensen, *Digte, 1904–41* (Poems), of which Jensen himself once said, "My poems represent a return to simple style and sound subject matter."

He died in 1950, at the age of seventy-seven.

Tom Kristensen is a Danish journalist and literary critic.
Translated by D. D. Paige.

THE 1944 PRIZE

By KJELL STRÖMBERG

During the years 1940–1943, no Nobel Prizes were awarded, by Royal decree. War was raging almost everywhere, and many countries, one after another, found it impossible to present candidates freely. In spite of this, the activities of the different Nobel Institutes were never interrupted, and each year the candidates were duly proposed and registered.

In 1944, most of Europe had been turned into a battlefield and disorder was at its height, but the end of the nightmare could be dimly foreseen. There was a strong feeling, by no means confined to the Scandinavian countries, that the Nobel Institutes should join in the general rise of spirits.

In fact, there was a major reason why the different Nobel groups should listen to these appeals: for the last four years—five in the case of the Peace Prize—no Nobel Prize had been presented, and if this shirking of obligations were repeated the whole existence of the Foundation would be in jeopardy, as the other legal heirs of the founder could claim that certain clauses of the founder's will had been broken. There was no obligation to present the Nobel Prizes every year; it was sufficient if each of the Prizes were presented once in every five years.

The Nobel Prizes, as it happened, were distributed practically every year except in time of war. War was an eventuality with which apparently neither the testator nor his executors had reckoned, because no reference has been made in the statutes to a comparable case of circumstances beyond control. On the other hand, if, in the case under consideration, the Nobel Prizes had been withheld for a further year until 1945, the statutes would still not have been formally violated, as the period of five years would have included the years 1941 to 1945 in this particular case, and not 1940 to 1944. Therefore, in order to eliminate the risk, the work of making all the awards, except for the Peace Prize, began again in 1944.

The last laureate of the Nobel Prize for Literature had been the Finnish novelist F. E. Sillanpää, who was honored in 1939, in the middle of the Russo-Finnish war. It was generally understood that this Prize was homage paid to the laureate's heroic little country as much as to Sillanpää himself.

During the course of the war years the Swedish Academy had regularly received proposals for the Prize for Literature, but of course in more limited numbers than usual. A great French name frequently appeared among these proposals, that of Georges Duhamel, who was particularly appreciated at that time as the ardent apostle of peace. There were also the names of Paul Valéry, and for the second time, Paul Claudel, who was proposed in 1941 by the Norwegians. Several English writers also appeared on the list, notably Edmund Blunden and Charles Morgan; an American, John Steinbeck, a future laureate who had attracted attention with a fine account of the Norwegian occupation, *The Moon Is Down;* and a Chinese, Lin Yu-Tang, who was proposed by Pearl Buck, the 1938 Nobel Prizewinner. Probably the most prominent non-Scandinavian candidates were the representatives of two neutral countries, the Swiss storyteller Charles-Ferdinand Ramuz—who was warmly endorsed by the former Prime Minister Hjalmar Hammarskjöld, president of the Nobel Foundation—and the Chilean poet Gabriela Mistral.

Everyone in Sweden expected that this time, after the tribute paid to Finland, a no less glowing one would be paid to one of the other friendly neighbor countries which had also been forced to endure war or occupation. Perhaps the warmest sympathy was shown toward Norway, where the very active resistance movement against the occupier had found its nominee in the person of the lyric poet Arnulf Överland. On the other hand, Denmark possessed an excellent novelist and poet of international repute in Johannes V. Jensen, who had already been a candidate for the Nobel Prize no fewer than eighteen times, and was now unanimously supported by the press. In spite of his being well on the wrong side of seventy, the Nobel Prize for 1944 was awarded him by a comfortable majority, for "the strength and fertility of his poetic imagination, with which is combined an intellectual curiosity of wide scope and a bold, freshly creative style."

The laureate himself was ill, and received the news of his award in a hospital bed in Copenhagen. It was not until the following year, when the Prize giving could once more be held with its customary ceremonial for the first time since 1938, that he went to Stockholm to be honored.

Translated by Camilla Sykes.